Law in Action

An Anthology of the Law in Literature

EDITED BY AMICUS CURIAE

With an Introduction by

ROSCOE POUND
Formerly Dean of the Harvard Law School

CROWN PUBLISHERS
New York

Contents

Part One

LIBERTY

Part Two

MORALS

Part Three

JUSTICE

Part Four

CRIME

Introduction

Roscoe Pound

B ARON MARTIN, a somewhat eccentric judge in England in the last
century, whose reading had long been confined to the law books,
noticed that his marshal was always quoting Shakespeare and
asked what play the marshal recommended him to read. *Measure
for Measure* was recommended. The Baron borrowed the marshal's copy
and duly read it. Handing it back, he shook his head saying, "I don't
think much of your friend Shakespeare. He lays down some very bad
law."

The administration of justice and the law in action touch human
life at so many vital points and offer so many dramatic situations that the
playwright and the writer of fiction turn to them constantly. Much of the
license of the poet must no doubt be allowed the lay writer. The exigen-
cies of his story may require the law to be fitted to them. Accurate adherence to the law and to the methods and usages of the forum may
spoil a thrilling scene or make dull a stirring episode. But the average
trial scene in the moving pictures today makes the lawyer shudder, and
as he reads even the best novelists, when their stories involve legal situations, he must needs sympathize with Baron Martin.

There are a few notable exceptions. Sir Walter Scott was a judge and
his accounts of the pedantic expounders of the modern Roman law and
Scots feudal land law in the latter part of the eighteenth century, as well
as his trial scenes, are true for the time and place. Dickens, too, was
usually accurate in his law and could describe a trial as it was actually
conducted in England of his time. Mr. Train wrote from experience as
a prosecutor in the courts of New York. But Mark Twain's satirical remark that the trial scene in *Pudd'nhead Wilson* (which calls for the mantle
of charity when the lawyer reads it) must be accurate because he submitted the manuscript to a rural Justice of the Peace shows he was conscious how much he had sacrificed a true picture of the procedure in a
court to the dramatic climax of comparison of the finger prints.

Moreover, there are certain established conventions of writing. In
mystery stories the official investigators are expected to be stupid, routine-
ridden, and obstinate. To make a good story they must over zealously

act on first appearances so that the lay genius for deduction can achieve a triumph at their expense. In novels the lawyers are expected to be bigoted and pedantic or else dishonest. Otherwise much dramatic interest will be lost. Also the judges must be arbitrary and tyrannical, or the trial scenes will lack in thrill. Nor is all this merely a literary tradition. Laymen who, sitting as arbitrators, will insist on technicalities which the law would instantly reject, and in rural corner grocery discussions will argue that a contract signed with a lead pencil is void for want of form, are quite sure that the lawyer systematically rejects the merits of a controversy in order to dispose of it on some quirk or quibble. The legal muckraker who writes for our periodicals finds no difficulty in finding an audience for the most absurd misstatements as to the laws under which we live, and the learned magazine writers on economics and government who, with scanty or no knowledge of the law, assume that they may read the dicta in the reports and pronounce judgment upon our legal systems on the basis thus afforded, obtain ready credence from a public disposed by tradition to believe that nothing can be too absurd, too mechanical, too out of accord with everyday life to be the law of the land.

Men have always been impatient of restraint and hence have railed at the law from the time that social control through law began. But apart from this general ground for human impatience of law, there are circumstances which make specially for lay misunderstanding of courts and judges and lawyers. Perhaps the most significant is the necessarily mechanical operation of rules, the circumstance that law must act to a large extent in gross, with rules made for the average case, and hence often must ignore elements in particular situations which seem controlling to the lay mind focused upon the one case exclusively. The more that certainty and uniformity and stability are insisted on, the more the law seeks to preclude all personal element in the administration of justice, the more it will seem to the layman, looking at single causes, that the law is arbitrary and technical and that it defeats the justice it is set up to maintain. But some periods of civil and legal development insist strongly upon certainty and stability in the law; and in the reaction from such periods the tradition always thrives.

Only less important in keeping alive a conception of law as a mass of arbitrary technicalities, used, if not devised, to defeat justice, is the necessary difference between law and public opinion with regard to their respective rates of growth. In a sense Spencer was well warranted in calling law a government of the living by the dead. We must pay a price for certainty and uniformity in judicial administration. If we refer the court to the formulated moral sentiments of the community expressed in laws, forbidding him to apply his personal ethical views where such formulations are at hand, we must recognize that only a fixed and settled public opinion may be formulated effectively, and, when it is so formulated, there can be no change until a change of public opinion has become reasonably complete and a new fixity has been attained. While moral or intellectual and economic changes are in progress, but before they are so complete as to have formulated new legal rules or principles or standards, an advanced, confident and clamorous minority may easily berate the backwardness of the general public in reality while in appearance accusing the obstinate conservatism and inveterate technicality of courts and judges and lawyers. In periods of rapid growth such as the present this backwardness inherent in a system of rules is felt acutely by the openest minds in the community and the timeworn tradition as to courts and lawyers gains ready acceptance.

Without going back to antiquity, the tradition may be found well established in the late Middle Ages, where it was an incident of the disputes between theology and law which began with the revival of the study of Roman law in the Italian universities in the twelfth century. We must remember that at one time the administration of justice and the practice of advising litigants and of advocacy were in the hands of the clergy. Indeed, for a time it seemed not unlikely that the universal church courts and church law would carry the day against the local courts and the local law. Naturally the clergy did not relinquish the practice of the law without a protest. From this period proceed such stories as the one of how the lawyers prayed for a patron saint: upon papal concession that the saint whose statue a representative lawyer, duly blindfolded, should select might be claimed and revered by the profession as their patron, an eminent advocate with bandaged eyes groped about the room, came upon the statue of St. Michael putting down Satan and as in duty bound embraced the statue of Satan.

At the Reformation, theological objections to law and lawyers were about the only thing on which Roman Catholic and Reformer were agreed. The part which Roman law had played in the Humanist movement and the prominent part taken by great French jurists of the sixteenth century in the Huguenot party easily led the pious Catholic to the conclusion that the lawyer was an enemy of religion. "The more that one is a great jurist," said one of the Catholic leaders, "so much the more is he a bad Christian." On the other hand, the authority which the lawyers conceded to the canon law and their universal ideas of law, which smacked suspiciously of Catholicism, aroused the animosity of Protestants. And this animosity was intensified by the distaste which Luther, as has happened in the case of other vigorous and impulsive personalities, felt for conventional rule and for attempts to confine the course of justice and to coerce the will. He was never weary of declaiming against lawyers and the tradition got its currency among the Protestant clergy of the next century through his writings.

Luther wrote and preached in a period of transition, when the reception of Roman law on the Continent required a process of adjustment to the needs of a new world. Hence his bitter epigrams were congenial to a people irritated by a legal situation not without parallel in the present, and gave rise to many popular sayings of similar import. Political jealousy due to the supplanting of the clergy by the lawyers in the conduct of the state, reinforced this tradition and handed it down. For, on the whole, down to the Reformation, the great offices of state had been the perquisites of the clergy. Clergymen had shared the reins of government at most only with soldiers. And in all the growing departments of governmental activity that had to do with the affairs of peace they had been supreme. When they found a new rival in the lawyer, and when this rival pushed them out of one after another of the great offices of state, the pious clergymen could perceive clearly the peril to religion and good morals which this change involved. The zeal which coined such phrases as *"Juristen böse Christen, ja diabolisten," "legum contortores, bonorum extortores," "legum doctores sunt legum dolores," "juris periti sunt juris perditi,"* was born of professional concern at the supercession of the clergy in the kingdoms of this world by the rise of the legal profession, and the natural disinclination of those who had been wont to lay down the law for both worlds to confine their attention to the less immediately profitable and immediately rewarded calling of preparing for the world to come.

In America the foregoing bit of history was repeated in such wise as to give new vitality to the twelfth-century clerical tradition. The Protestant tradition, averse to lawyers, was strong in Colonial America. Cromwell had found, as he put it, that the sons of Zeruiah were too hard for him and had retired from a single attempt to impose his ideas upon the English bar. This did not lead to a charitable view of the profession on the part of the Roundhead. Milton wrote of lawyers that they ground "their purposes, not on the prudent and heavenly contemplation of justice and equity, which was never taught them, but on the promising and pleasing thoughts of litigious terms, fat contentions and flowing fees." The pamphlet literature of the Commonwealth teemed with attacks upon the legal profession and the pious Puritan, apart from religious grounds, apart from his doctrine of consocation rather than subordination, apart from his belief in the individual conscience as the ultimate measure of conduct, was naturally disposed to regard law as "a dark and knavish business" and to regard lawyers as mischievous parasites upon society.

In New England the clergy were supreme throughout the seventeenth century. They conceived, as the non-lawyer usually does, that administration of justice was an easy matter, requiring no special skill, training or experience, and hence they were confident that all that was needed for just and righteous government of human relations might be found in their own consciences and in the word of God. Where today the question is one of law—does a proposed measure accord with the constitution, which is the supreme law of the land—then the question was one of theology—does the measure accord with the word of God. But the middle of the eighteenth century saw the rise of a legal profession. The last quarter of the century saw the firm establishment of a system of courts, and by the beginning of the nineteenth century executive justice and legislative justice, which had prevailed in the colonial period, were definitely superseded by judicial justice. Then followed the reception of the common law of England and the working over of the old English case law and the old English statutes into a common law of America which marks the period ending with the Civil War. The sceptre of justice had passed once more from the clergyman to the lawyer.

The reasons for this change are clear enough. Increasing complexity demands increasing specialization. A crude system of magisterial justice which will suffice for a pioneer community will not suffice for the commercial and industrial community of succeeding generations. With the development of society a scientific system of law was inevitable, and as in the case of any other science, this involved specialized training and a class of professional exponents. As the need for law grew, as the growing importance of the social interests in security of acquisitions and security of transactions called for more certainty and hence for greater detail of legal rule, the importance of the lawyer grew also. And our political system, with its elaborate legal machinery of checks and balances, demanded legal knowledge and invited legal interference in connection with almost every item of governmental activity. Hence, as Colonial America was the period of the clergyman, nineteenth-century America was the period of the lawyer. It was not merely that the administration of justice had passed into his hands. In nineteenth-century politics the sole rival of the lawyer was the soldier. From De Tocqueville to Bryce, observers were agreed as to the leadership of the lawyer in American communities.

It could not be expected that this passing of the hegemony from the pulpit to the bar would be acceptable to the learned and eloquent profession which had been displaced. Nor did the circumstance that the causes of this supersession were economic, or in other words, material, make it more acceptable. With their books full of the echoes of Luther's diatribes, it was but natural that the clergy should view the rise of law and consequent rise of the lawyer as a triumph of the material over the spiritual, a sacrifice of justice and right to the greed and craft of a parasitic class. Sermons of the first half of the nineteenth century are full of this, and nothing but the inexorable operation of economic conditions that demanded law enabled lawyers to overcome the violent hostility to their profession that persisted almost to the time of the Civil War.

In the present century we have been seeing the rise of new professions visibly contesting the leadership of the bar even in its own domain of the administration of justice. As to what effect this may have upon the tradition I will not speculate.

So much for the general attitude of much that has been written about law and courts and lawyers since the twelfth century. A few words more may be appropriate as to two of the selections.

H. B. Irving, the English criminologist, and Sir James Fitzjames Stephen in his *History of the Criminal Law of England* have shown that the portrait of Jeffreys in that brilliant Whig apologia, Macaulay's *History of England,* is much overdrawn. It is based on the accounts of those convicted before Jeffreys, ignores the criminal procedure and methods of prosecution and tradition of judicial conduct of criminal trials, and applies ideas of the nineteenth to the seventeenth century. But with all allowance for the background of his trials, Jeffreys leaves an abiding impression of unnecessary brutality of manner. Moreover, it was the Whig tradition as to Jeffreys and his obvious and vehement partisanship which was brought to America and had a marked effect on our attitude toward the trial judge. Those who escaped Jeffreys, and the widows and orphans and friends and neighbors of those convicted before him came to America just as we were setting up our court system and brought with them a picture of the common-law trial judge as a partisan monster. This had much to do with our characteristic American attitude toward the trial judge. We have persistently refused to trust him while on the other hand we entrust to judges of our appellate tribunals powers beyond what they have in England.

One of the selections, *Billy Budd* by Herman Melville, has to do with the perennial and hotly debated question as to military trials. After every war questions are raised as to the methods of these tribunals and the questions are far from easy to answer. They raise a fundamental issue of the science of law, namely, the balance between the general security and the individual life. Lord Acton tells us that all power corrupts; absolute power corrupts absolutely. Discipline in the armed forces demands large powers. Security must be upheld. Yet the individual, too, calls for security of his personality. This demands checks, and the checks threaten efficiency. When one reads about military tribunals he must bear in mind the deep-seated conflict of fundamental ideas to which both its good and its bad features must be referred.

But neither layman nor lawyer will read in the spirit of Baron Martin either the classical or the contemporary literature of the many problems of adjusting conflicting claims and ordering conduct and quest of justice which are raised by human life. Rather he will note in what a variety of ways the ideal relation among men has been sought for. He will perceive how differently attempts at administering justice whether according to law or without law have appealed to writers both in the past and in the present. He may observe how the layman has conceived he could solve the problems of adjusting relations and ordering behavior by simple offhand methods with little conception of the number and variety of interests which his supposedly common sense solutions ignore. Apart from the intrinsic interest of the situations and episodes and conditions which have been the theme of writers from antiquity to the present, from them and from the different ways in which they have been treated one may see something of how difficult is the task of law in maintaining the inner order of a politically organized society.

PART ONE

LIBERTY

========

No freeman shall be arrested, or detained in prison, or deprived of his freehold, or outlawed, or banished, or in any way molested; and we will not set forth against him, nor send against him, unless by the lawful judgment of his peers and by the law of the land.

MAGNA CARTA, *chap. 39 (1215).*

Jesus Before Pilate

Matthew, Mark, Luke and John

As Reported by Matthew

WHEN THE morning was come, all the chief priests and elders of the people took counsel against Jesus to put him to death: And when they had bound him, they led him away, and delivered him to Pontius Pilate the governor.

Then Judas, which had betrayed him, when he saw that he was condemned, repented himself, and brought again the thirty pieces of silver to the chief priests and elders, Saying, I have sinned in that I have betrayed the innocent blood. And they said, What is that to us? see thou to that. And he cast down the pieces of silver in the temple, and departed, and went and hanged himself. And the chief priests took the silver pieces, and said, It is not lawful for to put them into the treasury, because it is the price of blood. And they took counsel, and bought with them the potter's field, to bury strangers in. Wherefore that field was called, The field of blood, unto this day. Then was fulfilled that which was spoken by Jeremy the prophet, saying, And they took the thirty pieces of silver, the price of him that was valued, whom they of the children of Israel did value; and gave them for the potter's field, as the Lord appointed me. And Jesus stood before the governor: and the governor asked him, saying, Art thou the King of the Jews? And Jesus said unto him, Thou sayest. And when he was accused of the chief priests and elders, he answered nothing. Then said Pilate unto him, Hearest thou not how many things they witness against thee? And he answered him to never a word: insomuch that the governor marvelled greatly. Now at that feast the governor was wont to release unto the people a prisoner, whom they would. And they had then a notable prisoner, called Barabbas. Therefore when they were gathered together, Pilate said unto them, Whom will ye that I release unto you? Barabbas, or Jesus which is called Christ? For he knew that for envy they had delivered him.

When he was set down on the judgment seat, his wife sent unto him, saying, Have thou nothing to do with that just man: for I have suffered many things this day in a dream because of him. But the chief priests and elders persuaded the multitude that they should ask Barabbas, and

From *The New Testament*.

3

destroy Jesus. The governor answered and said unto them, Whether of the twain will ye that I release unto you? They said, Barabbas. Pilate saith unto them, What shall I do then with Jesus which is called Christ? They all say unto him, Let him be crucified.

And the governor said, Why, what evil hath he done? But they cried out the more, saying, Let him be crucified.

When Pilate saw that he could prevail nothing, but that rather a tumult was made, he took water, and washed his hands before the multitude, saying, I am innocent of the blood of this person: see ye to it. Then answered all the people, and said, His blood be on us, and on our children.

Then released he Barabbas unto them: and when he had scourged Jesus, he delivered him to be crucified.

As Reported by Mark

And straightway in the morning the chief priests held a consultation with the elders and scribes and the whole council, and bound Jesus, and carried him away, and delivered him to Pilate. And Pilate asked him, Art thou the King of the Jews? And he answering said unto him, Thou sayest it. And the chief priests accused him of many things: but he answered nothing. And Pilate asked him again, saying, Answerest thou nothing? behold how many things they witness against thee. But Jesus yet answered nothing; so that Pilate marvelled. Now at that feast he released unto them one prisoner, whomsoever they desired. And there was one named Barabbas, which lay bound with them that had made insurrection with him, who had committed murder in the insurrection. And the multitude crying aloud began to desire him to do as he had ever done unto them. But Pilate answered them, saying, Will ye that I release unto you the King of the Jews? For he knew that the chief priests had delivered him for envy. But the chief priests moved the people, that he should rather release Barabbas unto them. And Pilate answered and said again unto them, What will ye then that I shall do unto him whom ye call the King of the Jews? And they cried out again, Crucify him. Then Pilate said unto them, Why, what evil hath he done? And they cried out the more exceedingly, Crucify him.

And so Pilate, willing to content the people, released Barabbas unto them, and delivered Jesus, when he had scourged him, to be crucified.

As Reported by Luke

And the whole multitude of them arose, and led him unto Pilate. And they began to accuse him, saying, We found this fellow perverting the nation, and forbidding to give tribute to Caesar, saying that he himself is Christ a King. And Pilate asked him, saying, Art thou the King of the

Jews? And he answered him and said, Thou sayest it. Then said Pilate to the chief priests and to the people, I find no fault in this man. And they were the more fierce, saying, He stirreth up the people, teaching throughout all Jewry, beginning from Galilee to this place. When Pilate heard of Galilee, he asked whether the man were a Galilaean. And as soon as he knew that he belonged unto Herod's jurisdiction, he sent him to Herod, who himself also was at Jerusalem at that time.

And when Herod saw Jesus, he was exceeding glad: for he was desirous to see him for a long season, because he had heard many things of him; and he hoped to have seen some miracle done by him. Then he questioned with him in many words; but he answered him nothing. And the chief priests and scribes stood and vehemently accused him. And Herod with his men of war set him at nought, and mocked him, and sent him again to Pilate.

And the same day Pilate and Herod were made friends together: for before they were at enmity between themselves.

And Pilate, when he had called together the chief priests and the rulers and the people, Said unto them, Ye have brought this man unto me, as one that perverteth the people: and, behold, I, having examined him before you, have found no fault in this man touching those things whereof ye accuse him: No, nor yet Herod: for I sent you to him; and, lo, nothing worthy of death is done unto him. I will therefore chastise him, and release him. (For of necessity he must release one unto them at the feast.) And they cried out all at once, saying, Away with this man, and release unto us Barabbas: (Who for a certain sedition made in the city, and for murder, was cast into prison.) Pilate therefore, willing to release Jesus, spake again to them. But they cried, saying, Crucify him, crucify him. And he said unto them the third time, Why, what evil hath he done? I have found no cause of death in him: I will therefore chastise him, and let him go. And they were instant with loud voices, requiring that he might be crucified. And the voices of them and of the chief priests prevailed. And Pilate gave sentence that it should be as they required. And he released unto them him that for sedition and murder was cast into prison, whom they had desired; but he delivered Jesus to their will.

As Reported by John

Then the band and the captain and officers of the Jews took Jesus, and bound him, And led him away to Annas first; for he was father in law to Caiaphas, which was the high priest that same year. Now Caiaphas was he, which gave counsel to the Jews, that it was expedient that one man should die for the people.

And Simon Peter followed Jesus, and so did another disciple: that disciple was known unto the high priest, and went in with Jesus into the palace of the high priest. But Peter stood at the door without. Then went out that other disciple, which was known unto the high priest, and spake unto her that kept the door, and brought in Peter. Then saith the damsel that kept the door unto Peter, Art not thou also one of this man's disciples? He saith, I am not. And the servants and officers stood there, who had made a fire of coals; for it was cold: and they warmed themselves: and Peter stood with them, and warmed himself.

The high priest then asked Jesus of his disciples, and of his doctrine. Jesus answered him, I spake openly to the world; I ever taught in the synagogue, and in the temple, whither the Jews always report; and in secret have I said nothing. Why askest thou me? ask them which heard me, what I have said unto them: behold, they know what I said. And when he had thus spoken, one of the officers which stood by struck Jesus with the palm of his hand, saying, Answerest thou the high priest so? Jesus answered him, If I have spoken evil, bear witness to the evil: but if well, why smitest thou me? Now Annas had sent him bound unto Caiaphas the high priest. And Simon Peter stood and warmed himself. They said therefore unto him, Art not thou also one of his disciples? He denied it, and said, I am not. One of the servants of the high priest, being his kinsman whose ear Peter cut off, saith, Did not I see thee in the garden with him? Peter then denied again: and immediately the cock crew.

Then led they Jesus from Caiaphas unto the hall of judgment: and it was early; and they themselves went not into the judgment hall, lest they should be defiled; but that they might eat the passover. Pilate then went out unto them, and said, What accusation bring ye against this man? They answered and said unto him, If he were not a malefactor, we would not have delivered him up unto thee. Then said Pilate unto them, Take ye him, and judge him according to your law. The Jews therefore said unto him, It is not lawful for us to put any man to death: That the saying of Jesus might be fulfilled, which he spake, signifying what death he should die. Then Pilate entered into the judgment hall again, and called Jesus, and said unto him, Art thou the King of the Jews? Jesus answered him, Sayest thou this thing of thyself, or did others tell it thee of me? Pilate answered, Am I a Jew? Thine own nation and the chief priests have delivered thee unto me: what hast thou done? Jesus answered, My kingdom is not of this world: if my kingdom were of this world, then would my servants fight, that I should not be delivered to the Jews: but now is my kingdom not from hence. Pilate therefore said unto him, Art thou a king then? Jesus answered, Thou sayest I am a king. To this end I was born, and for this cause came I into the world, that I should bear witness unto the truth. Every one that is of the truth heareth my voice. Pilate saith unto him, What is truth? And when he said this, he went out again unto the Jews, and saith unto them, I find in him no fault at all. But ye have a custom, that I should release unto you one at the passover: will ye therefore that I release unto you the King of the Jews? Then cried they all again, saying, Not this man, but Barabbas. Now Barabbas was a robber. Then Pilate therefore took Jesus, and scourged him. And the soldiers platted a crown of thorns, and put it on his head, and they put on him a purple robe, And said, Hail, King of the Jews! and they smote him with their hands. Pilate therefore went forth again, and saith unto them, Behold, I bring him forth to you, that ye may know that I find no fault in him. Then came Jesus forth, wearing the crown of thorns, and the purple robe. And Pilate saith unto them, Behold the man! When the chief priests therefore and officers saw him, they cried out, Crucify him, crucify him. Pilate saith unto them, Take ye him, and crucify him: for I find no fault in him. The Jews answered him, We have a law, and by our law he ought to die, because he made himself the Son of God.

When Pilate therefore heard that saying, he was the more afraid: And went again into the judgment hall, and saith unto Jesus, Whence art thou? But Jesus gave him no answer. Then saith Pilate unto him, Speakest thou not unto me? knowest thou not that I have power to crucify thee, and have power to release thee? Jesus answered, Thou couldest have no power at all against me, except it were given thee from above; therefore he that delivered me unto thee hath the greater sin. And from thenceforth Pilate sought to release him: but the Jews cried out, saying, If thou let this man go, thou art not Caesar's friend: whosoever maketh himself a king speaketh against Caesar.

When Pilate therefore heard that saying, he brought Jesus forth, and sat down in the judgment seat in a place that is called the pavement, but in the Hebrew, Gabbatha. And it was the preparation of the passover, and about the sixth hour: and he saith unto the Jews, Behold your King! But they cried out, Away with him, away with him, crucify him. Pilate saith unto them, Shall I crucify your King? The chief priests answered, We have no king but Caesar. Then delivered he him therefore unto them to be crucified. And they took Jesus, and led him away. And he bearing his cross went forth into a place called the place of a skull, which is called in the Hebrew Golgotha: Where they crucified him, and two other with him, on either side one, and Jesus in the midst.

And Pilate wrote a title, and put it on the cross. And the writing was, JESUS OF NAZARETH THE KING OF THE JEWS. This title then read many of the Jews: for the place where Jesus was crucified was nigh to the city: and it was written in Hebrew, and Greek, and Latin. Then said the chief priests of the Jews to Pilate, Write not, The King of the Jews; but that he said, I am King of the Jews. Pilate answered, What I have written I have written.

Galileo and the Inquisition

Zsolt de Harsanyi

IT WAS APRIL 12th when they led him into the Council Room of the Holy Office. Two men supported him, the servant of the Embassy and a Dominican friar. They set him down in the anteroom. He was in great pain again, clenching his teeth and groaning; with all his strength he tried to control himself. From inside the Council Chamber came many voices, but their words were inaudible.

"Are those my judges?" he asked the Dominican.

"I can tell you nothing," the monk replied.

He waited, touching with his right hand his helpless left arm to move it slowly and carefully. Then he fingered the bandage of his rupture. He swallowed hard, his heart was pounding. The door opened and a monk called his name. They helped him up and into the room, which was large and well lighted. In the middle a long table with a crucifix. And on the other side of the table three priests: Firenzuola and two others. The accused was led to the center of the long table, face to face with his judges. The President of the Court, who sat between the other two, glanced up.

"Is the accused ill?" he asked in Latin.

"I have sharp pains in my joints and ought really to be in bed."

"Then we permit you to be seated throughout the trial. But before you sit you must take an oath. I declare the proceedings opened."

The servant and the Dominican were still at his side, and he leaned on them. The clerk had soon taken his description: Galileo Galilei, Court mathematician, seventy years old, of Florence. Then Firenzuola rose with the other two judges. He announced the oath: "I swear to speak the whole truth . . ."

"So help me God, the Blessed Virgin, and all the Saints of God."

The judges sat down again; a chair was brought for the prisoner. He lowered himself slowly with many groans. Firenzuola signed to the Dominican and the servant, who bowed and withdrew. "Let the accused say whether he knows the reason why he is summoned here before the Holy Office."

"I have no official knowledge of it. But I think it is to answer for my recently published work."

"Is this the book?" asked the President, holding up the copy.

"It is."

"Entitled *Dialogue,* etc. To save time we shall simply refer to it as *Dialogue,* throughout this trial, and shall not use its full title. Well, then. Do you acknowledge that you have written every word in this book yourself?"

"I do."

"Very well. Now let us turn to the preliminaries. Beginning with the year of Our Lord sixteen hundred and sixteen. Did the accused visit Rome in that year?"

"Yes, I did."

"What was the reason of your visit?"

"I had heard that the doctrine of the immobility of the sun and the movement of the earth, as stated by Copernicus, had various opponents in the Church. A certain Father Caccini preached against it in Florence and against its followers. I therefore came to Rome to assure myself as to the official viewpoint of the Church. This happened, not in 1616 but in December, 1615, though I stayed in Rome till the beginning of the following April."

"Never mind that. Let us say that you were here in 1616. Did you come by your own decision?"

"I did."

"Didn't you receive any call or summons?"

"No."

"Think again. Weren't you commanded by the Holy Office at that time to appear in Rome?"

"Not at all," he answered with surprise. "I had nothing to do with the Holy Office. I'd heard that there had been some denunciation; but the man Lorini didn't denounce me, only what he called my disciples."

"Are you quite sure that you hadn't been summoned? Have you any witness that you came of your own free will?"

"I discussed the journey with my Prince, His Highness Cosimo of blessed memory. The Prime Minister of Florence, Picchena, also knew of my decision. And Guicciardini, who was the Ambassador for Florence."

"I see. And all these are dead, of course."

Galileo did not answer. He began to see the trend of these questions. They wanted to prove that he had already been tried by the Inquisition. And in that case his offense would be judged with double severity. The instinct of the hunted animal sharpened his wits again.

"So you insist," the President said, "that you hadn't received any official summons and came to Rome of your own free will?"

"Yes, I remember it clearly; there cannot be any doubt of it. And if I had received any summons there would be a record of it in the archives.

But that record cannot be found, because I myself decided to take the journey."

"Very well, let's leave all that for now. Tell me, what clerical persons did you meet at that time in Rome?"

Galileo first mentioned Bellarmin. Then he named Father Grienberger, Count Querengo, Cardinal Del Monte, Orsini, the Dominican General Maraffi, Cardinal Gaetani. . . .

"Now tell us what you discussed with these men."

"Yes, Father. I'll leave Cardinal Bellarmin to the last, because with him I talked most and discussed the most important things. With Father Grienberger we talked mostly about my beloved late master, Father Clavius, but also about Copernicus. Count Querengo I had met in Padua. I discussed with him the essential meaning of the Copernican system and the possibility of influencing the Prelates of the Church in its favor. The same questions I discussed with Cardinal Del Monte and Cardinal Orsini, who enjoyed the special favor of Pope Paul. With Father Maraffi, I talked of the Dominicans who had attacked me. Cardinal Gaetani, an important official of the Holy Office, I asked to request Campanella, at that time still imprisoned at Naples, to give an expert opinion, which he did. But mostly I argued with Cardinal Bellarmin. He thought . . ."

He stopped suddenly. He had been going to say that Bellarmin thought the doctrine of Copernicus would threaten the whole spiritual and temporal structure of the Church. But if he told these people that, he would give them arms to use against him.

"Well, why do you hesitate?"

"Forgive me, I was only collecting my thoughts. Cardinal Bellarmin thought that the doctrine of Copernicus contradicted the literal meaning of certain passages in the Bible. We talked often and at great length about this, but I was unable to convince him."

"What, generally speaking, was the source of these conversations?"

"The interest shown by higher clergy. At that time proceedings had been started against the works of Foscarini, Zuniga, and Copernicus. The Prelates wished to be informed of the scientific essentials of the problem; therefore they consulted me, as an expert. But only in the capacity of an expert; I had no other status. I came freely to Rome; the proceedings of the Holy Office did not touch me personally. I was interested in them only as an astronomer. It was also important for me to know what the Holy Church said about this teaching in which I believed."

"Well, and what did the Church say?"

"The controversy on this teaching that the sun stands still and the earth moves was decided by the Holy Congregation of the Index as follows: To assert such an opinion directly is in contradiction to Holy Writ, and therefore forbidden; such an opinion must only be asserted in the way Copernicus asserted it, as a mathematical possibility."

"Was the accused informed of this? And if so, by whom?"

"I was informed. By Cardinal Bellarmin."

"Very well. Tell us exactly what His Eminence told you, whether he informed you of anything else, and what it was."

"His Eminence told me that it was permitted to maintain the doctrine of Copernicus as a hypothesis, just as Copernicus himself had done. His Eminence knew that I conceived the doctrine only as a hypothesis. This is proved by the letter which His Eminence sent to the Carmelite Provincial Foscarini, and of which I possess a duplicate."

He selected the letter from among his documents and laid it on the table.

"Dated April 12, 1615, a year before the decree of the Inquisition. I have underlined one sentence here. 'Your Reverence and Messer Galilei would do wisely, I think, if you would be content to treat this matter hypothetically, and make no positive assertions.' "

The letter caused surprise. One judge handed it to the other. Galileo had treasured it for seventeen years. The Lynxes had given him the duplicate. The President said a little sharply:

"There is no need to talk about 1615. We want to know what happened in February 1616."

"Yes, Father. In February, Cardinal Bellarmin informed me that the doctrine of Copernicus taken as reality was in contradiction to Holy Writ; therefore it was forbidden either to maintain or to defend it, but permitted to conceive of it as a theory and write about it in that sense. To prove this I have a document given to me by His Eminence Bellarmin on May 26, 1616, in which he says that the doctrine of Copernicus must not be directly asserted nor defended. Allow me to present a copy of it."

He drew forth this paper. For a long time he had been uncertain whether he should use or withhold it. In the end he decided that it must be shown. The points against him he could not explain away. But the judges could see that Bellarmin did not force his scientific integrity.

"When you were informed of this, were you alone with Cardinal Bellarmin?"

"No. Some Dominican Fathers were also present. But I didn't know them and haven't seen them since."

"Were you told of any interdiction at that time? Think carefully."

"I want to tell you everything I know. His Eminence sent for me one morning. He reminded me of certain matters to which he felt I must first draw the attention of His Holiness before I talked to anyone else about them."

"What's that you're saying?"

All the judges stared in surprise at Galileo, who did not answer. The President shook his head. Firenzuola's face became still icier as he spoke:

"That must be put into the records. The accused can continue."

"Thereafter the Cardinal explained to me that I must neither uphold nor defend the Copernican doctrine. I must only treat it as a theory."

"Only as a hypothesis. I see. Did anybody hear him saying that?"

"Perhaps the Dominican Fathers . . ."

The President suddenly changed in tone. Up to now he had been asking his questions monotonously. Now he shouted at the accused.

"Perhaps. You say—perhaps! What talk is this? Were the Dominican Fathers present or not?"

The old man winced. Something told him that now it was beginning. Now he must show absolute obedience and not a trace of argument.

"I don't remember. Seventeen years are a long time."

"So perhaps they weren't present at all?" Firenzuola continued his attack.

"Perhaps they weren't."

"So perhaps nobody heard the Cardinal say it?"

"Maybe. I don't remember."

"But if your memory is so bad, perhaps you can't even remember exactly what words the Cardinal said."

"He may have said something which I can't remember any more."

"Suppose that I refresh your memory? Suppose I read you the records of that hearing? Even then would you still be as forgetful?"

"I hardly think so, Monsignor."

"Well, listen to this. I have the record here in front of me."

Friday the twenty-sixth. In the Palace inhabited by His Grace the Cardinal and specifically in his private apartments, after the aforesaid Galilei was summoned and appeared, the Cardinal adjured Galilei in the presence of Fra Michelangelo Segnitius de Lauda, Chief Inquisitor of the Holy Office, to give up his erroneous convictions; immediately afterward the aforesaid Chief Inquisitor in my presence, in the presence of these witnesses, and likewise of His Grace Cardinal Bellarmin, commanded and prescribed Galilei in the name of His Holiness the Pope and the Holy Office to renounce completely the doctrine of the immobility of the Sun and the movement of the Earth, not to maintain it in any way, not to teach it, neither in writing nor orally, nor should he defend it, since otherwise the Holy Office would start proceedings against him. Galilei accepted this injunction and swore obedience. In witness whereof Nadino Nores etcetera, Augustino Mongard etcetera.

"What do you say now, accused?"

Galileo's temple throbbed. He remembered clearly that it had not happened in this way. Only Bellarmin spoke; the Dominicans had hovered around in silence. This record had either been drawn up falsely at that time, or someone had fabricated now a pseudo-memorandum containing the fatal expression "not to maintain it in any way, not to teach it . . . nor defend it." Not even in the form of a hypothesis! His first instinct was to cry out: "This document is a forgery!" But he could not. To accuse the Inquisition of forgery? His next step would be to the scaffold.

"Well, why don't you answer? Do you remember that it was thus?"

"I can't remember."

"You can't remember. But it might have been thus?"

Galileo was silent. He felt giddy. Firenzuola roared:

"Well? Might it have been thus? Or do you suggest that the records lie?"

The words came slowly, hoarsely, almost like groans from the tortured old man.

"It might have been thus."

"At last! So you received an unmistakable injunction?"

"I can't remember what was said."

"This protocol remembers better than you do, though, and you admit that it may have happened like this. Well, have you anything more to say?"

"I would humbly call the attention of Your Eminences to the fact that the document which His Eminence Bellarmin gave me does not contain the expressions 'neither to teach it orally nor in writing,' 'not to maintain it in any way.' "

"It doesn't contain them. But the records do. Well, who was it that issued the injunction?"

"His Eminence Cardinal Bellarmin."

"Haven't you heard with your own ears from the record that you were informed by the Chief Inquisitor of the Holy Office, in the name of His Holiness the Pope and the Inquisition?"

"I'd forgotten that. Nor do I seem to remember the presence of His Reverence the Chief Inquisitor."

"But he might have been present? Well? Speak! Speak!"

The accused had great difficulty in answering. He answered in a voice that could scarcely be heard:

"Yes . . . he might have been present."

"Good! So now we can sum up the following facts: The Holy Office ruled that this doctrine was blasphemous; the Chief Inquisitor officially forbade the accused in the name of His Holiness the Pope and the Holy Office to maintain such a theory in any way, or in any form. Now answer my question: Did you, after receiving this injunction, ever ask to be released from it to write your *Dialogue?*"

"No."

"And why did you not request such permission?"

"I didn't suppose that I had infringed an injunction by my book."

"You didn't suppose that you infringed an injunction which you had received? And in spite of which you wrote your book! Tell me, how did you get the imprimatur from the Reverend Father Chamberlain at the Vatican?"

Galileo related in detail his dealings with Riccardi.

"Did you tell the Father Chamberlain about the interdiction of 1616? No? Then why not?"

"Because my book does not directly teach Copernicus. I enumerate all the counter-arguments."

"And are they stronger? Well? Did you hear my question? According to the accused, which arguments are stronger in his book? Those for, or against, Copernicus?"

"Those . . . against . . . him . . ."

"And the arguments for him? Are they weak?"

Suddenly the accused broke into sobs. He was being asked to pronounce judgment against the work of fifty years.

"Yes, they are weak."

Angelus bells rang through the window. At once the judges were on their feet. The prisoner had to rise unaided, groaning and gasping for breath. The Inquisitors finished their silent prayer, and the President said:

"Before I close the proceedings, the accused must take another oath."

He had to swear to say nothing about this examination to anyone in word or writing. Two priests came to support him. He took the oath.

"So help me God and the Blessed Virgin and all God's Saints!"

And now the President gave his order.

Galileo thought that they were taking him to the torture chamber. He was still in tears as he limped away, leaning on two human crutches. Step by step they helped him down stairs and along passages. He was almost beside himself with fear. Instead they opened the door of a well-furnished suite—a suite of three rooms, all of them clean, light, and airy. He gazed around in timid amazement. This could not really be the truth. But at the same time came a knock at the door and the President of the Court himself entered.

"I hope that you'll find this suite to your liking."

"Are all the three rooms mine?"

"Yes, we've taken them temporarily from one of our Brothers, who has moved into another part of the building. You have the Florentine Embassy to thank for it. Her Excellency Signora Niccolini has already sent your luggage. Your servant is to sleep in the anteroom. As a special favor we are not going to lock your door, but you must not leave this part of the corridor. All this is an unheard-of concession."

The servant came to report that the prisoner's dinner had come from the Embassy.

"Very well, then I won't disturb him. If you need anything your servant can always find me in the building. Now sign this protocol of to-day's session. I wish you a very good appetite. . . ."

First that horrible cross-examination—and now this! Galileo thought that he was dreaming. Firenzuola left, and he crept into bed, where he ate his meal. Signora Niccolini had sent him all his favorite dishes and a flagon of her best wine, which he gulped down greedily, and fell fast asleep. He slept for sixteen hours—the first real sleep he had known for weeks. When he woke next day, the sunlight was streaming through his window. His first thought was about the proceedings. He winced, remembering the mental torture; but his physical pain was less than before. The quiet rest and the huge physical relief that there were no torture chambers to be faced had done his health good. On the third day he was able to get out of bed and totter around in the three rooms, leaning on his servant or clinging to the furniture. On the fifth day he dressed and went out into the corridor. He was only allowed the use of a short section of the long passage in which to exercise. He must not go beyond the turn of the wall. Sometimes he glanced into the courtyard, where fresh flowers looked gay and friendly. It was difficult to think that these were the flowers of the Inquisition.

On the fifth day Firenzuola visited him, with official news that the Holy Office had asked three experts to decide how far the *Dialogue* transgressed the injunction which its author had received seventeen years ago. Melchiore Inkhofer and Agustino Oregio found that the author had certainly maintained and defended the forbidden doctrine in his work; the third expert, Zaccaria Pasqualiga, thought that he had also taught it.

"I tell you this," Firenzuola said, "because it proves you guilty beyond all question. Therefore you may soon expect your punishment. Try to reconcile yourself and be contrite."

"What will be my punishment?" he stammered.

"Even if I knew, I couldn't tell you. But you must know that your crime is a very serious one, and probably your punishment will be heavy. The only comfort which now remains to you is to seek for repentance within yourself and regret deeply what you have done."

"Forgive me, Monsignor; could I hope for a milder punishment if I do public penance?"

"Penance done for reward shows no real contrition. Of course the judges will decide whether your penitence is sincere or only the usual mumming of the accused."

With that he departed. But Galileo was left with the terrible thought, "a heavy punishment." That could only mean one thing—the stake. Pope Urban thought that he had held him up in the figure of Simpiicio to the ridicule of the whole world. Therefore Pope Urban would burn him publicly. This was not such a wild idea. Pope Paul had had an unlucky man beheaded because he had compared Pope Gregory to Tiberius in a manuscript which had never even been published.

The physical improvement of the last few days was all spoiled by this visit. His pain returned, racking his body so that it was difficult not to scream. He dug his head into the pillows and moaned, panted, gnashed his teeth. Sometimes, when it was sheer impossibility any longer to bear this torture alone, he would send for his servant and grip his hand. "What will they do to me, Giovanni? Will they torture me? Will they burn me alive?" The servant could not bear the sight of such agony. He went to see the Inquisitor of his own accord. Firenzuola and Sincero, the attorney of the Inquisition, came into Galileo's room. They were astonished at his state. They questioned him about his ailment, even consoled him. Firenzuola promised to find something to ease his pain.

"I've brought you good news," he said next day. "The Holy Office is willing to permit your return to the villa of the Florentine Embassy. That is to say, when you can bear to move; for now you cannot."

"No, no—though I long to get back there."

"Well, well, come now! Take hold of yourself. We promise you that as soon as you can stand on your feet, you shall be taken back to the Embassy. But there is a condition attached."

"I'm willing to fulfill any condition."

"You must give some token of your full and complete repentance."

"Yes, Father. What token am I to give?"

"It will lose its meaning should I prescribe its nature. You must think of some way in which to show your deep contrition."

And so they left him with his pain, having set him a riddle. He himself must find what it was they wanted. Now he was prepared for everything, racked as he was from head to foot and in constant dread of being burned. His whole being longed for the Embassy, the consoling warmth of the Niccolinis.

He struggled for a whole week, sending for a copy of his book and reading certain passages with deep attention.

In a week the decision ripened in him; he would apologize humbly, asking only for his poor sickly life. He sent a message to Firenzuola.

"Monsignor, may I be received by the Holy Office? I want to make a declaration with full repentance."

"Very well. Repentance is always welcome to God, and we also can appreciate it. What is your state of health? Tomorrow, April 27th, we have a meeting. Can you appear then?"

"Yes. I'd even go there dying, because I can't stand this any longer. But, Monsignor, for God's sake, they won't send me to the stake if I show real penitence?"

"Are you setting conditions? What sort of a penitence is this? It displeases the Holy Office to hear such words."

"No, no, I have no stipulations. But look at me, Monsignor, I'm hardly alive. Even now, there's only a tiny spark of life left in me. I don't know what I'm saying. Be merciful to me. . . ."

"I told you that if you show real penitence we'll let you go back to the Embassy. Tomorrow you must appear before your judges and give a token of your remorse—but without stipulations."

All that day and night he thought of nothing but what he could say to his judges. Early next morning he was still repeating the humbling sentences. A strange instinct took hold of him: as if he had joined forces with his torturers and were helping them with savage lust to humiliate, torment the man who had been Galileo Galilei. "How I have sinned against myself," he thought suddenly in these moments of upheaval. Why did he punish himself so cruelly? He could find no answer.

In the early morning they led him before his judges. The three priests with crucifix in front of them sat waiting.

"We have been informed that the accused wishes to make a declaration."

"Yes, Monsignor," he answered softly, with bowed head, "if you will deign to hear me."

There was a pause. The well-prepared sentences would not come.

"Well? We are listening."

"Ever since my last examination," at last he began, "I have repeated your question in my mind and striven to collect my memories. Especially I tried to recall the injunction of seventeen years ago, that I must not maintain, defend, or even teach the doctrine of the earth's movement 'in any form.' Then I remembered that I hadn't read the *Dialogue* for three years, and ought to go through it again now, to see whether, against my best intentions, something hadn't slipped out of my quill in consequence of . . . in consequence . . ."

"Well? Well?"

"Forgive me, I'm very excited and short of breath. Whether something hadn't slipped from my quill in consequence of which the reader and the Church authorities could accuse me not merely of general disobedience but of having encouraged, in certain passages, the opinion that I had set myself up against the teaching of Holy Church. By the great kindness of the Holy Office I was able to send out my servant for a copy. I have read it very attentively, weighing every word. I hadn't read it for such a long time that it seemed to be a new book, written by a stranger. And I must acknowledge something most repentantly . . ."

"Speak."

"In several passages I perceived that a reader who did not know my method of thinking, might receive a false impression. Because, although I wanted to refute the false doctrine . . ."

He swallowed hard and stopped. He was now denying the whole scientific aim, faith, and conviction of his life. But nothing happened. Only something glinted for a moment in Firenzuola's eyes.

". . . the false doctrine," continued Galileo, "by accident I presented the arguments in such a way that the reader might have gathered the opposite impression."

He stopped again and collected his thoughts. Oh, yes, he wanted to mention the argument of the Pope and humiliate himself to the Jesuit Scheiner. If the Jesuits meant to send him to the stake, he must win their mercy.

"Especially I elaborated two arguments which might seem too extreme from one who was trying to prove the exact opposite. One was about the sunspots, the other about the problem of ebb and tide. I would like to explain how it happened. Since I wanted to disprove the false doctrine . . . the false doctrine, my method of composition required, especially in

such a dialogue form, that I should expound these fallacies as fully as
possible. Otherwise I couldn't have refuted them. But human vanity got
the better of me. I delighted in the skill of my mind, in my power of finding clever and easy arguments, even for falsehood—in possessing a finer
intellect than others. But though, like Cicero, *avidior sim gloriae quam
satis est,* if I had to write these passages now, I'd do them differently. I'd
take the strength out of them in such a way as to make them seem not
even plausible. Therefore I want to declare to my judges that I have been
at fault, out of vain ambition, carelessness, and . . . ignorance. . . ."

Galileo Galilei had denied truth and lied. He had spurned the sacred
birth of science. He looked eagerly at Firenzuola and the two other
judges. He waited for their praise—or at least approval. Surely they must
know what a terrible decision he had taken in these last weeks of infernal
agony, how in two minutes he had renounced the thought of his whole
life, was kneeling here in the dust to the Peripatetics. Firenzuola ought to
be feeling jubilant. Galilei as a scientist was dead. But the Inquisitor
showed no signs of satisfaction. He resumed in a monotonous voice:

"We take cognizance of this declaration and command the accused to
repeat it in writing with his own signature. This document will be enclosed in the records. Now you can go."

No praise, not a word about the Embassy, no reward for this unheard-
of betrayal. Galileo turned toward the door and began to cry.

"I want to go back," he said, sobbing, to the Dominican at the door.
"Let me go back. I want to say something else."

He dragged himself back. The judges were still in their places.

"I want to add something," he said in a weak, tearful voice. "Something more. Even more than this."

"Yes?"

"I want to make it even plainer that I don't consider this . . . this accursed doctrine of the moving earth and stationary sun. That I never
thought it was true. . . . I ask only for opportunity and time, Very Reverend Fathers. . . ."

"No tears! Collect yourself and speak."

"The three characters in my book had agreed to meet again in the future and discuss other questions of natural science. Therefore I have the
possibility to continue my work. I promise to enumerate again the arguments of the false and accursed doctrine and disprove them as far as the
merciful God enables me to do. I will prove that the earth is immobile and
the sun moves around it . . . the sun . . ."

His sobs made his words incoherent. He staggered and had to clutch
the edge of the table. He fell on his knees, weeping desperately.

"Mercy . . . don't burn me . . . don't . . . I implore you on my
knees. . . ."

They did not answer, but waited till his fit passed. When he calmed
down a little, Sincero helped him to his feet, while Firenzuola said:

"You can also put this new declaration into writing. Now I will ask the promised favor of His Holiness. Prepare to return today to the Embassy."

The old man began to sob again, but now with relief. Firenzuola declared the proceedings to be adjourned. Both he and the third judge came over to him, consoling, quieting Galileo.

"No more tears," Firenzuola insisted, "but listen, for I have something important to tell you. I am acting against the rules of the Sacred College, but I want to show you our special good will as reward for your penitence. There will be another hearing soon, when I shall command you to submit your defense within eight days to the Holy Office. Think it over. It must be very sincere, repentant, and especially very brief. And now return to your rooms and rest."

The same afternoon he moved back to the Embassy. It happened with surprising quickness: Firenzuola obtained this favor as soon as session rose. It was as though the Pope's permission had been all ready, waiting for the repentance of the accused. Niccolini had known nothing about it; the Holy Office kept its secrets. He received the old man with happy surprise, embraced him gently, and hastened to send a special courier to Florence with the glad news. Signora Niccolini wept for joy.

When Firenzuola gave him permission to depart, he warned him that he must tell the Ambassador nothing of the way in which his case had been tried. He was also forbidden to see visitors or leave the Medici villa. These last two stipulations meant nothing to him. If he was able to walk he could always sun himself in the beautiful garden of the villa. But it was very hard to keep silent about his case. He longed to go over it all with the Ambassador, ask his advice, find out about the probable punishment. But, humbled and terrified as he was, he dared not break the command.

He gave much thought to his written defense. A difficult business, since he would have to dart like a squirrel between falsehood and truth, and in such a way as not to wound the susceptibilities of the Holy Office. He could not question the full interdiction, acknowledgement of which had been forced out of him. He tore up several different versions before he hit on the final form. He made it short, as they had commanded. His line of thought was simple and clear. He had been informed of the injunction contained in that fatal memorandum. Yet at the same time Cardinal Bellarmin had given him a document which proved that he had never been commanded to deny officially any standpoint, and, though one sentence of this document mentioned interdiction of Copernicus, it did not use the expressions "in any way" or "not to teach." He had forgotten in these seventeen years the oral command, while he possessed the written directions of the Cardinal. Humanly it was quite understandable that he should forget the verbal information, while he clung to the document which did not forbid the form of hypothesis. He had written the *Dialogue* as a hypothesis, and if it caused any misunderstanding he was prepared to make every reparation: prepared to write a book refuting Copernicus.

Ten days passed without news of his case. But fate did not spare him other trials. Celeste sent alarming letters: the plague, already abating, had broken out more venomously. There were cases in the suburbs of Florence, and people were dying by scores in the city. Here at least was a subject of deep alarm he could discuss with the Niccolinis.

"Your Excellencies"—he showed them the letter—"fate has forced me into a horrible situation. Here I live in terror of the stake, while at home the plague threatens my family. I am full of fears. If my daughters die of the plague, my despair will kill me. Your Excellency, what is the sin for which God punishes me like this?"

"Wait a moment," said Signora Caterina. "I too have had a letter from Celeste. Let me read it to you—you'll feel calmer."

They read the letter together. It glowed with warm love and the certainty that her father was near the end of his troubles. Nobody else could offer such comfort, give such sweet peace. She was like the saints; her letter was like the pardoning hands which the blessed stretch out to souls in Purgatory.

On May 10th they summoned him again. Firenzuola in a dull official voice informed him that he had permission to compose and present within eight days his written defense. That ended the hearing. They permitted him to return to the Embassy.

Although up to now he had been almost mad with despair, now he fell into the opposite extreme. This denial of the greatest thought of his life seemed to him a monstrous sacrifice. Only life was worth more than that. He had paid the highest price for his bare existence, the most he could give, in exchange for his few remaining years; his judges must know what it had cost him. The Pope must hear how this victim of outraged vanity had gone to the last limits of self-abasement. If really he had secret organized enemies, they had won a full victory. What more could they want? Galileo felt like a man who had been taxed of everything save his life, and now as a pauper was meeting the bailiff. He had ceased to fear torture or burning alive. He knew that he would receive severe punishment, that he would have to add chapters to his *Dialogue* disproving Copernicus, that he himself would have to do penance. His scientific career was over, but the gentle joys of his old age remained.

He sent hopeful letters to all and sundry, avoiding carefully any reference to his case. But certain signs pointed to the fact that others were also spreading the news of a better turn in his affairs. Suddenly more letters began to arrive; many more congratulations, expressing joy at the results. One of them came from Ascanio Piccolomini, the young Archbishop of Siena. He sent warm greetings to the scientist, urging him to come to Siena and recuperate there from the strain and suffering. He promised him a litter and servants, an affectionate host who would do all he could. The pleasant tone of these letters gave him assurance. His health improved, his joints began to ache less, he could walk for a long time in the garden, and in general had begun to feel much better. All he wanted now was to hear his sentence soon.

But the Holy Office kept silence for many weeks. Niccolini tried to urge their decision, but the Inquisitors refused to discuss the matter—that would have been against the rules of the Holy Office. The Pope saw him once and gave him a noncommittal answer. The most he could do was to turn to Florence and ask the Grand Duke to intervene. But even this proved unexpectedly difficult. One night the servant who was putting Galileo to bed seemed to have something on his mind, but hesitated. Galileo noticed it and began to question him.

"Promise me, Your Honor, not to betray me."

"You can trust me, sirrah."

"I've heard something from their Excellencies' butler. He was listening one day when His Excellency and the Signora were talking about you. They were very angry with Lord Cioli of Florence. Because, if you don't mind my saying it, though I'm only a servant, Cioli is a bad man and is doing his best to spite Your Honor. He's written my master a letter saying that you ought not to be living here, and costing the Court a lot of money when you could lodge for nothing in the prison of the Holy Office. Their Excellencies were both very angry about it. The butler heard what His Excellency has written to Florence. He wrote to my Lord Cioli that you cost no more than fifteen scudi a month. So you could stay here for six months on a hundred scudi. And if the Government took objection to this, His Excellency would be glad to throw the money at their heads, out of his own pocket. But, for God's sake, Your Honor, don't tell on me, because we two servants would get into trouble . . ."

His host's kindness deeply touched Galileo. Although he could not betray his servant, he took the earliest opportunity to mention the cost of his stay to Niccolini. His host interrupted.

"Our Duke is no miser to haggle over a few gold pieces. Don't let that trouble you; you've trouble enough here. You can stay as long as you like; the rest is my business."

"I only mentioned it . . ."

"Don't waste your breath, old friend. I have more important news. I've received a summons for tomorrow morning from the Pope. I asked for an audience to plead your cause."

"Pleading is not enough, Your Excellency. Try to find out what my punishment is likely to be. Shall I be told to make a pilgrimage, or go for a certain time to a monastery? That is the sort of punishment the Holy Office inflicts if it is lenient, and perhaps you could ask what they mean to do with my book."

"I'll do my best. And as soon as I know I'll come back to tell you."

The Ambassador returned next day at noon and found Galileo in the garden.

"Your sentence is prepared, Messer, but I still can't find out what it is. It can't be very severe, but I'm afraid it won't be very mild either. I asked the Pope frankly. He told me that the sentence had been passed by the College of Cardinals in the Holy Office, according to the tribunal's report, but he didn't know it. Of course, that is impossible, since probably he has fixed it himself. But they always keep the verdicts of the Inquisition a strict secret till publication. When I insisted, he only said: 'We don't know in the least what will happen to him. He must be punished. The mildest sentence would be detention in a monastery for a certain time. After sentence has been passed, you must visit us again. Then we can discuss what we can do to spare him any really great sorrow.' This at least makes it clear that there's no danger at the stake or whatever else you were so afraid of. So let's hope for the best. We shall soon know now."

Three days later, on June 20th, the summons arrived: the accused was to be ready next morning at nine, at the Holy Office. He felt very much excited, but not terrified. He knew that they were going to let him live. He felt rather curious to know what they meant to offer him in exchange for forswearing himself and his life's whole work.

Next morning, at nine sharp, he faced his judges. He could stand again. There were still only three of them to judge him, and he felt surprised that in such an important case sentence should be pronounced with so little solemnity. Why had the Peripatetics of the Church refrained from making this an occasion for public rejoicing, a feast of triumph?

"We will question the accused again," Firenzuola said. "Take the usual oath."

He repeated it and was amazed. A new questioning? Was the Pope mistaken about the sentence being ready? When they allowed him to sit down he was still surprised.

"Has the accused any new declaration to make?"

"No."

"Let him tell the Court how long ago he began to believe that the earth moves round the sun, and whether he believes it still."

"A long time ago. That is to say, before the Holy Congregation of the Index decided the matter by decree, and I was not informed of it. I was still uncertain what to think, and considered both systems of the universe, those of Ptolemy and Copernicus, as possible. But once the Congregation had decided the matter, I was convinced by the wisdom of my superiors. Then every uncertainty was dispelled from my mind, and I knew at once that Ptolemy's theory of the earth's immobility and the sun's movement is indisputable."

"Why, then, did you write a book so long afterward, dealing with the very certainty? Can you deny that this work gives the impression that the accused believed in Copernicus in his secret soul?"

Galileo had begun to answer, but Firenzuola's face was suddenly hard again. He almost shouted:

"You've taken an oath to tell the truth! Answer us therefore truthfully and plainly. Did you and do you uphold this Copernican heresy? We aren't interested in what you are prepared to declare to us! Tell us what you believe in your heart! The truth!"

The old man trembled. He could not turn back on the road he had taken. They were forcing him to lie—under oath.

"As for my *Dialogue,* it wasn't written because I believed Copernican heresy. All I did was to try to serve the community by setting forth the astronomical arguments for these two cosmologies. I wanted to show that neither Ptolemy nor Copernicus brings decisive proof, and that, therefore, if we seek for certainty, we can only find it in higher teaching, only in the decision of Holy Church—as is shown by many passages in my book. I declare upon my conscience and oath that, after the decision of the Church, I did not and do not uphold the accursed teaching."

"These are idle words. The accused uses his tongue very skillfully, but he cannot convince. His arguments for Copernicus were much better! Prisoner, I warn you to tell the truth, because we have other instruments."

But Galileo answered stubbornly: "No. Once they forbade this doctrine, I turned away from it. That's all I can tell you. Here I am in your hands, Very Reverend Judges. Do with me whatever you wish."

The three judges rose. Galileo stumbled to his feet. The President of the Inquisition pointed to him and cried in a solemn voice:

"In the name of the Holy Office, I warn you for the last time to speak plain truth, or we shall use the instruments of torture."

Galileo blenched, but his nerves were steady. His brain worked with lightning speed. What should he say? If he altered anything he would both admit that he was a perjurer and had written his book with deliberate malice. He looked straight in Firenzuola's eyes:

"I came here to obey," his voice was tremulous but distinct. "I repeat that after the Church had decided, I ceased to believe in Copernicus."

Firenzuola thought for an instant, and then glanced at his two companions. They understood his questioning look, which remained a mystery to the prisoner. Both of them nodded. The President shrugged.

"Now go to the anteroom and wait till we call you."

He shuffled away and sank onto a bench suddenly, feeling a strong desire to sleep. His knees trembled. He became aware that he was sweating profusely. "Horrible! Horrible!" he muttered. Steps came down the corridor, and the noise tortured him so that he cried with pain. It was an endless wait. How were they going to torture him? And where? Here in the dungeons? Or in the Castel Sant' Angelo? He would never get over it. He would die. . . . Celeste, Celeste, why aren't you here? . . .

The door opened and they summoned him.

"We shall now read the record of your last examination."

They did. It was precise and faithful.

"Sign it."

He obeyed silently.

"Very good. Sentence on your case will be passed tomorrow. The proceedings are ended."

"May I go home?" he cried out happily.

"Not now. Our rules forbid it. You must sleep here tonight. You will sleep in the same rooms as before. Well, have you any request? Why do you hesitate?"

"The Ambassador is my very good friend; he will be anxious about me. Would it be possible to notify him that I am kept here and have suffered no harm?"

"Any harm you might or might not have suffered is an official secret in these proceedings. But we will notify the Florentine Ambassador that you remain here. You are dismissed."

They led him to his former rooms. He heard one sentence over and over again, like the promise of salvation: "This ends the proceedings." Now they would not torture him. Now—that at least was certain. For some reason known only to themselves they had wanted to make him forswear Copernicus under threat of the rack—and with Copernicus all he had taught and written, or publicly maintained, for sixteen years. All his enemies were suddenly in the right. Father Grassi, Scheiner, Chairomonti, everybody. Well, what did it matter? He would retire to the Jewel Villa, prune his vines, visit Celeste, sometimes play with his grandsons. Yes, but first he would have to do penance, as his judges prescribed. It did not matter. He wanted only a few years of peace in his hermitage at Arcetri.

In the afternoon came a servant with parcels from the Embassy, and a bunch of flowers from the embassy garden. Long before sundown he was in bed, but could get no sleep, although he had ceased to be in pain. A strange thought tormented him: All men die once; he would die twice. Already he was dead as a scientist.

Next morning he was early awake. He was so impatient to be up that he dressed without help and paced his room. It was almost noon before he was summoned, and then by no less a personage than Firenzuola, who gave him a document. Bells were ringing outside.

"Glance through this, and tell me at once whether you can read it fluently. Read a few lines aloud. . . ."

"I, Galileo Galilei, son of the late Vincenzo Galilei, seventy years of age and a citizen of Florence, appear in person before the Court, and kneeling at the feet of Your Eminences . . ."

"That will do," Firenzuola interrupted. "Run through it quickly. When your sentence has been pronounced you have to read this aloud on your knees. Be careful not to mumble and stutter. Read it on your way into Court. I shall go on ahead of you."

Firenzuola hurried away. Two Dominicans with lighted candles stood on either side of the prisoner. He read the scroll, which contained nothing surprising: a solemn abjuration of all he had taught. The punishment concerned him far more.

To his great surprise they led him into a church. The choir stalls right and left of the altar were not occupied today by Dominican monks, saying their office, but by Cardinals in all the glory of their purple—all doubtless members of the College of the Holy Office, assembled to punish the accused. The judges formed a separate group of three. The other benches were packed with bishops, canons, and monks, crowded together. Carmelites, Jesuits, Dominicans, Minorites, Franciscans, Theatines, and many more in brown, in black, and in white. The two Dominicans led him to a table. Between two burning candles stood a crucifix and a parchment-bound Bible. When he came to his place, Firenzuola rose, and in Latin asked the College's permission to pass sentence on Galileo Galilei. The Cardinals nodded all together. Firenzuola took a sheaf of documents and handed them to Cardinal Ginetti, the youngest among them, who began to read:

"We, Caspare Borgia, Cardinal of the Holy Cross of Jerusalem; Fra Felice Centino, Cardinal of Saint Anastasius; Guido Bentivoglio, Cardinal of Santa Maria del Popolo; Fra Desiderio Scaglia, Cardinal of Saint Charles; Fra Antonio Barberini, Cardinal of Saint Onufrius; Landivio Zacchia, Cardinal of Saint Peter; Berlingero, Cardinal of Saint Augustine; Fabrico Vereseppio, Cardinal of Saint Lawrence; Francesco Barberini, Cardinal of Saint Lawrence of Damascus; and Deacon Cardinal Marzio Ginetti, Cardinals of the Holy Roman Catholic Church by God's grace, Inquisitors against heresy appointed by Christ's mercy and the Holy and Apostolic See to purge all Christendom, declare as follows":

Galileo glanced at the men in red. He knew them all. Most of them had been his friends. Now they all stared at him. Probably he was being discussed. They were whispering in the back benches.

"Whereas you, Galilei," Ginetti continued, "son of Vincenzo Galilei, seventy years of age and a Florentine, were denounced in the year 1615, at this Holy Office . . ."

Denounced? So it was true? Those fears and nightmares had not been idle.

". . . for upholding certain false doctrines spread by many, namely, that the sun is the center of the universe and immobile, while the earth turns every day on its own axis; and, moreover, for corrupting pupils whom you instructed in this; furthermore, for spreading this heresy by letters which you wrote to certain mathematicians in Germany . . ."

Galileo was hardly listening. He heard only fragments:

" '. . . therefore the Holy Office . . . desiring to take steps against the confusion and damage caused to Our Holy Faith . . . contrary to Holy Writ . . . We were pleased to act leniently . . . on February 25, 1616, . . . a Congregation in the presence of His Holiness . . . requested His Eminence Cardinal Bellarmin . . . to enjoin you to give up the aforesaid heresy or, if you should prove obstinate and recalcitrant, the Inquisitor of the Holy Office was to call on you to abjure it, never to expound, defend, or instruct others in it. And should you not rest content in this command, you should be put into prison . . .

" 'In obedience to this decision, on the following day the aforesaid Cardinal Bellarmin reproved you mildly in his private apartments; the Inquisitor of the Holy Office at that time commanded you, in the presence of a public notary and witnesses, to give up completely the false doctrine, never to defend or teach it in the future in any form, verbally or in writing. To destroy the harmful theory completely and avoid its spreading further to the damage of Catholic truth, the Holy Congregation of the Index issued a decree prohibiting books defending it, while the doctrine itself was branded as false and contrary to Holy Writ.

" 'Now, last year a book was published in Florence. Its title page described you as the author. The Holy Office had taken cognizance of the fact, that as the result of this book, the false teaching of the moving earth and stationary sun had found more and more credit daily. Therefore we carefully examined the book and found in it an evident transgression of the interdiction of which you were informed, because you defended the already banned theory, although trying at the same time by all kinds of subterfuge to create the impression of not positively maintaining it, and only treating it as probable; this also being so, it was resolved at a sitting of our Holy Congregation, that His Eminence the Lord Cardinal Bellarmin should admonish you to renounce the aforesaid heresy . . . And should you refuse, the head of our Holy Office should strictly enjoin you to renounce it, neither to instruct others therein nor yourself defend it or expound it . . . and if then you should still prove recalcitrant to punish you with imprisonment.' "

All this had been forged, thought Galileo, seeing it all in a flash of memory; this record is forged. He had come to terms at once with Bellarmin; the Head of the Holy Office had been given no further say in the matter. The record was forged! Who could have forged it? Who could have given the Pope the satisfaction of finding the "original record?" He tried to keep his mind attentive to the droning voice. He listened, but his ears buzzed; he heard only fragments again:

"Therefore, at our command you have been summoned to the Holy Office, where under oath you acknowledge having written and published a book . . . acknowledge that in consequence of the book's composition, the arguments for the false doctrine could more easily lead the intellect astray than be refuted . . . when a date was set for preparing your defense, you presented a document written by His Eminence Cardinal Bellarmin personally . . . This document said that you had nothing to deny nor were you punished, but merely informed of the command not to maintain or defend the false doctrine. And, as this document did not contain the expressions of 'in any way' and 'not to teach,' according to you it is humanly possible that you had forgotten these expressions in so many years, and therefore did not mention them when asking for the permission of the Censorship. . . . But this document which you used for your defense was only an aggravation of your case, because it contained the statement that the doctrine was contrary to Holy Writ, and yet you dared to expound, defend, and maintain it. We considered that you did not confess everything sincerely in the matter of your intentions. Therefore we held a more strict examination, in the course of which you answered in a Catholic spirit . . . and so . . . weighing every circumstance . . . we have passed the following final sentence. . . ."

There was a slight movement in the benches. Galileo drew a deep sigh. Ginetti continued:

"In the name of Our Lord Jesus Christ and His Glorious Mother, Mary Immaculate, we announce, proclaim, and expound by means of this our definite and final sentence, which we sitting here as judges . . ." Yet still the sentence was not spoken; there came a long list of jurists, each with his titles minutely described . . . Galileo's whole body was trembling. Would he ever hear what lay in store for him? . . .

"That you laid yourself open to grave suspicion of heresy; that is to say, you believed and stubbornly maintained . . ."

This led to a long exposition of Copernican theory. Tirades which for the tenth time repeated what was already said. And still no sentence . . . Ah! At last!

". . . thereby you have exposed yourself to all the penalties prescribed by canon law and other general and special constitutions. Yet we are willing to acquit you of these as soon as you have denied and damned with a sincere heart, not with dissembling words, the aforesaid errors, heresies, and all divergencies from Catholic and Apostolic teaching, according to the text prepared by us. But in order not to leave your grave and damnable error and disobedience without punishment, to give you a warning for the future, and to create a dread example for others, we decree that the book entitled *Dialogue of Galileo Galilei* be placed under the public interdict; while, as to you, we sentence your person to imprisonment in the charge of this Holy Office, for a term which we ourselves shall decide; and as a penance you are enjoined to repeat the seven penitential psalms every week for three years; we also reserve the right to change, lessen, suspend, and ameliorate, fully or in part, these penalties. . . ."

Galileo felt faint. His heart beat madly. The prison of the Inquisition for an indefinite period: this was the end. Death. He had not expected this. But he had not even time to be terrified. Firenzuola began to speak:

"Galileo Galilei, have you understood your sentence?"

"Yes."

"Are you willing to renounce your errors in the form prescribed by Their Eminences?"

"I am."

"Then place your left hand on the Holy Bible and repeat the text aloud. Kneel now."

Galileo put his hand on the Holy Book. Heavily he crouched down on his knees. He tried to read, but his eyes were too misty. He had to wait. At last he began:

"I, Galileo Galilei, son of the late Vincenzo Galilei, seventy years of age, and a citizen of Florence, appear in person in front of the Court and, kneeling to Your Eminences, the Most Sincere Cardinals, Chief Inquisitors of heresy over all Christendom, looking with my eyes at Holy Writ, touching with my hands its parchment, do hereby swear that I always believed, believe, and with God's help shall believe, whatever the Holy Roman Catholic and Apostolic Church decides, maintains, and teaches. Yet, though the Holy Office commanded me by force of law to forswear completely my false belief in the sun as the center of the universe and immobile . . . whereas the earth is not its center and moves . . . furthermore, though I was forbidden to maintain this doctrine in any form whatsoever, whether verbally or in writing, to defend or teach it . . . nevertheless, I, though knowing that this doctrine contradicted Holy Writ, have written and published a book in which I expounded this already accursed teaching and defended it with strong arguments, although without drawing final conclusions, and so have been found most suspicious in heresy; for I maintained and proclaimed that the sun was the center of the universe and immobile, while the earth was not the center of the universe and moving. Since I wish to dispel this grave and well-founded suspicion in the presence of Your Eminences and all Catholic Christians; therefore, with a sincere heart and without dissembling I deny, damn, and condemn the aforesaid errors and heresies and all such teachings inimical to Holy Church. I swear furthermore that I shall never do or say in writing or verbally anything which could raise this suspicion against me; should I meet a heretic or one to be suspected of heresy, I shall denounce him to the Holy Office or the local Inquisitor or Bishop. I swear to comply with all the penances prescribed now or in future by the Holy Office. If, God forbid, I should break any of these promises, denials, or oaths, I will accept whatever penance or punishment either canon law or the general and special constitutions impose on such criminals. So help me God and this Holy Bible which I touch with my hand."

Firenzuola motioned him to rise. The two Dominicans came back to stand on either side of him, with their burning candles. His old legs, grown numb in the long kneeling, almost gave way under him. They guided him through the side door of the church into the monastery, but not into the unknown terrible prisons—only to his comfortable rooms. Only now they turned the key in the lock. "For an indefinite period." Probably till death. Celeste, Angela, Nencio, and the two grandchildren were gone from him forever.

He stretched himself on the bed and began to cry softly; his sobs became louder.

"So this is what you've betrayed everything for! For this? You wretch, you miserable wretch. . . ."

He beat his forehead with his fists. He would have liked to spit in his own face. He abused and damned his own soul. The door opened. They brought him food. Not the servant of the Embassy: one of the Dominicans. He shook his head and would not touch it. He was alone again with his shameful thoughts, which plagued him all the rest of that day. Sometimes he grew weary of self-torture, then it started again. Nobody came to him, only the Dominican in the evening to take away the untouched food and bring his supper. He ate a little now, but began to weep again, undressed himself, lay down and wept the whole night. The dark was full of ghosts and terrors which almost maddened him, so that he raved. He choked with fear and remorse, struck himself in the face for a coward, a wretched weakling, as though he were enraged with another man. He did not sleep at all. In the morning he dressed and continued his terrible self-destruction: he rolled about on his bed and abused himself horribly, almost like a madman.

Next day at noon Firenzuola came to him and made him sign the oath he had read in the church. He could not stop crying.

"Hush! You ought to be thankful to get off with such a mild punishment."

"But I'm not thankful," he burst out wildly. "What use is such a life to me? Take me to the torture chamber, break my bones, beat me; I deserve no better. Terrible, terrible . . ."

Now he roared, losing all restraint. Firenzuola could not hide his anxiety. He was afraid that the prisoner would go mad. He endeavored to soothe him.

"Listen! There's still some hope that His Holiness will forgive you. Think of that and . . ."

But he saw that this weeping old madman could think of nothing, and left him alone. When the key turned in the lock and the steps receded, the prisoner straightened, and yelled across the empty rooms:

"His Holiness may forgive me if he likes. But I shall never forgive myself. Never! Never! Never!"

And he sobbed again. It was like a flood bursting its gates: the abased, violated mind took its revenge. He realized that for seventy years he had had good reason to be proud of himself; and now, at the bitter end of his life, he had lost self-respect.

Judge Jeffreys and the Bloody Assizes

Thomas B. Macaulay

THE GREAT seal was left in Guilford's custody; but a marked indignity was at the same time offered to him. It was determined that another lawyer of more vigor and audacity should be called to assist in the administration. The person selected was Sir George Jeffreys, Chief Justice of the Court of King's Bench. The depravity of this man has passed into a proverb. Both the great English parties have attacked his memory with emulous violence; for the Whigs considered him as their most barbarous enemy, and the Tories found it convenient to throw on him the blame of all the crimes which had sullied their triumph. A diligent and candid inquiry will show that some frightful stories which have been told concerning him are false or exaggerated; yet the dispassionate historian will be able to make very little deduction from the vast mass of infamy with which the memory of the wicked judge has been loaded.

He was a man of quick and vigorous parts, but constitutionally prone to insolence and to the angry passions. When just emerging from boyhood, he had risen into practice at the Old Bailey bar, a bar where advocates have always used a license of tongue unknown in Westminster Hall. Here, during many years, his chief business was to examine and cross examine the most hardened miscreants of a great capital. Daily conflicts with prostitutes and thieves called out and exercised his powers so effectually that he became the most consummate bully ever known in his profession. All tenderness for the feelings of others, all self-respect, all sense of the becoming, were obliterated from his mind. He acquired a boundless command of the rhetoric in which the vulgar express hatred and contempt. The profusion of maledictions and vituperative epithets which composed his vocabulary could hardly have been rivaled in the fish-market or the beargarden. His countenance and his voice must always have been unamiable; but these natural advantages—for such he seems to have thought them—he had improved to such a degree that

From *History of England*.

there were few who, in his paroxysms of rage, could see or hear him without emotion. Impudence and ferocity sat upon his brow. The glare of his eyes had a fascination for the unhappy victim on whom they were fixed; yet his brow and eye were said to be less terrible than the savage lines of his mouth. His yell of fury, as was said by one who had often heard it, sounded like the thunder of the judgment day. These qualifications he carried, while still a young man, from the bar to the bench. He early became common sergeant, and then recorder of London. As judge at the city sessions he exhibited the same propensities which afterward, in a higher post, gained for him an unenviable immortality. Already might be remarked in him the most odious vice which is incident to human nature, a delight in misery merely as misery. There was a fiendish exultation in the way in which he pronounced sentence on offenders. Their weeping and imploring seemed to titillate him voluptuously; and he loved to scare them into fits by dilating with luxuriant amplification on all the details of what they were to suffer. Thus, when he had an opportunity of ordering an unlucky adventuress to be whipped at the cart's tail, "Hangman," he would exclaim, "I charge you to pay particular attention to this lady! Scourge her soundly, man! Scourge her till the blood runs down! It is Christmas; a cold time for madam to strip in! See that you warm her shoulders thoroughly!"* He was hardly less facetious when he passed judgment on Ludowick Muggleton, the drunken tailor who fancied himself a prophet. "Impudent rogue!" roared Jeffreys, "thou shalt have an easy, easy, easy punishment!" One part of this easy punishment was the pillory, in which the wretched fanatic was almost killed with brickbats.†

By this time the nature of Jeffreys had been hardened to that temper which tyrants require in their worst implements. He had hitherto looked therefore professed himself a Roundhead, and had always appeared to be in a higher state of exhilaration when he explained to popish priests that they were to be cut down alive, and were to see their own bodies burned, than when he passed ordinary sentences of death. But, as soon as he had got all that the city could give, he made haste to sell his forehead of brass and his tongue of venom to the court. Chiffinch, who was accustomed to act as broker in infamous contracts of more than one kind, lent his aid. He had conducted many amorous and many political intrigues, but he assuredly never rendered a more scandalous service to his masters than when he introduced Jeffreys to Whitehall. The renegade soon found a patron in the obdurate and revengeful James, but was always regarded with scorn and disgust by Charles, whose faults, great as they were, had no affinity with insolence and cruelty. "That man," said the king, "has no learning, no sense, no manners, and more impudence than

---

* Christmas Sessions Paper of 1678.
† The Acts of the Witnesses of the Spirit, Part vi. chapter v. In this work, Ludowick, after his fashion, revenges himself on the "bawling devil," as he calls Jeffreys, by a string of curses which Ernuhphus might have envied. The trial was in January, 1677.

ten carted street-walkers."* Work was to be done, however, which could be trusted to no man who reverenced law or was sensible of shame; and thus Jeffreys, at an age at which a barrister thinks himself fortunate if he is employed to lead an important cause, was made Chief Justice of the King's Bench.

His enemies could not deny that he possessed some of the qualities of a great judge. His legal knowledge, indeed, was merely such as he had picked up in practice of no very high kind; but he had one of those happily-constituted intellects which, across labyrinths of sophistry and through masses of immaterial facts, go straight to the true point. Of his intellect, however, he seldom had the full use. Even in civil causes his malevolent and despotic temper perpetually disordered his judgment. To enter his court was to enter the den of a wild beast, which none could tame, and which was as likely to be roused to rage by caresses as by attacks. He frequently poured forth on plaintiffs and defendants, barristers and attorneys, witnesses and jurymen, torrents of frantic abuse, intermixed with oaths and curses. His looks and tones had inspired terror when he was merely a young advocate struggling into practice. Now that he was at the head of the most formidable tribunal in the realm, there were few indeed who did not tremble before him. Even when he was sober, his violence was sufficiently frightful; but, in general, his reason was over-clouded, and his evil passions stimulated by the fumes of intoxication. His evenings were ordinarily given to revelry. People who saw him only over his bottle would have supposed him to be a man gross indeed, sottish, and addicted to low company and low merriment, but social and good-humored. He was constantly surrounded on such occasions by buffoons, selected, for the most part, from among the vilest pettifoggers who practiced before him. These men bantered and abused each other for his entertainment. He joined in their ribald talk, sang catches with them, and, when his head grew hot, hugged and kissed them in an ecstasy of drunken fondness. But, though wine at first seemed to soften his heart, the effect of a few hours later was very different. He often came to the judgment seat, having kept the court waiting long, and yet having but half slept off his debauch, his cheeks on fire, his eyes staring like those of a maniac. When he was in this state, his boon companions of the preceding night, if they were wise, kept out of his way, for the recollection of the familiarity to which he had admitted them inflamed his malignity, and he was sure to take every opportunity of overwhelming them with execration and invective. Not the least odious of his many odious peculiarities was the pleasure which he took in publicly browbeating and mortifying those whom, in his fits of maudlin tenderness, he had encouraged to presume on his favor.

The services which the government had expected from him were performed, not merely without flinching, but eagerly and triumphantly. His

---

* This saying is to be found in many cotemporary pamphlets. Titus Oates was never tired of quoting it.—See his Εἰκὼν βασιλική.

first exploit was the judicial murder of Algernon Sidney. What followed was in perfect harmony with this beginning. Respectable Tories lamented the disgrace which the barbarity and indecency of so great a functionary brought upon the administration of justice; but the excesses which filled such men with horror were titles to the esteem of James. Jeffreys, therefore, after the death of Charles, obtained a seat in the cabinet and a peerage. This last honor was a signal mark of royal approbation; for, since the judicial system of the realm had been remodeled in the thirteenth century, no chief justice had been a lord of Parliament.*

Guildford now found himself superseded in all his political functions, and restricted to his business as a judge in equity. At council he was treated by Jeffreys with marked incivility. The whole legal patronage was in the hands of the chief justice; and it was well known by the bar that the surest way to propitiate the chief justice was to treat the lord keeper with disrespect.

At Winchester the chief justice first opened his commission. Hampshire had not been the theater of war; but many of the vanquished rebels had, like their leader, fled thither. Two of them, John Hickes, a Nonconformist divine, and Richard Nelthorpe, a lawyer who had been outlawed for his share in the Rye House Plot, had sought refuge at the house of Alice, widow of John Lisle. John Lisle had sat in the Long Parliament and in the High Court of Justice, had been a commissioner of the great seal in the days of the Commonwealth, and had been created a lord by Cromwell. The titles given by the Protector had not been recognized by any government which had ruled England since the downfall of his house; but they appear to have been often used in conversation even by Royalists. John Lisle's widow was therefore commonly known as the Lady Alice. She was related to many respectable, and to some noble families, and she was generally esteemed even by the Tory gentlemen of her county; for it was well known to them that she had deeply regretted some violent acts in which her husband had borne a part, that she had shed bitter tears for Charles the First, and that she had protected and relieved many Cavaliers in their distress. The same womanly kindness which had led her to befriend the Royalists in their time of trouble would not suffer her to refuse a meal and a hiding-place to the wretched men who now entreated her to protect them. She took them into her house, set meat and drink before them, and showed them where they might take rest. The next morning her dwelling was surrounded by soldiers. Strict search was made. Hickes was found concealed in the malt-house, and Nelthorpe in the chimney. If Lady Alice knew her guests to have been concerned in the insurrection, she was undoubtedly guilty of what in

---

* The chief sources of information concerning Jeffreys are the State Trials and North's Life of Lord Guildford. Some touches of minor importance I owe to cotemporary pamphlets in verse and prose. Such are the Bloody Assizes, the Life and Death of George Lord Jeffreys, the Panegyric on the late Lord Jeffreys, the letter to the Lord Chancellor, Jeffrey's Elegy. See, also, Evelyn's Diary, Dec. 5, 1683, Oct. 31, 1685. I scarcely need advise every reader to consult Lord Campbell's excellent book.

strictness is a capital crime; for the law of principal and accessory, as respects high treason, then was, and is to this day, in a state disgraceful to English jurisprudence. In cases of felony, a distinction, founded on justice and reason, is made between the principal and the accessory after the fact. He who conceals from justice one whom he knows to be a murderer, though liable to punishment, is not liable to the punishment of murder; but he who shelters one whom he knows to be a traitor is, according to all our jurists, guilty of high treason. It is unnecessary to point out the absurdity and cruelty of a law which includes under the same definition, and visits with the same penalty, offenses lying at the opposite extremes of the scale of guilt. The feeling which makes the most loyal subject shrink from the thought of giving up to a shameful death the rebel who, vanquished, hunted down, and in mortal agony, begs for a morsel of bread and a cup of water, may be a weakness, but it is surely a weakness very nearly allied to virtue; a weakness which, constituted as human beings are, we can hardly eradicate from the mind without eradicating many noble and benevolent sentiments. A wise and good ruler may not think it right to sanction this weakness, but he will generally connive at it, or punish it very tenderly. In no case will he treat it as a crime of the blackest dye. Whether Flora Macdonald was justified in concealing the attainted heir of the Stuarts, whether a brave soldier of our own time was justified in assisting the escape of Lavalette, are questions on which casuists may differ; but to class such actions with the crimes of Guy Faux and Fieschi is an outrage to humanity and common sense. Such, however, is the classification of our law. It is evident that nothing but a lenient administration could make such a state of the law endurable. And it is just to say that, during many generations, no English government, save one, has treated with rigor persons guilty merely of harboring defeated and flying insurgents. To women especially has been granted, by a kind of tacit prescription, the right of indulging, in the midst of havoc and vengeance, that compassion which is the most endearing of all their charms. Since the beginning of the great civil war, numerous rebels, some of them far more important than Hickes or Nelthorpe, have been protected against the severity of victorious governments by female adroitness and generosity; but no English ruler who has been thus baffled, the savage and implacable James alone excepted, has had the barbarity even to think of putting a lady to a cruel and shameful death for so venial and amiable a transgression.

Odious as the law was, it was strained for the purpose of destroying Alice Lisle. She could not, according to the doctrine laid down by the highest authority, be convicted till after the conviction of the rebels whom she had harbored.* She was, however, sent to the bar before either Hickes or Nelthorpe had been tried. It was no easy matter in such a case to obtain a verdict for the crown. The witnesses prevaricated. The jury, consisting of the principal gentlemen of Hampshire, shrank from the

* See the preamble to the act reversing her attainder.

thought of sending a fellow-creature to the stake for conduct which seemed deserving rather of praise than of blame. Jeffreys was beside himself with fury. This was the first case of treason on the circuit, and there seemed to be a strong probability that his prey would escape him. He stormed, cursed, and swore in language which no well-bred man would have used at a race or a cock-fight. One witness named Dunne, partly from concern for Lady Alice, and partly from fright at the threats and maledictions of the chief justice, entirely lost his head, and at last stood silent. "Oh, how hard the truth is," said Jeffreys, "to come out of a lying Presbyterian knave." The witness, after a pause of some minutes, stammered a few unmeaning words. "Was there ever," exclaimed the judge, with an oath, "was there ever such a villain on the face of the earth? Dost thou believe that there is a God? Dost thou believe in hell fire? Of all the witnesses that I ever met with, I never saw thy fellow." Still the poor man, scared out of his senses, remained mute, and again Jeffreys burst forth: "I hope, gentlemen of the jury, that you take notice of the horrible carriage of this fellow. How can one help abhorring both these men and their religion? A Turk is a saint to such a fellow as this. A pagan would be ashamed of such villainy. Oh, blessed Jesus! What a generation of vipers do we live among." "I can not tell what to say, my lord," faltered Dunne. The judge again broke forth into a volley of oaths. "Was there ever," he cried, "such an impudent rascal? Hold the candle to him, that we may see his brazen face. You, gentlemen, that are of counsel for the crown, see that an information for perjury be preferred against this fellow." After the witnesses had been thus handled, the Lady Alice was called on for her defense. She began by saying, what may possibly have been true, that though she knew Hickes to be in trouble when she took him in, she did not know or suspect that he had been concerned in the rebellion. He was a divine, a man of peace. It had, therefore, never occurred to her that he could have borne arms against the government; and she had supposed that he wished to conceal himself because warrants were out against him for field preaching. The chief justice began to storm. "But I will tell you. There is not one of those lying, sniveling, canting Presbyterians but, one way or another, had a hand in the rebellion. Presbytery has all manner of villainy in it. Nothing but Presbytery could have made Dunne such a rogue. Show me a Presbyterian, and I'll show thee a lying knave." He summed up in the same style, declaimed during an hour against Whigs and Dissenters, and reminded the jury that the prisoner's husband had born a part in the death of Charles the First, a fact which was not proved by any testimony, and which, if it had been proved, would have been utterly irrelevant to the issue. The jury retired, and remained long in consultation. The judge grew impatient. He could not conceive, he said, how, in so plain a case, they should ever have left the box. He sent a messenger to tell them that, if they did not instantly return, he would adjourn the court and lock them up all night. Thus put to the torture, they came, but came to say that they doubted whether the charge had been made out. Jeffreys expostulated with them vehemently, and, after another consultation, they gave a reluctant verdict of Guilty.

On the following morning sentence was pronounced. Jeffreys gave directions that Alice Lisle should be burned alive that very afternoon. This excess of barbarity moved the pity and indignation even of that class which was most devoted to the crown. The clergy of Winchester Cathedral remonstrated with the chief justice, who, brutal as he was, was not mad enough to risk a quarrel on such a subject with a body so much respected by the Tory party. He consented to put off the execution five days. During that time the friends of the prisoner besought James to show her mercy. Ladies of high rank interceded for her. Feversham, whose recent victory had increased his influence at court, and who, it is said, had been bribed to take the compassionate side, spoke in her favor. Clarendon, the king's brother-in-law, pleaded her cause. But all was vain. The utmost that could be obtained was that her sentence should be commuted from burning to beheading. She was put to death on a scaffold in the market-place of Winchester, and underwent her fate with serene courage.*

In Hampshire Alice Lisle was the only victim; but, on the day following her execution, Jeffreys reached Dorchester, the principal town of the county in which Monmouth had landed, and the judicial massacre began.

The court was hung, by order of the chief justice, with scarlet; and this innovation seemed to the multitude to indicate a bloody purpose. It was also rumored that, when the clergyman who preached the assize sermon enforced the duty of mercy, the ferocious mouth of the judge was distorted by an ominous grin. These things made men augur ill of what was to follow.†

More than three hundred prisoners were to be tried. The work seemed heavy, but Jeffreys had a contrivance for making it light. He let it be understood that the only chance of obtaining pardon or respite was to plead guilty. Twenty-nine persons, who put themselves on their country and were convicted, were ordered to be tied up without delay. The remaining prisoners pleaded guilty by scores. Two hundred and ninety-two received sentence of death. The whole number hanged in Dorsetshire amounted to seventy-four.

From Dorchester Jeffreys proceeded to Exeter. The civil war had barely grazed the frontier of Devonshire. Here, therefore, comparatively few persons were capitally punished. Somersetshire, the chief seat of the rebellion, had been reserved for the last and most fearful vengeance. In this county two hundred and thirty-three prisoners were in a few days hanged, drawn, and quartered. At every spot where two roads met, on every market-place, on the green of every large village which had fur-

---

* Trial of Alice Lisle in the Collection of State Trials; Stat. 1 Gul. & Mar.; Burnet, i., 649; Caveat against the Whigs.
† Bloody Assizes.

nished Monmouth with soldiers, ironed corpses clattering in the wind, or heads and quarters stuck on poles, poisoned the air, and made the traveler sick with horror. In many parishes the peasantry could not assemble in the house of God without seeing the ghastly face of a neighbor grinning at them over the porch. The chief justice was all himself. His spirits rose higher and higher as the work went on. He laughed, shouted, joked, and swore in such a way that many thought him drunk from morning to night; but in him it was not easy to distinguish the madness produced by evil passions from the madness produced by brandy. A prisoner affirmed that the witnesses who appeared against him were not entitled to credit. One of them, he said, was a papist, and the other a prostitute. "Thou impudent rebel," exclaimed the judge, "to reflect on the king's evidence! I see thee, villain, I see thee already with the halter round thy neck." Another produced testimony that he was a good Protestant. "Protestant!" said Jeffreys; "you mean Presbyterian. I'll hold you a wager of it. I can smell a Presbyterian forty miles." One wretched man moved the pity even of bitter Tories. "My lord," they said, "this poor creature is on the parish." "Do not trouble yourselves," said the judge, "I will ease the parish of the burden." It was not only on the prisoners that his fury broke forth. Gentlemen and noblemen of high consideration and stainless loyalty, who ventured to bring to his notice any extenuating circumstance, were almost sure to receive what he called, in the coarse dialect which he had learned in the pot-houses of White Chapel, a lick with the rough side of his tongue. Lord Stawell, a Tory peer, who could not conceal his horror at the remorseless manner in which his poor neighbors were butchered, was punished by having a corpse suspended in chains at his park gate.* In such spectacles originated many tales of terror, which were long told over the cider by the Christmas fires of the farmers of Somersetshire. Within the last forty years, peasants in some districts well knew the accursed spots, and passed them unwillingly after sunset.†

Jeffreys boasted that he had hanged more traitors than all his predecessors together since the Conquest. It is certain that the number of persons whom he executed in one month, and in one shire, very much exceeded the number of all the political offenders who have been executed in our island since the Revolution. The insurrection of 1715 and 1745 were of longer duration, of wider extent, and of more formidable aspect than that which was put down at Sedgemoor. It has not been generally thought that, either after the rebellion of 1715, or after the rebellion of 1745, the house of Hanover erred on the side of clemency; yet all the executions of 1715 and 1745 added together will appear to have been few indeed when compared with those which disgraced the Bloody Assizes.

---

* Locke's Western Rebellion.
† This I can attest from my own childish recollections.

The number of the rebels whom Jeffreys hanged on this circuit was three hundred and twenty.*

Such havoc must have excited disgust even if the sufferers had been generally odious; but they were, for the most part, men of blameless life, and of high religious profession. They were regarded by themselves, and by a large proportion of their neighbors, not as wrong-doers, but as martyrs who sealed with blood the truth of the Protestant religion. Very few of the convicts professed any repentance for what they had done. Many, animated by the old Puritan spirit, met death, not merely with fortitude, but with exultation. It was in vain that the ministers of the Established Church lectured them on the guilt of rebellion and on the importance of priestly absolution. The claim of the king to unbounded authority in things temporal, and the claim of the clergy to the spiritual power of binding and loosing, moved the bitter scorn of the intrepid sectaries. Some of them composed hymns in the dungeon and chanted them on the fatal sledge. Christ, they sang while they were undressing for the butchery, would soon come to rescue Zion and to make war on Babylon, would set up his standard, would blow his trumpet, and would requite his foes tenfold for all the evil which had been inflicted on his servants. The dying words of these men were noted down; their farewell letters were kept as treasures; and, in this way, with the help of some invention and exaggeration, was formed a copious supplement to the Marian martyrology.†

A few cases deserve special mention. Abraham Holmes, a retired officer of the Parliamentary army, and one of those zealots who would own no king but King Jesus, had been taken at Sedgemoor. His arm had been frightfully mangled and shattered in the battle; and, as no surgeon was at hand, the stout old soldier amputated it himself. He was carried up to London and examined by the king in council, but would make no submission. "I am an aged man," he said, "and what remains to me of life is not worth a falsehood or a baseness. I have always been a Republican, and I am so still." He was sent back to the west and hanged. The people remarked with awe and wonder that the beasts which were to drag him to the gallows became restive and went back. Holmes himself doubted not that the Angel of the Lord, as in the old time, stood in the way, sword in hand, invisible to human eyes, but visible to the inferior animals. "Stop, gentlemen," he cried, "let me go on foot. There is more in this than you think. Remember how the ass saw him whom the prophet could not see." He walked manfully to the gallows, harangued the people with a smile, prayed fervently that God would hasten the downfall of anti-Christ and the deliverance of England, and went up the ladder with

---

* Lord Lonsdale says seven hundred; Burnet, six hundred. I have followed the list which the judges sent to the Treasury, and which may still be seen there in the letter-book of 1685. See the Bloody Assizes; Locke's Western Rebellion; the Panegyric on Lord Jeffreys; Burnet, i., 648; Eachard, iii., 775; Oldmixon, 705.

† Some of the prayers, exhortations, and hymns of the sufferers will be found in the Bloody Assizes.

an apology for mounting so awkwardly. "You see," he said, "I have but one arm."*

Not less courageously died Christopher Battiscombe, a young Templar of good family and fortune, who, at Dorchester, an agreeable provincial town proud of its taste and refinement, was regarded by all as the model of a fine gentleman. Great interest was made to save him. It was believed through the west of England that he was engaged to a young lady of gentle blood, the sister of the high sheriff; that she threw herself at the feet of Jeffreys to beg for mercy; and that Jeffreys drove her from him with a jest so hideous that to repeat it would be an offense against decency and humanity. Her lover suffered at Lyme piously and courageously.†

A still deeper interest was excited by the fate of two gallant brothers, William and Benjamin Hewling. They were young, handsome, accomplished, and well connected. Their maternal grandfather was named Kiffin. He was one of the first merchants in London, and was generally considered as the head of the Baptists. The chief justice behaved to William Hewling on the trial with characteristic brutality. "You have a grandfather," he said, "who deserves to be hanged as richly as you." The poor lad, who was only nineteen, suffered death with so much meekness and fortitude, that an officer of the army who attended the execution, and who had made himself remarkable by rudeness and severity, was strangely melted, and said, "I do not believe that my lord chief justice himself could be proof against this." Hopes were entertained that Benjamin would be pardoned. One victim of tender years was surely enough for one house to furnish. Even Jeffreys was, or pretended to be, inclined to lenity. The truth was, that one of his kinsmen, from whom he had large expectations, and whom, therefore, he could not treat as he generally treated intercessors, pleaded strongly for the afflicted family. Time was allowed for a reference to London. The sister of the prisoner went to Whitehall with a petition. Many courtiers wished her success; and Churchill, among whose numerous faults cruelty had no place, obtained admittance for her. "I wish well to your suit, with all my heart," he said, as they stood together in the ante-chamber; "but do not flatter yourself with hopes. This marble," and he laid his hand on the chimney-piece, "is not harder than the king." The prediction proved true. James was inexorable. Benjamin Hewling died with dauntless courage, amid lamentations in which the soldiers who kept guard round the gallows could not refrain from joining.‡

---

* Bloody Assizes; Locke's Western Rebellion; Lord Lonsdale's Memoirs; Account of the Battle of Sedgemoor in the Hardwicke Papers.
The story in Clarke's Life of James the Second, ii., 43, is not taken from the king's manuscripts, and sufficiently refutes itself.

† Bloody Assizes; Locke's Western Rebellion; Humble Petition of Widows and fatherless Children in the West of England; Panegyric on Lord Jeffreys.

‡ As to the Hewlings, I have followed Kiffin's Memoirs, and Mr. Hewling Luson's narrative, which will be found in the second edition of the Hughes Correspondence,

Yet those rebels who were doomed to death were less to be pitied than some of the survivors. Several prisoners to whom Jeffreys was unable to bring home the charge of high treason were convicted of misdemeanors, and were sentenced to scourging not less terrible than that which Oates had undergone. A woman, for some idle words such as had been uttered by half the women in the districts where the war had raged, was condemned to be whipped through all the market-towns in the county of Dorset. She suffered part of her punishment before Jeffreys returned to London; but, when he was no longer in the west, the jailers, with the humane connivance of the magistrates, took on themselves the responsibility of sparing her any further torture. A still more frightful sentence was passed on a lad named Tutchin, who was tried for seditious words. He was, as usual, interrupted in his defense by ribaldry and scurrility from the judgment seat. "You are a rebel; and all your family have been rebels since Adam. They tell me that you are a poet. I'll cap verses with you." The sentence was, that the boy should be imprisoned seven years, and should, during that period, be flogged through every market-town in Dorsetshire every year. The women in the galleries burst into tears. The clerk of the arraigns stood up in great disorder. "My lord," said he, "the prisoner is very young. There are many market-towns in our county. The sentence amounts to whipping once a fortnight for seven years." "If he is a young man," said Jeffreys, "he is an old rogue. Ladies, you do not know the villain as well as I do. The punishment is not half bad enough for him. All the interest in England shall not alter it." Tutchin, in his despair, petitioned, and probably with sincerity, that he might be hanged. Fortunately for him, he was, just at this conjuncture, taken ill of the small-pox and given over. As it seemed highly improbable that the sentence would ever be executed, the chief justice consented to remit it in return for a bribe which reduced the prisoner to poverty. The temper of Tutchin, not originally very mild, was exasperated to madness by what he had undergone. He lived to be known as one of the most acrimonious and pertinacious enemies of the house of Stuart and of the Tory party.*

The number of prisoners whom Jeffreys transported was eight hundred and forty-one. These men, more wretched than their associates who suffered death, were distributed into gangs, and bestowed on persons who enjoyed favor at court. The conditions of the gift were that the convicts should be carried beyond sea as slaves, that they should not be emancipated for ten years, and that the place of their banishment should be some West Indian island. This last article was studiously framed for the purpose of aggravating the misery of the exiles. In New England or New Jersey they would have found a population kindly disposed to them, and a climate not unfavorable to their health and vigor. It was therefore de-

---

vol. ii. Appendix. The accounts in Locke's Western Rebellion and in the Panegyric on Jeffreys are full of errors. Great part of the account in the Bloody Assizes was written by Kiffin, and agrees word for word with his Memoirs.

* See Tutchin's account of his own case in the Bloody Assizes.

termined that they should be sent to colonies where a Puritan could hope to inspire little sympathy, and where a laborer born in the temperate zone could hope to enjoy little health. Such was the state of the slave-market that these bondmen, long as was the passage, and sickly as they were likely to prove, were still very valuable. It was estimated by Jeffreys that, on an average, each of them, after all charges were paid, would be worth from ten to fifteen pounds. There was, therefore, much angry competition for grants. Some Tories in the west conceived that they had, by their exertions and sufferings during the insurrection, earned a right to share in the profits which had been eagerly snatched up by the sycophants of Whitehall. The courtiers, however, were victorious.*

The misery of the exiles fully equaled that of the negroes who are now carried from Congo to Brazil. It appears, from the best information which is now accessible, that more than one fifth of those who were shipped were flung to the sharks before the end of the voyage. The human cargoes were stowed close in the holds of small vessels. So little space was allowed that the wretches, many of whom were still tormented by unhealed wounds, could not all lie down at once without lying on one another. They were never suffered to go on deck. The hatchway was constantly watched by sentinels armed with hangers and blunderbusses. In the dungeon below all was darkness, stench, lamentation, disease, and death. Of ninety-nine convicts who were carried out in one vessel, twenty-two died before they reached Jamaica, although the voyage was performed with unusual speed. The survivors, when they arrived at their house of bondage, were mere skeletons. During some weeks coarse biscuit and fetid water had been doled out to them in such scanty measure that any one of them could easily have consumed the ration which was assigned to five. They were, therefore, in such a state, that the merchant to whom they had been consigned found it expedient to fatten them before selling them.†

Meanwhile, the property both of the rebels who had suffered death, and of those more unfortunate men who were withering under the tropical sun, was fought for and torn in pieces by a crowd of greedy informers. By law, a subject attainted of treason forfeits all his substance; and this law was enforced after the Bloody Assizes with a rigor at once cruel and ludicrous. The broken-hearted widows and destitute orphans of the laboring men whose corpses hung at the cross-roads were called upon by the agents of the Treasury to explain what had become of a basket, of a goose, of a flitch of bacon, of a keg of cider, of a sack of

---

* Sunderland to Jeffreys, Sept. 14, 1685; Jeffreys to the King, Sept. 19, 1685, in the State Paper Office.

† The best account of the sufferings of those rebels who were sentenced to transportation is to be found in a very curious narrative written by John Coad, an honest, God-fearing carpenter, who joined Monmouth, was badly wounded at Philip's Norton, was tried by Jeffreys, and was sent to Jamaica. The original manuscript was kindly lent to me by Mr. Phippard, to whom it belongs.

beans, of a truss of hay.* While the humbler retainers of the government were pillaging the families of the slaughtered peasants, the chief justice was fast accumulating a fortune out of the plunder of a higher class of Whigs. He traded largely in pardons. His most lucrative transaction of this kind was with a gentleman named Edmund Prideaux. It is certain that Prideaux had not been in arms against the government, and it is probable that his only crime was the wealth which he had inherited from his father, an eminent lawyer who had been high in office under the Protector. No exertions were spared to make out a case for the crown. Mercy was offered to some prisoners on condition that they would bear evidence against Prideaux. The unfortunate man lay long in jail, and at length, overcome by fear of the gallows, consented to pay fifteen thousand pounds for his liberation. This great sum was received by Jeffreys. He bought with it an estate, to which the people gave the name of Aceldama, from that accursed field which was purchased with the price of innocent blood.†

He was ably assisted in the work of extortion by the crew of parasites who were in the habit of drinking and laughing with him. The office of these men was to drive hard bargains with convicts under the strong terrors of death, and with parents trembling for the lives of children. A portion of the spoil was abandoned by Jeffreys to his agents. To one of his boon companions, it is said, he tossed a pardon for a rich traitor across the table during a revel. It was not safe to have recourse to any intercession except that of his creatures, for he guarded his profitable monopoly of mercy with jealous care. It was even suspected that he sent some persons to the gibbet solely because they had applied for the royal clemency through channels independent of him.‡

Some courtiers nevertheless contrived to obtain a small share of this traffic. The ladies of the queen's household distinguished themselves preeminently by rapacity and hard-heartedness. Part of the disgrace which they incurred falls on their mistress, for it was solely on account of the relation in which they stood to her that they were able to enrich themselves by so odious a trade; and there can be no question that she might, with a word or a look, have restrained them; but, in truth, she encouraged them by her evil example, if not by her express approbation. She seems to have been one of that large class of persons who bear adversity better than prosperity. While her husband was a subject and an exile, shut out from public employment, and in imminent danger of being deprived of his birth-right, the suavity and humility of her manners conciliated the kindness even of those who most abhorred her religion; but when her good fortune came, her good nature disappeared. The meek and affable

---

* In the Treasury records of the autumn of 1685 are several letters directing search to be made for trifles of this sort.

† Commons' Journals, Oct. 9, Nov. 10, Dec. 26, 1690; Oldmixon, 706; Panegyric on Jeffreys.

‡ Life and Death of Lord Jeffrey's; Panegyric on Jeffreys; Kiffin's Memoirs.

duchess turned out an ungracious and haughty queen.* The misfortunes which she subsequently endured have made her an object of some interest; but that interest would be not a little heightened if it could be shown that, in the season of her greatness, she saved, or even tried to save, one single victim from the most frightful proscription that England has ever seen. Unhappily, the only request that she is known to have preferred touching the rebels was that a hundred of those who were sentenced to transportation might be given to her.† The profit which she cleared on the cargo, after making large allowance for those who died of hunger and fever during the passage, can not be estimated at less than a thousand guineas. We can not wonder that her attendants should have imitated her unprincely greediness and her unwomanly cruelty. They exacted a thousand pounds from Roger Hoare, a merchant of Bridgewater, who had contributed to the military chest of the rebel army. But the prey on which they pounced most eagerly was one which it might have been thought that even the most ungentle natures would have spared. Already some of the girls who had presented the standard to Monmouth at Taunton had cruelly expiated their offense. One of them had been thrown into a prison where an infectious malady was raging. She had sickened and died there. Another had presented herself at the bar before Jeffreys to beg for mercy. "Take her, jailer," vociferated the judge, with one of those frowns which had often struck terror into stouter hearts than hers. She burst into tears, drew her hood over her face, followed the jailer out of court, fell ill of fright, and in a few hours was a corpse. Most of the young ladies, however, who had walked in the procession were still alive. Some of them were under ten years of age. All had acted under the orders of their schoolmistress, without knowing that they were committing a crime. The queen's maids of honor asked the royal permission to wring money out of the parents of the poor children, and the permission was granted. An order was sent down to Taunton that all these little girls should be seized and imprisoned. Sir Francis Warre, of Hestercombe, the Tory member for Bridgewater, was requested to undertake the office of exacting the ransom. He was charged to declare in strong language that the maids of honor would not endure delay; that they were determined to prosecute to outlawry, unless a reasonable sum were forthcoming; and that by a reasonable sum was meant seven thousand pounds. Warre excused himself from taking any part in a transaction so scandalous. The maids of honor then requested William Penn to act for them, and Penn accepted the commission; yet it should seem that a little of the

---

* Burnet, i., 368; Evelyn's Diary, Feb. 4, 1684-5, July 13, 1686. In one of the satires of that time are these lines:

> "When duchess, she was gentle, mild, and civil;
> When queen, she proved a raging, furious devil."

† Sunderland to Jeffreys, Sept. 14, 1685.

pertinacious scrupulosity which he had often shown about taking off his hat would not have been altogether out of place on this occasion. He probably silenced the remonstrances of his conscience by repeating to himself that none of the money which he extorted would go into his own pocket; that if he refused to be the agent of the ladies, they would find agents less humane; that by complying he should increase his influence at the court, and that his influence at the court had already enabled him, and might still enable him, to render great services to his oppressed brethren. The maids of honor were at last forced to content themselves with less than a third part of what they had demanded.*

No English sovereign has ever given stronger proofs of a cruel nature than James the Second; yet his cruelty was not more odious than his mercy; or, perhaps, it may be more correct to say that his mercy and his cruelty were that each reflects infamy on the other. Our horror at the fate of the simple clowns, the young lads, the delicate women, to whom he was inexorably severe, is increased when we find to whom and for what considerations he granted his pardon.

The rule by which a prince ought, after a rebellion, to be guided in selecting rebels for punishment is perfectly obvious. The ring-leaders, the men of rank, fortune, and education, whose power and whose artifices have led the multitude into error, are the proper objects of severity. The deluded populace, when once the slaughter on the field of battle is over, can scarcely be treated too leniently. This rule, so evidently agreeable to justice and humanity, was not only not observed, it was inverted. While those who ought to have been spared were slaughtered by hundreds, the few who might with propriety have been left to the utmost rigor of the law were spared. This eccentric clemency has perplexed some writers, and has drawn forth ludicrous eulogies from others. It was neither at all mysterious nor at all praiseworthy. It may be distinctly traced in every case either to a sordid or to a malignant motive, either to thirst for money or to thirst for blood.

In the case of Grey there was no mitigating circumstance. His parts and knowledge, the rank which he had inherited in the state, and the high command which he had borne in the rebel army, would have pointed him out to a just government as a much fitter object of punishment than Alice Lisle, than William Hewling, than any of the hundreds of ignorant peasants whose skulls and quarters were exposed in Somersetshire. But Grey's estate was large, and was strictly entailed. He had only a life interest in his property, and he could forfeit no more interest than he had. If he died, his lands at once devolved on the next heir. If he were pardoned, he would be able to pay a large ransom. He was therefore suffered to redeem himself by giving a bond for forty thousand

---

* Locke's Western Rebellion; Toulmin's History of Taunton, edited by Savage; Letter of the Duke of Somerset to Sir F. Warre; Letter of Sunderland to Penn, Feb. 13, 1685-6, from the State Paper Office, in the Mackintosh Collection.

pounds to the lord treasurer, and smaller sums to other courtiers.*

Sir John Cochrane had held among the Scotch rebels the same rank which had been held by Grey in the west of England. That Cochrane should be forgiven by a prince vindictive beyond all example, seemed incredible; but Cochrane was the younger son of a rich family; it was therefore only by sparing him that money could be made out of him. His father, Lord Dundonald, offered a bribe of five thousand pounds to the priests of the royal household, and a pardon was granted.†

Samuel Storey, a noted sower of sedition, who had been commissary in the rebel army, and who had inflamed the ignorant populace of Somersetshire by vehement harangues in which James had been described as an incendiary and a poisoner, was admitted to mercy; for Storey was able to give important assistance to Jeffreys in wringing fifteen thousand pounds out of Prideaux.‡

None of the traitors had less right to expect favor than Wade, Goodenough, and Ferguson. These three chiefs of the rebellion had fled together from the field of Sedgemoor, and had reached the coast in safety; but they had found a frigate cruising near the spot where they had hoped to embark. They had then separated. Wade and Goodenough were soon discovered and brought up to London. Deeply as they had been implicated in the Rye House Plot, conspicuous as they had been among the chiefs of the western insurrection, they were suffered to live, because they had it in their power to give information which enabled the king to slaughter and plunder some persons whom he hated, but to whom he had never yet been able to bring home any crime.§

How Ferguson escaped was, and still is, a mystery. Of all the enemies of the government, he was, without doubt, the most deeply criminal. He was the original author of the plot for assassinating the royal brothers. He had written that declaration which, for insolence, malignity, and mendacity, stands unrivaled even among the libels of those stormy times. He had instigated Monmouth first to invade the kingdom, and then to usurp the crown. It was reasonable to expect that a strict search would be made for the arch-traitor, as he was often called; and such a search a man of so singular an aspect and dialect could scarcely have eluded. It was confidently reported in the coffee-houses of London that Ferguson was taken, and this report found credit with men who had excellent opportunities of knowing the truth. The next thing that was heard of him was that he was safe on the Continent. It was strongly suspected that he had been in constant communication with the government against which he was constantly plotting; and that he had, while urging his associates to every excess of rashness, sent to Whitehall just so much information about their

---

* Burnet, i., 646, and Speaker Onslow's note; Clarendon to Rochester, May 8, 1686.
† Burnet, i., 634.
‡ Calamy's Memoirs; Commons' Journals, Dec. 26, 1690; Privy Council Book, Feb. 26, 1685-6.
§ Lansdowne MS., 1152; Harl. MS., 6485; London Gazette, July 20, 1685.

proceedings as might suffice to save his own neck, and that, therefore, orders had been given to let him escape.*

And now Jeffreys had done his work, and returned to claim his reward. He arrived at Windsor from the west, leaving carnage, mourning, and terror behind him. The hatred with which he was regarded by the people of Somersetshire has no parallel in our history. It was not to be quenched by time or by political changes, was long transmitted from generation to generation, and raged fiercely against his innocent progeny. When he had been many years dead, when his name and title were extinct, his granddaughter, the Countess of Pomfret, traveling along the western road, was insulted by the populace, and found that she could not safely venture herself among the descendants of those who had witnessed the bloody assizes.†

But at the court Jeffreys was cordially welcomed. He was a judge after his master's own heart. James had watched the circuit with interest and delight. In his drawing-room and at his table he had frequently talked of the havoc which was making among his disaffected subjects with a glee at which the foreign ministers stood aghast. With his own hand he had penned accounts of what he facetiously called his lord chief justice's campaign in the west. Some hundreds of rebels, his majesty wrote to the Hague, had been condemned. Some of them had been hanged; more should be so; and the rest should be sent to the plantations. It was to no purpose that Ken wrote to implore mercy for the misguided people, and described with pathetic eloquence the frightful state of his diocese. He complained that it was impossible to walk along the highways without seeing some terrible spectacle, and that the whole air of Somersetshire was tainted with death. The king read, and remained, according to the saying of Churchill, hard as the marble chimney-pieces of Whitehall. At Windsor the great seal of England was put into the hands of Jeffreys, and in the next London Gazette it was solemnly notified that this honor was

---

* Many writers have asserted, without the slightest foundation, that a pardon was granted to Ferguson by James. Some have been so absurd as to cite this imaginary pardon, which, if it were real, would prove only that Ferguson was a court spy, in proof of the magnanimity and benignity of the prince who beheaded Alice Lisle and burned Elizabeth Gaunt. Ferguson was not only not specially pardoned, but was excluded by name from the general pardon published in the following spring.—(London Gazette, March 15, 1685-6.) If, as the public suspected, and as seems probable, indulgence was shown to him, it was indulgence on which James was, not without reason, ashamed, and which was, as far as possible, kept secret. The reports which were current in London at the time are mentioned in the Observator, Aug. 1, 1685. Sir John Reresby, who ought to have been well informed, positively affirms that Ferguson was taken three days after the battle of Sedgemoor; but Sir John was certainly wrong as to the date, and may therefore have been wrong as to the whole story. From the London Gazette, and from Goodenough's confession (Lansdowne MS, 1152), it is clear that, a fortnight after the battle, Ferguson had not been caught, and was supposed to be still lurking in England.

† Granger's Biographical History, "Jeffreys."

the reward of the many eminent and faithful services which he had rendered to the crown.*

At a later period, when all men of all parties spoke with horror of the bloody assizes, the wicked judge and the wicked king attempted to vindicate themselves by throwing the blame on each other. Jeffreys, in the Tower, protested that, in his utmost cruelty, he had not gone beyond his master's express orders; nay, that he had fallen short of them. James, at Saint Germain's, would willingly have had it believed that his own inclinations had been on the side of clemency, and that unmerited obloquy had been brought on him by the violence of his minister; but neither of these hard-hearted men must be absolved at the expense of the other. The plea set up for James can be proved under his own hand to be false in fact. The plea of Jeffreys, even if it be true in fact, is utterly worthless.

---

* Burnet, i., 648; James to the Prince of Orange, Sept. 10 and 24, 1685; Lord Lonsdale's Memoirs; London Gazette, Oct. 1, 1685.

The Trial of John Brown

Leonard Ehrlich

THE CROWDS gape, jostle. A great excitement eddies in the open square, where only a week before boys and men with old guns, the Jefferson Guards, rushed into line. Suddenly the ancient bell in the court-house dome clangs deep, jagged; instantly following and mingling unseen drums roll out upon the sharp autumn air. The great crowd-voice veers tenser, the heads are craning, every eye holds the door of the jail. It opens. Militiamen are beginning to file down the steps into the street. In column of twos they move raggedly up on either side of the short narrow path that leads to the court-house, a high building, pillared and venerable. They halt, face each other. The rear rank of each file swings to the right about. "Port arms!" The fixed bayonets gleam, a bristling avenue is formed. The crowds surge up close. From the ends of the square cannon are trained upon the scene.

Now two men come out of the jail door, the county sheriff and Avis the keeper. Next, two armed guards. A hush, expectant, almost absolute, has fallen; faintly somewhere a child is crying, pigeons whir low and swiftly by. A black-bearded man appears on the threshold. His arm is heavy about the shoulders of a huge young Negro; his head is swathed in bandages. Together they go slowly down the three steps, the bearded man tottering. Another Negro follows, young too, straight and slender as a javelin. And last, the old man and the Quaker youth, manacled to each other.

The militiamen are standing set against the crowd, but from it, for all the hate, there is no hostile move, only a staring silence. Something about these five prisoners moving slowly and silently between the bayonet files, stifles the jeers, something like an aura, a single deep doomed pride, moves darkly with them. There too is Stevens faltering, pitifully faint, with his handsome face bloodless white above the black beard and his jet eyes gleaming and torn. He has three musket wounds in his head, two slugs in his right breast and a deep raw forehead gash. And the old man walking by the side of the boy. The old man with the blood-stained bandages about his head. The long white beard; and the face like slate, sabre-slashed. Eyes fierce, sunken, glittering. No, there are no jeers, no taunts; only the deep staring silence.

Down the court-room aisle they walk, through the restless sea of turned pitiless faces. Now as before there is the hush; they can feel the stabbing weight of five hundred eyes. The air is stifling, reeking with odor of human bodies and stale smoke. The prisoners are led to the bench. The morning light streams through the high dirty uncurtained windows and falls about the five in a wan pool. Smoke from the old pipe woodstove is further polluting the air. The bare plank floor is strewn with chestnut shells and scraps of paper. The gavel sharply raps, and in this room of whitewashed walls stained with handsmears, in this room where farmers and tradespeople come, and debts and acres and vagrants are given judgment, the old man and the four youths, white and black, look up at the cold sober countenances of the magistrates, eight in a row behind the table; face the power of the Virginia Commonwealth. The gavel has rapped, the trial is on.

"Do the prisoners have counsel?"

Harding, county-attorney, rises to put the question. He is a short man; heavy. He has a raw bloated face, a hooked nose and brutal eyes, the face of a wastrel. Some political stream threw him up on Jefferson County. He will get fifty dollars for trying this case. He is sober now; savagely his voice rasps out; every word, every gesture reveals his attitude: no frills, quick work and a hanging. "Do you have counsel, or do you want counsel to be assigned by the court?"

The four young prisoners, uncertain, look as one toward the old man. He presses his bony hand on Copeland's shoulder (the young doctor Starry who saved you from the lynching gave you a chance to go like a man, Copeland) and rises painfully from the bench. His angered eyes hold Harding's for an instant. Then he turns, and now is facing, not the prosecutor, not the bench, but the spectators. Yet the eyes are distant from them too; the hewn Hebraic face is raised high. Beyond this old courthouse is a vastness, great cities, plains, the mountains, seas rushing, the millions the poised vastness a nation. Speak, Brown of Osawatomie, hold the innumerable condemning eyes, speak in the profound silence, passionately to your countrymen:

"Virginians! I did not ask for quarter at the time I was taken! I did not ask to have my life spared. The Governor of the State of Virginia tendered me his assurance that I should have a fair trial. But under no circumstances whatever will I be able to have a fair trial. If you seek my blood, you can have it at any moment, without this mockery. I've had no counsel, I have not been able to advise with anyone. I know nothing about the feelings of my fellow prisoners, and I am utterly unable to attend in any way to my own defence. My memory don't serve me, my health is insufficient, though improving. There are mitigating circumstances that I would urge in our favor, if a fair trial is to be allowed us, but if we are to be forced with a mere form, a trial for execution, you might spare yourselves that trouble. I am ready for my fate. I don't ask a trial. I beg for no mockery of a trial, no insult, nothing but that which conscience gives or cowardice would drive you to practice. I ask again to be excused from the mockery of a trial. I do not even know what the special design of this examination is. I do not know what is to be the benefit of it to the Commonwealth. I have now little further to ask, other than that I may not be foolishly insulted only as cowardly barbarians insult those who fall into their power."

The silence endures. The old man is sinking back to the bench, breathing hard, and ashen with the strain.

The Court designates C. J. Faulkner and Lawson Botts as counsel for the defendants. Are the defendants willing to accept?

"If I am to have nothing but the mockery of a trial I do not care anything about counsel." The old man does not rise, he speaks feebly now. "It is unnecessary to trouble any gentleman with that duty."

Harding swells and bristles: "You are, sir, to have a fair trial."

"I have sent for counsel to the north. I am a stranger here. I do not know the disposition or character of the gentlemen named. I could have my own counsel if I am not to be hurried to execution before they can reach me."

"Answer the question, sir! Do you desire the aid of Messrs. Faulkner and Botts? Answer yes or no!"

"I cannot regard this as an examination under any circumstances. I would prefer that they exercise their own pleasure. I feel as if it were a matter of little account to me."

Mr. Faulkner rises instantly, speaks with indignation. He resents the prisoner's criticism of his and Mr. Botts' appointment. Moreover he helped in the fighting against the raiders, and has since then expressed strong opinions about their guilt. Also he has important professional engagements elsewhere. He wishes to be relieved of the assignment.

Will Mr. Green serve as counsel for the defendants?

The mayor of Charlestown stands up to a swift angular height; drawls, "I accept the honor."

Will Mr. Botts serve?

Yes, he too (a small thin-knit man) will serve. He feels it his duty, despite the graceless intimations of the prisoner, to carry on the case.

The heads are wagging throughout the room, the eyes relay the stir. Why, the prisoners have the two best lawyers in Jefferson County. No ordinary criminals ever get such able defence. But, the eyes are saying, the minds flashing, but it's no use, it's all a formality. These men have no chance. There's the evidence and the law. Let the witnesses be examined, let the statements be sworn to, the indictments will come in, they will be found true and binding. These men are doomed. Aye, and a just thing. Nigger-stealers. Traitors. Midnight assassins.

Now the witnesses are being called by Harding.

Lewis Washington. Yes, he was one of the engine-house hostages. Yes, the prisoners did . . . Yes . . . Yes . . . Mr. Brua . . . Mr. Kitzmiller . . . Yes . . . Yes . . . Yes . . . And the old man is sitting there his eyes closed, as if he has no slightest interest in the proceedings. Later the minutes will read: "Sundry witnesses were examined, and the Court being unanimously of the opinion that the Prisoners are guilty of the offence with which they stand charged, it is ordered and considered by the Court that they be sent on to the Circuit-Court for trial according to law."

It was twenty-four hours after the first arraignment. The Court was waiting; the prisoners had been ordered in to plead to the indictments. (Outside, the town leaned forward, cocked its head. Militia trod the narrow streets. Against the closed shops, the startled familiar peace, waves of restlessness broke. Citizens went about carrying rifles.) Again the room was tight-wedged with spectators and newspaper men. Judge Parker sat in the presiding chair. He was a smallish man, with a straight close mouth and a strong jaw; the steady gray eyes were gentle. Now as he waited he was thinking: this would be difficult, he was bound in duty to judge men whose actions deep in his heart he execrated; the traditions of his revered Virginia called powerfully upon his sympathies. But he was a man of law, he reverenced his calling even beyond those traditions; with every power, then, he could summon, this trial would be conducted with judicial decency and impartiality. The whole South was crying for the blood of these men; he must make no smallest concession to the popular frenzy, he must be steel against the passion of the moment. They would be denied no presumption, benefit, or right to which they were entitled; the honor of the State of Virginia was equally on trial before the judgment of the—

The prisoners were coming through the door, led by Avis the jailer . . . Coppoc. Copeland. Emperor Green. Then Stevens, borne on a mattress by four attendants. Finally, the old man. They carried him in on a cot; he had been weakened by the previous day's exertion.

The two wounded men lay within the counsel's railing, near Botts and Mayor Green, and directly before the bench. In the silence Steven's breathing sounded up like a rattle. He's dying, flashed through the crowd-mind, he'll die of his wounds if they don't hang him promptly. Andrew Hunter, special prosecutor for the Commonwealth, thought with anger: the old murderer, he can walk as well as I can, he's going to try to hold up the case, he's out to get every smallest delay. But he has me to face now, not Harding alone, he'll earn every delay, in ten days I'll have him on the gallows. The formal procedure had already begun; now, even as Hunter was thinking, the old man threw off the counterpane and struggled to his feet. He motioned for assistance. A bailiff came and stood by him. There was a stir in the room; the people remembered the defiant courage of the first day, the impassioned "Virginians!"—the room went very quiet. He began—a manacle hung from his right wrist; he wore loose black carpet-slippers—low and uncertain:

"Your honor . . . I do not intend to detain the Court, but barely wish to say, as I have been promised a fair trial, that I am not now in circumstances that enable me to attend to a trial, owing to the state of my health. I have a severe wound in the back, or rather in one kidney, which enfeebles me very much. But I am doing well and only ask for a short delay of my trial, and I think I may be able to listen to it, and I merely ask this, that, as the saying is, the devil may have his dues, no more. I wish to say further that my hearing is impaired and rendered indistinct in consequence of wounds I have about my head. I cannot hear distinctly at all. I could not hear what the Court said this morning. I would be glad to hear what is said on my trial, and am now doing better than I could expect under the circumstances. A very short delay would be all I would ask. I don't presume to ask more than a very short delay, so that I may in some degree recover, and be able at least to listen to my trial, and hear what questions are asked of the citizens, and what their answers are. If that could be allowed me I should be very much obliged."

Judge Parker's gentle eyes rested upon some invisible point high above the rear door; and the voice mild but firm spoke slowly from the bench:

Before passing on the defendant's plea it was necessary for the indictments to be read. Would the prisoners stand in accordance with the dignity of the Court? Would the clerk of the Court read the indictments?

The three young fellows stood; Coppoc quivering a little, but withal, resolute; Copeland proudly; Emperor Green huge, glistening black, dazed. Two attendants lifted white-faced Stevens, held him limp under the arms.

". . . John Brown, Aaron C. Stevens, Edwin Coppoc, white persons . . . Shields Green, John Copeland, Negroes . . . evil-minded and traitorous persons . . . not having the fear of God before their eyes, but being moved and seduced by the false and malignant counsel of other evil and traitorous persons and the instigation of the devil . . . are hereby charged with:

"One, confederating to make rebellion and levy war against the State of Virginia . . .

"Two, with conspiring to induce slaves to make rebellion and insurrection . . .

"Three, with committing murder upon Thomas Boerley, Fontaine Beckham, Luke Quin, white persons, and Shephard Heyward, a free Negro . . ."

The prisoners had heard the arraignment, said the Court. The plea was in order. Guilty or not guilty.

John Brown?

Not guilty.

Aaron C. Stevens?

Not guilty . . . not guilty . . . not guilty . . .

Mr. Botts rose: the prisoners had elected to be tried separately.

Quickly Andrew Hunter and Harding conferred; announced: It was the choice of the prosecution to try the commander of the Provisional Army first. They believed the immediate selection of the jurors was in order.

Mr. Green protested: He wished to urge the justice of Captain Brown's appeal for postponement before a jury was impanelled. They had had little opportunity for examing the indictment or preparing the defence. Moreover the client was ill. It was obvious to all eyes.

Mr. Hunter answered sharply. He opposed the motion for delay. The prisoner's wounds were at worst superficial. There must be no further subterfuges for gaining time. The trial must be swift, the efficiency of the Virginia law must be demonstrated.

"Dr. Mason," said Judge Parker. The court-physician stood up in the second row. "You have recently examined the prisoner. Is the nature of his wounds such as to justify a stay of his trial?"

"I believe the prisoner fit to stand the requirements of the trial, your Honor. Neither his hearing or his mind is impaired by the injuries."

"The request for delay is denied. The impanelling will begin at once."

Richard Timberlake.

Are you a free-holder of this county? Have you expressed any opinions as to the guilt of the prisoner? This man will be hung if you find him guilty. Do you have any conscientious scruples which will prevent you from finding him guilty because the death penalty may be his punishment? Do you . . . have you . . .

William Rightsdale . . . George W. Tapp . . . Isaac Dust. . . . The voices went on, rumbling, high-pitched, timid, drawling; and the old man lay there with his eyes closed, the counterpane drawn up to his white beard.

It happened with startling suddenness.

The procedure of the third day had just begun; the first formalities were being gotten through; the voice of Judge Parker was low and calm over the packed room, the sea of eyes. Harding was nodding off his last night's whiskey. Andrew Hunter, by his side, was glancing hurriedly over some notes, ignoring his colleague. The old man lay again on the pallet within the counsel's railing, alone this time; very still; his eyes smoldered upon Botts' face. The small wiry lawyer was leaning forward in his chair, his thin legs coiled around the supports. He was like a spring poised to leap out. Judge Parker's voice halted. Botts rose quickly.

"Your Honor!"

In all urgency he wished to plead again for postponement. Counsel for the defence (Hunter stirred angrily: another evasion, another subterfuge) had in their hands new testimony of startling significance. It was a telegram (the old man's eyes were slits of fire) which had been received late last night. They wished, in consideration of its obvious and important bearing upon the defence, to reveal its purport to the Court.

Indeed, indeed, assented the Court.

Green slipped a paper from the table and handed it to Botts. The audience strained. The old man's body took on a hawk-like rigidity. The thin lawyer began to read:

"Akron, Ohio, Thursday, October Twenty-seventh, Eighteen Fifty-nine. . . . To C. J. Faulkner and Lawson Botts. . . . John Brown, leader of the insurrection at Harper's Ferry, and several of his family, have resided in this county many years. Insanity is hereditary in that family. His mother's sister died with it, and a daughter of that sister has been two years in a lunatic asylum. A son and daughter of his mother's brother have also been confined in the lunatic asylum, and another son of that brother is now insane and under close restraint. These facts can be conclusively proven by witnesses residing here, who will doubtless attend the trial if desired. . . . A. H. Lewis."

Order! Silence in this room!

Slowly, at length, the excited whispering died; but a throbbing was in the court, like a great pulse. Botts went on quickly: he thought it only fair to state that the defendant had refused to avail himself of the plea of insanity (Hunter's lips curled) and that the movement had been undertaken without his approval or concurrence and was unknown to him until the receipt of the despatch—

"Your Honor!"

The old man was raising himself from the pallet. He stood up, swaying, holding the blanket to him. The haggard face blazed with scorn.

"I will add, if the Court will allow me, that I look upon it as a miserable artifice and pretext of those who ought to take a different course in regard to me, if they took any at all, and I view it with contempt more than otherwise. As I remarked to Mr. Green, insane persons, so far as experience goes, have but little ability to judge of their own sanity, and if I am insane, of course I should think I know more than all the rest of the world. But I do not think so. I am perfectly unconscious of insanity, and I reject, so far as I am capable, any attempt to interfere in my behalf on that score."

It was like a bolt from clear skies. The hush hung. Every eye followed him down to the mattress, beheld him kneel, trembling with faintness. Then the startled murmur broke, swelled higher, higher, drowning the gavel; hubbub ruled.

It was astounding! Andrew Hunter was staring; Judge Parker's discreet eyebrows had gone up perceptibly. Even the sodden Harding blinked from his dimness. The old scoundrel had been fighting for time every inch of the way, desperately "playing possum." Now here was the first real chance to hold up the trial indefinitely, even more, a chance for very life, and he was rejecting it utterly! Chagrin began to mingle with Hunter's perplexity; there was some cunning here and he did not know how to meet it. The Virginian's eyes bored into the wounded fanatic, as if he would penetrate to the very workings of the secret mind. Crazy old cutthroat!

Not this, God. Not this . . . Do not let the madhouse be the end of my search. . . . For twenty years I have fought against slavery, according to your word. . . . I have sinned, I know I have sinned. But have I not mingled the blood of my children with your despised poor? Oh God, let some good arise from this ruin. . . . Israel Green snatched up a light dress-blade instead of a sabre; in the engine-house the blade thrust for my life, and did not find it. Oh let it be spared for a good death! Let this end of my time, in some way yet unknown and inscrutable, serve you.

Only not this. Not this, God.

". . . I look upon it as a miserable artifice and pretext of those who ought to take a different course in regard to me, and I view it with contempt more than otherwise. . . . I am perfectly unconscious of insanity and I reject so far as I am capable any attempt to interfere in my behalf on that score."

Botts looked helplessly at his associate. Green rose. (His face was tight, expressive: see what we are up against; the man thwarts us at every turn; but we are men of law, and though we detest all he stands for, we will do our duty by him.) "Your Honor. We confess extreme embarrassment in urgin' a defence which the client has publicly repudiated. But the course open to us is single, it's obvious. We plead adjournment; the existin' circumstances cry out for 'n investigation."

"I object," said Andrew Hunter. "There is no proper cause for postponement."

"The objection is sustained. In the absence of sworn testimony supporting the plea of insanity there is no true legal question before the Court. The trial will proceed."

The old man sank back upon the pallet. He drew the blanket about himself. He closed his eyes.

". . . and you sent the boy?" asked Higginson.

"He ought to be here tonight," said LeBarnes.

Outside, the narrow Boston street lay quiet and coldly dappled. The sun cut sharp through the elms. A bell chimed faint and clear, twice in the autumn distance.

"Bowditch was dubious. He said they'd suspect him."

"Damn Bowditch! He's against every plan I've broached. He can't see that it's no time for caution. Impossible, wild, hopeless! What does he think this is, a business deal? Why, the boy's very youth will throw them off. They'll think he's some impulsive fledgling lawyer who's rushed down to help the old man. They'll never suspect."

"They may. Does Massachusetts need a stripling to represent her in a trial of this importance? . . . Well, we can't lose much."

"I told him to watch everything closely. To see and talk with him, and get to us anything he may want to say. I told him to make a plan of the town. How many troops, and where they're placed. The site of the jail and exactly how it's guarded. The nature of the surrounding country. Do you see?"

"Yes . . . yes . . . it may help. . . . But let's get to these other matters. It's too slow, LeBarnes, the whole thing's going too slowly! He'll be gone before we stir."

Eagerly they talked. . . . The son in Ohio, the eldest . . . coming east with men . . . the German radicals, a hundred of them under a firebrand, Metternich, down from New York . . . Kansas jay-hawkers . . . outside Charlestown, a swift dash on the town, the escape on the horses of the cavalry companies . . . Orsini bombs, hand-grenades. . . . The countryside paralyzed . . .

Aye, and that other desperate scheme, all else failing: the Governor of the State of Virginia spirited away by night . . . out to sea in a fast tug, faster by many knots than the single gunboat off Richmond . . .

Henry Wise, hostage for Osawatomie Brown . . .

It was the fourth morning. The frail beardless boy came into the courtroom. Amid a profound astonishment he spoke:

"I am George Henry Hoyt. I am a member of the Massachusetts bar and I have come to assist in Captain Brown's defence."

The room was astir with derision and mistrust. Andrew Hunter instantly protested: "Mr. Hoyt is unknown to us. Let him prove his position under the Massachusetts bar, his right to practice in this court."

"We have no need of assistance," said Botts coldly.

"I do not know Mr. Hoyt," said the old man. "But I request his help, as one in sympathy with me."

"I regret that I have no formal proof at the moment," said the youth. "But I shall be willing to take no active part until my status is established."

Spy, thought Andrew Hunter, damned Yankee spy.

"I see no reason," said Judge Parker, "to object against additional counsel. I suggest that formal proof be dispensed with for the present. Let the oath be administered."

". . . so help me God. . . ." George Henry Hoyt entered within the counsel's railing; took a place beside the old man's pallet. The prosecution continued, Hunter addressing the Court:

". . . And the evidence shows without a shadow of a question that when the defendant went to Virginia and planted his feet at Harper's Ferry, he came there to reside, and to hold the place permanently. True, he occupied a farm four or five miles off in Maryland, but not for the legitimate purpose of establishing his domicile there. No, for the hellish purpose of rallying forces into the Commonwealth and establishing himself at the Ferry, as the starting point for a new government. Whatever it was, whether tragical, or farcial and ridiculous, as the learned counsel for the defence have just presented it, his conduct showed, if his declarations were insufficient, that his provisional government was a real thing and no debating society, and in holding office under it and exercising its functions, he was clearly guilty of treason. As to conspiring with slaves and rebels the law says the prisoner is equally guilty, whether insurrection is made or not. Advice may be given by actions as well as words. When you put pikes in the hands of slaves and have their masters captive, that is advice to rebel. It is punishable with death."

Now Harding began the examination of witnesses to support his colleague's denunciation. Lew Washington . . . Joseph Brua. . . . And once again by these brief sober affirmations the whole mad Ferry thrust was evoked. Then Andrew Hunter rose. He drew some papers from the old black carpet-bag on the table. He began, without comment, to read:

"Whereas, Slavery, throughout its existence . . . is none other than a most barbarous, unprovoked War of one portion of its citizens upon . . . Therefore we . . . and the oppressed people . . . do ordain and establish for ourselves the following Provisional Constitution . . ."

Andrew Hunter moved to the pallet, handed down the sheets to old Brown.

"Do you recognize this writing?"

"It is mine."

Hunter moved back to the counsel's bench. He took up another paper; without a single word, began to read.

". . . It is mine."

". . . Yes, I held such a belief. I hold it now."

". . . Yes . . . Yes . . "

By noon the prosecution rested: treason, insurrection, murder.

". . . and I ask that the penalty be visited on the prisoner, whom the law denounces, whom reason denounces, the penalty which our safety requires and which the laws of God and man approve."

During the midday recess young Hoyt was closeted with John Brown. A half hour before the session was again to open, Botts and Green entered the jail. The young fellow had a startled incredulous look upon his face; the eyes of the wounded prisoner shone with a proud fervent yet strangely softened light. The two were not speaking; they were sitting silent, as if between them words lay.

"We begin the defence this afternoon," said Botts, frigidly pointed.

"I do not know the Virginia law," said the boy. "I have nothing as yet to suggest."

"How did you expect to help?"

". . . I was not sure. . . . But I felt I might help . . . in some way. Even if it was only to bring to Captain Brown the knowledge that we in the North had not forgotten him."

"Undoubtedly." Botts turned to the old man. "You still insist that we go on with the defence as you have suggested?"

"Yes, I think it is best so."

"Very well then. But the responsibility is yours. You are insisting that we concentrate the defence upon details that the Court will inevitably consider irrelevant. Your case is desperate even with the best kind of a defence, yet—"

"Here," said the old man. "I have written down these points for you to follow."

Botts read the paper; then silently handed it to Green. The angular man's eyes moved swiftly, a flush began to redden up his leathery neck.

"Damn me," he drawled. "What fool stuff'll you have *us* workin' upon? Thar's no use, don't you see it? All's been brought out over'n over again."

"Yes. But I wish it so."

"Damn me. Thar, see this for a rock-hard defence." Green in a helpless anger flipped the paper into young Hoyt's lap:

We gave to numerous prisoners perfect liberty—get all their names. We allowed other prisoners to visit their families, to quiet their fears—get all their names. We treated all our prisoners with the utmost kindness and humanity—get all their names, so far as may be. Our orders from the first and throughout were that no unarmed person should be injured, under any circumstances whatever—prove that by all the prisoners. We committed no destruction or waste of property—prove that.

"Thar, see this for a rock-hard defence."

Aye, what do you know of my dream?

In the afternoon the defence began.

". . . My name is John Dangerfield . . . I am a clerk in the armory . . . yes, I was there . . .

". . . At night the firing stopped. You see, it was pitch black in the engine-house and we couldn't see anything. I talked a lot with Mr. Brown that night. I found him a very brave man, and I found him sensible on all subjects except slavery. He believed it was his duty to free slaves, even if he lost his own life. . . . During a sharp fight one of his sons was killed. He fell, then he tried to raise himself, and he said, it is all over with me. Brown did not leave his post at the porthole, but when the fighting was over he walked to his son's body. He stretched out the limbs and took off the dead fellow's trappings. Then he said to me, this is the third son I have lost in this cause. Another son had been shot in the morning and was then moaning so you could hardly bear to listen. They brought him in from the street, all ripped with slugs. He was dying. But when his men wanted to fire on someone passing, Mr. Brown would stop them, saying, don't shoot, that man is unarmed. . . ."

"You are a Virginian, are you not, Mr. Dangerfield? . . . And you, of course, have no slightest sympathy in principle with the prisoner? . . . And yet you are testifying in his favor?"

"Yes, I feel it's my duty. He made me a prisoner, he had me and other men in his full power and could have killed us. But he spared our lives. When his sons were shot down beside him, almost any other man would have taken life for life . . ."

"Your Honor!" said Andrew Hunter. "I object strenuously to the introduction of such testimony at this time! There is nothing in these facts which the jury can consider. What difference will it make if a thousand witnesses should testify to the defendant's kindness, or his merciful instructions to his men? Mr. Brown's so-called humanity has already been brought out again and again, and as to the nobility of his motives, that has even less relevance in a court of law. The point in question is the prisoner's guilt under the charges of the indictment. Treason, insurrection, murder! This entire testimony is a sheer waste of time! It has no more bearing on the case than the dead languages!"

Objection overruled. . . .

"My name is David Sinn. . . . I was in command of the Fredericksburg militia during the raid . . .

". . . and I have never seen any man show more courage and forebearance than John Brown showed that night under those terrible circumstances. . . . Besides my admiration for the man, I am testifying for Captain Brown so Northern men will have no opportunity to say that

Southern men were not willing to appear as witnesses in behalf of one whose ideas they hated. . . ."

". . . My name's Benjamin Mills. Most people call me Ben. . . I'm the master-armorer. I been that for six years now. Before that I was twenty years doin' . . . eh? . . .

. . . Well, then one of the old man's boys went out with a handkerchief for a truce. He was shot down. Then he came crawlin' in—

(Oh stilled young hearts!)

"—to the gates. I gave him some water, tried to ease him, but there wasn't no use. . . . The old man didn't seem to hold no grudge, he only said kind of choked that our citizens had done it like . . . like barbarians. . . . He was expectin' reinforcements all along. When his men got to losin' hope he would say, it'll soon be night, and he kept sayin', Owen, Owen. He said to shoot no one save they was bearin' arms, and if they do let them have it. . . . It kind of seemed to me he wanted to make terms more for our sake than to be safe his own self. . . ."

". . . and nothing but the truth, so help. . . . I am Harry Hunter. . . . Fontaine Beckham was my uncle. . . . He was shot down on the trestle. . . . Chambers and I ran to the hotel. The Thompson fellow was tied up there. We were going to shoot him but Miss Foukes got in front of him and shielded him. I guess she was afraid we'd spoil her carpet. So we dragged him up to the railroad bridge, right to the spot where they'd killed my uncle. We gave it to him, dropped his body—" (as the prosecutor's son calmly drawled on there was no sound of sympathy or horror in all the court-rom, save on the pallet the old man suddenly groaning aloud) "—to the rocks in the river. I don't regret it. They killed my uncle. He was the best friend I ever had. I'd have killed anyone I could get my hands on . . . Sir? . . . Yes, I'd have killed them all, truce or no truce."

Thomas Osbourne?

Silence.

Joseph Wiltshire?

Silence.

(Scoff, call all this irrelevant— what do you know of my dream? I cherish no illusion, the sands of my time have to run out, long ago my body's life was forfeit. But the dream—Almighty Father! speak through me, speak through me to the hearts of men. Grant me a little time to reach them. Not Virginia, not men of a jury. But the North, the South, my land, my country!)

Reason Cross?

Silence.

Abraham Avey?

Silence.

The old man suddenly struggled to his feet:

"May it please the Court! I discover that notwithstanding all the assurances I have received of a fair trial, nothing like a fair trial is to be given me! I gave the names, as soon as I could get them, of the persons I wished to have called as witnesses, and was assured that they would be subpoenaed. I wrote down a memorandum to that effect, saying where those parties were, but it appears that they have not been subpoenaed as far as I can learn, and now I ask, if I am to have anything at all deserving the name and shadow of a fair trial, that this proceeding be deferred until tomorrow morning, for I have no counsel, as I before stated, in whom I feel that I can rely; but I am in hopes counsel may arrive who will attend to seeing that I get the witnesses who are necessary for my defence. I am myself unable to attend to it. I have given all the attention I possibly could to it, but am unable to see or know about them, and can't even find out their names, and I have nobody to do any errands, for my money was all taken when I was sacked and stabbed, and I have not a dime. I had two hundred and fifty or sixty dollars in gold and silver taken from my pocket, and now I have no possible means of getting anybody to go my errands for me, and I have not had all the witnesses subpoenaed. They are not within reach, and are not here. I ask at least until tomorrow morning to have something done, if anything is designed. If not, I am ready for anything that may come up."

Green sprang up furious: Mr. Brown had openly charged them with bad faith, had cast reflections upon their professional conduct! They could no longer go on with the case! They had represented the prisoner to the very best of their ability, they had faithfully followed his instructions, even against their own judgment, had performed every duty which law and honor committed them to! Now, since their motives were questioned and a lack of confidence in them expressed in open court, they would resign and leave the case in the hands of the gentleman from Massachusetts!

Blanched, stunned, in the midst of the stir and the hostile derisive eyes, young Hoyt sat. Then he rose, his thin hands frantically clutching the back of his chair, and said:

"I have just come from Boston. I have travelled night and day. I have had no time to read the indictment, and I know nothing of the criminal code of Virginia. . . . Other counsel from the North are due in Charlestown tonight. I beg in fairness to Captain Brown that the case be postponed until their arrival."

"Exception!" cried Hunter violently. "These delays are making a farce of the trial!"

"I second Mr. Hoyt's appeal," said Botts. "His difficulties demand consideration. Mr. Green and myself can no longer act in behalf of the prisoner, but if the Court will grant a postponement we will devote every spare moment to prepare him for his duties. We will put our notes and knowledge at Mr. Hoyt's command."

"The trial is adjourned until tomorrow morning."

The light in Botts' office burned steadily into the early hours. The thin lawyer and the boy sat talking, talking, the great books and the papers cluttered before them. At four in the morning the boy's eyes closed, with sheer exhaustion his head slipped to the table; he was dead asleep. Botts quietly rose, turned out the light. He walked home through the dark silent lanes. He felt a sorrow in his heart, he felt it in the night, a sorrow vast and moving, yet impersonal.

(*Trampled bloodwet fields of Manassas, oh brothers locked in anguish falling to the long bleached sleep!*

"*Lawson Botts: Colonel, Second Regiment Virginia Volunteers, Army of the Confederacy. 1823-1862.*")

At ten o'clock the next morning the Court resumed session. There were two new faces; eminent lawyers from the North, Samuel Chilton of Washington, and Hiram Griswold of Cleveland. Immediately they requested a delay of a few hours: the case was curiously confused; Mr. Griswold was unacquainted with the Virginia law.

"The request is denied. The prisoner has had able counsel. He has had the fullest opportunities for defence. He has chosen to make a change, the responsibility is his alone. I should at once accede to the request, however, if this were the only case on the calendar. But the end of the term is near; in fairness to the other defendants and to the State the action must be undelayed. The trial will proceed."

The end was nearing. Young Hoyt, peaked and shaken, continued the defence along the lines the old man had laid down to Green and Botts: summoning of the engine-house hostages to establish his humanity to them. In the afternoon, Chilton, seeking time, submitted a motion that the State elect one count of the indictment and abandon the other two. It was, he said, gravely difficult for the prisoner to defend himself against the three distinct charges at once. No, ruled Judge Parker, the trial had begun under the complete indictment; it must continue under it. The most that could be granted was a motion for arrest of judgment at the conclusion of the trial. He ordered the prosecution to begin summing up. Late that afternoon the Court adjourned. There would be a respite of a single day, the Sabbath.

On Monday morning, Andrew Hunter, addressing the jury, concluded the case for the Commonwealth of Virginia:

". . . Administer justice according to your law. Acquit the prisoner if you can. But if justice requires you by your verdict to take his life, stand by it uprightly. Let retributive justice, if he is guilty, send him before that Maker who will settle the question forever and forever."

"Gentlemen of the Jury, what say you? Is the prisoner at the bar—John Brown—guilty or not guilty?"

"*Guilty.*"

"Guilty of treason, guilty of conspiring with slaves to rebel, guilty of murder in the first degree?"

"*Guilty.*"

"Does the prisoner have anything to say why sentence should not be pronounced on him?"

The gas-lit room is packed with people. They are filling every square inch from the counsel's railing out to the wide hall, out to the corridors and the entrance steps. Just as last night to hear the verdict they stood silent and moved, agitated by one hope and dreadful expectancy, so now spreading out into the dusk of the streets do they strain to witness, to hear the last of the doomed old man. He is sitting on the bench beside the pale boy counsel, gazing fixedly at the Judge. In a flat quivering voice the clerk asks the question, the question quivers into the rapt silence: does the prisoner have anything to say why sentence should not be pronounced on him? John Brown turns his head to stare at the clerk; then sits unmoving, as if stunned. Hoyt whispers hurriedly to him. The old man shakes his head twice. A moment goes by; now slowly he is rising to his feet. He grips the table before him, leans over it a little, his face working with consternation. Oh, is his thought, I am not ready, I am not ready. He stands unsteadily so for many minutes, bent over a little, gaunt and tragic in the green flickering light; the deep silence endures. Then slowly, haltingly, he speaks:

"I have, may it please the Court, a few words to say. . . .

"It is unjust that I should suffer such a penalty. Had I interfered in the manner which I admit, and which I admit has been fairly proved—for I admire the truthfulness and candor of the greater portion of the witnesses who have testified in this case—had I so interfered in behalf of the rich, the powerful, the intelligent, the so-called great, or in behalf of any of their friends, either father, mother, brother, sister, wife or children, or any of that class, and suffered and sacrificed what I have in this interference, I would have been all right. Every man in this Court would have deemed it an act worthy of reward rather than punishment. . . .

"This Court acknowledges too, as I suppose, the validity of the law of God. I see a book kissed, which I suppose to be the Bible, or at least the New Testament, which teaches me that all things whatsoever I would that men should do to me, I should do even so to them. It teaches me, further, to remember them that are in bonds as bound with them. I endeavored to act up to that instruction. I say I am yet too young to understand that God is any respecter of persons. I believe that to have interfered as I have done, as I have always freely admitted I have done, in behalf of His despised poor, I did no wrong, but right. Now, if it is deemed necessary that I should forfeit my life for the furtherance of the ends of justice, and mingle my blood further with the blood of my children and with the blood of millions in this slave country whose rights are disregarded by wicked, cruel, and unjust enactments, I say, let it be done. . . ."

". . . I pronounce the sentence of death . . . Friday, the Second of December . . . hanged by the neck till dead . . . dead . . . dead . . ."

The Commission in Lunacy

Honoré de Balzac

Dedicated to Monsieur le Contre-Amiral Bazoche, Governor of the Isle of Bourbon, by the grateful writer,

De Balzac.

IN 1828, at about one o'clock one morning, two persons came out of a large house in the Rue du Faubourg Saint-Honore, near the Elysee-Bourbon. One was a famous doctor, Horace Bianchon; the other was one of the most elegant men in Paris, the Baron de Rastignac; they were friends of long standing. Each had sent away his carriage, and no cab was to be seen in the street; but the night was fine, and the pavement dry.

"We will walk as far as the Boulevard," said Eugene de Rastignac to Bianchon. "You can get a hackney cab at the club; there is always one to be found there till daybreak. Come with me as far as my house."

"With pleasure."

"Well, and what have you to say about it?"

"About that woman?" said the doctor coldly.

"There I recognize my Bianchon!" exclaimed Rastignac.

"Why, how?"

"Well, my dear fellow, you speak of the Marquise d'Espard as if she were a case for your hospital."

"Do you want to know what I think, Eugene? If you throw over Madame de Nucingen for this Marquise, you will swap a one-eyed horse for a blind one."

"Madame de Nucingen is six-and-thirty, Bianchon."

"And this woman is three-and-thirty," said the doctor quickly.

"Her worst enemies only say six-and-twenty."

"My dear boy, when you really want to know a woman's age, look at her temples and the tip of her nose. Whatever women may achieve with their cosmetics, they do nothing against those incorruptible witnesses to their experiences. There each year of life has left its stigmata. When a women's temples are flaccid, seamed, withered in a particular way; when at the tip of her nose you see those minute specks, which look like the imperceptible black smuts which are shed in London by the chimneys in which coal is burnt. . . . Your servant, sir! That woman is more than thirty. She may be handsome, witty, loving—whatever you please, but she is past thirty, she is arriving at maturity. I do not blame men who attach themselves to that kind of woman; only, a man of your superior distinction must not mistake a winter pippin for a little summer apple, smiling on the bough, and waiting for you to crunch it. Love never goes to study the registers of birth and marriage; no one loves a woman because she is handsome or ugly, stupid or clever; we love because we love."

"Well, for my part, I love for quite other reasons. She is Marquise d'Espard; she was a Blamont-Chauvry; she is the fashion; she has soul; her foot is as pretty as the Duchess de Berri's; she has perhaps a hundred thousand francs a year—some day, perhaps, I may marry her! In short, she will put me into a position which will enable me to pay my debts."

"I thought you were rich," interrupted Bianchon.

"Bah! I have twenty thousand francs a year—just enough to keep up my stables. I was thoroughly done, my dear fellow, in that Nucingen business; I will tell you about that.—I have got my sisters married; that is the clearest profit I can show since we last met; and I would rather have them provided for than have five hundred thousand francs a year. Now, what would you have me do? I am ambitious. To what can Madame de Nucingen lead? A year more and I shall be shelved, stuck in a pigeon-hole like a married man. I have all the discomforts of marriage and of single life, without the advantages of either; a false position, to which every man must come who remains tied too long to the same apron-string."

"So you think you will come upon a treasure here?" said Bianchon. "Your Marquise, my dear fellow, does not hit my fancy at all."

"Your liberal opinions blur your eyesight. If Madame d'Espard were a Madame Rabourdin . . ."

"Listen to me. Noble or simple, she would still have no soul; she would be still a perfect type of selfishness. Take my word for it, medical men are accustomed to judge of people and things; the sharpest of us read the soul while we study the body. In spite of that pretty boudoir where we have spent this evening, in spite of the magnificence of the house, it is quite possible that Madame le Marquise is in debt."

"What makes you think so?"

"I do not assert it; I am supposing. She talked of her soul as Louis XVIII. used to talk of his heart. I tell you this: That fragile, fair woman, with her chestnut hair, who pities herself that she may be pitied, enjoys an iron constitution, and appetite like a wolf's and the strength and cowardice of a tiger. Gauze, and silk, and muslin were never more cleverly twisted round a lie! *Ecco.*"

"Bianchon, you frighten me! You have learned a good many things, then, since we lived in the Maison Vauquer?"

"Yes; since then, my boy, I have seen puppets, both dolls and mannikins. I know something of the ways of the fine ladies whose bodies we attend to, saving that which is dearest to them, their child—if they love it—or their pretty faces, which they always worship. A man spends his nights by their pillow, wearing himself to death to spare them the slightest loss of beauty in any part; he succeeds, he keeps their secret like the dead; they send to ask for his bill, and think it horribly exhorbitant. Who saved them? Nature. Far from recommending him, they speak ill of him, fearing lest he should become the physician of their best friends.

"My dear fellow, those women of whom you say, 'They are angels!' I— I—have seen stripped of the little grimaces under which they hide their soul, as well as of the frippery under which they disguise their defects— without manners and without stays; they are not beautiful.

"We saw a great deal of mud, a great deal of dirt, under the waters of the world when we were aground for a time on the shoals of the Maison Vauquer.—What we saw there was nothing. Since I have gone into higher society, I have seen monsters dressed in satin, Michonneaus in white gloves, Poirets bedizened with orders, fine gentlemen doing more usurious business than old Gobseck! To the shame of mankind, when I have wanted to shake hands with Virtue, I have found her shivering in a loft, persecuted by calumny, half starving on an income or a salary of fifteen hundred francs a year, and regarded as crazy, or eccentric, or imbecile.

"In short, my dear boy, the Marquise is a woman of fashion, and I have a particular horror of that kind of woman. Do you want to know why? A woman who has a lofty soul, fine taste, gentle wit, a generously warm heart, and who lives a simple life, has not a chance of being the fashion. *Ergo:* A woman of fashion and a man in power are analogous; but there is this difference: the qualities by which a man raises himself above others ennoble him and are a glory to him; whereas the qualities by which a woman gains power for a day are hideous vices; she belies her nature to hide her character, and to live the militant life of the world she must have iron strength under a frail appearance.

"I, as a physician, know that a sound stomach exudes a good heart. Your woman of fashion feels nothing; here rage for pleasure has its source in a longing to heat up her cold nature, a craving for excitement and enjoyment, like an old man who stands night after night by the footlights at the opera. As she has more brain than heart, she sacrifices genuine passion and true friends to her triumph, as a general sends his most devoted subalterns to the front in order to win a battle. The woman of fashion ceases to be a woman; she is neither mother, nor wife, nor lover. She is, medically speaking, sex in the brain. And your Marquise, too, has all the characteristics of her monstrosity, the beak of a bird of prey, the clear, cold eye, the gentle voice—she is as polished as the steel of a machine, she touches everything except the heart."

"There is some truth in what you say, Bianchon."

"Some truth?" replied Bianchon. "It is all true. Do you suppose that I was not struck to the heart by the insulting politeness by which she made me measure the imaginary distance which her noble birth sets between us? That I did not feel the deepest pity for her catlike civilities when I remembered what her object was? A year hence she will not write one word to do me the slightest service, and this evening she pelted me with smiles, believing that I can influence my uncle Popinot, on whom the success of her case—"

"Would you rather she should have played the fool with you, my dear fellow?—I accept your diatribe against women of fashion; but you are beside the mark. I should always prefer for a wife a Marquise d'Espard to the most devout and devoted creature on earth. Marry an angel! you would have to go and bury your happiness in the depths of the country! The wife of a politician is a governing machine, a contrivance that makes compliments and courtesies. She is the most important and most faithful tool which an ambitious man can use; a friend, in short, who may compromise herself without mischief, and whom he may belie without harmful results. Fancy Mahomet in Paris in the nineteenth century! His wife would be a Rohan, a Duchess de Chevreuse of the Fronde, as keen and as flattering as an Ambassadress, as wily as Figaro. Your loving wives lead nowhere; a woman of the world leads to everything; she is the diamond with which a man cuts every window when he has not the golden key which unlocks every door. Leave humdrum virtues to the humdrum, ambitious vices to the ambitious.

"Besides, my dear fellow, do you imagine that the love of a Duchesse de Langeais, or de Maufrigneuse, or of a Lady Dudley does not bestow immense pleasure? If only you know how much value the cold, severe style of such women gives to the smallest evidence of their affection! What a delight it is to see a periwinkle piercing through the snow! A smile from below a fan contradicts the reserve of an assumed attitude, and is worth all the unbridled tenderness of your middle-class women with their mortgaged devotion; for, in love, devotion is nearly akin to speculation.

"And, then, a woman of fashion, A Blamont-Chauvry, has her virtues too! Her virtues are fortune, power, effect, a certain contempt for all that is beneath her—"

"Thank you!" said Bianchon.

"Old curmudgeon!" said Rastignac, laughing. "Come—do not be common; do like your friend Desplein; be a Baron, a Knight of Saint-Michael; become a peer of France, and marry your daughters to dukes."

"I! May the five hundred thousand devils—"

"Come, come! Can you be superior only in medicine! Really, you distress me. . . ."

"I hate that sort of people; I long for a revolution to deliver us from them forever."

"And so, my dear Robespierre of the lancet, you will not go to-morrow to your uncle Popinot?"

"Yes, I will," said Bianchon; "for you I would go to hell and fetch water. . . ."

"My good friend, you really touch me. I have sworn that a commission shall sit on the Marquis. Why, here is even a long-saved tear to thank you."

"But," Bianchon went on, "I do not promise to succeed as you wish with Jean-Jules Popinot. You do not know him. However, I will take him to see your Marquise the day after to-morrow; she may get round him if she can. I doubt it. If all the truffles, all the Duchesses, all the mistresses, and all the charmers in Paris were there in the full bloom of their beauty; if the King promised him the *pairie,* and the Almighty gave him the Order of Paradise with the revenues of Purgatory, not one of all these powers would induce him to transfer a single straw from one saucer of his scales into the other. He is a judge, as Death is Death."

The two friends had reached the office of the Minister for Foreign Affairs, at the corner of the Boulevard des Capucines.

"Here you are at home," said Bianchon, laughing, as he pointed to the ministerial residence. "And here is my carriage," he added, calling a hackney cab. "And these—express our fortune."

"You will be happy at the bottom of the sea, while I am still struggling with the tempests on the surface, till I sink and go to ask you for a corner in your grotto, old fellow!"

"Till Saturday," replied Bianchon.

"Agreed," said Rastignac. "And you promise me Popinot?"

"I will do all my conscience will allow. Perhaps this appeal for a commission covers some little dramorama, to use a word of our good bad times."

"Poor Bianchon! he will never be anything but a good fellow," said Rastignac to himself as the cab drove off.

"Rastignac has given me the most difficult negotiation in the world," said Bianchon to himself, remembering, as he rose next morning, the delicate commission intrusted to him. "However, I have never asked the smallest service from my uncle in Court, and have paid more than a thousand visits gratis for him. And, after all, we are not apt to mince matters between ourselves. He will say Yes or No, and there an end."

After this little soliloquy the famous physician bent his steps, at seven in the morning, towards the Rue du Fouarre, where dwelt Monsieur Jean-Jules Popinot, judge of the Lower Court of the Department of the Seine. The Rue du Fouarre—an old word meaning straw—was in the thirteenth century the most important street in Paris. There stood the Schools of the University, where the voices of Abélard and of Gerson were heard in the world of learning. It is now one of the dirtiest streets of the Twelfth Arrondissement, the poorest quarter of Paris, that in which two-thirds of the population lack firing in winter, which leaves most brats at the gate of the Foundling Hospital, which sends most beggars to the poorhouse, most rag-pickers to the street corners, most decrepit old folks to bask against the walls on which the sun shines, most delinquents to the police courts.

Half-way down this street, which is always damp, and where the gutter carries to the Seine the blackened waters from some dye-works, there is an old house, restored no doubt under Francis I., and built of bricks held together by a few courses of masonry. That it is substantial seems proved by the shape of its front wall, not uncommonly seen in some parts of Paris. It bellies, so to speak, in a manner caused by the protuberance of its first floor, crushed under the weight of the second and third, but upheld by the strong wall of the ground floor. At first sight it would seem as though the piers between the windows, though strengthened by the stone mullions, must give away; but the observer presently perceives that, as in the tower of Bologna, the old bricks and old time-eaten stones of this house persistently preserve their center of gravity.

At every season of the year the solid piers of the ground floor have the yellow tone and the imperceptible sweating surface that moisture gives to stone. The passer-by feels chilled as he walks close to this wall, where worn cornerstones ineffectually shelter him from the wheels of vehicles. As is always the case in houses built before carriages were in use, the vault of the doorway forms a very low archway not unlike the barbican of a prison. To the right of this entrance there are three windows, protected outside by iron gratings of so close a pattern, that the curious cannot possibly see the use made of the dark, damp rooms within, and the panes too are dirty and dusty; to the left are two similar windows, one of which is sometimes open, exposing to view the porter, his wife, and his children; swarming, working, cooking, eating, and screaming, in a floored and wainscoted room where everything is dropping to pieces, and into which you descend two steps—a depth which seems to suggest the gradual elevation of the soil of Paris.

If on a rainy day some foot-passenger takes refuge under the long vault, with projecting lime-washed beams, which leads from the door to the staircase, he will hardly fail to pause and look at the picture presented by the interior of this house. To the left is a square garden-plot, allowing of not more than four long steps in each direction, a garden of black soil, with trellises bereft of vines, and where, in default of vegetation under the shade of two trees, papers collect, old rags, potsherds, bits of mortar fallen from the roof; a barren ground, where time has shed on the walls, and on the trunks and branches of the trees, a powdery deposit like cold soot. The two parts of the house, set at a right angle, derive light from this garden-court shut in by two adjoining houses built on wooden piers, decrepit and ready to fall, where on each floor some grotesque evidence is to be seen of the craft pursued by the lodger within. Here long poles are hung with immense skeins of dyed worsted put out to dry; there, on ropes, dance clean-washed shirts; higher up, on a shelf, volumes display their freshly marbled edges; women sing, husbands whistle, children shout; the carpenter saws his planks, a copper-turner makes the metal screech; all kinds of industries combine to produce a noise which the number of instruments renders distracting.

The general system of decoration in this passage, which is neither courtyard, garden, nor vaulted way, though a little of all, consists of wooden pillars resting on square stone blocks, and forming arches. Two archways open on to the little garden; two others, facing the front gateway, lead to a wooden staircase, with an iron balustrade that was once a miracle of smith's work, so whimsical are the shapes given to the metal; the worn steps creak under every tread. The entrance to each flat has an architrave dark with dirt, grease, and dust, and outer doors, covered with Utrecht velvet set with brass nails, once gilt, in a diamond pattern. These relics of splendor show that in the time of Louis XIV. the house was the residence of some Councilor to the *Parlement,* some rich priests, or some treasurer of the ecclesiastical revenue. But these vestiges of former luxury bring a smile to the lips by the artless contrast of past and present.

M. Jean-Jules Popinot lived on the first floor of this house, where the gloom, natural to all first floors in Paris houses, was increased by the narrowness of the street. This old tenement was known to all the twelfth *arrondissement,* on which Providence had bestowed this lawyer, as it gives a beneficent plant to cure or alleviate every malady. Here is a sketch of the man whom the brilliant Marquise d'Espard hoped to fascinate.

M. Popinot, as is seemly for a magistrate, was always dressed in black— a style which contributed to make him ridiculous in the eyes of those who were in the habit of judging everything from a superficial examination. Men who are jealous of maintaining the dignity required by this color ought to devote themselves to constant and minute care of their person; but our dear M. Popinot was incapable of forcing himself to the puritanical cleanliness which black demands. His trousers, always threadbare, looked like camlet—the stuff of which attorneys' gowns are made; and his habitual stoop set them in time, in such innumerable creases, that in places they were traced with lines, whitish, rusty, or shiny, betraying either sordid avarice, or the most unheeding poverty. His coarse worsted stockings were twisted anyhow in his ill-shaped shoes. His linen had the tawny tinge acquired by long sojourn in a wardrobe, showing that the late lamented Madame Popinot had had a mania for much linen; in the Flemish fashion, perhaps, she had given herself the trouble of a great wash no more than twice a year. The old man's coat and waistcoat were in harmony with his trousers, shoes, stockings, and linen. He always had the luck of his carelessness; for, the first day he put on a new coat, he unfailingly matched it with the rest of his costume by staining it with incredible promptitude. The good man waited till his housekeeper told him that his hat was too shabby before buying a new one. His necktie was always crumpled and starchless, and he never set his dog's-eared shirt collar straight after his judge's bands had disordered it. He took no care of his gray hair, and shaved but twice a week. He never wore gloves, and generally kept his hands stuffed into his empty trousers' pockets; the soiled pocket-holes, almost always torn, added a final touch to the slovenliness of his person.

Anyone who knows the Palais de Justice at Paris, where every variety of black attire may be studied, can easily imagine the appearance of M. Popinot. The habit of sitting for days at a time modifies the structure of the body, just as the fatigue of hearing interminable pleadings tells on the expression of a magistrate's face. Shut up as he is in courts ridiculously small, devoid of architectural dignity, and where the air is quickly vitiated, a Paris judge inevitably acquires a countenance puckered and seamed by reflection, and depressed by weariness; his complexion turns pallid, acquiring an earthly or greenish hue according to his individual temperament. In short, within a given time the most blooming young man is turned into an "inasmuch" machine—an instrument which applies the Code to individual cases with the indifference of clockwork.

Hence, nature having bestowed on M. Popinot a not too pleasing exterior, his life as a lawyer had not improved it. His frame was graceless and angular. His thick knees, huge feet, and broad hands formed a contrast with a priest-like face having a vague resemblance to a calf's head, meek to unmeaningness, and but little brightened by divergent, bloodless eyes, divided by a straight flat nose, surmounted by a flat forehead, flanked by enormous ears, flabby and graceless. His thin, weak hair showed the baldness through various irregular partings.

One feature only commended this face to the physiognomist. This man had a mouth to whose lips divine kindness lent its sweetness. They were wholesome, full, red lips, finely wrinkled, sinuous, mobile, by which nature had given expression to noble feeling; lips which spoke to the heart and proclaimed the man's intelligence and lucidity, a gift of second sight, and a heavenly temper; and you would have judged him wrongly from looking merely at his sloping forehead, his fireless eyes, and his shambling gait. His life answered to his countenance; it was full of secret labor, and hid the virtue of a saint. His superior knowledge of law proved so strong a recommendation at the time when Napoleon was reorganizing it in 1808 and 1811, that, by the advice of Cambacérès, he was one of the first men named to sit on the Imperial High Court of Justice at Paris. Popinot was no schemer. Whenever any demand was made, any request preferred for an appointment, the Minister would overlook Popinot, who never set foot in the house of the High Chancellor or the Chief Justice. From the High Court he was sent down to the Common Court, and pushed to the lowest rung of the ladder by active struggling men. There he was appointed supernumerary judge. There was a general outcry among the lawyers: "Popinot a supernumerary!" Such injustice struck the legal world with dismay—the attorneys, the registrars, everybody but Popinot himself, who made no complaint. The first clamor over, everybody was satisfied that all was for the best in the best of all possible worlds, which must certainly be the legal world. Popinot remained supernumerary judge till the day when the most famous Great Seal under the Restoration avenged the oversights heaped on this modest and uncomplaining man by the Chief Justices of the Empire. After being a supernumerary for twelve years, M. Popinot would no doubt die a puisne judge of the Court of the Seine.

To account for the obscure fortunes of one of the superior men of the legal profession, it is necessary to enter here into some details which will serve to reveal his life and character, and which will, at the same time, display some of the wheels of the great machine known as Justice. M. Popinot was classed by the three Presidents who successively controlled the Court of the Seine under the category of possible Judges, the stuff of which judges are made. Thus classified, he did not achieve the reputation for capacity which his previous labors had deserved. Just as a painter is invariably included in a category as a landscape painter, a portrait painter, a painter of history, of sea pieces, or of genre, by a public consisting of artists, connoisseurs, and simpletons, who, out of envy, or critical omnipotence, or prejudice, fence in his intellect, assuming, one and all, that there are ganglions in every brain—a narrow judgment which the world applies to writers, to statesmen, to everybody who begins with some specialty before being hailed as omniscient; so Popinot's fate was sealed, and he was hedged round to do a particular kind of work. Magistrates, attorneys, pleaders, all who pasture on the legal common, distinguish two elements in every case—law and equity. Equity is the outcome of facts, law is the application of principles to facts. A man may be right in equity but wrong in law, without any blame to the judge. Between his conscience and the facts there is a whole gulf of determining reasons unknown to the judge, but which condemn or legitimize the act. A judge is not God; his duty is to adapt facts to principles, to judge cases of infinite variety while measuring them by a fixed standard.

France employs about six thousand judges; no generation has six thousand great men at her command, much less can she find them in the legal profession. Popinot, in the midst of the civilization of Paris, was just a very clever cadi, who, by the character of his mind, and by dint of rubbing the letter of the law into the essence of facts, had learned to see the error of spontaneous and violent decisions. By the help of his judicial second sight he could pierce the double casing of lies in which advocates hide the heart of a trial. He was a judge, as the great Desplein was a surgeon; he probed men's consciences as the anatomist probed their bodies. His life and habits had led him to an exact appreciation of their most secret thoughts by a thorough study of facts.

He sifted a case as Cuvier sifted the earth's crust. Like that great thinker, he proceeded from deduction to deduction before drawing his conclusion, and reconstructed the past career of a conscience as Cuvier reconstructed an Anoplotherium. When considering a brief he would often wake in the night, startled by a gleam of truth suddenly sparkling in his brain. Struck by the deep injustice, which is the end of these contests, in which everything is against the honest man, everything to the advantage of the rogue, he often summed up in favor of equity against law in such cases as bore on questions of what may be termed divination.

Hence he was regarded by his colleagues as a man not of a practical mind; his arguments on two lines of deduction made their deliberations lengthy. When Popinot observed their dislike to listening to him he gave his opinion briefly; it was said that he was not a good judge in this class of cases; but as his gift of discrimination was remarkable, his opinion lucid, and his penetration profound, he was considered to have a special aptitude for the laborious duties of an examining judge. So an examining judge he remained during the greater part of his legal career.

Although his qualifications made him eminently fitted for its difficult functions, and he had the reputation of being so learned in criminal law that his duty was a pleasure to him, the kindness of his heart constantly kept him in torture, and he was nipped as in a vice between his conscience and his pity. The services of an examining judge are better paid than those of a judge in civil actions, but they do not therefore prove a temptation; they are too onerous. Popinot, a man of modest and virtuous learning, without ambition, an indefatigable worker, never complained of his fate; he sacrificed his tastes and his compassionate soul to the public good, and allowed himself to be transported to the noisome pools of criminal examinations, where he showed himself alike severe and beneficent. His clerk sometimes would give the accused some money to buy tobacco, or a warm winter garment, as he led him back from the judge's office to the *Souricière,* the mouse-trap—the House of Detention where the accused are kept under the orders of the Examining Judge. He knew how to be an inflexible judge and a charitable man. And no one extracted a confession so easily as he without having recourse to judicial trickery. He had, too, all the acumen of an observer. This man, apparently so foolishly good-natured, simple, and absent-minded, could guess all the cunning of a prison wag, unmask the astutest street hussy, and subdue a scoundrel. Unusual circumstances had sharpened his perspicacity; but to relate these we must intrude on his domestic history, for in him the judge was the social side of the man; another man, greater and less known, existed within.

Twelve years before the beginning of this story, in 1816, during the terrible scarcity which coincided disastrously with the stay in France of the so-called Allies, Popinot was appointed President of the Commission Extraordinary, formed to distribute food to the poor of his neighborhood, just when he had planned to move from the Rue du Fouarre, which he as little liked to live in as his wife did. The great lawyer, the clear-sighted criminal judge, whose superiority seemed to his colleagues a form of aberration, had for five years been watching legal results without seeing their causes. As he scrambled up into lofts, as he saw the poverty, as he studied the desperate necessities which gradually bring the poor to criminal acts, as he estimated their long struggles, compassion filled his soul. The judge then became the Saint Vincent de Paul of these grown-up children, these suffering toilers. The transformation was not immediately complete. Beneficence has its temptations as vice has. Charity consumes a saint's purse, as roulette consumes the possessions of a gambler, quite gradually. Popinot went from misery to misery, from charity to charity; then, by the time he had lifted all the rags which cover public pauperism, like a bandage under which an inflamed wound lies festering, at the end of a year he had become the Providence incarnate of that quarter of the town. He was a member of the Benevolent Committee and of the Charity Organization. Wherever any gratuitous services were needed he was ready, and did everything without fuss, like the *man with the short cloak,* who spends his life in carrying soup round the markets and other places where there are starving folks.

Popinot was fortunate in acting on a larger circle and in a higher sphere; he had an eye on everything, he prevented crime, he gave work to the unemployed, he found a refuge for the helpless, he distributed aid with discernment wherever danger threatened, he made himself the counselor of the widow, the protector of homeless children, the sleeping partner of small traders. No one at the Courts, no one in Paris, knew of this secret life of Popinot's. There are virtues so splendid that they necessitate obscurity; men make haste to hide them under a bushel. As to those whom the lawyer succored, they, hard at work all day and tired at night, were little able to sing his praises; theirs was the gracelessness of children, who can never pay because they owe too much. There is such compulsory ingratitude; but what heart that has sown good to reap gratitude can think itself great?

By the end of the second year of his apostolic work, Popinot had turned the storeroom at the bottom of his house into a parlor, lighted by the three iron-barred windows. The walls and ceiling of this spacious room were whitewashed, and the furniture consisted of wooden benches like those seen in schools, a clumsy cupboard, a walnut-wood writing-table, and an armchair. In the cupboard were his registers of donations, his tickets for orders for bread, and his diary. He kept his ledger like a tradesman, that he might not be ruined by kindness. All the sorrows of the neighborhood were entered and numbered in a book, where each had its little account, as merchants' customers have theirs. When there was any question as to a man or a family needing help, the lawyer could always command information from the police.

Lavienne, a man made for his master, was his aid-de-camp. He redeemed or renewed pawn-tickets, and visited the districts most threatened with famine, while his master was in court.

From four till seven in the morning in summer, from six till nine in winter, this room was full of women, children, and paupers, while Popinot gave audience. There was no need for a stove in winter; the crowd was so dense that the air was warmed; only Lavienne strewed straw on the wet floor. By long use the benches were as polished as varnished mahogany; at the height of a man's shoulders the wall had a coat of dark, indescribable color, given to it by the rags and tattered clothes of these poor creatures. The poor wretches loved Popinot so well that when they assembled before his door was opened, before daybreak on a winter's morning, the women warming themselves with their foot-braziers, the men swinging their arms for circulation, never a sound had disturbed his sleep. Rag-pickers and other toilers of the night knew the house, and often saw a light burning in the lawyer's private room at unholy hours. Even thieves, as they passed by, said, "That is his house," and respected it. The morning he gave to the poor, the midday hours to criminals, the evening to law work.

Thus the gift of observation that characterized Popinot was necessarily *bifrons;* he could guess the virtues of a pauper—good feelings nipped, fine actions in embryo, unrecognized self-sacrifice, just as he could read at the bottom of a man's conscience the faintest outlines of a crime, the slenderest threads of wrongdoing, and infer all the rest.

Popinot's inherited fortune was a thousand crowns a year. His wife, sister to M. Bianchon *senior,* a doctor at Sancerre, had brought him about twice as much. She, dying five years since, had left her fortune to her husband. As the salary of a supernumerary judge is not large, and Popinot had been a fully salaried judge only for four years, we may guess his reasons for parsimony in all that concerned his person and mode of life, when we consider how small his means were and how great his beneficence. Besides, is not such indifference to dress as stamped Popinot an absent-minded man, a distinguishing mark of scientific attainment, of art passionately pursued, of a perpetually active mind? To complete this portrait, it will be enough to add that Popinot was one of the few judges of the Court of the Seine on whom the ribbon of the Legion of Honor had not been conferred.

Such was the man who had been instructed by the President of the Second Chamber of the Court—to which Popinot had belonged since his reinstatement among the judges in civil law—to examine the Marquis d'Espard at the request of his wife, who sued for a Commission in Lunacy.

The Rue du Fouarre, where so many unhappy wretches swarmed in the early morning, would be deserted by nine o'clock, and as gloomy and squalid as ever. Bianchon put his horse to a trot in order to find his uncle in the midst of his business. It was not without a smile that he thought of the curious contrast the judge's appearance would make in Madame d'Espard's room; but he promised himself that he would persuade him to dress in a way that should not be too ridiculous.

"If only my uncle happens to have a new coat!" said Bianchon to himself as he turned into the Rue du Fouarre, where a pale light shone from the parlor windows. "I shall do well, I believe, to talk that over with Lavienne."

At the sound of wheels half a score of startled paupers came out from under the gateway, and took off their hats on recognizing Bianchon; for the doctor, who treated gratuitously the sick recommended to him by the lawyer, was not less well known than he to the poor creatures assembled there.

Bianchon found his uncle in the middle of the parlor, where the benches were occupied by patients presenting such grotesque singularities of costume as would have made the least artistic passer-by turn round to gaze at them. A draughtsman—a Rembrandt, if there were one in our day—might have conceived of one of his finest compositions from seeing these children of misery, in artless attitudes, and all silent.

Here was the rugged countenance of an old man with a white beard and an apostolic head—a Saint Peter ready to hand; his chest, partly uncovered, showed salient muscles, the evidence of an iron constitution which had served him as a fulcrum to resist a whole poem of sorrows. There a young woman was suckling her youngest-born to keep it from crying, while another of about five stood between her knees. Her white bosom, gleaming amid rags, the baby with its transparent flesh-tints, and the brother, whose attitude promised a street Arab in the future, touched the fancy with pathos by its almost graceful contrast with the long row of faces crimson with cold, in the midst of which sat this family group. Further away, an old woman, pale and rigid, had the repulsive look of rebellious pauperism, eager to avenge all its past woes in one day of violence.

There, again, was the young workman, weakly and indolent, whose brightly intelligent eye revealed fine faculties crushed by necessity struggled within vain, saying nothing of his sufferings, and nearly dead for lack of an opportunity to squeeze between the bars of the vast stews where the wretched swim round and round and devour each other.

The majority were women; their husbands, gone to their work, left it to them, no doubt, to plead the cause of the family with the ingenuity which characterizes the woman of the people, who is almost always queen in her hovel. You would have seen a torn bandana on every head, on every form a skirt deep in mud, ragged kerchiefs, worn and dirty jackets, but eyes that burnt like live coals. It was a horrible assemblage, raising at first sight a feeling of disgust, but giving a certain sense of terror the instant you perceived that the resignation of these souls, all engaged in the struggle for every necessary of life, was purely fortuitous, a speculation on benevolence. The two tallow candles which lighted the parlor flickered in a sort of fog caused by the fetid atmosphere of the ill-ventilated room.

The magistrate himself was not the least picturesque figure in the midst of this assembly. He had on his head a rusty cotton night-cap; as he had no cravat, his neck was visible, red with cold and wrinkled, in contrast with the threadbare collar of his old dressing-gown. His worn face had the half-stupid look that comes of absorbed attention. His lips, like those of all men who work, were puckered up like a bag with the strings drawn tight. His knitted brows seemed to bear the burden of all the sorrows confided to him: he felt, analyzed, and judged them all. As watchful as a Jew money-lender, he never raised his eyes from his books and registers but to look into the very heart of the persons he was examining, with the flashing glance by which a miser expresses his alarm.

Lavienne, standing behind his master, ready to carry out his orders, served no doubt as a sort of police, and welcomed new-comers by encouraging them to get over their shyness. When the doctor appeared there was a stir on the benches. Lavienne turned his head, and was strangely surprised to see Bianchon.

"Ah! It is you, old boy!" exclaimed Popinot, stretching himself. "What brings you so early?"

"I was afraid lest you should make an official visit about which I wish to speak to you before I could see you."

"Well," said the lawyer, addressing a stout little woman who was still standing close to him, "if you do not tell me what it is you want, I cannot guess it, child."

"Make haste," said Lavienne. "Do not waste other people's time."

"Monsieur," said the woman at last, turning red, and speaking so low as only to be heard by Popinot and Lavienne, "I have a green-grocery truck, and I have my last baby out at nurse, and I owe for his keep. Well, I had hidden my little bit of money—"

"Yes; and your man took it?" said Popinot, guessing the sequel.

"Yes, sir."

"What is your name?"

"La Pomponne."

"And your husband's?"

"Toupinet."

"Rue du Petit-Banquier?" said Popinot, turning over his register. "He is in prison," he added, reading a note at the margin of the section in which this family was described.

"For debt, my kind Monsieur."

Popinot shook his head.

"But I have nothing to buy any stock for my truck; the landlord came yesterday and made me pay up; otherwise I should have been turned out."

Lavienne bent over his master, and whispered in his ear.

"Well, how much do you want to buy fruit in the market?"

"Why, my good Monsieur, to carry on my business, I should want— Yes, I should certainly want ten francs."

Popinot signed to Lavienne, who took ten francs out of a large bag, and handed them to the woman, while the lawyer made a note of the loan in his ledger. As he saw the thrill of delight that made the poor hawker tremble, Bianchon understood the apprehensions that must have agitated her on her way to the lawyer's house.

"You next," said Lavienne to the the old man with the white beard.

Bianchon drew the servant aside, and asked him how long this audience would last.

"Monsieur has had two hundred persons this morning, and there are eighty to be turned off," said Lavienne. "You will have time to pay your early visit, sir."

"Here, my boy," said the lawyer, turning round and taking Horace by the arm; "here are two addresses near this—one in the Rue de Seine, and the other in the Rue de l'Arbalète. Go there at once. Rue de Seine, a young girl has just asphyxiated herself; and Rue de l'Arbalète, you will find a man to remove to your hospital. I will wait breakfast for you."

Bianchon returned an hour later. The Rue du Fouarre was deserted; day was beginning to dawn there; his uncle had gone up to his rooms; the last poor wretch whose misery the judge had relieved was departing, and Lavienne's money bag was empty.

"Well, how are they going on?" asked the old lawyer, as the doctor came in.

"The man is dead," replied Bianchon; "the girl will get over it."

Since the eye and hand of a woman had been lacking, the flat in which Popinot lived had assumed an aspect in harmony with its master's. The indifference of a man who is absorbed in one dominant idea had set its stamp of eccentricity on everything. Everywhere lay unconquerable dust, every object was adapted to a wrong purpose with a pertinacity suggestive of a bachelor's home. There were papers in the flower vases, empty ink-bottles on the tables, plates that had been forgotten, matches used as tapers for a minute when something had to be found, drawers or boxes half turned out and left unfinished; in short, all the confusions and vacancies resulting from plans for order never carried out. The lawyer's private room, especially disordered by this incessant rummage, bore witness to his unresting pace, the hurry of a man overwhelmed with business, hunted by contradictory necessities. The bookcase looked as if it had been sacked; there were books scattered over everything, some piled up open, one on another, others on the floor face downwards; registers of proceedings laid on the floor in rows, lengthwise, in front of the shelves; and that floor had not been polished for two years.

The tables and shelves were covered with *ex votos,* the offerings of the grateful poor. On a pair of blue glass jars which ornamented the chimney-shelf there were two glass balls, of which the core was made up of many colored fragments, giving them the appearance of some singular natural product. Against the wall hung frames of artificial flowers, and decorations in which Popinot's initials were surrounded by hearts and everlasting flowers. Here were boxes of elaborate and useless cabinet work; there letter-weights carved in the style of work done by convicts in penal servitude. These masterpieces of patience, enigmas of gratitude, and withered bouquets gave the lawyer's room the appearance of a toy-shop. The good man used these works of art as hiding-places which he filled with bills, worn-out pens, and scraps of paper. All these pathetic witnesses to his divine charity were thick with dust, dingy, and faded.

Some birds, beautifully stuffed, but eaten by moth, perched in this wilderness of trumpery, presided over by an Angora cat, Madame Popinot's pet, restored to her no doubt with all the graces of life by some impecunious naturalist, who thus repaid a gift of charity with a perennial treasure. Some local artist whose heart had misguided his brush had painted portraits of M. and Madame Popinot. Even in the bedroom there were embroidered pin-cushions, landscapes, in cross-stitch, and crosses in folded paper, so elaborately cockled as to show the senseless labor they had cost.

The window-curtains were black with smoke, and the hangings absolutely colorless. Between the fireplace and the large square table at which the magistrate worked, the cook had set two cups of coffee on a small table, and two armchairs, in mahogany and horsehair, awaited the uncle and nephew. As daylight, darkened by the windows, could not penetrate to this corner, the cook had left two dips burning, whose unsnuffed wicks showed a sort of mushroom growth, giving the red light which promises length of life to the candle from slowness of combustion —a discovery due to some miser.

"My dear uncle, you ought to wrap yourself more warmly when you go down to that parlor."

"I cannot bear to keep them waiting, poor souls!—Well, and what do you want of me?"

"I have come to ask you to dine to-morrow with the Marquise d'Espard."

"A relation of ours?" asked Popinot, with such genuine absence of mind that Bianchon laughed.

"No, uncle; the Marquise d'Espard is a high and puissant lady, who has laid before the Courts a petition desiring that a Commission in Lunacy should sit on her husband, and you are appointed—"

"And you want me to dine with her! Are you mad?" said the lawyer, taking up the code of proceedings. "Here, only read this article, prohibiting any magistrate's eating or drinking in the house of either of two parties whom he is called upon to decide between. Let her come and see me, your Marquise, if she has anything to say to me. I was in fact to go to examine her husband to-morrow, after working the case up to-night."

He rose, took up a packet of papers that lay under a weight where he could see it, and after reading the title, he said—

"Here is the affidavit. Since you take an interest in this high and puissant lady, let us see what she wants."

Popinot wrapped his dressing-gown across his body, from which it was constantly slipping and leaving his chest bare; he sopped his bread in the half-cold coffee, and opened the petition, which he read, allowing himself to throw in a parenthesis now and then, and some discussions, in which his nephew took part:—

" 'To Monsieur the President of the Civil Tribunal of the Lower

Court of the Department of the Seine, sitting at the Palais de Justice.

" 'Madame Jeanne Clémentine Athénaïs de Blamont-Chauvry, wife of M. Charles Maurice Marie Andoche, Comte de Nègrepelisse, Marquis d'Espard'—a very good family—'landowner, the said Mms. d'Espard living in the Rue du Faubourg Saint-Honoré, No. 104, and the said M. d'Espard in the Rue de la Montagne-Sainte-Geneviève, No. 22.'—To be sure, the President told me he lived in this part of the town—'having for her solicitor Maitre Desroches'—Desroches! a pettifogging jobber, a man looked down upon by his brother lawyers, and who does his clients no good—"

"Poor fellow!" said Bianchon, "unluckily he has no money, and he rushes round like the Devil in holy water—That is all."

" 'Has the honor to submit to you, Monsieur the President, that for a year past the moral and intellectual powers of her husband, M. d'Espard, have undergone so serious a change, that at the present day they have reached the state of dementia and idiocy provided for by Article 448 of the Civil Code, and require the application of the remedies set forth by that article, for the security of his fortune and his person, and to guard the interest of his children whom he keeps to live with him.

" 'That, in point of fact, the mental condition of M. d'Espard, which for some years has given grounds for alarm based on the system he has pursued in the management of his affairs, has reached, during the last twelvemonth, a deplorable depth of depression; that his infirm will was the first thing to show the results of the malady; and that its effete state leaves M. the Marquis d'Espard exposed to all the perils of his incompetency, as is proved by the following facts:—

" 'For a long time all the income accruing from M. d'Espard's estates are paid, without any reasonable cause, or even temporary advantage, into the hands of an old woman, whose repulsive ugliness is generally remarked on, named Madame Jeanrenaud, living sometimes in Paris, Rue de la Vrillière, No. 8, sometimes at Villeparisis, near Claye, in the Department of Seine at Marne, and for the benefit of her son, aged thirty-six, an officer in the ex-Imperial Guards, whom the Marquis d'Espard has placed by his influence in the King's Guards as Major in the First Regiment of Cuirassiers. These two persons, who in 1814 were in extreme poverty, have since then purchased house-property of considerable value; among other items, quite recently, a large house in the Grande Rue Verte, where the said Jeanrenaud is laying out considerable sums in order to settle there with the woman Jeanrenaud, intending to marry; these sums amount already to more than a hundred thousand francs. The marriage has been arranged by the intervention of M. d'Espard with his banker, one Mongenod, whose niece he has asked in marriage for the said Jeanrenaud, promising to use his influence to procure him the title and dignity of Baron. This has in fact been secured by his Majesty's letters patent, dated December 29th of last year, at the request of the Marquis d'Espard, as can be proved by his Excellency the Keeper of the Seals, if the Court should think proper to require his testimony.

" 'That no reason, not even such as morality and the law would concur in disapproving, can justify the influence which the said Mme. Jeanrenaud exerts over M. d'Espard, who, indeed, sees her very seldom; nor account for his strange affection for the said Baron Jeanrenaud, Major, with whom he has but little intercourse. And yet their power is so considerable, that whenever they need money, if only to gratify a mere whim, this lady or her son—' Heh, heh! *no reason even such as morality and the law concur in disapproving!* What does the clerk or the attorney mean to insinuate?" said Popinot.

Bianchon laughed.

" 'This lady, or her son, obtain whatever they ask of the Marquis d'Espard without demur; and if he has not ready money, M. d'Espard draws bills to be paid by the said Mongenod, who has offered to give evidence to that effect for the petitioner.

" 'That, moreover, in further proof of these facts, lately, on the occasion of the renewal of the leases on the Espard estate, the farmers having paid a considerable premium for the renewal of their leases on the old terms, M. Jeanrenaud at once secured the payment of it into his own hands.

" 'That the Marquis d'Espard parts with these sums of money so little of his own free-will, that when he was spoken to on the subject he seemed to remember nothing of the matter; that whenever anybody of any weight has questioned him as to his devotion to these two persons, his replies have shown so complete an absence of ideas and of sense of his own interests, that there obviously must be some occult cause at work to which the petitioner begs to direct the eye of justice, inasmuch as it is impossible but that this cause should be criminal, malignant, and wrongful, or else of a nature to come under medical jurisdiction; unless this influence is of the kind which constitutes an abuse of moral power—such as can only be described by the word *possession*—' The devil!" exclaimed Popinot. "What do you say to that, doctor? These are strange statements."

"They might certainly," said Bianchon, "be an effect of magnetic force."

"Then do you believe in Mesmer's nonsense, and his tub, and seeing through walls?"

"Yes, uncle," said the doctor gravely. "As I heard you read that petition I thought of that. I assure you that I have verified, in another sphere of action, several analogous facts proving the unlimited influence one man may acquire over another. In contradiction to the opinion of my brethren, I am perfectly convinced of the power of the will regarded as a motor force. All collusion and charlatanism apart, I have seen the results of such a possession. Actions promised during sleep by a magnetized patient to the magnetizer have been scrupulously performed on waking. The will of one had become the will of the other."

"Every kind of action?"

"Yes."

"Even a criminal act?"

"Even a crime."

"If it were not from you, I would not listen to such a thing."

"I will make you witness it," said Bianchon.

"Hm, hm," muttered the lawyer, "But supposing that this so-called possession fell under this class of facts, it would be difficult to prove it as legal evidence."

"If this woman Jeanrenaud is so hideously old and ugly, I do not see what other means of fascination she can have used," observed Bianchon.

"But," observed the lawyer, "in 1814, the time at which this fascination is supposed to have taken place, this woman was fourteen years younger; if she had been connected with M. d'Espard ten years before that, these calculations take us back four-and-twenty years, to a time when the lady may have been young and pretty, and have won for herself and her son a power over M. d'Espard which some men do not know how to evade. Though the source of this power is reprehensible in the sight of justice, it is justifiable in the eye of nature. Madame Jeanrenaud may have been aggrieved by the marriage, contracted probably at about that time, between the Marquis d'Espard and Mademoiselle de Blamont-Chauvry, and at the bottom of all this there may be nothing more than the rivalry of two women, since the Marquis has for a long time lived apart from Mme. d'Espard."

"But her repulsive ugliness, uncle."

"Power of fascination is in direct proportion to ugliness," said the lawyer; "that is an old story. And then think of the smallpox, doctor. But to proceed.

" 'That so long ago as in 1815, in order to supply the sums of money required by these two persons, the Marquis d'Espard went with his two children to live in the Rue de la Montagne-Sainte-Geneviève, in rooms quite unworthy of his name and rank'—well, we may live as we please— 'that he keeps his two children there, the Comte Clément d'Espard and Vicomte Camille d'Espard, in a style of living quite unsuited to their future prospects, their name and fortune; that he often wants money, to such a point, that not long since the landlord, one Mariast, put in an execution on the furniture in the rooms; that when this execution was carried out in his presence, the Marquis d'Espard helped the bailiff, whom he treated like a man of rank, paying him all the marks of attention and respect which he would have shown to a person of superior birth and dignity to himself.' "

The uncle and nephew glanced at each other and laughed.

" 'That, moreover, every act of his life, besides the facts with reference to the widow Jeanrenaud and the Baron Jeanrenaud, her son, are those of a madman; that for nearly ten years he has given his thoughts exclusively to China, its customs, manners, and history; that he refers everything to a Chinese origin; that when he is questioned on the subject, he confuses the events of the day and the business of yesterday with facts relating to China; that he censures the acts of the Government and the conduct of the King, though he is personally much attached to him, by comparing them with the politics of China;

" 'That this monomania has driven the Marquis d'Espard to conduct devoid of all sense: against the customs of men of rank, and, in opposition to his own professed ideas as to the duties of the nobility, he has joined a commercial undertaking, for which he constantly draws bills which, as they fall due, threaten both his honor and his fortune, since they stamp him as a trader, and in default of payment may lead to his being declared insolvent; that these debts, which are owing to stationers, printers, lithographers, and print-colorists, who have supplied the materials for his publication, called *A Picturesque History of China,* now coming out in parts, are so heavy that these tradesmen have requested the petitioner to apply for a Commission in Lunacy with regard to the Marquis d'Espard in order to save their own credit.' "

"The man is mad!" exclaimed Bianchon.

"You think so, do you?" said his uncle. "If you listen to only one bell, you hear only one sound."

"But it seems to me——" said Bianchon.

"But it seems to me," said Popinot, "that if any relation of mine wanted to get hold of the management of my affairs, and if, instead of being a humble lawyer, whose colleagues can, any day, verify what his condition is, I were a duke of the realm, an attorney with a little cunning, like Desroches, might bring just such a petition against me.

" 'That his children's education has been neglected for this monomania; and that he has taught them, against all the rules of education, the facts of Chinese history, which contradict the tenets of the Catholic Church. He also has them taught the Chinese dialects.' "

"Here Desroches strikes me as funny," said Bianchon.

"The petition is drawn up by his head clerk Godeschal, who, as you know, is not strong in Chinese," said the lawyer.

" 'That he often leaves his children destitute of the most necessary things; that the petitioner, notwithstanding her entreaties, can never see them; that the said Marquis d'Espard brings them to her only once a year; that, knowing the privations to which they are exposed, she makes vain efforts to give them the things most necessary for their existence, and which they require——' Oh! Madame la Marquise, this is preposterous. By proving too much you prove nothing.—My dear boy," said the old man, laying the document on his knee, "where is the mother who ever lacked heart and wit and yearning to such a degree as to fall below the inspirations suggested by her animal instinct? A mother is as cunning to get at her children as a girl can be in the conduct of a love intrigue. If your Marquise really wanted to give her children food and clothes, the Devil himself would not have hindered her, heh? That is rather too big a fable for an old lawyer to swallow!—To proceed.

" 'That at the age the said children have now attained it is necessary that steps should be taken to preserve them from the evil effects of such an education; that they should be provided for as beseems their rank, and that they should cease to have before their eyes the sad example of their father's conduct;

" 'That there are proofs in support of these allegations which the Court can easily order to be produced. Many times has M. d'Espard spoken of the judge of the Twelfth Arrondissement as a mandarin of the third class; he often speaks of the professors of the Collège Henri IV. as "men of letters" '—and that offends them! 'In speaking of the simplest things, he says, "They were not done so in China"; in the course of the most ordinary conversation he will sometimes allude to Madame Jean-renaud, or sometimes to events which happened in the time of Louis XIV., and then sit plunged in the darkest melancholy; sometimes he fancies he is in China. Several of his neighbors, among others, one Edmé Becker, medical student, and Jean Baptiste Frémiot, a professor, living under the same roof, are of opinion, after frequent intercourse with the Marquis d'Espard, that his monomania with regard to everything Chinese is the result of a scheme laid by the said Baron Jeanrenaud and the widow his mother to bring about the deadening of all the Marquis d'Espard's mental faculties, since the only service which Mme. Jeanrenaud appears to render M. d'Espard is to procure him everything that relates to the Chinese Empire;

" 'Finally, that the petitioner is prepared to show to the Court that the moneys absorbed by the said Baron and Mme. Jeanrenaud between 1814 and 1828 amount to not less than one million francs.

" 'In confirmation of the facts herein set forth, the petitioner can bring the evidence of persons who are in the habit of seeing the Marquis d'Espard, whose names and professions are subjoined, many of whom have urged her to demand a commission in lunacy to declare M. d'Espard incapable of managing his own affairs, as being the only way to preserve his fortune from the effects of his maladministration and his children from his fatal influence.

" 'Taking all this into consideration, M. le Président, and the affidavits subjoined, the petitioner desires that it may please you, inasmuch as the foregoing facts sufficiently prove the insanity and incompetency of the Marquis d'Espard herein described with his titles and residence, to order that, to the end that he may be declared incompetent by law, this petition and the documents in evidence may be laid before the King's public prosecutor; and that you will charge one of the judges of this Court to make his report to you on any day you may be pleased to name, and thereupon to pronounce judgment,' etc.

"And here," said Popinot, "is the President's order instructing me!— Well, what does the Marquise d'Espard want with me? I know everything. But I shall go to-morrow with my registrar to see

M. le Marquis, for this does not seem at all clear to me."

"Listen, my dear uncle, I have never asked the least little favor of you that had to do with your legal functions; well, I now beg you to show Madame d'Espard the kindness which her situation deserves. If she came here, you would listen to her?"

"Yes."

"Well, then, go and listen to her in her own house. Madame d'Espard is a sickly, nervous, delicate woman, who would faint in your rat's hole of a place. Go in the evening, instead of accepting her dinner, since the law forbids your eating or drinking at your client's expense."

"And does not the law forbid you from taking any legacy from your dead?" said Popinot, fancying that he saw a touch of irony on his nephew's lips.

"Come, uncle, if it were only to enable you to get at the truth of this business, grant my request. You will come as the examining judge, since matters do not seem to you very clear. Deuce take it! It is as necessary to cross-question the Marquise as it is to examine the Marquis."

"You are right," said the lawyer. "It is quite possible that it is she who is mad. I will go."

"I will call for you. Write down in your engagement book: 'To-morrow evening at nine, Madame d'Espard.'—Good!" said Bianchon, seeing his uncle make a note of the engagement.

Next evening at nine Bianchon mounted his uncle's dusty staircase, and found him at work on the statement of some complicated judgment. The coat Lavienne had ordered of the tailor had not been sent, so Popinot put on his old stained coat, and was the Popinot unadorned whose appearance made those laugh who did not know the secrets of his private life. Bianchon, however, obtained permission to pull his cravat straight, and to button his coat, and he hid the stains by crossing the breast of it with the right side over the left, and so displaying the new front of the cloth. But in a minute the judge rucked the coat up over his chest by the way in which he stuffed his hands into his pockets, obeying an irresistible habit. Thus the coat, deeply wrinkled both in front and behind, made a sort of hump in the middle of the back, leaving a gap between the waistcoat and trousers through which his shirt showed. Bianchon, to his sorrow, only discovered this crowning absurdity at the moment when his uncle entered the Marquise's room.

A brief sketch of the person and the career of the lady in whose presence the doctor and the judge now found themselves is necessary for an understanding of her interview with Popinot.

Madame d'Espard had, for the last seven years, been very much the fashion in Paris, where Fashion can raise and drop by turns various personages who, now great and now small, that is to say, in view or forgotten, are at last quite intolerable—as discarded ministers are, and every kind of decayed sovereignty. These flatterers of the past, odious with their stale pretensions, know everything, speak ill of everything, and, like ruined profligates, are friends with all the world. Since her husband had separated from her in 1815, Madame d'Espard must have married in the beginning of 1812. Her children, therefore, were aged respectively fifteen and thirteen. By what luck was the mother of a family, about three-and-thirty years of age, still the fashion?

Though Fashion is capricious, and no one can foresee who shall be her favorites, though she often exalts a banker's wife, or some woman of very doubtful elegance and beauty, it certainly seems supernatural when Fashion puts on constitutional airs and gives promotion for age. But in this case Fashion had done as the world did, and accepted Madame d'Espard as still young.

The Marquise, who was thirty-three by her register of birth, was twenty-two in a drawing-room in the evening. But by what care, what artifice! Elaborate curls shaded her temples. She condemned herself to live in twilight, affecting illness so as to sit under the protecting tones of light filtered through muslin. Like Diane de Poitiers, she used cold water in her bath, and, like her again, the Marquise slept on a horsehair mattress, with morocco-covered pillows to preserve her hair; she ate very little, only drank water, and observed monastic regularity in the smallest actions of her life.

This severe system has, it is said, been carried so far as to the use of ice instead of water, and nothing but cold food, by a famous Polish lady of our day who spends a life, now verging on a century old, after the fashion of a town belle. Fated to live as long as Marion Delorme, whom history has credited with surviving to be a hundred and thirty, the old vice-queen of Poland, at the age of nearly a hundred, has the heart and brain of youth, a charming face, an elegant shape; and in her conversation, sparkling with brilliancy like faggots in the fire, she can compare the men and books of our literature with the men and books of the eighteenth century. Living in Warsaw, she orders her caps of Herbault in Paris. She is a great lady with the amiability of a mere girl; she swims, she runs like a schoolboy, and can sink on to a sofa with the grace of a young coquette; she mocks at death, and laughs at life. After having astonished the Emperor Alexander, she can still amaze the Emperor Nicholas by the splendor of her entertainments. She can still bring tears to the eyes of a youthful lover, for her age is whatever she pleases, and she has the exquisite self-devotion of a *grisette*. In short, she is herself a fairy tale, unless, indeed, she is a fairy.

Had Madame d'Espard known Madame Zayonseck? Did she mean to imitate her career? Be that as it may, the Marquise proved the merits of the treatment; her complexion was clear, her brow unwrinkled, her figure, like that of Henri II.'s lady-love, preserved the litheness, the freshness, the covered charms which bring a woman love and keep it alive. The simple precautions of this course, suggested by art and nature, and perhaps by experience, had met in her with a general system which confirmed the results. The Marquise was absolutely indifferent to everything that was not herself: men amused her, but no man had ever caused her those deep agitations which stir both natures to their depths, and wreck one on the other. She knew neither hatred nor love. When she was offended, she avenged herself coldly, quietly, at her leisure, waiting for the opportunity to gratify the ill-will she cherished against anybody who dwelt in her unfavorable remembrance: She made no fuss, she did not excite herself; she talked, because she knew that by two words a woman may cause the death of three men.

She had parted from M. d'Espard with the greatest satisfaction. Had he not taken with him two children who at present were troublesome, and in the future stand in the way of her pretensions? Her most intimate friends, as much as her least persistent admirers, seeing about her none of Cornelia's jewels, who come and go, and unconsciously betray their mother's age, took her for quite a young woman. The two boys, about whom she seemed so anxious in her petition, were, like their father, as unknown in the world as the northwest passage is unknown to navigators. M. d'Espard was supposed to be an eccentric personage, who had deserted his wife without having the smallest cause for complaint against her.

Mistress of herself at two-and-twenty, and mistress of her fortune of twenty-six thousand francs a year, the Marquise hesitated long before deciding on a course of action and ordering her life. Though she benefited by the expenses her husband had incurred in his house, though she had all the furniture, the carriages, the horses, in short, all the details of a handsome establishment, she lived a retired life during the years 1816, 17, and 18, a time when families were recovering from the disasters resulting from political tempests. She belonged to one of the most important and illustrious families of the Faubourg Saint-Germain, and her parents advised her to live with them as much as possible after the separation forced upon her by her husband's inexplicable caprice.

In 1820 the Marquise roused herself from her lethargy; she went to Court, appeared at parties, and entertained in her own house. From 1821 to 1827 she lived in great style, and made herself remarked for her taste and her dress; she had a day, an hour, for receiving visits, and ere long she had seated herself on the throne, occupied before her by Madame la Vicomtesse de Beauséant, the Duchess de Langeais, and Madame Firmiani—who on her marriage with M. de Camps had resigned the scepter in favor of the Duchesse de Maufrigneuse, from whom Madame d'Espard snatched it. The world knew nothing beyond this of the private life of the Marquise d'Espard. She seemed likely to shine for long on the Parisian horizon, like the sun near its setting, but which will never set.

The Marquise was on terms of great intimacy with a duchess as famous for beauty as for her attachment to a prince just now in banishment, but accustomed to play a leading part in every prospective government. Madame d'Espard was also the friend of a foreign lady, with whom a famous and very wily Russian diplomat was in the habit of discussing public affairs. And then an antiquated countess, who was accustomed to shuffle the cards for the great game of politics, had adopted her in a maternal fashion. Thus, to any man of high ambitions, Madame d'Espard was preparing a covert but very real influence to follow the public and frivolous ascendency she now owed to fashion. Her drawing-room was acquiring political individuality: "What do they say at Madame d'Espard's?" "Are they against the measure in Madame d'Espard's drawing-room?" were questions repeated by a sufficient number of simpletons to give the flock of the faithful who surrounded her the importance of a coterie. A few damaged politicians whose wounds she had bound up, and whom she flattered, pronounced her as capable in diplomacy as the wife of the Russian ambassador to London. The Marquise had indeed several times suggested to deputies or to peers words and ideas that had rung through Europe. She had often judged correctly of certain events on which her circle of friends dared not express an opinion. The principal persons about the Court came in the evening to play whist in her rooms.

Then she also had the qualities of her defects; she was thought to be— and she was—discreet. Her friendship seemed to be stanch; she worked for her protégés with a persistency which showed that she cared less for patronage than for increased influence. This conduct was based on her dominant passion: Vanity. Conquests and pleasure, which so many women love, to her seemed only means to an end; she aimed at living on every point of the largest circle that life can describe.

Among the men still young, and to whom the future belonged, who crowded her drawing-room on great occasions, were to be seen MM. de Marsay and de Ronquerolles, de Montriveau, de la Roche-Hugon, de Sérizy, Ferraud, Maxime de Trailles, de Listomère, the two Vandenesses, du Châtelet, and others. She would frequently receive a man whose wife she would not admit, and her power was great enough to induce certain ambitious men to submit to these hard conditions, such as two famous royalist bankers, M. de Nucingen and Ferdinand du Tillet. She had so thoroughly studied the strength and the weakness of Paris life, that her conduct had never given any man the smallest advantage over her. An enormous price might have been set on a note or letter, by which she might have compromised herself, without one being produced.

If an arid soul enabled her to play her part to the life, her person was no less available for it. She had a youthful figure. Her voice was, at will, soft and fresh, or clear and hard. She possessed in the highest degree the secret of that aristocratic pose by which a woman wipes out the past. The Marquise knew well the art of setting an immense space between herself and the sort of man who fancies he may be familiar after some chance advances. Her imposing gaze could deny everything. In her conversation fine and beautiful sentiments and noble resolutions flowed naturally, as it seemed, from a pure heart and soul; but in reality she was all self, and quite capable of blasting a man who was clumsy in his negotiations, at the very time when she was shamefully making a compromise for the benefit of her own interest.

Rastignac, in trying to fasten on to this woman, had discerned her to be the cleverest of tools, but he had not yet used it; far from handling it, he was already finding himself crushed by it. This young *Condottiere* of the brain, condemned, like Napoleon, to give battle constantly, while knowing that a single defeat would prove the grave of his fortunes, had met a dangerous adversary in his protectress. For the first time in his turbulent life, he was playing a game with a partner worthy of him. He saw a place as Minister in the conquest of Madame d'Espard, so he was her tool till he could make her his—a perilous beginning.

The Hôtel d'Espard needed a large household, and the Marquise had a great number of servants. The grand receptions were held in the ground-floor rooms, but she lived on the first floor of the house. The perfect order of a fine staircase splendidly decorated, and rooms fitted in the dignified style which formerly prevailed at Versailles, spoke of an immense fortune. When the judge saw the carriage gates thrown open to admit his nephew's cab, he took in with a rapid glance the lodge, the porter, the courtyard, the stables, the arrangement of the house, the flowers that decorated the stairs, the perfect cleanliness of the banisters, walls, and carpets, and counted the footmen in livery who, as the bell rang, appeared on the landing. His eyes, which only yesterday in his parlor had sounded the dignity of misery under the muddy clothing of the poor, now studied with the same penetrating vision the furniture and splendor of the rooms he passed through, to pierce to the misery of grandeur.

"M. Popinot.—M. Bianchon."

The two names were pronounced at the door of the boudoir where the Marquise was sitting, a pretty room recently refurnished, and looking out on the garden behind the house. At the moment Madame d'Espard was seated in one of the old *rococo* armchairs of which Madame had set the fashion. Rastignac was at her left hand on a low chair, in which he looked settled like an Italian lady's "cousin." A third person was standing by the corner of the chimney-piece. As the shrewd doctor had suspected, the Marquise was a woman of a parched and wiry constitution. But for her regimen her complexion must have taken the ruddy tone that is produced by constant heat; but she added to the effect of her acquired pallor by the strong colors of the stuffs she hung her rooms with, or in which she dressed. Reddish-brown, marone, bistre with a golden light in it, suited her to perfection. Her boudoir, copied from that of a famous lady then at the height of fashion in London, was in tan-colored velvet; but she had added various details of ornament which moderated the pompous splendor of this royal hue. Her hair was dressed like a girl's in bands ending in curls, which emphasized the rather long oval of her face; but an oval face is as majestic as a round one is ignoble.

The mirrors, cut with facets to lengthen or flatten the face at will, amply prove the rule as applied to the physiognomy.

On seeing Popinot, who stood in the doorway craning his neck like a startled animal, with his left hand in his pocket, and the right hand holding a hat with a greasy lining, the Marquise gave Rastignac a look where lay a germ of mockery. The good man's rather foolish appearance was so completely in harmony with his grotesque figure and sacred looks, that Rastignac, catching sight of Bianchon's dejected expression of humiliation through his uncle, could not help laughing, and turned away. The Marquise bowed a greeting, and made a great effort to rise from her seat, falling back again, not without grace, with an air of apologizing for her incivility by affected weakness.

At this instant the person who was standing between the fireplace and the door bowed slightly, and pushed forward two chairs, which he offered by a gesture to the doctor and the judge; then, when they had seated themselves, he leaned against the wall again, crossing his arms.

A word as to this man. There is living now, in our day, a painter—Decamps—who possesses in the very highest degree the art of commanding your interest in everything he sets before your eyes, whether it be a stone or a man. In this respect his pencil is more skillful than his brush. He will sketch an empty room and leave a broom against the wall. If he chooses, you shall shudder; you shall believe that this broom has just been the instrument of crime, and is dripping with blood; it shall be the broom which the widow Bancal used to clean out the room where Fualdès was murdered. Yet, the painter will touzle that broom like a man in a rage; he will make each hair of it stand on end as though it were on your own bristling scalp; he will make it the interpreter between the secret poem of his imagination and the poem that shall have its birth in yours. After terrifying you by the aspect of that broom, to-morrow he will draw another, and lying by it a cat, asleep, but mysterious in its sleep, shall tell you that this broom is that on which the wife of a German cobbler rides off to the Sabbath on the Brocken. Or it will be a quite harmless broom, on which he will hang the coat of a clerk in the Treasury. Decamps had in his brush what Paganini had in his bow—a magnetically communicative power.

Well, I should have to transfer to my style that striking genius, that marvelous knack of the pencil, to depict the upright, tall, lean man dressed in black, with black hair, who stood there without speaking a word. This gentleman had a face like a knife-blade, cold and harsh, with a color like Seine water when it is muddy and strewn with fragments of charcoal from a sunken barge. He looked at the floor, listening and passing judgment. His attitude was terrifying. He stood there like the dreadful broom to which Decamps has given the power of revealing a crime. Now and then, in the course of conversation, the Marquise tried to get some tacit advice; but however eager her questioning, he was as grave and as rigid as the statue of the Commendatore.

The worthy Popinot, sitting on the edge of his chair in front of the fire, his hat between his knees, stared at the gilt chandeliers, the clock, and the curiosities with which the chimney-shelf was covered, the velvet and trimmings of the curtains, and all the costly and elegant nothings that a woman of fashion collects about her. He was roused from his homely meditations by Madame d'Espard, who addressed him in a piping tone—

"Monsieur, I owe you a million thanks——"

"A million thanks," thought he to himself, "that is too many; it does not mean one."

"For the trouble you condescend——"

"Condescend!" thought he; "she is laughing at me."

"To take in coming to see an unhappy client, who is too ill to go out——"

Here the lawyer cut the Marquise short by giving her an inquisitorial look, examining the sanitary condition of the unhappy client.

"As sound as a bell," said he to himself.

"Madame," said he, assuming a respectful mien, "you owe me nothing. Although my visit to you is not in strict accordance with the practice of the Court, we ought to spare no pains to discover the truth in cases of this kind. Our judgment is then guided less by the letter of the law than by the promptings of our conscience. Whether I seek the truth here or in my own consulting-room, so long as I find it, all will be well."

While Popinot was speaking, Rastignac was shaking hands with Bianchon; the Marquise welcomed the doctor with a little bow full of gracious significance.

"Who is that?" asked Bianchon in a whisper of Rastignac indicating the dark man.

"The Chevalier d'Espard, the Marquis's brother."

"Your nephew told me," said the Marquise to Popinot, "how much you are occupied, and I know too that you are so good as to wish to conceal your kind actions, so as to release those whom you oblige from the burden of gratitude. The work in Court is most fatiguing, it would seem. Why have they not twice as many judges?"

"Ah, Madame, that would not be difficult; we should be none the worse if they had. But when that happens, fowls will cut their teeth!"

As he heard this speech, so entirely in character with the lawyer's appearance, the Chevalier measured him from head to foot, out of one eye, as much as to say, "We shall easily manage him!"

The Marquise looked at Rastignac, who bent over her. "That is the sort of man," murmured the dandy in her ear, "who is trusted to pass judgments on the life and interests of private individuals."

Like most men who have grown old in a business, Popinot readily let himself follow the habits he had acquired, more particularly habits of mind. His conversation was all of "the shop." He was fond of questioning those he talked to, forcing them to unexpected conclusions, making them tell more than they wished to reveal. Pozzo di Borgo, it is said, used to amuse himself by discovering other folks' secrets, and entangling them in his diplomatic snares, and thus, by invincible habit showed how his mind was soaked in wiliness. As soon as Popinot had surveyed the ground, so to speak, on which he stood, he saw that it would be necessary to have recourse to the cleverest subtleties, the most elaborately wrapped up and disguised, which were in use in the Court, to detect the truth.

Bianchon sat cold and stern, as a man who has made up his mind to endure torture without revealing his sufferings; but in his heart he wished that his uncle could only trample on this woman as we trample on a viper—a comparison suggested to him by the Marquise's long dress, by the curve of her attitude, her long neck, small head, and undulating movements.

"Well, Monsieur," said Madame d'Espard, "however great my dislike to be or seem selfish, I have been suffering too long to wish that you may settle matters at once. Shall I soon get a favorable decision?"

"Madame, I will do my best to bring matters to a conclusion," said Popinot, with an air of frank good-nature. "Are you ignorant of the reason which made the separation necessary which now subsists between you and the Marquis d'Espard?"

"Yes Monsieur," she replied, evidently prepared with a story to tell. "At the beginning of 1816 M. d'Espard, whose temper had completely changed within three months or so, proposed that we should go to live on one of his estates near Briançon, without any regard for my health, which that climate would have destroyed, or for my habits of life; I refused to go. My refusal gave rise to such unjustifiable reproaches on his part, that from that hour I had my suspicions as to the soundness of his mind. On the following day he left me, leaving me his house and the free use of my income, and he went to live in the Rue de la Montagne-Saint-Geneviève, taking with him my two children——"

"One moment, Madame," said the lawyer, interrupting her. "What was that income?"

"Twenty-six thousand francs a year," she replied parenthetically. "I at once consulted old M. Bordin as to what I ought to do," she went on; "but it seems that there are so many difficulties in the way of depriving a father of the care of his children, that I was forced to resign myself to remaining alone at the age of twenty-two—an age at which many young women do very foolish things. You have read my petition, no doubt Monsieur; you know the principal facts on which I rely to procure a Commission in Lunacy with regard to M. d'Espard?"

"Have you ever applied to him, Madame, to obtain the care of your children?"

"Yes, Monsieur; but in vain. It is very hard on a mother to be deprived of the affection of her children, particularly when they can give her such happiness as every woman clings to."

"The elder must be sixteen," said Popinot.

"Fifteen," said the Marquise eagerly.

Here Bianchon and Rastignac looked at each other. Madame d'Espard bit her lips.

"What can the age of my children matter to you?"

"Well, Madame," said the lawyer, without seeming to attach any importance to his words, "a lad of fifteen and his brother, of thirteen, I suppose, have legs and their wits about them; they might come to see you on the sly. If they do not, it is because they obey their father, and to obey him in that matter they must love him very dearly."

"I do not understand," said the Marquise.

"You do not know, perhaps," replied Popinot, "that in your petition your attorney represents your children as being very unhappy with their father?"

Madame d'Espard replied with charming innocence—

"I do not know what my attorney may have put into my mouth."

"Forgive my inferences," said Popinot, "but Justice weighs everything. What I ask you, Madame, is suggested by my wish thoroughly to understand the matter. By your account M. d'Espard deserted you on the most frivolous pretext. Instead of going to Briançon, where he wished to take you, he remained in Paris. This point is not clear. Did he know this Madame Jeanrenaud before his marriage?"

"No Monsieur," replied the Marquise, with some asperity, visible only to Rastignac and the Chevalier d'Espard.

She was offended at being cross-questioned by this lawyer when she had intended to beguile his judgment; but as Popinot still looked stupid from sheer absence of mind, she ended by attributing his interrogatory to the Questioning Spirit of Voltaire's bailiff.

"My parents," she went on, "married me at the age of sixteen to M. d'Espard, whose name, fortune, and mode of life were such as my family looked for in the man who was to be my husband. M. d'Espard was then six-and-twenty; he was a gentleman in the English sense of the word; his manners pleased me, he seemed to have plenty of ambition, and I like ambitious people," she added, looking at Rastignac. "If M. d'Espard had never met that Madame Jeanrenaud, his character, his learning, his acquirements would have raised him—as his friends then believed—to high office in the Government. King Charles X., at that time Monsieur, had the greatest esteem for him, and a peer's seat, an appointment at Court, some important post certainly would have been his. That woman turned his head, and has ruined all the prospects of my family."

"What were M. d'Espard's religious opinions at that time?"

"He was, and is still, a very pious man."

"You do not suppose that Madame Jeanrenaud may have influenced him by mysticism?"

"No, Monsieur."

"You have a very fine house, Madame," said Popinot suddenly, taking his hands out of his pockets, and rising to pick up his coat-tails and warm himself. "This boudoir is very nice, those chairs are magnificent, the whole apartment is sumptuous. You must indeed be most unhappy when, seeing yourself here, you know that your children are ill lodged; ill clothed, and ill fed. I can imagine nothing more terrible for a mother."

"Yes, indeed. I should be so glad to give the poor little follows some amusement, while their father keeps them at work from morning till night at that wretched history of China."

"You give handsome balls; they would enjoy them, but they might acquire a taste for dissipation. However, their father might send them to you once or twice in the course of the winter."

"He brings them here on my birthday and on New Year's Day. On those days M. d'Espard does me the favor of dining here with them."

"It is very singular behavior," said the judge, with an air of conviction. "Have you ever seen this Dame Jeanrenaud?"

"My brother-in-law one day, out of interest in his brother——"

"Ah! Monsieur is M. d'Espard's brother?" said the lawyer, interrupting her.

The Chevalier bowed, but did not speak.

"M. d'Espard, who has watched this affair, took me to the Oratoire, where this woman goes to sermon, for she is a Protestant. I saw her; she is not in the least attractive; she looks like a butcher's wife, extremely fat, horribly marked with the smallpox; she has feet and hands like a man's, she squints; in short, she is monstrous!"

"It is inconceivable," said the judge, looking like the most imbecile judge in the whole kingdom. "And this creature lives near here, Rue Verte, in a fine house? There are no plain folks left, it would seem?"

"In a mansion on which her son has spent absurd sums."

"Madame," said Popinot, "I live in the Faubourg Saint-Marceau; I know nothing of such expenses. What do you call absurd sums?"

"Well," said the Marquise, "a stable with five horses and three carriages, a phaeton, a brougham, and a cabriolet."

"That costs a large sum, then?" asked Popinot in surprise.

"Enormous sums!" said Rastignac, intervening. "Such an establishment would cost, for the stables, the keeping the carriages in order, and the liveries for the men, between fifteen and sixteen thousand francs a year."

"Should you think so, Madame?" said the judge, looking much astonished.

"Yes, at least," replied the Marquise.

"And the furniture, too, must have cost a lot of money?"

"More than a hundred thousand francs," replied Madame d'Espard, who could not help smiling at the lawyer's vulgarity.

"Judges, Madame, are apt to be incredulous; it is what they are paid for, and I am incredulous. The Baron Jeanrenaud and his mother must have fleeced M. d'Espard most preposterously, if what you say is correct. There is a stable establishment which, by your account, costs sixteen thousand francs a year. Housekeeping, servants' wages, and the gross expenses of the house itself must run to twice as much; that makes a total of from fifty to sixty thousand francs a year. Do you suppose that these people, formerly so extremely poor, can have so large a fortune? A million yields scarcely forty thousand a year."

"Monsieur, the mother and son invested the money given them by M. d'Espard in the Funds when they were at 60 to 80. I should think their income must be more than sixty thousand francs. And then the son has fine appointments."

"If they spend sixty thousand francs a year," said the judge, "how much do you spend?"

"Well," said Madame d'Espard, "about the same." The Chevalier started a little, the Marquise colored; Bianchon looked at Rastignac; but Popinot preserved an expression of simplicity which quite deceived Madame d'Espard. The Chevalier took no part in the conversations; he saw that all was lost.

"These people, Madame, might be indicted before the superior Court," said Popinot.

"That was my opinion," exclaimed the Marquise, enchanted. "If threatened with the police, they would have come to terms."

"Madame," said Popinot, "when M. d'Espard left you, did he not give you a power of attorney enabling you to manage and control your own affairs?"

"I do not understand the object of all these questions," said the Marquise with petulance. "It seems to me that if you would only consider the state in which I am placed by my husband's insanity, you ought to be troubling yourself about him, and not about me."

"We are coming to that, Madame," said the judge. "Before placing in your hands, or in any others, the control of M. d'Espard's property, supposing he were pronounced incapable, the Court must inquire as to how you have managed your own. If M. d'Espard gave you power, he would have shown confidence in you, and the Court would recognize the fact. Had you any power from him? You might have bought or sold house property or invested money in business?"

"No, Monsieur, the Blamont-Chauvrys are not in the habit of trading," said she, extremely nettled in her pride as an aristocrat, and forgetting the business in hand. "My property is intact, and M. d'Espard gave me no power to act."

The Chevalier put his hand over his eyes not to betray the vexation he felt at his sister-in-law's short-sightedness, for she was ruining herself by her answers. Popinot had gone straight to the mark in spite of his apparent doublings.

"Madame," said the lawyer, indicating the Chevalier, "this gentleman, of course, is your near connection? May we speak openly before these other gentlemen?"

"Speak on," said the Marquise, surprised at this caution.

"Well, Madame, granting that you spend only sixty thousand francs a year, to anyone who sees your stables, your house, your train of servants, and a style of housekeeping which strikes me as far more luxurious than that of the Jeanrenauds, that sum would seem well laid out."

The Marquise bowed an agreement.

"But," continued the judge, "if you have no more than twenty-six thousand francs a year, you may have a hundred thousand francs of debts. The Court would therefore have a right to imagine that the motives which prompt you to ask that your husband may be deprived of the control of his property are complicated by self-interest and the need for paying your debts—if—you—have—any. The requests addressed to me have interested me in your position; consider fully and make your confession. If my suppositions have hit the truth, there is yet time to avoid the blame which the Court would have a perfect right to express in the saying clauses of the verdict if you could not show your attitude to be absolutely honorable and clear.

"It is our duty to examine the motives of the applicant as well as to listen to the plea of the witness under examination, to ascertain whether the petitioner may not have been prompted by passion, by a desire for money, which is unfortunately too common——"

The Marquise was on Saint Laurence's gridiron.

"And I must have explanations on this point. Madame, I have no wish to call you to account; I only want to know how you have managed to live at the rate of sixty thousand francs a year, and that for some years past. There are plenty of women who achieve this in their housekeeping, but you are not one of those. Tell me, you may have the most legitimate resources, a royal pension, or some claim on the indemnities lately granted; but even then you must have had your husband's authority to receive them."

The Marquise did not speak.

"You must remember," Popinot went on, "that M. d'Espard may wish to enter a protest, and his counsel will have a right to find out whether you have any creditors. This boudoir is newly furnished, your rooms are not now furnished with the things left to you by M. d'Espard in 1816. If, as you did me the honor of informing me, furniture is costly for the Jeanrenauds, it must be yet more so for you, who are a great lady. Though I am a judge, I am but a man; I may be wrong—tell me so. Remember the duties imposed on me by law, and the rigorous inquiries it demands, when the case before it is the suspension from all his functions of the father of a family in the prime of life. So you will pardon me, Madame la Marquise, for laying all these difficulties before you; it will be easy for you to give me an explanation.

"When a man is pronounced incapable of the control of his own affairs, a trustee has to be appointed. Who will be the trustee?"

"His brother," said the Marquise.

The Chevalier bowed. There was a short silence, very uncomfortable for the five persons who were present. The judge, in sport as it were, had laid open the woman's sore place. Popinot's countenance of common, clumsy good-nature, at which the Marquise, the Chevalier, and Rastignac had been inclined to laugh, had gained importance in their eyes. As they stole a look at him, they discerned the various expressions of that eloquent mouth. The ridiculous mortal was a judge of acumen. His studious notice of the boudoir was accounted for: he had started from the gilt elephant supporting the chimney-clock, examining all this luxury, and had ended by reading this woman's soul.

"If the Marquis d'Espard is mad about China, I see that you are not less fond of its products," said Popinot, looking at the porcelain on the chimney-piece. "But perhaps it was from M. le Marquis that you had these charming Oriental pieces," and he pointed to some precious trifles.

This irony, in very good taste, made Bianchon smile and petrified Rastignac, while the Marquise bit her thin lips.

"Instead of being protector of a woman placed in a cruel dilemma— an alternative between losing her fortune and her children, and being regarded as her husband's enemy," she said, "you accuse me, Monsieur! You suspect my motives! You must own that your conduct is strange!"

"Madame," said the judge eagerly, "the caution exercised by the Court in such cases as these might have given you, in any other judge, a perhaps less indulgent critic than I am.—And do you suppose that M. d'Espard's lawyer will show you any great consideration? Will he not be suspicious of motives which may be perfectly pure and disinterested? Your life will be at his mercy; he will inquire into it without qualifying his search by the respectful deference I have for you."

"I am much obliged to you, Monsieur," said the Marquise satirically. "Admitting for the moment that I owe thirty thousand, or fifty thousand francs, in the first place, it would be a mere trifle to the d'Espards and the de Blamont-Chauvrys. But if my husband is not in the possession of his mental faculties, would that prevent his being pronounced incapable?"

"No, Madame," said Popinot.

"Although you have questioned me with a sort of cunning which I should not have expected in a judge, and under circumstances where straightforwardness would have answered your purpose," she went on, "I will tell you without subterfuge that my position in the world, and the efforts I have to make to keep up my connection, are not in the least to my taste. I began my life by a long period of solitude; but my children's interest appealed to me; I felt that I must fill their father's place. By receiving my friends, by keeping up all this connection, by contracting these debts, I have secured their future welfare; I have prepared for them a brilliant career where they will find help and favor; and to have what has thus been acquired, many a man of business, lawyer or banker, would gladly pay all it has cost me."

"I appreciate your devoted conduct, Madame," replied Popinot. "It does you honor, and I blame you for nothing. A judge belongs to all; he must know and weigh every fact."

Madame d'Espard's tact and practice in estimating men made her understand that M. Popinot was not to be influenced by any consideration. She had counted on an ambitious lawyer, she had found a man of conscience. She at once thought of finding other means for securing the success of her side.

The servants brought in tea.

"Have you any further explanations to give me, Madame?" said Popinot, seeing these preparations.

"Monsieur," she replied haughtily, "do your business your own way; question M. d'Espard, and you will pity me, I am sure." She raised her head, looking Popinot in the face with pride, mingled with impertinence; the worthy man bowed himself out respectfully.

"A nice man is your uncle," said Rastignac to Bianchon. "Is he really so dense? Does not he know what the Marquise d'Espard is, what her influence means, her unavowed power over people? The Keeper of the Seals will be with her to-morrow——"

"My dear fellow, how can I help it?" said Bianchon. "Did not I warn you? He is not a man you can get over."

"No," said Rastignac; "he is a man you must run over."

The doctor was obliged to make his bow to the Marquise and her mute Chevalier to catch up Popinot, who, not being the man to endure an embarrassing position, was pacing through the rooms.

"That woman owes a hundred thousand crowns," said the judge, as he stepped into his nephew's cab.

"And what do you think of the case?"

"I?" said the judge. "I never have an opinion till I have gone into everything. To-morrow early I will send to Madame Jeanrenaud to call on me in my private office at four o'clock, to make her explain the facts which concern her, for she is compromised."

"I should very much like to know what the end will be."

"Why, bless me, do not you see that the Marquise is the tool of that tall lean man who never uttered a word? There is a strain of Cain in him, but of the Cain who goes to the Law Courts for his bludgeon, and there, unluckily for him, we keep more than one Damocles' sword."

"Oh, Rastignac! what brought you into that boat, I wonder?" exclaimed Bianchon.

"Ah, we are used to seeing these little family conspiracies," said Popinot. "Not a year passes without a number of verdicts of 'insufficient evidence' against applications of this kind. In our state of society such an attempt brings no dishonor, while we send a poor devil to the galleys if he breaks a pane of glass dividing him from a bowl full of gold. Our Code is not faultless."

"But these are the facts?"

"My boy, do you not know all the judicial romances with which clients impose on their attorneys? If the attorneys condemned themselves to state nothing but the truth, they would not earn enough to keep their office open."

Next, day, at four in the afternoon, a very stout dame, looking a good deal like a cask dressed up in a gown and belt, mounted Judge Popinot's stairs, perspiring and panting. She had, with great difficulty, got out of a green landau, which suited her to a miracle; you could not think of the woman without the landau, or the landau without the woman.

"It is I, my dear sir," said she, appearing in the doorway of the judge's room. "Madame Jeanrenaud, whom you summoned exactly as if I were a thief, neither more nor less."

The common words were spoken in a common voice, broken by the wheezing of asthma, and ending in a cough.

"When I go through a damp place, I can't tell what I suffer, sir. I shall never make old bones, saving your presence. However, here I am."

The lawyer was quite amazed at the appearance of this supposed Maréchale d'Ancre. Madame Jeanrenaud's face was pitted with an infinite number of little holes, was very red, with a pug nose and a low forehead, and was as round as a ball; for everything about the good woman was round. She had the bright eyes of a country woman, an honest gaze, a cheerful tone, and chestnut hair held in place by a bonnet cap under a green bonnet decked with a shabby bunch of auriculas. Her stupendous bust was a thing to laugh at, for it made one fear some grotesque explosion every time she coughed. Her enormous legs were of the shape which makes the Paris street boy describe such a woman as being built on piles. The widow wore a green gown trimmed with chinchilla, which looked on her as a splash of dirty oil would look on a bride's veil. In short, everything about her harmonized with her last words: "Here I am."

"Madame," said Popinot, "you are suspected of having used some seductive arts to induce M. d'Espard to hand over to you very considerable sums of money."

"Of what! of what!" cried she. "Of seductive arts? But, my dear sir, you are a man to be respected, and, moreover, as a lawyer you ought to have some good sense. Look at me. Tell me if I am likely to seduce anyone. I cannot tie my own shoes, nor even stoop. For these twenty years past, the Lord be praised, I have not dared to put on a pair of stays under pain of sudden death. I was as thin as an asparagus stalk when I was seventeen, and pretty too—I may say so now. So I married Jeanrenaud, a good fellow, and headman on the salt-barges. I had my boy, who is a fine young man; he is my pride, and it is not holding myself cheap to say he is my best piece of work. My little Jeanrenaud was a soldier who did Napoleon credit, and who served in the Imperial Guard. But, alas! at the death of my old man, who was drowned, times changed for the worse. I had the smallpox. I was kept two years in my room without stirring, and I came out of it the size you see me, hideous for ever, and as wretched as could be. These are my seductive arts."

"But what, then, can the reasons be that you have induced M. d'Espard to give you sums——?"

"Hugious sums, Monsieur, say the word; I do not mind. But as to his reasons, I am not at liberty to explain them."

"You are wrong. At this moment, his family, very naturally alarmed, are about to bring an action——"

"Heaven above us!" said the good woman, starting up. "Is it possible that he should be worried on my account? That king of men, a man that has not his match! Rather than he should have the smallest trouble, or a hair less on his head I could almost say, we would return every sou, Monsieur. Write that down on your papers. Heaven above us! I will go at once and tell Jeanrenaud what is going on! A pretty thing indeed!"

And the little old woman went out, rolled herself downstairs, and disappeared.

"That one tells no lies," said Popinot to himself. "Well, to-morrow I shall know the whole story, for I shall go to see the Marquis d'Espard."

People who have outlived the age when a man wastes his vitality at random, know how great an influence may be exercised on more important events by apparently trivial incidents, and will not be surprised at the weight here given to the following minor fact. Next day Popinot had an attack of coryza, a complaint which is not dangerous, and generally known by the absurd and inadequate name of a cold in the head.

The judge, who could not suppose that the delay could be serious, feeling himself a little feverish kept his room, and did not go to see the Marquis d'Espard. This day lost was, to this affair, what on the Day of Dupes the cup of soup had been, taken by Marie de Medici, which, by delaying her meeting with Louis XIII., enabled Richelieu to arrive at Saint-Germain before her, and recapture his royal slave.

Before accompanying the lawyer and his registering clerk to the Marquis d'Espard's house, it may be as well to glance at the home and the private affairs of this father of sons whom his wife's petition represented to be a madman.

Here and there in the old parts of Paris a few buildings may still be seen in which the archaeologist can discern an intention of decorating the city, and that love of property which leads the owner to give a durable character to the structure. The house in which M. d'Espard was then living in the Rue de la Montagne-Sainte Geneviève, was one of these old mansions, built in stone, and not devoid of a certain richness of style; but time had blackened the stone, and revolutions in the town had damaged it both outside and inside. The dignitaries who formerly

dwelt in the neighborhood of the University having disappeared with the
great ecclesiastical foundations, this house had become the home of industries and of inhabitants whom it was never destined to shelter. During
the last century a printing establishment had worn down the polished
floors, soiled the carved wood, blackened the walls, and altered the principal internal arrangements. Formerly the residence of a Cardinal, this
fine house was now divided among plebeian tenements. The character of
the architecture showed that it had been built under the reigns of Henry
III., Henry IV., and Louis XIII., at the time when the hotels Mignon and
Serpente were erected in the same neighborhood, with the palace of the
Princess Palatine, and the Sorbonne. An old man could remember having
heard it called, in the last century, the hotel Duperron, so it seemed probable that the illustrious Cardinal of that name had built, or perhaps merely
lived in it.

There still exists, indeed, in the corner of the courtyard, a *perron* or
flight of several outer steps by which the house is entered; and the way
into the garden on the garden front is down a similar flight of steps. In
spite of dilapidations, the luxury lavished by the architect on the balustrade
and entrance porch crowning these two *perrons* suggests the simple-minded
purpose of commemorating the owner's name, a sort of sculptured pun
which our ancestors often allowed themselves. Finally, in support of this
evidence, archaeologists can still discern in the medallions which show on
the principal front some traces of the cords of the Roman hat.

M. le Marquis d'Espard lived on the ground floor, in order, no doubt,
to enjoy the garden, which might be called spacious for that neighborhood,
and which lay open to the south, two advantages imperatively necessary
for his children's health. The situation of the house, in a street on a steep
hill, as its name indicates, secured these ground-floor rooms against ever
being damp. M. d'Espard had taken them, no doubt, for a very moderate
price, rents being low at the time when he settled in that quarter, in order
to be among the schools and to superintend his boys' education. Moreover, the state in which he found the place, with everything to repair, had
no doubt induced the owner to be accommodating. Thus M. d'Espard had
been able to go to some expense to settle himself suitably without being
accused of extravagance. The loftiness of the rooms, the paneling, of
which nothing survived but the frames, the decoration of the ceilings, all
displayed the dignity which the prelacy stamped on whatever it attempted
or created, and which artists discern to this day in the smallest relic that
remains, though it be but a book, a dress, the panel of a bookcase, or an
armchair.

The Marquis had the rooms painted in the rich brown tones beloved
of the Dutch and of the citizens of Old Paris, hues which lend such good
effects to the painter of *genre*. The panels were hung with plain paper in
harmony with the paint. The window curtains were of inexpensive materials, but chosen so as to produce a generally happy result; the furniture

was not too crowded and judiciously placed. Anyone on going into this home could not resist a sense of sweet peacefulness, produced by the perfect calm, the stillness which prevailed, by the unpretentious unity of color, the keeping of the picture, in the words a painter might use. A certain nobleness in the details, the exquisite cleanliness of the furniture, and a perfect concord of men and things, all brought the word "suavity" to the lips.

Few persons were admitted to the rooms used by the Marquis and his two sons, whose life might perhaps seem mysterious to their neighbors. In a wing towards the street, on the third floor, there are three large rooms which had been left in the state of dilapidation and grotesque barrenness to which they had been reduced by the printing works. These three rooms, devoted to the evolution of the *Picturesque History of China,* were contrived to serve as a writing-room, a depository, and a private room, where M. d'Espard sat during part of the day; for after breakfast till four in the afternoon the Marquis remained in this room on the third floor to work at the publication he had undertaken. Visitors wanting to see him commonly found him there, and often the two boys on their return from school resorted thither. Thus the ground-floor rooms were a sort of sanctuary where the father and sons spent their time from the hour of dinner till the next day, and his domestic life was carefully closed against the public eye.

His only servants were a cook—an old woman who had long been attached to his family, and a man-servant forty years old, who was with him when he married Mademoiselle de Blamont. His children's nurse had also remained with them, and the minute care to which the apartment bore witness revealed the sense of order and the maternal affection expended by this woman in her master's interest, in the management of his house, and the charge of his children. These three good souls, grave and uncommunicative folks, seemed to have entered into the idea which ruled the Marquis's domestic life. And the contrast between their habits and those of most servants was a peculiarity which cast an air of mystery over the house, and fomented the calumny to which M. d'Espard himself lent occasion. Very laudable motives had made him determine never to be on visiting terms with any of the other tenants in the house. In undertaking to educate his boys he wished to keep them from all contact with strangers. Perhaps, too, he wished to avoid the intrusion of neighbors.

In a man of his rank, at a time when the Quartier Latin was distracted by Liberalism, such conduct was sure to rouse in opposition a host of petty passions, of feelings whose folly is only to be measured by their meanness, the outcome of porters' gossip and malevolent tattle from door to door, all unknown to M. d'Espard and his retainers. His man-servant was stigmatized as a Jesuit, his cook as a sly fox; the nurse was in collusion with Madame Jeanrenaud to rob the madman. The madman was the Marquis. By degrees the other tenants came to regard as proofs of madness a num-

ber of things they had noticed in M. d'Espard, and passed through the
sieve of their judgment without discerning any reasonable motive for
them.

Having no belief in the success of the *History of China,* they had managed to convince the landlord of the house that M. d'Espard had no money
just at a time when, with the forgetfulness which often befalls busy men,
he had allowed the tax-collector to send him a summons for non-payment
of arrears. The landlord had forthwith claimed his quarter's rent from
January 1st by sending in a receipt, which the porter's wife had amused
herself by detaining. On the 15th a summons to pay was served on M.
d'Espard, the portress had delivered it at her leisure, and he supposed it
to be some misunderstanding, not conceiving of any incivility from a man
in whose house he had been living for twelve years. The Marquis was
actually seized by a bailiff at the time when his man-servant had gone to
carry the money for the rent to the landlord.

This arrest, insidiously reported to the persons with whom he was in
treaty for his undertaking, had alarmed some of them who were already
doubtful of M. d'Espard's solvency in consequence of the enormous sums
which Baron Jeanrenaud and his mother were said to be receiving from
him. And, indeed, these suspicions on the part of the tenants, the creditors,
and the landlord had some excuse in the Marquis's extreme economy in
housekeeping. He conducted it as a ruined man might. His servants always paid in ready money for the most trifling necessaries of life, and acted
as not choosing to take credit; if now they had asked for anything on
credit, it would probably have been refused, calumnious gossip had been
so widely believed in the neighborhood. There are tradesmen who like
those of their customers who pay badly when they see them often, while
they hate others, and very good ones, who hold themselves on too high a
level to allow of any familiarity as *chums,* a vulgar but expressive word.
Men are made so; in almost every class they will allow to a gossip, or a
vulgar soul that flatters them, facilities and favors they refuse to the superiority they resent, in whatever form it may show itself. The shopkeeper
who rails at the Court has his courtiers.

In short, the manners of his Marquis and his children were certain to
arouse ill-feeling in their neighbors, and to work them up by degrees to
the pitch of malevolence when men do not hesitate at an act of meanness
if only it may damage the adversary they have themselves created.

M. d'Espard was a gentleman, as his wife was a lady, by birth and
breeding; noble types, already so rare in France that the observer can
easily count the persons who perfectly realize them. These two characters
are based on primitive ideas, on beliefs that may be called innate, on habits
formed in infancy, and which have ceased to exist. To believe in pure
blood, in a privileged race, to stand in thought above other men, must we
not from birth have measured the distance which divides patricians from
the mob? To command, must we not have never met our equal? And
finally, must not education inculcate the ideas with which Nature inspires

those great men on whose brow she has placed a crown before their mother has ever set a kiss there? These ideas, this education, are no longer possible in France, where for forty years past chance has arrogated the right of making noblemen by dipping them in the blood of battles, by gilding them with glory, by crowning them with the halo of genius; where the abolition of entail and of eldest sonship, by frittering away estates, compels the nobleman to attend to his own business instead of attending to affairs of state, and where personal greatness can only be such greatness as is acquired by long and patient toil: quite a new era.

Regarded as a relic of that great institution known as feudalism, M. d'Espard deserved respectful admiration. If he believed himself to be by blood the superior of other men, he also believed in all the obligations of nobility; he had the virtues and the strength it demands. He had brought up his children in his own principles, and taught them from the cradle the religion of their caste. A deep sense of their own dignity, pride of name, the conviction that they were by birth great, gave rise in them to a kingly pride, the courage of knights, and the protecting kindness of a baronial lord; their manners, harmonizing with their notions, would have become princes, and offended all the world of the Rue de la Montagne-Sainte Geneviève—a world, above all others, of equality, where everyone believed that M. d'Espard was ruined, and where all, from the lowest to the highest, refused the privileges of nobility to a nobleman without money, because they all were ready to allow an enriched bourgeois to usurp them. Thus the lack of communion between this family and other persons were as much moral as it was physical.

In the father and the children alike, their personality harmonized with the spirit within. M. d'Espard, at this time about fifty, might have sat as a model to represent the aristocracy of birth in the nineteenth century. He was slight and fair; there was in the outline and general expression of his face a native distinction which spoke of lofty sentiments, but it bore the impress of a deliberate coldness which commanded respect a little too decidedly. His aquiline nose bent at the tip from left to right, a slight crookedness which was not devoid of grace; his blue eyes, his high forehead, prominent enough at the brows to form a thick ridge that checked the light and shaded his eyes, all indicated a spirit of rectitude, capable of perseverance and perfect loyalty, while it gave a singular look to his countenance. This pent-house forehead might, in fact, hint at a touch of madness, and his thick-knitted eyebrows added to the apparent eccentricity. He had the white well-kept hands of a gentleman; his foot was high and narrow. His hesitating speech—not merely as to his pronunciation, which was that of a stammerer, but also in the expression of his ideas, his thought, and language—produced on the mind of the hearer the impression of a man who, in familiar phraseology, comes and goes, feels his way, tries everything, breaks off his gestures, and finishes nothing. This defect was purely superficial, and in contrast with the decisiveness of a firmly-set mouth, and the strongly-marked character of his physiognomy. His rather jerky gait matched his mode of speech. These peculiarities helped to affirm his supposed insanity. In spite of his elegant appearance, he was systematically parsimonious in his personal expenses, and wore the same black frock-coat for three or four years, brushed with extreme care by his old man-servant.

As to the children, they both were handsome, and endowed with a grace which did not exclude an expression of aristocratic disdain. They had the bright coloring, the clear eye, the transparent flesh which reveal habits of purity, regularity of life, and a due proportion of work and play. They both had black hair and blue eyes, and a twist in their nose, like their father; but their mother, perhaps, had transmitted to them the dignity of speech, of look and mien, which are hereditary in the Blamont-Chauvrys. Their voices, as clear as crystal, had an emotional quality, the softness which proves so seductive; they had, in short, the voice a woman would willingly listen to after feeling the flame of their looks. But, above all, they had the modesty of pride, a chaste reserve, a *touch-me-not* which at a maturer age might have seemed intentional coyness so much did their demeanor inspire a wish to know them. The elder, Comte Clément de Nègrepelisse, was close upon his sixteenth year. For the last two years he had ceased to wear the pretty English round jacket which his brother, Vicomte Camille d'Espard, still wore. The Count, who for the last six months went no more to the Collège Henri IV., was dressed in the style of a young man enjoying his first pleasures of fashion. His father had not wished to condemn him to a year's useless study of philosophy; he was trying to give his knowledge some consistency by the study of transcendental mathematics. At the same time, the Marquis was having him taught Eastern languages, the international law of Europe, heraldry, and history from the original sources—charters, early documents, and collections of edicts. Camille had lately begun to study rhetoric.

The day when Popinot arranged to go to question M. d'Espard was a Thursday, a holiday. At about nine in the morning, before their father was awake, the brothers were playing in the garden. Clément was finding it hard to refuse his brother, who was anxious to go to the shooting gallery for the first time, and who begged him to second his request to the Marquis. The Viscount always rather took advantage of his weakness, and was very fond of wrestling with his brother. So the couple were quarreling and fighting in play like schoolboys. As they ran in the garden, chasing each other, they made so much noise as to wake their father, who came to the window without their perceiving him in the heat of the fray. The Marquis amused himself with watching his two children twisted together like snakes, their faces flushed by the exertion of their strength; their complexion was rose and white, their eyes flashed sparks, their limbs writhed like cords in the fire; they fell, sprang up again, and caught each other like athletes in a circus, affording their father one of those moments of happiness which would make amends for the keenest anxieties of a busy life. Two other persons, one on the second and one on the first floor, were also looking into the garden, and saying that the old madman was amusing himself by making his children fight. Immediately a number of heads appeared at the windows; the Marquis, noticing them, called a word to his sons, who at once climbed up to the window and jumped into his room, and Clément obtained the permission asked by Camille.

All through the house everyone was talking of the Marquis's new form of insanity. When Popinot arrived at about twelve o'clock, accompanied by his clerk, the portress, when he asked for M. d'Espard, conducted him to the third floor, telling him "as how M. d'Espard, no longer ago than that very morning, had set on his two children to fight, and laughed like the monster he was seeing the younger biting the elder till he bled, and as how no doubt he longed to see them kill each other.—Don't ask me the reason why," she added; "he doesn't know himself!"

Just as the woman spoke these decisive words, she had brought the judge to the landing on the third floor, face to face with a door covered with notices announcing the successful numbers of the *Picturesque History of China*. The muddy floor, the dirty banisters, the door where the printers had left their marks, the dilapidated window, and the ceiling on which the apprentices had amused themselves with drawing monstrosities with the smoky flare of their tallow dips, the piles of paper and litter heaped up in the corners, intentionally or from sheer neglect—in short, every detail of the picture lying before his eyes agreed so well with the facts alleged by the Marquise that the judge, in spite of his impartiality, could not help believing them.

"There you are, gentlemen," said the porter's wife; "there is the manifactor, where the Chinese swallow up enough to feed the whole neighborhood."

The clerk looked at the judge with a smile, and Popinot found it hard to keep his countenance. They went together into the outer room, where sat an old man, who, no doubt, performed the functions of office clerk, shopman, and cashier. This old man was the Maitre Jacques of China. Along the walls ran long shelves, on which the published numbers lay in piles. A partition in wood, with a grating lined with green curtains, cut off the end of the room, forming a private office. A till with a slit to admit or disgorge crown pieces indicated the cash-desk.

"M. d'Espard?" said Popinot, addressing the man, who wore a gray blouse.

The shopman opened the door into the next room, where the lawyer and his companion saw a venerable old man, white-headed and simply dressed, wearing the Cross of Saint-Louis, seated at a desk. He ceased comparing some sheets of colored prints to look up at the two visitors. This room was an unpretentious office, full of books and proof-sheets. There was a black wood table at which someone, at the moment absent, no doubt was accustomed to work.

"The Marquis d'Espard?" said Popinot.

"No, Monsieur," said the old man, rising; "what do you want with him?" he added, coming forward, and showing by his demeanor the dignified manners and habits due to a gentlemanly education.

"We wish to speak to him on business exclusively personal to himself," replied Popinot.

"D'Espard, here are some gentlemen who want to see you," then said the old man, going into the furthest room, where the Marquis was sitting by the fire, reading the newspaper.

This innermost room had a shabby carpet, the windows were hung with gray holland curtains; the furniture consisted of a few mahogany chairs, two armchairs, a desk with a revolving front, an ordinary office table, and, on the chimney-shelf, a dingy clock and two old candlesticks. The old man led the way for Popinot and his registrar, and pulled forward two chairs, as though he were master of the place; M. d'Espard left it to him. After the preliminary civilities, during which the judge watched the supposed lunatic, the Marquis naturally asked what was the object of this visit. On this Popinot glanced significantly at the old gentleman and the Marquis.

"I believe, Monsieur le Marquis," said he, "that the character of my functions, and the inquiry that has brought me here, make it desirable that we should be alone, though it is understood by law that in such cases the inquiries have a sort of family publicity. I am judge of the Inferior Court of Appeal for the Department of the Seine, and charged by the President with the duty of examining you as to certain facts set forth in a petition for a Commission in Lunacy on the part of the Marquise d'Espard."

The old man withdrew. When the lawyer and the Marquis were alone, the clerk shut the door, and seated himself unceremoniously at the office table, where he laid out his papers and prepared to take down his notes. Popinot had still kept his eye on M. d'Espard; he was watching the effect on him of this crude statement, so painful for a man in full possession of his reason. The Marquise d'Espard, whose face was usually pale, as are those of fair men, suddenly turned scarlet with anger; he trembled for an instant, sat down, laid his paper on the chimney-piece, and looked down. In a moment he had recovered his gentlemanly dignity, and looked steadily at the judge, as if to read in his countenance the indications of his character.

"How is it, Monsieur," he asked, "that I have had no notice of such a petition?"

"Monsieur le Marquis, persons on whom such a commission is held, not being supposed to have the use of their reason, any notice of the petition is unnecessary. The duty of the Court chiefly consists in verifying the allegations of the petitioner."

"Nothing can be fairer," replied the Marquis. "Well, then, Monsieur, be so good as to tell me what I ought to do—"

"You have only to answer my questions, omitting nothing. However delicate the reasons may be which may have led you to act in such a manner as to give Madame d'Espard a pretext for her petition, speak without fear. It is unnecessary to assure you that lawyers know their duties, and that in such cases the profoundest secrecy—"

"Monsieur," said the Marquis, whose face expressed the sincerest pain, "if my explanations should lead to any blame attached to Madame d'Espard's conduct, what will be the result?"

"The Court may add its censure to its reason for its decision."

"Is such censure optional? If I were to stipulate with you, before replying, that nothing should be said that could annoy Madame d'Espard in the event of your report being in my favor, would the Court take my request into consideration?"

The judge looked at the Marquis, and the two men exchanged sentiments of equal magnanimity.

"Noël," said Popinot to his registrar, "go into the other room. If you can be of use, I will call you in.—If, as I am inclined to think," he went on, speaking to the Marquis when the clerk had gone out, "I find that there is some misunderstanding in this case, I can promise you, Monsieur, that on your application the Court will act with due courtesy.

"There is a leading fact put forward by Madame d'Espard, the most serious of all, of which I must beg for an explanation," said the judge after a pause. "It refers to the dissipation of your fortune to the advantage of a certain Madame Jeanrenaud, the widow of a barge-master—or rather, to that of her son, Colonel Jeanrenaud, for whom you are said to have procured an appointment, to have exhausted your influence with the King, and at last to have extended such protection as secures him a good marriage. The petition suggests that such a friendship is more devoted than any feelings, even those which morality must disapprove—"

A sudden flush crimsoned the Marquis's face and forehead, tears even started to his eyes, for his eyelashes were wet, then wholesome pride crushed the emotions, which in a man are accounted a weakness.

"To tell you the truth, Monsieur," said the Marquis, in a broken voice, "you place me in a strange dilemma. The motives of my conduct were to have died with me. To reveal them I must disclose to you some secret wounds, must place the honor of my family in your keeping, and must speak of myself, a delicate matter, as you will fully understand. I hope, Monsieur, that it will all remain a secret between us. You will, no doubt, be able to find in the formulas of the law one which will allow of judgment being pronounced without any betrayal of my confidences."

"So far as that goes, it is perfectly possible, Monsieur le Marquis."

"Some time after my marriage," said M. d'Espard, "my wife having run into considerable expenses, I was obliged to have recourse to borrowing. You know what was the position of noble families during the Revolution; I had not been able to keep a steward or a man of business. Nowadays gentlemen are for the most part obliged to manage their affairs themselves. Most of my title-deeds had been brought to Paris, from Languedoc, Provence, or Le Comtat, by my father, who dreaded, and not without reason, the inquisition which family title-deeds, and what were then styled the 'parchments' of the privileged class, brought down on the owners.

"Our name is Nègrepelisse; d'Espard is a title acquired in the time of Henry IV. by a marriage which brought us the estates and titles of the house of d'Espard, on condition of our bearing an escutcheon of pretense on our coat-of-arms, those of the house of d'Espard, an old family of Béarn, connected in the female line with that of Albret: quarterly, paly of or and sable, and azure two griffins' claws armed, gules in saltire, with the famous motto *Des partem leonis*. At the time of this alliance we lost Nègrepelisse, a little town which was as famous during the religious struggles as was my ancestor who then bore the name. Captain de Nègrepelisse was ruined by the burning of all his property, for the Protestants did not spare a friend of Montluc's.

"The Crown was unjust to M. de Nègrepelisse; he received neither a marshal's baton, nor a post as governor, nor any indemnity; King Charles IX., who was fond of him, died without being able to reward him; Henri IV. arranged his marriage with Mademoiselle d'Espard, and secured him the estates of that house, but all those of the Nègrepelisses had already passed into the hands of his creditors.

"My great-grandfather, the Marquis d'Espard, was, like me, placed early in life at the head of his family by the death of his father, who, after dissipating his wife's fortune, left his son nothing but the entailed estates of the d'Espards, burdened with a jointure. The young Marquis was all the more straitened for money because he held a post at Court. Being in great favor with Louis XIV., the King's goodwill brought him a fortune. But here, Monsieur, a blot stained our escutcheon, an unconfessed and horrible stain of blood and disgrace which I am making it my business to wipe out. I discovered the secret among the deeds relating to the estate of Nègrepelisse and the packets of letters."

At this solemn moment the Marquis spoke without hesitation or any of the repetition habitual with him; but it is a matter of common observation that persons who, in ordinary life, are afflicted with these two defects, are freed from them as soon as any passionate emotion underlies their speech.

"The Revocation of the Edict of Nantes was decreed," he went on. "You are no doubt aware, Monsieur, that this was an opportunity for many favorites to make their fortunes. Louis XIV. bestowed on the magnates about his Court the confiscated lands of those Protestant families who did not take the prescribed steps for the sale of their property. Some persons in high favor went 'Protestant-hunting,' as the phrase was. I have ascertained beyond a doubt that the fortune enjoyed to this day by two ducal families is derived from lands seized from hapless merchants.

"I will not attempt to explain to you, a man of law, all the maneuvers employed to entrap the refugees who had large fortunes to carry away. It is enough to say that the lands of Nègrepelisse, comprising twenty-two churches and rights over the town, and those of Gravenges which had formerly belonged to us, were at that time in the hands of a Protestant family. My grandfather recovered them by gifts from Louis XIV. This gift was effected by documents hall-marked by atrocious iniquity. The owner of these two estates, thinking he would be able to return, had gone through the form of a sale, and was going to Switzerland to join his family, whom he had sent in advance. He wished, no doubt, to take advantage of every delay granted by the law, so as to settle the concerns of his business.

"This man was arrested by order of the governor, the trustee confessed the truth, the poor merchant was hanged, and my ancestor had the two estates. I would gladly have been able to ignore the share he took in the plot; but the governor was his uncle on the mother's side; and I have unfortunately read the letter in which he begged him to apply to Deodatus, the name agreed upon by the Courts to designate the King. In this letter there is a tone of jocosity with reference to the victim, which filled me with horror. In the end, the sums of money sent by the refugee family to ransom the poor man's life were kept by the governor, who dispatched the merchant all the same."

The Marquis paused, as though the memory of it were still too heavy for him to bear.

"This unfortunate family were named Jeanrenaud," he went on. "That name is enough to account for my conduct. I could never think without keen pain of the secret disgrace that weighed on my family. That fortune enabled my grandfather to marry a demoiselle de Navarreins-Lansac, heiress to the younger branch of that house, who were at that time much richer than the elder branch of the Navarreins. My father thus became one of the largest landowners in the kingdom. He was able to marry my mother, a Grandlieu of the younger branch. Though ill-gotten, this property has been singularly profitable.

"For my part, being determined to remedy the mischief, I wrote to Switzerland, and knew no peace till I was on the traces of the Protestant victim's heirs. At last I discovered that the Jeanrenauds, reduced to abject want, had left Fribourg and returned to live in France. Finally, I found in Mr. Jeanrenaud, lieutenant in a cavalry regiment under Napoleon, the sole heir of this unhappy family. In my eyes, Monsieur, the rights of the Jeanrenauds were clear. To establish a prescriptive right is it not necessary that there should have been some possibility of proceeding against those who are in the enjoyment of it? To whom could these refugees have appealed? Their Court of Justice was on high, or rather, Monsieur, it was here," and the Marquis struck his hand on his heart. "I did not choose that my children should be able to think of me as I have thought of my father and of my ancestors. I aim at leaving them an unblemished inheritance and escutcheon. I did not choose that nobility should be a lie in my person. And, after all, politically speaking, ought those *émigrés* who are now appealing against revolutionary confiscations, to keep the property derived from antecedent confiscations by positive crimes?

"I found in Mr. Jeanrenaud and his mother the most perverse honesty; to hear them you would suppose that they were robbing me. In spite of all I could say, they will accept no more than the value of the lands at the time when the King bestowed them on my family. The price was settled between us at the sum of eleven hundred thousand francs, which I was to pay at my convenience and without interest. To achieve this I had to forego my income for a long time. And then, Monsieur, began the destruction of some illusions I had allowed myself as to Madame d'Espard's character. When I proposed to her that we should leave Paris and go into the country, where we could live respected on half of her income, and so more rapidly complete a restitution of which I spoke to her without going into the more serious details, Madame d'Espard treated me as a madman. I then understood my wife's real character. She would have approved of my grandfather's conduct without a scruple, and have laughed at the Huguenots. Terrified by her coldness, and her little affection for her children, whom she abandoned to me without a regret, I determined to leave her the command of her fortune, after paying our common debts. It was no business of hers, as she told me, to pay for my follies. As I then had not enough to live on and pay for my sons' education, I determined to educate them myself, to make them gentlemen and men of feeling. By investing my money in the Funds I have been enabled to pay off my obligations sooner than I had dared to hope, for I took advantage of the opportunities afforded by the improvement in prices. If I had kept four thousand francs a year for my boys and myself, I could only have paid off twenty thousand crowns a year, and it would have taken almost eighteen years to achieve my freedom. As it is, I have lately repaid the whole of the eleven hundred thousand francs that were due. Thus I enjoy the happiness of having made this restitution without doing my children the smallest wrong.

"These, Monsieur, are the reasons for the payments made to Madame Jeanrenaud and her son."

"So Madame d'Espard knew the motives of your retirement?" said the judge, controlling the emotion he felt at this narrative.

"Yes, Monsieur."

Popinot gave an expressive shrug; he rose and opened the door in the next room.

"Noël, you can go," said he to his clerk.

"Monsieur," he went on, "though what you have told me is enough to enlighten me thoroughly, I should like to hear what you have to say to the other facts put forward in the petition. For instance, you are here carrying on a business such as is not habitually undertaken by a man of rank."

"We cannot discuss that matter here," said the Marquis, signing to the judge to quit the room. "Nouvion," said he to the old man, "I am going down to my rooms; the children will soon be in; dine with us."

"Then, Monsieur le Marquis," said Popinot on the stairs, "that is not your apartment?"

"No, Monsieur; I took those rooms for the office of this undertaking. You see," and he pointed to an advertisement sheet, "the *History* is being brought out by one of the most respectable firms in Paris, and not by me."

The Marquis showed the lawyer into the ground-floor rooms, saying, "This is my apartment."

Popinot was quite touched by the poetry, not aimed at but pervading this dwelling. The weather was lovely, the windows were open, the air from the garden brought in a wholesome earthy smell, the sunshine brightened and gilded the woodwork, of a rather gloomy brown. At the sight Popinot made up his mind that a madman would hardly be capable of inventing the tender harmony of which he was at that moment conscious.

"I should like just such an apartment," thought he. "You think of leaving this part of the town?" he inquired.

"I hope so," replied the Marquis. "But I shall remain till my younger son has finished his studies, and till the children's character is thoroughly formed, before introducing them to the world and to their mother's circle. Indeed, after giving them the solid information they possess, I intend to complete it by taking them to travel to the capitals of Europe, that they may see men and things, and become accustomed to speak the languages they have learned. And, Monsieur," he went on, giving the judge a chair in the drawing-room, "I could not discuss the book on China with you, in the presence of an old friend of my family, the Comte de Nouvion, who, having emigrated, has returned to France without any fortune whatever, and who is my partner in this concern, less for my profit than his. Without telling him what my motives were, I explained to him that I was as poor as he, but that I had enough money to start a speculation in which he might be usefully employed. My tutor was the Abbé Grozier, whom Charles X. on my recommendation appointed Keeper of the Books at the Arsenal, which were returned to that Prince when he was still Monsieur. The Abbé Grozier was deeply learned with regard to China, its manners and customs; he made me heir to his knowledge at an age when it is difficult not to become a fanatic for the things we learn. At five-and-twenty I knew Chinese, and I confess I have never been able to check myself in an exclusive admiration for that nation, who conquered their conquerors, whose annals extend back indisputably to a period more remote than mythological or Biblical times, who by their immutable institutions have preserved the integrity of their empire, whose monuments are gigantic, whose administration is perfect, among whom revolutions are impossible, who have regarded ideal beauty as a barren element in art, who have luxury and industry to such a pitch that we cannot outdo them in anything, while they are our equals in things where we believe ourselves superior.

"Still, Monsieur, though I often make a jest of comparing China with the present condition of European states, I am not a Chinaman, I am a French gentleman. If you entertain any doubts as to the financial side of this undertaking, I can prove to you that at this moment we have two thousand five hundred subscribers to this work, which is literary, icono-graphical, statistical, and religious; its importance has been generally ap-preciated; our subscribers belong to every nation in Europe, we have but twelve hundred in France. Our book will cost about three hundred francs, and the Comte de Nouvion will derive from it from six to seven thousand francs a year, for his comfort was the real motive of the under-taking. For my part, I aimed only at the possibility of affording my chil-dren some pleasures. The hundred thousand francs I have made, quite in spite of myself, will pay for their fencing lessons, horses, dress, and theatres, pay the masters who teach them accomplishments, procure them canvases to spoil, the books they may wish to buy, in short, all the little fancies which a father finds so much pleasure in gratifying. If I had been com-pelled to refuse these indulgences to my poor boys, who are so good and work so hard, the sacrifice I have made to the honor of my name would have been doubly painful.

"In point of fact, the twelve years I have spent in retirement from the world to educate my children have led to my being completely forgotten at Court. I have given up my career of politics; I have lost my historical fortune, and all the distinctions which I might have acquired and be-queathed to my children; but our house will have lost nothing; my boys will be men of mark. Though I have missed the senatorship, they will win it nobly by devoting themselves to the affairs of the country, and do-ing such service as is not soon forgotten. While purifying the past record of my family, I have insured it a glorious future; and is not that to have achieved a noble task, though in secret and without glory?—And now, Monsieur, have you any other explanations to ask of me?"

At this instant the tramp of horses was heard in the courtyard.

"Here they are!" said the Marquis. In a moment the two lads, fashion-ably but plainly dressed, came into the room, booted, spurred, and gloved, and flourishing their riding-whips. Their beaming faces brought in the freshness of the outer air; they were brilliant with health. They both grasped their father's hand, giving him a look, as friends do, a glance of unspoken affection, and then they bowed coldly to the lawyer. Popinot felt that it was quite unnecessary to question the Marquis as to his rela-tions towards his sons.

"Have you enjoyed yourselves?" asked the Marquis.

"Yes, father; I knocked down six dolls in twelve shots at the first trial!" cried Camille.

"And where did you ride?"

"In the Bois; we saw my mother."

"Did she stop?"

"We were riding so fast just then that I dare say she did not see us," replied the young Count.

"But, then, why did you not go to speak to her?"

"I fancy I have noticed, father, that she does not care that we should speak to her in public," said Clément, in an undertone. "We are a little too big."

The judge's hearing was keen enough to catch these words, which brought a cloud to the Marquis's brow. Popinot took pleasure in contemplating the picture of the father and his boys. His eyes went back with a sense of pathos to M. d'Espard's face; his features, his expression, and his manner all expressed honesty in its noblest aspect, intellectual and chivalrous honesty, nobility in all its beauty.

"You—you see, Monsieur," said the Marquis, and his hesitation had returned, "you see that Justice may look in—in here at any time—yes, at any time—here. If there is anybody crazy, it can only be the children—the children—who are a little crazy about their father, and the father who is very crazy about his children—but that sort of madness rings true."

At this juncture Madame Jeanrenaud's voice was heard in the ante-room, and the good woman came bustling in, in spite of the man-servant's remonstrances.

"I take no roundabout ways, I can tell you!" she exclaimed. "Yes, Monsieur le Marquis, I want to speak to you, this very minute," she went on, with a comprehensive bow to the company. "By George, and I am too late as it is, since Monsieur the criminal Judge is before me."

"Criminal!" cried the two boys.

"Good reasons why I did not find you at your own house, since you were here. Well, well! the Law is always to the fore when there is mischief brewing.—I came, Monsieur le Marquis, to tell you that my son and I are of one mind to give you everything back, since our honor is threatened. My son and I, we had rather give you back everything than cause you the smallest trouble. My word, they must be as stupid as pans without handles to call you a lunatic—"

"A lunatic! My father?" exclaimed the boys, clinging to the Marquis. "What is this?"

"Silence, Madame," said Popinot.

"Children, leave us," said the Marquis.

The two boys went into the garden without a word, but very much alarmed.

"Madame," said the judge, "the moneys paid to you by Monsieur le Marquis were legally due, though given to you in virtue of a very far-reaching theory of honesty. If all the people possessed of confiscated goods, by whatever cause, even if acquired by treachery, were compelled to make restitution every hundred and fifty years, there would be few legitimate owners in France. The possessions of Jacques Coeur enriched twenty noble families; the confiscations pronounced by the English to the advantage of their adherents at the time when they held a part of France made the fortune of several princely houses.

"Our law allows M. d'Espard to dispose of his income without accounting for it, or suffering him to be accused of its misapplication. A Commission in Lunacy can only be granted when a man's actions are devoid of reason; but in this case, the remittances made to you have a reason based on the most sacred and most honorable motives. Hence you may keep it all without remorse, and leave the world to misinterpret a noble action. In Paris, the highest virtue is the object of the foulest calumny. It is, unfortunately, the present condition of society that makes the Marquis's actions sublime. For the honor of my country, I would that such deeds were regarded as a matter of course; but, as things are, I am forced by comparison to look upon M. d'Espard as a man to whom a crown should be awarded, rather than that he should be threatened with a Commission in Lunacy.

"In the course of a long professional career, I have seen and heard nothing which has touched me more deeply than that I have just seen and heard. But it is not extraordinary that virtue should wear its noblest aspect when it is practiced by men of the highest class.

"Having heard me express myself in this way, I hope, Monsieur le Marquis, that you feel certain of my silence, and that you will not for a moment be uneasy as to the decision pronounced in the case—if it comes before the Court."

"There, now! Well said," cried Madame Jeanrenaud. "That is something like a judge! Look here, my dear sir, I would hug you if I were not so ugly; you speak like a book."

The Marquis held out his hand to Popinot, who gently pressed it with a look full of sympathetic comprehension at this great man in private life, and the Marquis responded with a pleasant smile. These two natures, both so large and full—one commonplace but divinely kind, the other lofty and sublime—had fallen into unison gently, without a jar, without a flash of passion, as though two pure lights had been merged into one. The father of a whole district felt himself worthy to grasp the hand of this man who was doubly noble, and the Marquis felt in the depths of his soul an instinct that told him that the judge's hand was one of those from which the treasures of inexhaustible beneficence perennially flow.

"Monsieur le Marquis," added Popinot, with a bow, "I am happy to be able to tell you that, from the first words of this inquiry, I regarded my clerk as quite unnecessary."

He went close to M. d'Espard, led him into the window-bay, and said: "It is time that you should return home, Monsieur. I believe that Madame le Marquise has acted in this matter under an influence which you ought at once to counteract."

Popinot withdrew; he looked back several times as he crossed the courtyard, touched by the recollection of the scene. It was one of those which take root in the memory to blossom again in certain hours when the soul seeks consolation.

"Those rooms would just suit me," said he to himself as he reached home. "If d'Espard leaves them, I will take up his lease."

The next day, at about ten in the morning, Popinot, who had written out his report the previous evening, made his way to the Palais de Justice, intending to have prompt and righteous justice done. As he went into the robing-room to put on his gown and bands, the usher told him that the President of his Court begged him to attend in his private room, where he was waiting for him. Popinot forthwith obeyed.

"Good morning, my dear Popinot," said the President, "I have been waiting for you."

"Why, Monsieur le Président, is anything wrong?"

"A mere silly trifle," said the President. "The Keeper of the Seals, with whom I had the honor of dining yesterday, led me apart into a corner. He had heard that you had been to tea with Madame d'Espard, in whose case you were employed to make inquiries. He gave me to understand that it would be as well that you should not sit on this case—"

"But Monsieur le Président, I can prove that I left Madame d'Espard's house at the moment when tea was brought in. And my conscience—"

"Yes, yes; the whole Bench, the two Courts, all the profession know you. I need not repeat what I said about you to his Eminence; but, you know, 'Caesar's wife must not be suspected.' So we shall not make this foolish trifle a matter of discipline, but only of the properties. Between ourselves, it is not on your account, but on that of the Bench."

"But, Monsieur, if you only knew the kind of woman—" said the judge, trying to pull his report out of his pocket.

"I am perfectly certain that you have proceeded in this matter with the strictest independence of judgment. I myself in the provinces, have often taken more than a cup of tea with the people I had to try; but the fact that the Keeper of the Seals should have mentioned it and that you might be talked about, is enough to make the Court avoid any discussion of the matter. Any conflict with public opinion must always be dangerous for a constitutional body, even when the right is on its side against the public, because their weapons are not equal. Journalism may say or suppose anything, and our dignity forbids us even to reply. In fact, I have spoken of the matter to your President, and M. Camusot has been appointed in your place on your retirement, which you will signify. It is a family matter, so to speak. And now I beg you to signify your retirement from the case as a personal favor. To make up, you will get the Cross of the Legion of Honor, which has so long been due to you. I make that my business."

When he saw M. Camusot, a judge recently called to Paris from a provincial Court of the same class, as he went forward bowing to the Judge and the President, Popinot could not suppress an ironical smile. This pale, fair young man, full of covert ambition, looked ready to hang and unhang, at the pleasure of any earthly king, the innocent and the guilty alike, and to follow the example of a Laubardemont rather than that of a Molé.

Popinot withdrew with a bow; he scorned to deny the lying accusation that had been brought against him.

Imprisonment for Debt

Sir Walter Scott

THE PARTY, consisting of the Antiquary, his nephew, and the old beggar, now took the sands toward Mussel-crag—the former in the very highest mood of communicating information, and the others, under a sense of former obligation, and some hope for future favors, decently attentive to receive it. The uncle and nephew walked together, the mendicant about a step and a half behind, just near enough for his patron to speak to him by a slight inclination of his neck, and without the trouble of turning round. (Petrie, in his Essay on Goodbreeding, dedicated to the magistrates of Edinburgh, recommends, upon his own experience, as tutor in a family of distinction, this attitude to all led captains, tutors, dependants, and bottle-holders of every description.) Thus escorted, the Antiquary moved along full of his learning, like a lordly man of war, and every now and then yawing to starboard and larboard to discharge a broadside upon his followers.

"And so it is your opinion," said he to the mendicant, "that this windfall—this *arca auri,* as Plautus has it, will not greatly avail Sir Arthur in his necessities?"

"Unless he could find ten times as much," said the beggar, "and that I am sair doubtful of;—I heard Puggie Orrock, and the tother chief of a sheriff-officer, or messenger, speaking about it—and things are ill aff when the like o' them can speak crousely about my gentleman's affairs. I doubt Sir Arthur will be in stane wa's for debt, unless there's swift help and certain."

"You speak like a fool," said the Antiquary. "Nephew, it is a remarkable thing, that in this happy country no man can be legally imprisoned for debt."

"Indeed, sir?" said M'Intyre; "I never knew that before—that part of our law would suit some of our mess well."

"And if they arena confined for debt," said Ochiltree, "what is't that tempts sae mony puir creatures to bide in the tolbooth o' Fairport yonder? —they a' say they were put there by their creditors—Od! they maun like it better than I do, if they're there o' free will."

From *The Antiquary.*

"A very natural observation, Edie, and many of your betters would make the same; but it is founded entirely upon ignorance of the feudal system. Hector, be so good as to attend, unless you are looking out for another—Ahem!" (Hector compelled himself to give attention at this hint.) "And you, Edie, it may be useful to you *rerum cognoscere causas.* The nature and origin of warrant for caption is a thing *haud alienum a Scaevolae studiis.*—You must know then, once more, that nobody can be arrested in Scotland for debt."

"I haena muckle concern wi' that, Monkbarns," said the old man, "for naebody wad trust a bodle to a gaberlunzie."

"I pr'ythee, peace, man—As a compulsitor, therefore, of payment, that being a thing to which no debtor is naturally inclined, as I have too much reason to warrant from the experience I have had with my own,—we had first letters of four forms, a sort of gentle invitation, by which out sovereign lord the king, interesting himself, as a monarch should, in the regulation of his subjects' private affairs, at first by mild exhortation, and afterwards by letters of more strict enjoinment and more hard compulsion—What do you see extraordinary about that bird, Hector?—it's but a seamaw."

"It's a pictarnie, sir," said Edie.

"Well, what an if it were—what does that signify at present?—But I see you're impatient; so I will waive the letters of four forms, and come to the modern process of diligence.—You suppose, now, a man's committed to prison, because he cannot pay his debt? Quite otherwise: the truth is, the king is so good as to interfere at the request of the creditor, and to send the debtor his royal command to do him justice within a certain time —fifteen days, or six, as the case may be. Well, the man resists and disobeys; what follows? Why, that he be lawfully and rightfully declared a rebel to our gracious sovereign, whose command he has disobeyed, and that by three blasts of a horn at the market-place of Edinburgh, the metropolis of Scotland. And he is then legally imprisoned, not on account of any civil debt, but because of his ungrateful contempt of the royal mandate. What do you say to that, Hector?—there's something you never knew before."*

"No, uncle; but, I own, if I wanted money to pay my debts, I would rather thank the king to send me some, than to declare me a rebel for not doing what I could not do."

"Your education has not led you to consider these things," replied his uncle; "you are incapable of estimating the elegance of the legal fiction, and the manner in which it reconciles that duress, which, for the protection of commerce, it has been found necessary to extend towards refractory

---

* The doctrine of Monkbarns on the origin of imprisonment for civil debt in Scotland may appear somewhat whimsical, but was referred to, and admitted to be correct, by the Bench of the Supreme Scottish Court, on the 5th December, 1828, in the case of Thom *v.* Black. In fact, the Scottish law is in this particular more jealous of the personal liberty of the subject than any other code in Europe.

debtors, with the most scrupulous attention to the liberty of the subject."

"I don't know, sir," replied the unenlightened Hector; "but if a man must pay his debt or go to jail, it signifies but little whether he goes as a debtor or a rebel, I should think. But you say this command of the king's gives a license of so many days—Now, egad, were I in the scrape, I would beat a march and leave the king and the creditors to settle it among themselves before they came to extremities."

"So wad I," said Edie; "I wad gie them leg-bail to a certainty."

"True," replied Monkbarns: "but those whom the law suspects of being unwilling to abide her formal visit, she proceeds with by means of a shorter and more unceremonious call, as dealing with persons on whom patience and favor would be utterly thrown away."

"Ay," said Ochiltree, "that will be what they ca' the fugie-warrants—I hae some skeel in them. There's Border-warrants too in the south country, unco rash uncanny things;—I was taen up on ane at Saint James's Fair; and keepit in the auld kirk at Kelso the haill day and night; and a cauld goustie place it was, I'se assure ye."

Contempt of Court

Arthur Train

The court can't determine what is honor.—Chief Baron Bowes, 1743.

I know what my code of honor is, my lord, and I intend to adhere to it.—John O'Conner, M. P., in Parnell Commission's Proceedings, 103d Day; Times Rep. pt. 28, pp. 19 ff.

Well, honor is the subject of my story.—Julius Caesar, Act I, Sc. 2.

WHAT HAS become of Katie—the second waitress?" asked Miss Althea Beekman of Dawkins, her housekeeper, as she sat at her satinwood desk after breakfast. "I didn't see her either last night or this morning."

Dawkins, who was a mid-Victorian, flushed awkwardly.

"I really had to let the girl go, ma'am!" she explained with an outraged air. "I hardly know how to tell you—such a thing in this house! I couldn't possibly have her around. I was afraid she might corrupt the other girls, ma'am—and they are such a self-respecting lot—almost quite ladylike, ma'am. So I simply paid her and told her to take herself off."

Miss Beekman looked pained.

"You shouldn't have turned her out into the street like that, Dawkins!" she expostulated. "Where has she gone?"

Dawkins gazed at her large feet in amazement.

"I don't know, ma'am," she admitted. "I didn't suppose you'd want her here so I sent her away. It was quite inconvenient, too—with the servant problem what it is. But I'm hoping to get another this afternoon from Miss Healey's."

Miss Beekman was genuinely annoyed.

"I am seriously displeased with you, Dawkins!" she returned severely. "Of course, I am shocked at any girl in my household misbehaving herself, but—I—wouldn't want her to be sent away—under such circumstances. It would be quite heartless. Yes, I am very much disturbed!"

"I'm sorry, ma'am," answered the housekeeper penitently. "But I was only thinking of the other girls."

"Well, it's too late to do anything about it now," repeated her mistress. "But I'm sorry, Dawkins; very sorry, indeed. We have responsibilities toward these people! However—this is Thursday, isn't it?—we'll have veal for lunch as usual—and she was so pretty!" she added inconsequently.

"H'm. That was the trouble!" sniffed the housekeeper. "We're well rid of her. You'd think a girl would have some consideration for her employer—if nothing else. In a sense she's a guest in the house and should behave herself as such!"

"Yes, that is quite true!" agreed her employer. "Still—yes, Brown Betty is very well for dessert. That will do, Dawkins."

Behind the curtain of this casual conversation had been enacted a melodrama as intensely vital and elemental as any of Shakespeare's tragedies, for the day Dawkins had fired Katie O'Connell—"for reasons," as she said—and told her to go back where she came from or anywhere she liked for that matter, so long as she got out of her sight, Katie's brother Shane in the back room of McManus' gin palace gave Red McGurk—for the same "reasons"—a certain option and, the latter having scornfully declined to avail himself of it, had then and there put a bullet through his neck. But this, naturally, Miss Beekman did not know.

As may have been already surmised Miss Althea was a gracious, gentle and tender-hearted lady who never knowingly would have done a wrong to anybody and who did not believe that simply because God had been pleased to call her into a state of life at least three stories higher than her kitchen she was thereby relieved from her duty toward those who occupied it. Nevertheless, from the altitude of those three stories she viewed them as essentially different from herself, for she came of what is known as "a long line of ancestors." As, however, Katie O'Connell and Althea Beekman were practically contemporaries, it is somewhat difficult to understand how one of them could have had a succession of ancestors that was any longer than that of the other. Indeed, Miss Beekman's friend, Prof. Abelard Samothrace, of Columbia University, probably would have admitted that just as the two lived in the same house—albeit at different levels—on Fifth Avenue, so their forebears at some prehistoric period had, likely as not, occupied the same cave and had in company waded on frosty mornings the ice-skimmed swamps of Mittel Europa in pursuit of the cave bear, the mastodon and the woolly rhinoceros, and for afternoon relaxation had made up twosomes for hunting wives with stone clubs instead of mashies in their hairy prehensile hands.

It would seem, therefore, that—whatever of tradition might have originated in the epoch in question—glimmerings of sportsmanship, of personal pride, of tribal duty or of conscience ought to have been the common heritage of them both. For it was assuredly true that while Miss Katie's historic ancestors had been Celtiberians, clad on occasion only in a thin coating of blue paint, Miss Althea's had dwelt in the dank marshes of the Elbe and had been unmistakably Teutonic, though this curse had been largely removed by racial intermarriage during subsequent thousands of years. Indeed, it may well have been that in the dimmer past some Beekman serf on bended knee had handed a gilded harp to some King O'Connell on his throne. If the O'Connells were foreigners the Beekmans, from the point of view of the aboriginal American, were no less so simply because they had preceded them by a couple of hundred years.

Tradition is not a matter of centuries but of ages. If Katie inherited some of hers from the peat bogs adjacent to Tara's Halls in that remote period when there were still snakes in Ireland, Miss Althea had vicariously acquired others from the fur-clad barbarians described by Tacitus who spent their leisure time in drinking, gambling or splitting each other's skulls with stone mallets. On this subject see Spencer's "Data of Ethics" and Lecky's "History of European Morals." But all this entirely escaped Miss Althea, who suffered from the erroneous impression that because she was a Beekman and lived in a stone mansion facing Central Park she differed fundamentally not only from the O'Connells but from the Smiths, the Pasquales, the Ivanovitches and the Ginsbergs, all of whom really come of very old families. Upon this supposed difference she prided herself.

Because she was, in fact, mistaken and because the O'Connells shared with the Beekmans and the Ginsbergs a tradition reaching back to a period when revenge was justice, and custom of kinsfolk the only law, Shane O'Connell had sought out Red McGurk and had sent him unshriven to his God. The only reason why this everyday Bowery occurrence excited any particular attention was not that Shane was an O'Connell but that McGurk was the son of a political boss of much influence and himself one of the leaders of a notorious cohort of young ruffians who when necessary could be relied upon to stuff a ballot box or otherwise to influence public opinion. As Red was a mighty man in Gideon, so his taking off was an event of moment, and he was waked with an elegance unsurpassed in the annals of Cherry Hill.

"An' if ye don't put the son of a— who kilt me b'y in th' chair, ye name's mud—see?" the elder McGurk had informed District Attorney Peckham the next morning. "I've told the cops who done it. Now you do the rest—understand?"

Peckham understood very well. No one seeing the expression on McGurk's purple countenance could have failed to do so.

"We'll get him! Don't you worry!" Peckham had assured the desolated father with a manner subtly suggesting both the profoundest sympathy and the prophetic glories of a juridical revenge in which the name of McGurk would be upon every lip and the picture of the deceased, his family, and the home in which they dwelt would be featured on the front page of every journal. "We'll get him, all right!"

"See to it that ye do!" commented his visitor meaningly.

Therefore, though no one had seen him commit the crime, word was passed along the line to pick up Shane O'Connell for the murder of Red McGurk. It mattered not there was no evidence except the report of a muttered threat or two and the lie passed openly the week before.

Everybody knew that Shane had done it, and why; though no one could tell how he knew it. And because everybody knew, it became a political necessity for Peckham to put him under arrest with a great fanfare of trumpets and a grandiose announcement of the celerity with which the current would be turned through his body.

The only fly in the ointment was the fact that O'Connell had walked into the district attorney's office as soon as the rumor reached him and quietly submitted to being arrested, saying merely: "I heard you wanted me. Well, here I am!"

But though they badgered him for hours, lured him by every pretext to confess, put a stool pigeon in the same cell with him, and resorted to every trick, device, and expedient known to the prosecutor's office to trap him into some sort of an admission, they got nothing for their pains. It was just one of those cases where the evidence simply wasn't forthcoming. And yet Peckham was aware that unless he convicted O'Connell his name would indeed be mud—or worse. This story, however, is concerned less with the family honor of the O'Connells than with that of the Beekmans.

Miss Althea was the last surviving member of her branch of the family. Though she would probably have regarded it as slightly vulgar to have been referred to as "one hundred per cent American" she was so nearly so—except for a reminiscent affection for "the late dear Queen"—that the phrase in her case would have been substantially correct. Her mother had been the daughter of a distinguished Revolutionary statesman who had been a signer of the Declaration of Independence, an ambassador and justice of the Supreme Court as well; her father a celebrated newspaper editor.

She had been born in the Prue and I period in Gramercy Park near what is now The Players' Club, and the old colonial house with its white trimmings and ornamental ironwork had been the scene of many a modest gayety at a time when Emerson, Lowell, and George William Curtis were viewed less as citizens than as high priests of Culture, sharing equally in sanctity with the goddess thereof. She could just remember those benign old gentlemen, as well as the many veterans of the Civil War who dined at her father's decorous mahogany and talked of the preservation of the Constitution and those other institutions to found which it is generally assumed the first settlers landed on the Atlantic seaboard and self-sacrificingly accepted real estate from the wily native in return for whisky and glass beads. She was forty-seven years of age, a Colonial Dame, a Daughter of the American Revolution, a member of the board of directors of several charitable institutions, and she was worth a couple of million dollars in railroad securities. On Sundays she always attended the church in Stuyvesant Square frequented by her family, and as late as 1907 did so in the famous Beekman C-spring victoria driven by an aged Negro coachman.

But besides being full of rectitude and good works—which of themselves so often fail of attraction—Miss Althea was possessed of a face so charming even in its slightly faded prettiness that one wondered how it was possible that she could successfully have withstood the suitors who must have crowded about her. Her house on Fifth Avenue was full of old engravings of American patriots, and the library inherited from her editorial parent was replete with volumes upon subjects which would have filled a Bolshevik with disgust. Briefly, if ever Trotzky had become Commissar of the Soviet of Manhattan, Miss Althea and those like her would have been the first candidates for a drumhead court-martial.

She prided herself equally upon her adherence to religious principle and the Acts of Congress. For the law, merely as law, she had the profoundest veneration, viewing the heterogeneous statutes passed from time to time by desultory legislators much as if they had in some mysterious way been handed down from Mount Sinai along with the Ten Commandments.

For any violator of the law she had the uttermost abhorrence, and the only weakness in her ethics rose out of her failure to discriminate between relative importances, for she undoubtedly regarded the sale of a glass of beer after the closing hour as being quite as reprehensible as grand larceny or the bearing of false witness. To her every judge must be a learned, wise and honorable man because he stood for the enforcement of the law of the land, and she never questioned whether or not that law was wise or otherwise, which latter often—it must be confessed—it was not.

In a word, though there was nothing progressive about Miss Althea she was one of those delightful, cultivated, loyal and enthusiastic female citizens who are rightfully regarded as vertebrae in the backbone of a country which, after it has got its back up, can undoubtedly lick any other nation on earth. It was characteristic of her that carefully folded inside the will drawn for her by her family solicitor was a slip of paper addressed to her heirs and next of kin requesting that at her funeral the national anthem should be played and that her coffin should be draped with the American flag.

But there was a somewhat curious if not uncommon inconsistency in Miss Beekman's attitude toward lawbreakers in that once they were in prison they instantly became objects of her gentlest solicitude. Thus she was a frequent visitor at the Tombs, where she brought spiritual, and more often, it must be frankly admitted, bodily comfort to those of the inmates who were recommended by the district attorney and prison authorities as worthy of her attention; and Prosecutor Peckham being not unmindful of the possible political advantage that might accrue from being on friendly terms with so well-known a member of the distinguished family of Beekman, lost no opportunity to ingratiate himself with her and gave orders to his subordinates to make her path as easy as possible. Thus quite naturally she had heard of Tutt & Tutt, and had a casual acquaintance with the senior partner himself.

"That O'Connell is a regular clam—won't tell me anything at all!" remarked Mr. Tutt severely, hanging up his hat on the office tree with one hand while he felt for a match in his waistcoat pocket with the other, upon the afternoon of the day that Miss Beekman had had the conversation with Dawkins with which this story opens.

"National temperament," answered Bonnie Doon, producing the desired match. "It's just like an Irishman to refuse point-blank to talk to the lawyer who has been assigned to defend him. He's probably afraid he'll make some admission from which you will infer he's guilty. No Irishman ever yet admitted that he was guilty of anything!"

"Well, I've never met a defendant of any other nationality who would, either," replied Mr. Tutt, pulling vigorously at his stogy. "Even so, this chap O'Connell is a puzzle to me. 'Go ahead and defend me,' said he to-day, 'but don't ask me to talk about the case, because I won't.' I give it up. He wouldn't even tell me where he was on the day of the murder."

Bonnie grunted dubiously.

"There may be a very good reason for that!" he retorted. "If what rumor says is true he simply hunted for McGurk until he found him and put a lead pellet back of his ear."

"And also, if what rumor says is true," supplemented Tutt, who entered at this moment, "a good job it was, too. McGurk was a treacherous, dirty blackguard, the leader of a gang of criminals, even if he was, as they all agree, a handsome rascal who had every woman in the district on tenterhooks. Any girl in this case?"

Bonnie shrugged his shoulders.

"They claim so; only there's nothing definite. The O'Connells are well spoken of."

"If there was, that would explain why he wouldn't talk," commented Mr. Tutt. "That's the devil of it. You can't put in a defense under the unwritten law without besmirching the very reputation you are trying to protect."

The senior partner of Tutt & Tutt wheeled his swivel chair to the window and crossing his congress boots upon the sill gazed contemplatively down upon the shipping.

"Unwritten law!" sarcastically exclaimed Tutt from the doorway. "There ain't no such animal in these parts!"

"You're quite wrong!" retorted his elder partner. "Most of our law—ninety-nine per cent of it, in fact—is unwritten."

"Excuse me!" interjected Bonnie Doon, abandoning his usual flippancy. "What is that you said, Mr. Tutt?"

"That ninety-nine per cent of the laws by which we are governed are unwritten laws, just as binding as the printed ones upon our statute books, which after all are only the crystallization of the sentiments and opinions of the community based upon its traditions, manners, customs and religious beliefs. For every statute in print there are a hundred that have no tangible existence, based on our sense of decency, of duty and of honor, which are equally controlling and which it has never been found necessary to reduce to writing, since their infraction usually brings its own penalty or infringes the more delicate domain of private conscience where the crude processes of the criminal law cannot follow. The laws of etiquette and fair play are just as obligatory as legislative enactments—the Ten Commandments as efficacious as the Penal Code."

"Don't you agree with that, Tutt?" demanded Bonnie. "Every man's conscience is his own private unwritten law."

Tutt looked skeptical.

"Did you say every man had a conscience?" he inquired.

"And it makes a lot of trouble sometimes," continued Mr. Tutt, ignoring him. "You remember when old Cogswell was on the bench and a man was brought before him for breaking his umbrella over the head of a fellow who had insulted the defendant's wife, he said to the jury: 'Gentlemen, if this plaintiff had called my wife a name like that I'd have smashed my umbrella over his head pretty quick. However, that's not the law! Take the case, gentlemen!'"

"Well, I guess I was wrong," admitted Tutt. "Of course, that is unwritten law. People don't like to punish a man for resenting a slur upon his wife's reputation."

"But you see where that leads you?" remarked his partner. "The so-called unwritten law is based on our inherited idea of chivalry. A lady's honor and reputation were sacred, and her knight was prepared instantly to defend it with the last drop of his blood. A reflection on her honesty was almost as unbearable as one upon her virtue. Logically, the unwritten law ought to permit women to break their contracts and do practically anything they see fit."

"They do, don't they—the dear things!" sighed Bonnie.

"I remember," interjected Tutt brightly, "when it was the unwritten law of Cook County, Illinois—that's Chicago, you know—that any woman could kill her husband for the life-insurance money. Seriously!"

"There's no point of chivalry that I can see involved in that—it's merely good business," remarked Mr. Doon, lighting another cigarette. "All the same it's obvious that the unwritten law might be stretched a long way. It's a great convenience, though, on occasion!"

"We should be in an awful stew if nowadays we substituted ideas of chivalry for those of justice," declared Mr. Tutt. "Fortunately the danger is past. As someone has said, 'The women, once our superiors, have become our equals!' "

"We don't even give 'em our seats in the subway," commented Tutt complacently. "No, we needn't worry about the return of chivalry—in New York at any rate."

"I should say not!" exclaimed Miss Wiggin, entering at that moment with a pile of papers, as nobody rose.

"But," insisted Bonnie, "all the same there are certainly plenty of cases where if he had to choose between them any man would obey his conscience rather than the law."

"Of course, there are such cases," admitted Mr. Tutt. "But we ought to discourage the idea as much as possible."

"Discourage a sense of honor?" exclaimed Miss Wiggin. "Why, Mr. Tutt!"

"It depends on what you mean by honor," he retorted. "I don't take much stock in the kind of honor that makes an heir apparent 'perjure himself like a gentleman' about a card game at a country house."

"Neither do I," she returned, "any more than I do in the kind of honor that compels a man to pay a gambling debt before he pays his tailor, but I do believe that there may be situations where, though it would not be permissible to perjure oneself, honor would require one to refuse to obey the law."

"That's a pretty dangerous doctrine," reflected Mr. Tutt. "For everybody would be free to make himself the judge of when he ought to respect the law and when he oughtn't. We can easily imagine that the law would come out at the small end of the horn."

"In matters of conscience—which, I take it, is the same thing as one's sense of honor—one has got to be one's own judge," declared Miss Wiggin firmly.

"The simplest way," announced Tutt, "is to take the position that the law should always be obeyed and that the most honorable man is he who respects it the most."

"Yes, the safest and also the most cowardly!" retorted Miss Wiggin. "Supposing the law required you to do something which you personally regarded not only as morally wrong but detestable, would you do it?"

"It wouldn't!" protested Tutt with a grimace. "The law is the perfection of reason."

"But I am entitled, am I not, to suppose, for purposes of argument, that it might?" she inquired caustically. "And I say that our sense of honor is the most precious thing we've got. It's our duty to respect our institutions and obey the law whether we like it or not, unless it conflicts with our conscience, in which case we ought to defy it and take the consequences!"

"Dear me!" mocked Tutt. "And be burned at the stake?"

"If necessary; yes!"

"I don't rightly get all this!" remarked Bonnie. "Me for the lee side of the law, every time!"

"It's highly theoretical," commented Tutt. "As usual with our discussions."

"Not so theoretical as you might think!" interrupted his senior, hastening to reenforce Miss Wiggin. "Nobody can deny that to be true to oneself is the highest principle of human conducts, and that ' 'tis man's perdition to be safe when for the truth he ought to die.' That's why we reverence the early Christian martyrs. But when it comes to choosing between what we loosely call honor and what the law requires—"

"But I thought the law embodied our ideas of honor!" replied Tutt. "Didn't you say so—a few hours earlier in this conversation? As our highest duty is to the state, it is a mere play on words, in my humble opinion, to speak of honor as distinguished from law or the obligation of one's oath in a court of justice. I bet I can find plenty of authorities to that effect in the library!"

"Of course you can," countered Miss Wiggin. "You can find an authority on any side of any proposition you want to look for. That's why one's own sense of honor is so much more reliable than the law. What is the law, anyhow? It's what some judge says is the law—until he's reversed. Do you suppose I'd surrender my own private ideas of honor to a casual ruling from a judge who very likely hadn't the remotest idea of what I think is honorable?"

"You'll be jailed for contempt before you get through!" Tutt warned her.

"The fact of the matter is," concluded Mr. Tutt, "that honor and law haven't anything to do with one another. The courts have constantly pointed that out from the earliest days, though judges like, when they can, to make the two seem one and the same. Chief Baron Bowes, I remember, said in some case in 1743, 'The court can't determine what is honor.' No, no; the two are different, and that difference will always make trouble. Isn't it nearly tea time?"

Miss Beekman was just stepping off the elevator on the first floor of the Tombs the next afternoon on one of her weekly visits when she came face to face with Mr. Tutt.

She greeted him cordially, for she had taken rather a fancy to the shabby old man, drawn to him, in spite of her natural aversion to all members of the criminal bar, by the gentle refinement of his weather-beaten face. "I hope you have had a successful day."

The lawyer shook his head in a pseudo-melancholy manner.

"Unfortunately, I have not," he answered whimsically. "My only client refuses to speak to me! Perhaps you could get something out of him for me."

"Oh, they all talk to me readily enough!" she replied. "I fancy they know I'm harmless. What is his name?"

"Shane O'Connell."

"What is his offense?"

"He is charged with murder."

"Oh!"

Miss Althea recoiled. Her charitable impulses did not extend to defendants charged with homicide. There was too much notoriety connected with them, for one thing; there was nothing she hated so much as notoriety.

"Seriously," he went on with earnestness, "I wish you'd have a word with him. It's pretty hard to have to defend a man and not to know a thing about his side of the case. It's almost your duty, don't you think?"

Miss Althea hesitated, and was lost.

"Very well," she answered reluctantly, "I'll see what I can do. Perhaps he needs some medicine or letter paper or something. I'll get an order from the warden and go right back and see him."

Twenty minutes later Shane O'Connell faced Miss Beekman sullenly across the deal table of the counsel room. A ray of late sunshine fell through the high grating of the heavily barred window upon a face quite different from those which Miss Althea was accustomed to encounter in these surroundings, for it showed no touch of depravity or evil habits, and confinement had not yet deprived its cheeks of their rugged mantle of crimson or its eyes of their bold gleam.

He was little more than a boy, this murderer, as handsome a lad as ever swaggered out of County Kerry.

"An' what may it be that leads you to send for such as me, Miss Beekman!" he demanded, glowering at her.

She felt suddenly unnerved, startled and rather shocked at his use of her name. Where could he have discovered it? From the keeper, probably, she decided. All her usual composure, her quiet self-possession, her aloof and slightly condescending sweetness—had deserted her.

"I thought," she stammered—"I might—possibly—be of help to you."

" 'Tis too late to make up for the harm ye've done!" His coal-black eyes reached into her shrinking body as if to tear out her heart.

"I!" she gasped. "I—do harm! What do you mean?"

"Did not my sister Katie work for yez?" he asked, and his words leaped and curled about her like hissing flames. "Did you see after her or watch her comings and goings, as she saw after you—she a mere lass of sixteen? Arrah! No!"

With a sensation of horror Miss Althea realized that at last she was in a murder case in spite of herself! This lad, the brother of Katie, the waitress whom she had discharged! How curious! And how unfortunate! His charge was preposterous; nevertheless a faint blush stole to her cheek and she looked away.

"How ridiculous!" she managed to say. "It was no part of my obligation to look after her! How could I?"

His hawk's eyes watched her every tremor.

"Did ye not lock her out the night of the ball when she went wid Mc-Gurk?"

"I—how absurd!"

Suddenly she faltered. An indistinct accusing recollection turned her faint—of the housekeeper having told her that one of the girls insisted on going to a dance on an evening not hers by arrangement, and how she had given orders that the house should be closed the same as usual at ten o'clock for the night. If the girl couldn't abide by the rules of the Beekman ménage she could sleep somewhere else. What of it? Supposing she had done so? She could not be held responsible for remote, unreasonable and discreditable consequences!

And then by chance Shane O'Connell made use of a phrase that indirectly saved his life, a phrase curiously like the one used on a former occasion by Dawkins to Miss Althea:

"Katie was a member of your household; ye might have had a bit of thought for her!" he asserted bitterly.

Dawkins had said: "You'd think a girl would have some consideration for her employer, if nothing else. In a sense she is a guest in the house and should behave herself as such."

There was no sense in it! There was no parallel, no analogy. There was no obligation to treat the girl as a guest, even though the girl should have acted like one. Miss Beekman knew it. And yet there was—something! Didn't she owe some sort of duty at any rate toward those in her employment—those who slept under her roof?

" 'Twould have been better to have been kind to her then than to be kind to me now!" said he with sad conviction.

The proud Miss Althea Beekman, the dignified descendant of a long line of ancestors, turned red. Heretofore serenely confident of her own personal virtue and her own artificial standards of democracy, she now found herself humiliated and chagrined before this rough young criminal.

"You—are—quite right!" she confessed, her eyes smarting with sudden tears. "My position is quite—quite illogical. But of course I had no idea! Please, please let me try to help you—if I can—and Katie, too—if it isn't too late."

Shane O'Connell experienced contrition. After all it was not seemly that the likes of him should be dictating to the likes of her. And he could never abide seeing a woman—particularly a pretty woman—cry.

"Forgive me, madam!" he begged, lowering his head.

"You were quite justified in all you said!" she assured him. "Please tell me everything that has happened. I have influence with the district attorney and—in other places. No doubt I can be of assistance to you. Of course, you can absolutely trust me!"

Shane O'Connell, looking into her honest gray eyes, knew that he could trust her. Slowly—brokenly—tensely, he told her how he had killed Red McGurk, and why.

The corridors were full of shadows when Althea Beekman put her hands on Shane O'Connell's shoulders and bade him good night. Though she abominated his crime and loathed him for having committed it she felt in some way partially responsible, and she also perceived that, by the code of the O'Connell's, Shane had done what he believed to be right. He had taken the law into his own hands and he was ready to pay the necessary penalty. He would have done the same thing all over again. To this extent at least he had her respect.

She found Mr. Tutt waiting for her on the bench by the warden's office.

"Well?" he asked with a smile, rising to greet her and tossing away his stogy.

"I haven't very good news for you," she answered regretfully. "He's confessed to me—told me everything—why he shot him and where he bought the pistol. He's a brave boy, though! It's a sad case! But what can you do with people who believe themselves justified in doing things like that?"

She did not notice Detective Eddie Conroy, of the D. A.'s office, standing behind an adjacent pillar, ostentatiously lighting a cigar; nor see him smile as he slowly walked away.

"Talk about luck!" exulted O'Brien, the yellow dog of the district attorney's office, an hour later to his chief. "What do you think, boss? Eddie Conroy heard Miss Beekman telling old man Tutt over in the Tombs that O'Connell had confessed to her! Say, how's that? Some evidence—what?"

"What good will that do us?" asked Peckham, glancing up with a scowl from his desk. "She won't testify for us."

"But she'll have to testify if we call her, won't she?" demanded his assistant.

The district attorney drummed on the polished surface before him.

"We—ell, I suppose so," he admitted hesitatingly. "But you can't just subpoena a woman like that without any warning and put her on the stand and make her testify. It would be too rough!"

"It's the only way to do it!" retorted O'Brien with a sly grin. "If she knew in advance that we were thinking of calling her she'd beat it out of town."

"That's true," agreed his chief. "That's as far as she'd go, too, in defying the law. But I don't much like it. Those Beekmans have a lot of influence, and if she got sore she could make us a heap of trouble! Besides it's sort of a scaly trick making her give up on him like that."

O'Brien raised his brows.

"Scaly trick! He's a murderer, isn't he! And he'll get off if we don't call her. It's a matter of duty, as I see it."

"All the same, my son, your suggestion has a rotten smell to it. We may have to do it—I don't say we won't—but it's risky business!" replied Peckham dubiously.

"It's a good deal less risky than not doing it, so far as your candidacy next autumn is concerned!" retorted his assistant. "We won't let her suspect what we're goin' to do; and the last minute I'll call her to the stand and cinch the case! She won't even know who called her! Perhaps I can arrange with Judge Babson to call her on some other point and then pretend to sort of stumble onto the fact of the confession and examine her himself. That would let us out. I can smear it over somehow."

"You'd better," commented Peckham, "unless you want a howl from the papers! It would make quite a story if Miss Althea Beekman got on the rampage. She could have your scalp, my boy, if she wanted it!"

"And McGurk could have yours!" retorted O'Brien with the impudence born of knowledge.

The prosecution of Shane O'Connell, which otherwise might have slowly languished and languishing died, took on new life owing to the evidence thus innocently delivered into the hands of the district attorney; in fact it became a *cause célèbre.* The essential elements to convict were now all there—the *corpus delicti,* evidence of threats on the part of the defendant, of motive, of opportunity, and—his confession. The law which provides that the statement of an accused "is not sufficient to warrant his conviction without additional proof that the crime charged had been committed" would be abundantly satisfied—though without his confession there would have been no proof whatever that the crime charged had been committed by him.

Thus, without her knowing it, Miss Beekman was an essential witness and, in fact, the pivot upon which the entire case turned.

The day of the great sporting event came. With it arrived in full panoply the McGurks, their relatives and followers. All Cherry Hill seemed to have packed itself into Part I of the Supreme Court. There was an atmosphere somehow suggestive of the races or a prize fight. But it was a sporting event which savoured of a sure thing—really more like a hanging. They were there to make holiday over the law's revenge for the killing of the darling of the Pearl Button Kids. Peckham personally assured McGurk that everything was copper-fastened.

"He's halfway up the river already!" he said jocularly.

And McGurk, swelling with importance and emotion, pulled a couple of cigars from his pocket and the two smoked the pipe of peace.

But the reader is not particularly concerned with the progress of the trial, for he has already attended many. It is enough to say that a jury

with undershot jaws, who had proved by previous experience their indifference to capital punishment and to all human sympathy, were finally
selected and that the witnesses were duly called, and testified to the usual
facts, while the Pearl Button Kids and the rest, spitting surreptitiously
beneath the benches, eagerly drank in every word. There was nothing for
Mr. Tutt to do; nothing for him to deny. The case built itself up, brick by
brick. And Shane O'Connell sat there unemotionally, hardly listening.
There was nothing in the evidence to reflect in any way upon the honor
of the O'Connells in general or in particular. He had done that which
that honor demanded and he was ready to pay the penalty—if the law
could get him. He assumed that it would get him. So did the Tutts.

But when toward the end of the third day nothing had yet been brought
forward to connect him with the crime Tutt leaned over and whispered
to Mr. Tutt, "D'ye know, I'm beginning to have a hunch there isn't any
case!"

Mr. Tutt made an imperceptible gesture of assent.

"Looks that way," he answered out of the corner of his mouth. "Probably they'll spring the connecting evidence at the end and give us the
coup de grâce."

At that moment a police witness was released from the stand and
O'Brien stepped to the bench and whispered something to the judge, who
glanced at the clock and nodded. It was twenty minutes of four, and the
jury were already getting restless, for the trial had developed into a humdrum, cut-and-dried affair.

Miss Beekman sitting far back in the rear of the court room suddenly
heard O'Brien call her name, and a quiver of apprehension passed through
her body. She had never testified in any legal proceeding, and the idea of
getting up before such a crowd of people and answering questions filled
her with dismay. It was so public! Still, if it was going to help O'Connell—

"Althea Beekman," bellowed Cap. Phelan, "to the witness chair!"

Althea Beekman! The gentle lady felt as if she had been rudely stripped
of all her protective clothing. Althea! Did not the law do her the courtesy
of calling her even "Miss"? Nerving herself to the performance of her
duty she falteringly made her way between the crowded benches, past
the reporters' table, and round back of the jury box. The judge, apparently
a pleasant-faced, rather elderly man, bowed gravely to her, indicated
where she should sit and administered the oath to her himself, subtly
dwelling upon the phrase "the whole truth," and raising his eyes heaven-
ward as he solemnly pronounced the words "so help you God!"

"I do!" declared Miss Beekman primly but decidedly.

Behind her upon the court-room wall towered in its flowing draperies
the majestic figure of the Goddess of the Law, blindfolded and holding
aloft the scales of justice. Beside her sat in the silken robes of his sacred
office a judge who cleverly administered that law to advance his own
interests and those of his political associates. In front of her, treacherously

smiling, stood the cynical, bullet-headed O'Brien. At a great distance Mr. Tutt leaned on his elbows at a table beside Shane O'Connell. To them she directed her gaze and faintly smiled.

"Miss Beekman," began O'Brien as courteously as he knew how, "you reside, do you not, at Number 1000 Fifth Avenue, in this city and county?"

"I do," she answered with resolution.

"Your family have always lived in New York, have they not?"

"Since 1630," she replied deprecatingly and with more confidence.

"You are prominent in various philanthropic, religious and civic activities?"

"Not prominent; interested," she corrected him.

"And you make a practise of visiting prisoners in the Tombs?"

She hesitated. What could this be leading to?

"Occasionally," she admitted.

"Do you know this defendant, Shane O'Connell?"

"Yes."

"Did you see him on the twenty-third day of last month?"

"I think so—if that was the day."

"What day do you refer to?"

"The day I had the talk with him."

"Oh, you had a talk with him?"

"Yes."

"Where did you have that talk with him?"

"In the counsel room of the Tombs."

O'Brien paused. Even his miserable soul revolted at what he was about to do.

"What did he say?" he asked, nervously looking away.

Something in his hangdog look warned Miss Beekman that she was being betrayed, but before she could answer Mr. Tutt was on his feet.

"One moment!" he cried. "May I ask a preliminary question?"

The court signified acquiescence.

"Was that conversation which you had with the defendant a confidential one?"

"I object to the question!" snapped O'Brien. "The law recognizes no confidential communications as privileged except those made to a priest, a physician or an attorney. The witness is none of these. The question is immaterial and irrelevant."

"That is the law," announced the judge, "but under all the circumstances I will permit the witness to answer."

Miss Beekman paused.

"Why," she began, "of course it was confidential, Mr. Tutt. O'Connell wouldn't have told me anything if he had supposed for one moment I was going to repeat what he said. Besides, I suggested that I might be able to help him. Yes, certainly our talk was confidential."

"I am sorry," gloated O'Brien, "but I shall have to ask you what it was."

"That is not a question," said Mr. Tutt calmly.

"What did the defendant say to you in the counsel room of the Tombs on the twenty-third of last month?" cautiously revised O'Brien.

"I object!" thundered Mr. Tutt, his form towering until seemingly it matched that of the blind goddess in height. "I object to the answer as requiring a breach of confidence which the law could not tolerate."

Judge Babson turned politely to Miss Beekman.

"I regret very much that I shall be obliged to ask you to state what the defendant said to you. You will recall that you yourself volunteered the information that you had had the talk in question. Otherwise"—he coughed and put up his hand—"we might possibly never have learned of it. A defendant cannot deprive the people of the right to prove what he may have divulged respecting his offense merely by claiming that it was in confidence. Public policy could never allow that. It may be unpleasant for you to answer the question but I must ask you to do so."

"But," she protested, "you certainly cannot expect me to betray a confidence! I asked O'Connell to tell me what he had done so that I could help him—and he trusted me!"

"But you are not responsible for the law! He took his chance!" admonished the judge.

Slowly Miss Althea's indignation rose as she perceived the dastardly trick which O'Brien had played upon her. Already she suspected that the judge was only masquerading in the clothing of a gentleman. With a white face she turned to Mr. Tutt.

"Does the law require me to answer, Mr. Tutt?" she inquired.

"Do not ask questions—answer them," ordered Babson brusquely, feeling the change in her manner. "You are a witness for the people—not the defendant."

"I am not a witness against O'Connell!" she declared. "This man"—indicating O'Brien scornfully—"has in some way found out that I— Oh, surely the law doesn't demand anything so base as that!"

There was silence. The wheels of justice hung on a dead center.

"Answer the question," remarked His Honor tartly.

All Miss Beekman's long line of ancestors turned in their graves. In her Beekman blood the chief justice, the ambassador, the great editor, the signer of the Declaration of Independence, stirred, awoke, rubbed their eyes and sternly reared themselves. And that blood—blue though it was instead of scarlet like the O'Connells'—boiled in her veins and burned through the delicate tissue of her cheeks.

"My conscience will not permit me to betray a confidence!" she cried angrily.

"I direct you to answer!" ordered the judge.

"I object to the court's threatening the witness!" interjected Mr. Tutt. "I wish it to appear upon the record that the manner of the court is most unjudicial and damaging to the defendant."

"Take your seat, sir!" barked Babson, his features swelling with anger. "Your language is contemptuous!"

The jury was leaning forward intently. Trained militiamen of the gibbet, they nevertheless admired this little woman's fearlessness and the old lawyer's pugnacity. On the rear wall the yellow face of the old self-regulating clock, that had gayly ticked so many men into the electric chair, leered shamelessly across at the blind goddess.

"Answer the question, madam! If, as you claim, you are a patriotic citizen of this commonwealth, having due respect for its institutions and for the statutes, you will not set up your own ideas of what the law ought to be in defiance of the law as it stands. I order you to answer! If you do not I shall be obliged to take steps to compel you to do so."

In the dead silence that followed, the stones in the edifice of Miss Beekman's inherited complacency, with each beat of the clock, fell one by one to the ground until it was entirely demolished. Vainly she struggled to test her conscience by her loyalty to her country's laws. But the task was beyond her.

Tightly compressing her lips she sat silent in the chair, while the delighted reporters scribbled furious messages to their city editors that Miss Althea Beekman, one of the Four Hundred, was defying Judge Babson, and to rush up a camera man right off in a taxi, and to look her up in the morgue for a front-page story. O'Brien glanced uneasily at Babson. Possible defiance on the part of this usually unassuming lady had not entered into his calculations. The judge took a new tack.

"You probably do not fully understand the situation in which you are placed," he explained. "You are not responsible for the law. Neither are you responsible in any way for the consequences to this defendant, whatever they may be. The matter is entirely out of your hands. You are compelled to do as the court orders. As a law-abiding citizen you have no choice in the matter."

Miss Althea's modest intellect reeled, but she stood her ground, the ghost of the Signer at her elbow.

"I am sorry," she replied, "but my own self-respect will not allow me to answer."

"In that case," declared Babson, playing his trump card, "it will be my unpleasant duty to commit you for contempt."

There was a bustle of excitement about the reporters' table. Here was a story!

"Very well," answered Miss Beekman proudly. "Do as you see fit, and as your own duty and conscience demand."

The judge could not conceal his annoyance. The last thing in the world that he wished to do was to send Miss Althea to jail. But having threatened her he must carry out his threat or forever lose face.

"I will give the witness until to-morrow morning at half after ten o'clock to make up her mind what she will do," he announced after a hurried conference with O'Brien. "Adjourn court!"

Miss Beekman did not go to bed at all that night. Until a late hour she conferred in the secrecy of her Fifth Avenue library with her gray-haired solicitor, who, in some mysterious way, merely over the telephone, managed to induce the newspapers to omit any reference to his client's contemptuous conduct in their morning editions.

"There's no way out of it, my dear," he said finally as he took his leave —he was her father's cousin and very fond of her—"this judge has the power to send you to jail if he wants to—and dares to! It's an even chance whether he will dare to or not. It depends on whether he prefers to stand well with the McGurks or with the general public. Of course I respect your attitude, but really I think you are a little quixotic. Points of honor are too emphemeral to be debated in courts of justice. To do so would be to open the door to all kinds of abuses. Dishonest witnesses would constantly avail themselves of the opportunity to avoid giving evidence."

"Dishonest witnesses would probably lie in the first place!" she quavered.

"True! I quite overlooked that!" he smiled, gazing down at her in an avuncular manner. "But to-day the question isn't open. It is settled, whether we like it or not. No pledge of privacy, no oath of secrecy—can avail against demand in a court of justice. Even confessions obtained by fraud are admissible—though we might wish otherwise."

Miss Beekman shrugged her shoulders.

"Nothing you have said seems to me to alter the situation."

"Very well," he replied. "I guess that settles it. Knowing you and the Beekman breed! There's one thing I must say," he added as he stood in the doorway after bidding her good night—"that old fellow Tutt has behaved pretty well, leaving you entirely alone this way. I always had an idea he was a sort of shyster. Most attorneys of that class would have been sitting on your doorstep all the evening trying to persuade you to stick to your resolution not to give their client away, and to do the square thing. But he's done nothing of the sort. Rather decent on the whole!"

"Perhaps he recognizes a woman of honor when he sees one!" she retorted.

"Honor!" he muttered as he closed the door. "What crimes are sometimes committed in thy name!"

But on the steps he stopped and looked back affectionately at the library window.

"After all, Althea's a good sport!" he remarked to himself.

At or about the same moment a quite dissimilar conference was being held between Judge Babson and Assistant District Attorney O'Brien in the café of the Passamaquoddy Club.

"She'll cave!" declared O'Brien, draining his glass. "Holy Mike! No woman like her is going to stay in jail! Besides, if you don't commit her everybody will say that you were scared to—yielded to influence. You're in the right and it will be a big card for you to show that you aren't afraid of anybody!"

Babson pulled nervously on his cigar.

"Maybe that's so," he said, "but I don't much fancy an appellate court sustaining me on the law and at the same time roasting hell out of me as a man!"

"Oh, they won't do that!" protested O'Brien. "How could they? All they're interested in is the law!"

"I've known those fellows to do queer things sometimes," answered the learned judge. "And the Beekmans are pretty powerful people."

"Well, so are the McGurks!" warned O'Brien.

"Now, Miss Beekman," said Judge Babson most genially the next morning, after that lady had taken her seat in the witness chair and the jury had answered to their names, "I hope you feel differently to-day about giving your testimony. Don't you think that after all it would be more fitting if you answered the question?"

Miss Althea firmly compressed her lips.

"At least let me read you some of the law on the subject," continued His Honor patiently. "Originally many people, like yourself, had the mistaken idea that what they called their honor should be allowed to intervene between them and their duty. And even the courts sometimes so held. But that was long ago—in the sixteenth and seventeenth centuries. To-day the law wisely recognizes no such thing. Let me read you what Baron Hotham said, in Hill's Trial in 1777, respecting the testimony of a witness who very properly told the court what the accused had said to him. It is very clearly put:

" 'The defendant certainly thought him his friend, and he'—the defendant—'therefore did disclose all this to him. Gentlemen, one has only to say further that if this point of honor was to be so sacred as that a man who comes by knowledge of this sort from an offender was not to be at liberty to disclose it the most atrocious criminals would every day escape punishment; and therefore it is that the wisdom of the law knows nothing of that point of honor.' "

Miss Beekman listened politely.

"I am sorry," she replied with dignity. "I shall not change my mind. I refuse to answer the question, and—and you can do whatever you like with me."

"Do you understand that you are in contempt of this court? Do you intend to show contempt for this court?" he demanded wrathfully.

"I do," answered Miss Althea. "I have contempt for this court."

A titter danced along the benches and some fool in the back of the room clapped his hands.

Judge Babson's face grew hard and his eyes narrowed to steel points.

"The witness stands committed for contempt," he announced bitingly. "I direct that she be confined in the city prison for thirty days and pay a fine of two hundred and fifty dollars. Madam, you will go with the officer."

Miss Althea rose while the ghost of the Signer encircled her with his arm.

Mr. Tutt was already upon his feet. He knew that the ghost of the Signer was there.

"May I ask the court if the witness, having been committed for the contemptuous conduct of which she is obviously guilty, may remain in your chambers until adjournment, in order that she may arrange her private affairs?"

"I will grant her that privilege," agreed Judge Babson with internal relief. "The request is quite reasonable. Captain Phelan, you may take the witness into my robing room and keep her there for the present."

With her small head erect, her narrow shoulders thrown back, and with a resolute step as befitted the descendant of a long line of ancestors Miss Althea passed behind the jury box and disappeared.

The twelve looked at one another dubiously. Both Babson and O'Brien seemed nervous and undecided.

"Well, call your next witness," remarked the judge finally.

"But I haven't any more witnesses!" growled O'Brien. "And you know it almighty well, you idiot!" he muttered under his breath.

"If that is the people's case I move for the defendant's immediate discharge," cried Mr. Tutt, jumping to his feet. "There is no evidence connecting him with the crime."

McGurk, furious, sprang toward the bar.

"See here! Wait a minute! Hold on, judge! I can get a hundred witnesses—"

"Sit down!" shouted one of the officers, thrusting him back. "Keep quiet!"

Babson looked at O'Brien and elevated his forehead. Then as O'Brien gave a shrug the judge turned to the expectant jury and said in apologetic tones:

"Gentlemen of the jury, where the people have failed to prove the defendant's guilt beyond a reasonable doubt it is the duty of the court to direct a verdict. In this case, though by inference the testimony points strongly toward the prisoner, there is no direct proof against him and I am accordingly constrained—much as I regret it—to instruct you to return a verdict of not guilty."

In the confusion which followed the rendition of the verdict a messenger entered breathlessly and forcing his way through the crowd delivered a folded paper to Mr. Tutt, who immediately rose and handed it to the clerk; and that official, having hurriedly perused it and pursed his lips in surprise, passed it over the top of the bench to the judge.

"What's this?" demanded Babson. "Don't bother me now with trifles!"

"But it's a writ of habeas corpus, Your Honor, signed by Judge Winthrop, requiring the warden to produce Miss Beekman in Part I of the Supreme Court, and returnable forthwith," whispered Mr. McGuire in an awe-stricken voice. "I can't disregard that, you know!"

"What!" cried Babson. "How on earth could he have issued a writ in this space of time? The thing's impossible!"

"If Your Honor please," urbanely explained Mr. Tutt, "as—having known Miss Beekman's father—I anticipated that the witness would pursue the course of conduct which, in fact, she has, I prepared the necessary papers early this morning and as soon as you ordered her into custody my partner, who was waiting in Judge Winthrop's chambers, presented them to His Honor, secured his signature and brought the writ here in a taxicab."

Nobody seemed to be any longer interested in O'Connell. The reporters had left their places and pushed their way into the inclosure before the dais. In the rear of the room O'Brien was vainly engaged in trying to placate the Pearl Button Kids, who were loudly swearing vengeance upon both him and Peckham. It was a scene as nearly turbulent as the old yellow clock had ever witnessed. Even the court officers abandoned any effort to maintain order and joined the excited group about Mr. Tutt before the bench.

"Does Your Honor desire that this matter be argued before the Supreme Court?" inquired Mr. Tutt suavely. "If so I will ask that the prisoner be paroled in my custody. Judge Winthrop is waiting."

Babson had turned pale. Facing a dozen newspapermen, pencils in hand, he quailed. To hell with "face." Why, if he went on any longer with the farce the papers would roast the life out of him. With an apology for a smile that was, in fact, a ghastly grin, he addressed himself to the waiting group of jurymen, lawyers and reporters.

"Of course, gentlemen," he said, "I never had any real intention of dealing harshly with Miss Beekman. Undoubtedly she acted quite honestly and according to her best lights. She is a very estimable member of society. It will be unnecessary, Mr. Tutt, for you to argue the writ before Judge Winthrop. The relator, Althea Beekman, is discharged."

"Thank you, Your Honor!" returned Mr. Tutt, bowing profoundly, and lowering an eyelid in the direction of the gentlemen of the press. "You are indeed a wise and upright judge!"

The wise and upright judge rose grandly and gathered his robes about the judicial legs.

"Good morning, gentlemen," he remarked from his altitude to the reporters.

"Good morning, judge," they replied in chorus. "May we say anything about the writ?"

Judge Babson paused momentarily in his flight.

"Oh! Perhaps you might as well let the whole thing go," he answered carelessly. "On the whole I think it better that you should."

As they fought their way out of the doorway Charley Still, of the *Sun,* grinned at "Deacon" Terry, of the *Tribune,* and jocosely inquired: "Say Deac., did you ever think why one calls a judge 'Your Honor'?"

The Deacon momentarily removed his elbow from the abdomen of the gentleman beside him and replied sincerely though breathlessly, "No! You can search me!"

And "Cap." Phelan, who happened to be setting his watch at just that instant, affirms that he will make affidavit that the old yellow clock winked across the room at the Goddess of Justice, and that beneath her bandages she unmistakably smiled.

The Devil and Daniel Webster

Stephen Vincent Benét

IT'S A STORY they tell in the border country, where Massachusetts joins Vermont and New Hampshire.

Yes, Dan'l Webster's dead—or, at least, they buried him. But every time there's a thunderstorm around Marshfield, they say you can hear his rolling voice in the hollows of the sky. And they say that if you go to his grave and speak loud and clear, "Dan'l Webster—Dan'l Webster!" the ground'll begin to shiver and the trees begin to shake. And after a while you'll hear a deep voice saying, "Neighbor, how stands the Union?" Then you better answer the Union stands as she stood, rock-bottomed and copper-sheathed, one and indivisible, or he's liable to rear right out of the ground. At least, that's what I was told when I was a youngster.

You see, for a while, he was the biggest man in the country. He never got to be President, but he was the biggest man. There were thousands that trusted in him right next to God Almighty, and they told stories about him that were like the stories of patriarchs and such. They said, when he stood up to speak, stars and stripes came right out in the sky, and once he spoke against a river and made it sink into the ground. They

From *Selected Works of Stephen Vincent Benét,* published by Rinehart & Co., Inc. Copyright, 1931, by Stephen Vincent Benét.

said, when he walked the woods with his fishing rod, Killall, the trout would jump out of the streams right into his pockets, for they knew it was no use putting up a fight against him; and, when he argued a case, he could turn on the harps of the blessed and the shaking of the earth underground. That was the kind of man he was, and his big farm up at Marshfield was suitable to him. The chickens he raised were all white meat down to the drumsticks, the cows were tended like children, and the big ram called Goliath had horns with a curl like a morning-glory vine and could butt through an iron door. But Dan'l wasn't one of your gentlemen farmers; he knew all the ways of the land, and he'd be up by candlelight to see that the chores got done. A man with a mouth like a mastiff, a brow like a mountain and eyes like burning anthracite—that was Dan'l Webster in his prime. And the biggest case he argued never got written down in the books, for he argued it against the devil, nip and tuck and no holds barred. And this is the way I used to hear it told.

There was a man named Jabez Stone, lived at Cross Corners, New Hampshire. He wasn't a bad man to start with, but he was an unlucky man. If he planted corn, he got borers; if he planted potatoes, he got blight. He had good-enough land, but it didn't prosper him; he had a decent wife and children, but the more children he had, the less there was to feed them. If stones cropped up in his neighbor's field, boulders boiled up in his; if he had a horse with the spavins, he'd trade it for one with the staggers and give something extra. There's some folks bound to be like that, apparently. But one day Jabez Stone got sick of the whole business.

He'd been plowing that morning and he'd just broke the plowshare on a rock that he could have sworn hadn't been there yesterday. And as he stood looking at the plowshare, the off horse began to cough—that ropy kind of cough that means sickness and horse doctors. There were two children down with the measles, his wife was ailing, and he had a whitlow on his thumb. It was about the last straw for Jabez Stone. "I vow," he said, and he looked around him kind of desperate—"I vow it's enough to make a man want to sell his soul to the devil! And I would, too, for two cents!"

Then he felt a kind of queerness come over him at having said what he'd said; though, naturally, being a New Hampshireman, he wouldn't take it back. But, all the same, when it got to be evening and, as far as he could see, no notice had been taken, he felt relieved in his mind, for he was a religious man. But notice is always taken, sooner or later, just like the Good Book says. And, sure enough, next day, about suppertime, a soft-spoken, dark-dressed stranger drove up in a handsome buggy and asked for Jabez Stone.

Well, Jabez told his family it was a lawyer, come to see him about a legacy. But he knew who it was.

He didn't like the looks of the stranger, nor the way he smiled with his teeth. They were white teeth, and plentiful—some say they were filed to a point, but I wouldn't vouch for that. And he didn't like it when the dog took one look at the stranger and ran away howling, with his tail between his legs. But having passed his word, more or less, he stuck to it, and they went out behind the barn and made their bargain. Jabez Stone had to prick his finger to sign, and the stranger lent him a silver pin. The wound healed clean, but it left a little white scar.

After that, all of a sudden, things began to pick up and prosper for Jabez Stone. His cows got fat and his horses sleek, his crops were the envy of the neighborhood, and lightning might strike all over the valley, but it wouldn't strike his barn. Pretty soon, he was one of the prosperous people of the county; they asked him to stand for selectman, and he stood for it; there began to be talk of running him for state senate. All in all, you might say the Stone family was as happy and contented as cats in a dairy. And so they were, except for Jabez Stone.

He'd been contented enough, the first few years. It's a great thing when bad luck turns; it drives most other things out of your head. True, every now and then, especially in rainy weather, the little white scar on his finger would give him a twinge. And once a year, punctual as clockwork, the stranger with the handsome buggy would come driving by. But the sixth year, the stranger lighted, and, after that, his peace was over for Jabez Stone.

The stranger came up through the lower field, switching his boots with a cane—they were handsome black boots, but Jabez Stone never liked the look of them, particularly the toes. And, after he'd passed the time of day, he said, "Well, Mr. Stone, you're a hummer! It's a very pretty property you've got here, Mr. Stone."

"Well, some might favor it and others might not," said Jabez Stone, for he was a New Hampshireman.

"Oh, no need to decry your industry!" said the stranger, very easy, showing his teeth in a smile. "After all, we know what's been done, and it's been according to contract and specifications. So when—ahem—the mortgage falls due next year, you shouldn't have any regrets."

"Speaking of that mortgage, mister," said Jabez Stone, and he looked around for help to the earth and the sky, "I'm beginning to have one or two doubts about it."

"Doubts?" said the stranger, not quite so pleasantly.

"Why, yes," said Jabez Stone. "This being the U. S. A. and me always having been a religious man." He cleared his throat and got bolder. "Yes, sir," he said, "I'm beginning to have considerable doubts as to that mortgage holding in court."

"There's courts and courts," said the stranger, clicking his teeth. "Still, we might as well have a look at the original document." And he hauled out a big black pocketbook, full of papers. "Sherwin, Slater, Stevens, Stone," he muttered. "I, Jabez Stone, for a term of seven years—— Oh, it's quite in order, I think."

But Jabez Stone wasn't listening, for he saw something else flutter out of the black pocketbook. It was something that looked like a moth, but it wasn't a moth. And as Jabez Stone stared at it, it seemed to speak to him in a small sort of piping voice, terrible small and thin, but terrible human. "Neighbor Stone!" it squeaked. "Neighbor Stone! Help me! For God's sake, help me!"

But before Jabez Stone could stir his hand or foot, the stranger whipped out a big bandanna handkerchief, caught the creature in it, just like a butterfly, and started tying up the ends of the bandanna.

"Sorry for the interruption," he said. "As I was saying——"

But Jabez Stone was shaking all over like a scared horse.

"That's Miser Stevens' voice!" he said, in a croak. "And you've got him in your handkerchief!"

The stranger looked a little embarrassed.

"Yes, I really should have transferred him to the collecting box," he said with a simper, "but there were some rather unusual specimens there and I didn't want them crowded. Well, well, these little contretemps will occur."

"I don't know what you mean by contertan," said Jabez Stone, "but that was Miser Stevens' voice! And he ain't dead! You can't tell me he is! He was just as spry and mean as a woodchuck, Tuesday!"

"In the midst of life——" said the stranger, kind of pious. "Listen!" Then a bell began to toll in the valley and Jabez Stone listened, with the sweat running down his face. For he knew it was tolled for Miser Stevens and that he was dead.

"These long-standing accounts," said the stranger with a sigh; "one really hates to close them. But business is business."

He still had the bandanna in his hand, and Jabez Stone felt sick as he saw the cloth struggle and flutter.

"Are they all as small as that?" he asked hoarsely.

"Small?" said the stranger. "Oh, I see what you mean. Why, they vary." He measured Jabez Stone with his eyes, and his teeth showed. "Don't worry, Mr. Stone," he said. "You'll go with a very good grade. I wouldn't trust you outside the collecting box. Now, a man like Dan'l Webster, of course—well, we'd have to build a special box for him, and even at that, I imagine the wing spread would astonish you. But, in your case, as I was saying——"

"Put that handkerchief away!" said Jabez Stone, and he began to beg and to pray. But the best he could get at the end was a three years' extension, with conditions.

But till you make a bargain like that, you've got no idea of how fast four years can run. By the last months of those years, Jabez Stone's known all over the state and there's talk of running him for governor—and it's dust and ashes in his mouth. For every day, when he gets up, he thinks, "There's one more night gone," and every night when he lies down, he thinks of the black pocketbook and the soul of Miser Stevens, and it makes him sick at heart. Till, finally, he can't bear it any longer, and, in the last days of the last year, he hitches up his horse and drives off to seek Dan'l Webster. For Dan'l was born in New Hampshire, only a few miles from Cross Corners, and it's well known that he has a particular soft spot for old neighbors.

It was early in the morning when he got to Marshfield, but Dan'l was up already, talking Latin to the farm hands and wrestling with the ram, Goliath, and trying out a new trotter and working up speeches to make against John C. Calhoun. But when he heard a New Hampshireman had come to see him, he dropped everything else he was doing for that was Dan'l's way. He gave Jabez Stone a breakfast that five men couldn't eat, went into the living history of every man and woman in Cross Corners, and finally asked him how he could serve him.

Jabez Stone allowed that it was a kind of mortgage case.

"Well, I haven't pleaded a mortgage case in a long time, and I don't generally plead now, except before the Supreme Court," said Dan'l, "but if I can, I'll help you."

"Then I've got hope for the first time in ten years," said Jabez Stone, and told him the details.

Dan'l walked up and down as he listened, hands behind his back, now and then asking a question, now and then plunging his eyes at the floor, as if they'd bore through it like gimlets. When Jabez Stone had finished, Dan'l puffed out his cheeks and blew. Then he turned to Jabez Stone and a smile broke over his face like the sunrise over Monadnock.

"You've certainly given yourself the devil's own row to hoe, Neighbor Stone," he said, "but I'll take your case."

"You'll take it?" said Jabez Stone, hardly daring to believe.

"Yes," said Dan'l Webster. "I've got about seventy-five other things to do and the Missouri Compromise to straighten out, but I'll take your case. For if two New Hampshiremen aren't a match for the devil, we might as well give the country back to the Indians."

Then he shook Jabez Stone by the hand and said, "Did you come down here in a hurry?"

"Well, I admit I made time," said Jabez Stone.

"You'll go back faster," said Dan'l Webster, and he told 'em to hitch up Constitution and Constellation to the carriage. They were matched grays with one white forefoot, and they stepped like greased lightning.

Well, I won't describe how excited and pleased the whole Stone family was to have the great Dan'l Webster for a guest, when they finally got there. Jabez Stone had lost his hat on the way, blown off when they overtook a wind, but he didn't take much account of that. But after supper he sent the family off to bed, for he had most particular business with Mr. Webster. Mrs. Stone wanted them to sit in the front parlor, but Dan'l Webster knew front parlors and said he preferred the kitchen. So it was there they sat, waiting for the stranger, with a jug on the table between them and a bright fire on the hearth—the stranger being scheduled to show up on the stroke of midnight, according to specifications.

Well, most men wouldn't have asked for better company than Dan'l Webster and a jug. But with every tick of the clock Jabez Stone got sadder and sadder. His eyes roved round, and though he sampled the jug you could see he couldn't taste it. Finally, on the stroke of 11:30 he reached over and grabbed Dan'l Webster by the arm.

"Mr. Webster, Mr. Webster!" he said, and his voice was shaking with fear and a desperate courage. "For God's sake, Mr. Webster, harness your horses and get away from this place while you can!"

"You've brought me a long way, neighbor, to tell me you don't like my company," said Dan'l Webster, quite peaceable, pulling at the jug.

"Miserable wretch that I am!" groaned Jabez Stone. "I've brought you a devilish way, and now I see my folly. Let him take me if he wills. I don't hanker after it, I must say, but I can stand it. But you're the Union's stay and New Hampshire's pride! He mustn't get you, Mr. Webster! He mustn't get you!"

Dan'l Webster looked at the distracted man, all gray and shaking in the firelight, and laid a hand on his shoulder.

"I'm obliged to you, Neighbor Stone," he said gently. "It's kindly thought of. But there's a jug on the table and a case in hand. And I never left a jug or a case half finished in my life."

And just at that moment there was a sharp rap on the door.

"Ah," said Dan'l Webster, very coolly, "I thought your clock was a trifle slow, Neighbor Stone." He stepped to the door and opened it. "Come in!" he said.

The stranger came in—very dark and tall he looked in the firelight. He was carrying a box under his arm—a black, japanned box with little air holes in the lid. At the sight of the box, Jabez Stone gave a low cry and shrank into a corner of the room.

"Mr. Webster, I presume," said the stranger, very polite, but with his eyes glowing like a fox's deep in the woods.

"Attorney of record for Jabez Stone," said Dan'l Webster, but his eyes were glowing too. "Might I ask your name?"

"I've gone by a good many," said the stranger carelessly. "Perhaps Scratch will do for the evening. I'm often called that in these regions."

Then he sat down at the table and poured himself a drink from the jug. The liquor was cold in the jug, but it came steaming into the glass.

"And now," said the stranger, smiling and showing his teeth, "I shall call upon you, as a law-abiding citizen, to assist me in taking possession of my property."

Well, with that the argument began—and it went hot and heavy. At first, Jabez Stone had a flicker of hope, but when he saw Dan'l Webster being forced back at point after point, he just scrunched in his corner, with his eyes on that japanned box. For there wasn't any doubt as to the deed or the signature—that was the worst of it. Dan'l Webster twisted and turned and thumped his fist on the table, but he couldn't get away from that. He offered to compromise the case; the stranger wouldn't hear of it.

He pointed out the property had increased in value, and state senators ought to be worth more; the stranger stuck to the letter of the law. He was a great lawyer, Dan'l Webster, but we know who's the King of Lawyers, as the Good Book tells us, and it seemed as if, for the first time, Dan'l Webster had met his match.

Finally, the stranger yawned a little. "Your spirited efforts on behalf of your client do you credit, Mr. Webster," he said, "but if you have no more arguments to adduce, I'm rather pressed for time"—and Jabez Stone shuddered.

Dan'l Webster's brow looked dark as a thundercloud.

"Pressed or not, you shall not have this man!" he thundered. "Mr. Stone is an American citizen, and no American citizen may be forced into the service of a foreign prince. We fought England for that in '12 and we'll fight all hell for it again!"

"Foreign?" said the stranger. "And who calls me a foreigner?"

"Well, I never yet heard of the dev—of your claiming American citizenship," said Dan'l Webster with surprise.

"And who with a better right?" said the stranger, with one of his terrible smiles. "When the first wrong was done to the first Indian, I was there. When the first slaver put out for the Congo, I stood on her deck. Am I not in your books and stories and beliefs, from the first settlements on? Am I not spoken of, still, in every church in New England? 'Tis true the North claims me for a Southerner and the South for a Northerner, but I am neither, I am merely an honest American like yourself—and of the best descent—for, to tell the truth, Mr. Webster, though I don't like to boast of it, my name is older in this country than yours."

"Aha!" said Dan'l Webster, with the veins standing out in his forehead. "Then I stand on the Constitution! I demand a trial for my client!"

"The case is hardly one for an ordinary court," said the stranger, his eyes flickering. "And, indeed, the lateness of the hour——"

"Let it be any court you choose, so it is an American judge and an American jury!" said Dan'l Webster in his pride. "Let it be the quick or the dead; I'll abide the issue!"

"You have said it," said the stranger, and pointed his finger at the door. And with that, and all of a sudden, there was a rushing of wind outside and a noise of footsteps. They came, clear and distinct, through the night. And yet, they were not like the footsteps of living men.

"In God's name, who comes so late?" cried Jabez Stone, in an ague of fear.

"The jury Mr. Webster demands," said the stranger, sipping at his boiling glass. "You must pardon the rough appearance of one or two; they will have come a long way."

And with that the fire burned blue and the door blew open and twelve men entered, one by one.

If Jabez Stone had been sick with terror before, he was blind with terror now. For there was Walter Butler, the loyalist, who spread fire and horror through the Mohawk Valley in the times of the Revolution; and there was Simon Girty, the renegade, who saw white men burned at the stake and whooped with the Indians to see them burn. His eyes were green, like a catamount's, and the stains on his hunting shirt did not come from the blood of the deer. King Philip was there, wild and proud as he had been in life, with the great gash in his head that gave him his death wound, and cruel Governor Dale, who broke men on the wheel. There was Morton of Merry Mount, who so vexed the Plymouth Colony, with his flushed, loose, handsome face and his hate of the godly. There was Teach, the bloody pirate, with his black beard curling on his breast. The Reverend John Smeet, with his strangler's hands and his Geneva gown, walked as daintily as he had to the gallows. The red print of the rope was still around his neck, but he carried a perfumed handkerchief in one hand. One and all, they came into the room with the fires of hell still upon them, and the stranger named their names and their deeds as they came, till the tale of twelve was told. Yet the stranger had told the truth—they had all played a part in America.

"Are you satisfied with the jury, Mr. Webster?" said the stranger mockingly, when they had taken their places.

The sweat stood upon Dan'l Webster's brow, but his voice was clear.

"Quite satisfied," he said. "Though I miss General Arnold from the company."

"Benedict Arnold is engaged upon other business," said the stranger, with a glower. "Ah, you asked for a justice, I believe."

He pointed his finger once more, and a tall man, soberly clad in Puritan garb, with the burning gaze of the fanatic, stalked into the room and took his judge's place.

"Justice Hathorne is a jurist of experience," said the stranger. "He presided at certain witch trials once held in Salem. There were others who repented of the business later, but not he."

"Repent of such notable wonders and undertakings?" said the stern old justice. "Nay, hang them—hang them all!" And he muttered to himself in a way that struck ice into the soul of Jabez Stone.

Then the trial began, and, as you might expect, it didn't look anyways good for the defense. And Jabez Stone didn't make much of a witness in his own behalf. He took one look at Simon Girty and screeched, and they had to put him back in his corner in a kind of swoon.

It didn't halt the trial, though; the trial went on, as trials do. Dan'l Webster had faced some hard juries and hanging judges in his time, but this was the hardest he'd ever faced, and he knew it. They sat there with a kind of glitter in their eyes, and the stranger's smooth voice went on and on. Every time he'd raise an objection, it'd be "Objection sustained," but whenever Dan'l objected, it'd be "Objection denied." Well, you couldn't expect fair play from a fellow like this Mr. Scratch.

It got to Dan'l in the end, and he began to heat, like iron in the forge. When he got up to speak he was going to flay that stranger with every trick known to the law, and the judge and jury too. He didn't care if it was contempt of court or what would happen to him for it. He didn't care any more what happened to Jabez Stone. He just got madder and madder, thinking of what he'd say. And yet, curiously enough, the more he thought about it, the less he was able to arrange his speech in his mind.

Till, finally, it was time for him to get up on his feet, and he did so, all ready to bust out with lightnings and denunciations. But before he started he looked over the judge and jury for a moment, such being his custom. And he noticed the glitter in their eyes was twice as strong as before, and they all leaned forward. Like hounds just before they get the fox, they looked, and the blue mist of evil in the room thickened as he watched them. Then he saw what he'd been about to do, and he wiped his forehead, as a man might who's just escaped falling into a pit in the dark.

For it was him they'd come for, not only Jabez Stone. He read it in the glitter of their eyes and in the way the stranger hid his mouth with one hand. And if he fought them with their own weapons, he'd fall into their power; he knew that, though he couldn't have told you how. It was his own anger and horror that burned in their eyes; and he'd have to wipe that out or the case was lost. He stood there for a moment, his black eyes burning like anthracite. And then he began to speak.

He started off in a low voice, though you could hear every word. They say he could call on the harps of the blessed when he chose. And this was just as simple and easy as a man could talk. But he didn't start out by condemning or reviling. He was talking about the things that make a country a country, and a man a man.

And he began with the simple things that everybody's known and felt—the freshness of a fine morning when you're young, and the taste of food when you're hungry, and the new day that's every day when you're a child. He took them up and he turned them in his hands. They were good things for any man. But without freedom, they sickened. And when he talked of those enslaved, and the sorrows of slavery, his voice got like a big bell. He talked of the early days of America and the men who had made those days. It wasn't a spread-eagle speech, but he made you see it. He admitted all the wrong that had ever been done. But he showed how, out of the wrong and the right, the suffering and the starvations, something new had come. And everybody had played a part in it, even the traitors.

Then he turned to Jabez Stone and showed him as he was—an ordinary man who'd had hard luck and wanted to change it. And, because he'd wanted to change it, now he was going to be punished for all eternity. And yet there was good in Jabez Stone, and he showed that good. He was hard and mean, in some ways, but he was a man. There was sadness in being a man, but it was a proud thing too. And he showed what the pride of it was till you couldn't help feeling it. Yes, even in hell, if a man was a man, you'd know it. And he wasn't pleading for any one person any more, though his voice rang like an organ. He was telling the story and the failures and the endless journey of mankind. They got tricked and trapped and bamboozled, but it was a great journey. And no demon that was ever foaled could know the inwardness of it—it took a man to do that.

The fire began to die on the hearth and the wind before morning to blow. The light was getting gray in the room when Dan'l Webster finished. And his words came back at the end to New Hampshire ground, and the one spot of land that each man loves and clings to. He painted a picture of that, and to each one of that jury he spoke of things long forgotten. For his voice could search the heart, and that was his gift and his strength. And to one, his voice was like the forest and its secrecy, and to another like the sea and the storms of the sea; and one heard the cry of his lost nation in it, and another saw a little harmless scene he hadn't remembered for years. But each saw something. And when Dan'l Webster finished he didn't know whether or not he'd saved Jabez Stone. But he knew he'd done a miracle. For the glitter was gone from the eyes of judge and jury, and, for the moment, they were men again, and knew they were men.

"The defense rests," said Dan'l Webster, and stood there like a mountain. His ears were still ringing with his speech, and he didn't hear anything else till he heard Judge Hathorne say, "The jury will retire to consider its verdict."

Walter Butler rose in his place and his face had a dark, gay pride on it.

"The jury has considered its verdict," he said, and looked the stranger full in the eye. "We find for the defendant, Jabez Stone."

With that, the smile left the stranger's face, but Walter Butler did not flinch.

"Perhaps 'tis not strictly in accordance with the evidence," he said, "but even the damned may salute the eloquence of Mr. Webster."

With that, the long crow of a rooster split the gray morning sky, and judge and jury were gone from the room like a puff of smoke and as if they had never been there. The stranger turned to Dan'l Webster, smiling wryly.

"Major Butler was always a bold man," he said. "I had not thought him quite so bold. Nevertheless, my congratulations, as between two gentlemen."

"I'll have that paper first, if you please," said Dan'l Webster, and he took it and tore it into four pieces. It was queerly warm to the touch. "And now," he said, "I'll have you!" and his hand came down like a bear trap on the stranger's arm. For he knew that once you bested anybody like Mr. Scratch in fair fight, his power on you was gone. And he could see that Mr. Scratch knew it too.

The stranger twisted and wriggled, but he couldn't get out of that grip. "Come, come, Mr. Webster," he said, smiling palely. "This sort of thing is ridic—ouch!—is ridiculous. If you're worried about the costs of the case, naturally, I'd be glad to pay——"

"And so you shall!" said Dan'l Webster, shaking him till his teeth rattled. "For you'll sit right down at that table and draw up a document, promising never to bother Jabez Stone nor his heirs or assigns nor any other New Hampshireman till doomsday! For any hades we want to raise in this state, we can raise ourselves, without assistance from strangers."

"Ouch!" said the stranger. "Ouch! Well, they never did run very big to the barrel, but—ouch!—I agree!"

So he sat down and drew up the document. But Dan'l Webster kept his hand on his coat collar all the time.

"And, now, may I go?" said the stranger, quite humble, when Dan'l had seen the document was in proper and legal form.

"Go?" said Dan'l, giving him another shake. "I'm still trying to figure out what I'll do with you. For you've settled the costs of the case, but you haven't settled with me. I think I'll take you back to Marshfield," he said, kind of reflective. "I've got a ram there named Goliath that can butt through an iron door. I'd kind of like to turn you loose in his field and see what he'd do."

Well, with that the stranger began to beg and to plead. And he begged and he pled so humble that finally Dan'l, who was naturally kind-hearted, agreed to let him go. The stranger seemed terrible grateful for that and said, just to show they were friends, he'd tell Dan'l's fortune before leaving. So Dan'l agreed to that, though he didn't take much stock in fortune-tellers ordinarily. But, naturally, the stranger was a little different.

Well, he pried and he peered at the lines in Dan'l's hands. And he told him one thing and another that was quite remarkable. But they were all in the past.

"Yes, all that's true, and it happened," said Dan'l Webster. "But what's to come in the future?"

The stranger grinned, kind of happily, and shook his head.

"The future's not as you think it," he said. "It's dark. You have a great ambition, Mr. Webster."

"I have," said Dan'l firmly, for everybody knew he wanted to be President.

"It seems almost within your grasp," said the stranger, "but you will not attain it. Lesser men will be made President and you will be passed over."

"And, if I am, I'll still be Daniel Webster," said Dan'l. "Say on."

"You have two strong sons," said the stranger, shaking his head. "You look to found a line. But each will die in war and neither reach greatness."

"Live or die, they are still my sons," said Dan'l Webster. "Say on."

"You have made great speeches," said the stranger. "You will make more."

"Ah," said Dan'l Webster.

"But the last great speech you will make will turn many of your own against you," said the stranger. "They will call you Ichabod; they will call you by other names. Even in New England, some will say you have turned your coat and sold your country, and their voices will be loud against you till you die."

"So it is an honest speech, it does not matter what men say," said Dan'l Webster. Then he looked at the stranger and their glances locked.

"One question," he said. "I have fought for the Union all my life. Will I see that fight won against those who would tear it apart?"

"Not while you live," said the stranger, grimly, "but it will be won. And after you are dead, there are thousands who will fight for your cause, because of words that you spoke."

"Why, then, you long-barreled, slab-sided, lantern-jawed, fortune-telling note shaver!" said Dan'l Webster, with a great roar of laughter, "be off with you to your own place before I put my mark on you! For, by the thirteen original colonies, I'd go to the Pit itself to save the Union!"

And with that he drew back his foot for a kick that would have stunned a horse. It was only the tip of his shoe that caught the stranger, but he went flying out of the door with his collecting box under his arm.

"And now," said Dan'l Webster, seeing Jabez Stone beginning to rouse from his swoon, "let's see what's left in the jug, for it's dry work talking all night. I hope there's pie for breakfast, Neighbor Stone."

But they say that whenever the devil comes near Marshfield, even now, he gives it a wide berth. And he hasn't been seen in the state of New Hampshire from that day to this. I'm not talking about Massachusetts or Vermont.

A Question of Citizenship

B. Traven

THIRTY FRANCS, no matter how you get them, don't last very long. Money always goes sooner than you expect it will. The same with really fine people.

Hanging around the docks one day, I saw two guys walking along and caught a few words of their conversation. There is something queer about languages. The English say that we can't speak English, while we say that what the English talk is a sort of ancient Scotch, because no serious-minded person can ever guess what they mean when they start talking about races or movies or, worse, politics. That's why the first English settlers couldn't get along as well with the Indians as we can, because the Indians are hundred-per-centers, and the English are not.

But whatever language the limeys talk, I am not crazy about them. They don't like us, either, and never did. It's been going on now for more than a hundred and fifty years—ever since the tea-party that had no bridge-partners. The war made things worse.

You come into a port where the limeys are thick, and they shout as though they owned the world. Maybe in Australia, or in China, or along the coast of the Indian Sea. You step into a tavern like a good and decent sailor who is ashore for a couple of hours and wants to wash down the salt from his throat.

You don't have to say who you are. You just step across to the bar and you say: "Hello, pal, gimme a shot. No, straight. Make it two."

That's all you need to say, and hell is let loose.

"Hey you, Yank. Who won the war?"

Now, as a decent sailor, what can you say to that? What has that to do with me? I didn't win the war. Of that I am sure. Those who say they won it would rather that nobody reminded them of it, true or not true.

Again: "Hey, Yank, you're a smart sailor. Tell the world who won the war!"

What do I care? I am drinking my hard washer, and ask for another,

From *The Death Ship*, by B. Traven. Copyright, 1934, by Alfred A. Knopf, Inc. and B. Traven. By permission of Alfred A. Knopf, Inc.

straight. Mother told me long ago not to meddle with boys who are not
honest and who seek only trouble.

Now there are about two dozen of the limeys. Grinning and laughing.
I am alone. I don't know where the other fellows from my can are right
now. Not very likely to drop in here, anyhow.

"Make this one a doubler. Mother's son is thirsty."

"Hey, submarine admiral, Nancy of the gobs. Tell us real sailors who
won the war."

I do not even look at the drunks. I punish them with my profound
disrespect. But they cannot leave a guy in peace, especially since I am all
alone. I don't even know if the barman will keep neutral. I guess I shall
have to say something. The honor of my country is at stake. No matter
what it may cost me.

Now what can I say? If I say: "We," there will be roaring laughter and
a big fight. If I say: "The Frenchies," there will be a fight. If I say: "I won
it," there will be a fight, and most likely the jail afterwards and then the
hospital. If I say: "The Canadians, the Australians, the Africans, and the
New Zealanders," there will be a fight. If I stay on saying nothing, it will
be taken to mean: "We Americans won it," which, I know, will surely result in the biggest fight. I could say: "You English, you won the war."
This would be a lie, and that reminds me again of my mother, who told
me a thousand times never to tell a lie, and always to think of the cherry-
tree that was responsible for a president. So what else can be done about
it? There is a fight on. That's the way they treat the fine guys whom
they called, when they needed them badly, "our cousins across the sea."
Not my cousins, no, siree.

So that's why I am not so crazy about the limeys. But whether I liked
them or despised them made no difference now. I had to be friendly, for
they were all I had to rely on.

"What bucket are you from, chaps?"

"Hello, Yankey, what're you doing here?"

"I was mixed up with a jane who had a sick mother. Had to take her
to the hospital myself. So I was skipped, see?"

"Now it is too hot here for you, isn't it? Polishing anchor-chains, hey?"

"You said it. How about stowing with you?"

"It might be done. Always a free hand for a sailor feller."

"Where are you making for?" I asked.

"Lisbon and old Malta, and then Egypt. Can't take ye that far, but
welcome to Boulogne. From there on, you have to look out for your own
future."

"Boulogne will be okay with me."

"See, the bos'n we have is a bloody devil, he is. If it were not for him,
we could take you round the world sightseeing. Now, tell ye what we'll
do for you. You come round about eight at night. Then the bos'n will be
so filled up he'll be kicking over the rim. Doesn't see anything and
doesn't hear anything. Now, you just come up. We'll wait for you at the

railing. Just look at me. If I tip my cap over onto my neck, everything is shipshape and you just hop on. But if anybody finds you aboard, don't ever say who heaved you up. Sailor's word."

"Understand. I'll be there at eight."

I was there. The cap was cocked onto his neck. The bos'n was so well drenched that it lasted until Bolougne. There I got off, and that's how I came to France.

I changed my money for French coin. Then I went to the depot. I bought a ticket to the first station on the way to Paris. The Paris Express. I boarded it.

The French are very polite gents. No one molested me to show my ticket.

The train pulled in at what they call a *gare,* which means their depot. So I came to Paris, which is supposed to be the paradise for Americans who have become sick of God's country.

Now the tickets were asked for.

The police are quick in Paris. Since I had no ticket for Paris, and I had ridden all the way down from Boulogne on a very soft seat unmolested by anybody, I had become a case for the Paris criminal investigation police department, or something that sounded as high-falutin' as that.

I knew a few words of French, and I hoped that this would save me, but these cops knew more about the English language than I shall ever be able to pick up. They must have had better teachers than we usually have.

Where did I come from? Boulogne. How did I come to Boulogne? On a ship. What ship? The *Abraham Lincoln.* No *Abraham Lincoln* lately to Boulogne. Where is my sailor's card? Haven't got any.

"You mean to say you have no—"

"No, I have no sailor's card."

I had become so used to that question that I would understand it even in Hindustani, whatever that may be. The tune of the words, and the gestures, and the lifted eyebrows that always accompany the question are so unmistakably alike among all the bureaucrats and policemen of the world that there never can be any doubt about what is asked.

"And I have no passport either. Nor have I an identification card of the French authorities. No immigration stamp. No customs-house seal. I have no papers at all. Never in all my life did I ever have any papers."

I rattled off all this to spare them the work of questioning me for an hour. I could easily pass the toughest examination for immigration officers, because I have had the best schooling any guy ever can have.

The chief, who had wanted to spend an easy hour or two with me, became confused. He looked at me with dying eyes. He seemed to feel that I had taken from him all his upholstered authority. He pushed around some papers lying on his desk to find a few questions for me. After a while, trying to compose himself, he gave up for the day.

Next day there was a hearing, of which I did not grasp a single word, since everyone spoke in French. When it was all over, somebody tried his best to explain to me that I had got ten days in prison for cheating the French railroad out of the money for a ticket to Paris. I learned later that in France one might get for such an offense as much as two years, but someone in court had said that I was too dumb to understand the French Law and it would be an injustice to load two years on me.

That was the welcome the French gave a good American who had been willing to help them win democracy.

I have never been in prison back home. When home I am very decent and dull, just like all the home folks. When living among baboons, do as the baboons do. Life is easier that way, and you may find a dame who thinks you are a great guy—in fact, the greatest guy on earth. But in foreign countries everything is different, and so am I. That's why travel is educating. You never get educated staying home, because you stay dumb like the rest. If you show only a bit of intelligence above the average, everybody says you must be a crank, or something else must be wrong with you, or else you would not act the way you do and upset everything. Back home in Sconsin I would never have told a good story. Everybody would have said that I was silly, and I'd better buy the gas-station Mr. Jorgson is offering for sale. So I do not know how prison life is at home.

In Paris it was this way:

First day: Registration. Bath. Health examination. Bedclothes obtained. A book from the prison library. Cell assigned. Take possession of cell. First day gone.

Second day: The money they found on me was handed over to the treasurer of the prison. I had to make several statements as to whether it was my money, whether any of it was missing, whether the coins were exactly the same as far as I could remember. All this was written in three thick books. Also information was asked as to other valuables found on my person, of which there were none, and which I had to testify to several times, signing my name about two dozen times in as many books and on as many blanks. Afternoon: Called for by the minister of the prison. Sort of Protestant or Calvinist. He spoke good English. It must have been the English William the Conqueror spoke before he landed on the coast of old England. I did not understand one word of his English. I was in France, therefore I was more courteous than at home, where one is thought silly when courteous; so I did not let the minister feel that I did not understand what he was talking about. Whenever he mentioned God, I thought he was talking about a goat. That was the way he pronounced it. Not my fault. So the second day came to an end.

Third day: In the morning I was asked by about fifteen different officers if I had ever in my life sewn strings on aprons. I said that I had not, and that I had not the slightest idea as to how it is done. Afternoon: I am called for by eight or nine prison officials who inform me that I have been assigned to the sewing department to sew on apron-strings. I have to sign my name on dozens of blanks, which takes all the afternoon.

Fourth day: I have to appear in the store, where I receive a pair of scissors, one needle, about five yards of thread, and a thimble. The thimble did not fit any of my fingers. I complained, but I was told to be quiet; they had no other thimble to satisfy my peculiarities. I had to sign my name in books several times. Each time, before signing my name, I was asked if I had the needle, and if the needle was still good, or if I thought it looked as though it had a dull point. Afternoon: I was shown how to set up in the middle of my cell a little bench in such a way that it would be seen from the peep-hole in the door. On this bench I had to lay out in open view the scissors, the needle, the thread, and the thimble. These things were not laid out any old way. They had to be arranged in a special manner, which took me all afternoon to learn, because every time I thought it was right, the officer told me it was wrong and I had to do it all over again until he was satisfied. But he added that there was still something lacking in accuracy. Outside my door a cardboard sign was put above the peep-hole, which stated that the resident of the cell had scissors, a needle, a thread, and a thimble. When this sign had been put on my door, the fourth day was gone.

Fifth day: Sunday. Something said about good behavior, and the Lord will do all the rest.

Sixth day: In the morning I am taken to the shop in which I have to work. Afternoon: I am given a place to sit and to work. Sixth day gone.

Seventh day: In the morning a prisoner is introduced to me as the professor who is going to teach me how to sew on apron-strings. Afternoon: The prof shows me how to use the needle, and how to get in the thread without biting up too much of it. Seventh day gone.

Eighth day: The prisoner in charge of my education shows me how he himself sews on apron-strings. Afternoon: Bathing and weighing. I am asked if I have any complaints as to treatment or food. I tell them that I am used to better food and a better sort of coffee. No one takes any notice of my complaints; they only say it is all right, they cannot grow a special coffee for me. The eighth day is gone.

Ninth day: During the morning I am sent for to see the chief warden. He asks my name, and wants to know if I am the guy whose name I said was mine. I answered: "Yes, sir." Then he asks me if I have any complaints. I tell him that I am not much satisfied with the food and the coffee. He says: "The French law is the best law in the world, and there is no country more civilized than France." I have to sign my name in two books. Afternoon: I am shown how to sew on apron-strings. The ninth day is gone.

Tenth day: During the morning I sew on one apron-string. The guy who teaches me how to do it examines the string it took me an hour and a half, perhaps two hours to sew on. Then he says that it is not sewn as well as he had thought I would do it, and that he feels sorry that he has no other remedy but to cut off the string and have me do it all over again. Afternoon: When I am half-way through sewing on the string again, I am called to the chief warden, who tells me that tomorrow morning my time is up. Then he says that he is sorry that I have to leave, but it is the law; he has been satisfied with my good behavior, and I have been an example to other prisoners. After this is over, I am weighed and examined by the doctor, who asks me if I am all right. Then I am called to the receiving hall, where I have to return the prison garment. For a while I have to wait in an open cell without anything on but a towel. Then I have to go to a desk where I am handed my civilian clothes. I am asked if anything is missing. I say: "No, sir." Then I am allowed to dress in my own clothes. The tenth day is over.

I am called the next morning very early and asked if I wish to have breakfast here or if I want to get out in a hurry. I say that I would prefer to have breakfast in town. So everything is hurried up, and I don't have to wait until breakfast-time. I am taken to the treasurer, who returns my money. He asks if the amount is correct. I have to sign my name in three books. Then I am notified that I have earned fifteen centimes while working here. These fifteen centimes are paid out, and I have to sign my name again in three or four books. I am asked again if I have any complaints. I say: "No, sir, thank you, mercy beaucoup," which means the same. I am now discharged, and taken to the gate, where another warden looks me over, reads some papers, and then opens the gate, where another warden looks me over, reads some papers, and then opens the gate and says: "Marshey," which means in French: "Scram!"

I do not think that the French government made much money out of me. And there is still a question whether the French railroad will be convinced now that my ticket was paid for by sending me up.

When I had gone hardly twenty feet, two policemen met me and said that they had waited for me only to tell me that I had to leave France within exactly fifteen days by the same road I had come in, and if I am still found in France after the fifteen days have expired, the law will take care of me and not with very soft gloves; so the best thing for me to do would be to leave even before the last of the fifteen days. They did not tell me how the law would take care of me. Perhaps by shipping me to their Devil's Island and keeping me there until death do us part. Every age has its Inquisition. Our age has the passport to make up for the tortures of mediaeval times. And unemployment.

"You ought to have some papers to show who you are," the police officer advised me.

"I do not need any paper; I know who I am," I said.

"Maybe so. Other people are also interested in knowing who you are. Of course, I can get you the prison release paper. Somehow, I think it would not do you much good. I have no authority to furnish you with any other paper."

"But you have authority to put me in jail, haven't you?"

"That is my duty. That is what I am paid for. What did you say? I do not understand you. Now you may go. I have warned you officially that

you have to be out of the country within fifteen days. How you manage
it is not my business. You came in some way; you may go out the same
way. If you are still here, then I shall find you, be sure of that. Why don't
you go to Germany? A big country, and a very fine country at that. Try
the Germans; they like fellows like you. Well, good luck! I hope never
to see you again."

There must be something wrong somewhere, that the police of all the
countries I have been in want to ship me off to Germany. The reason may
be that everybody wants to help the Germans pay off the reparations, or
everybody seems to think that Germany is the freest country in Europe.
How can that be, with a socialist president who is more nationalistic than
old man Bismarck ever was?

I stayed in Paris for several days. Just to see what would happen. Unexpected happenings often help you more and push you further ahead
than plans worked out carefully. I now had a right to walk the streets
and boulevards of Paris. My railroad ticket had been paid for, so I did
not owe the French nation a cent, and I was entitled to make use of their
sidewalks and their street illuminations. I have to admit that I did not
see for a moment the American paradise that I had been sure I would find
at every corner and in each nook.

I felt bored, and I did not know what to do, where to go, or how to
entertain myself. So I hit upon the idea that the cheapest way to have fun
would be to see my consul. I had a desire to find out if he had passed a
different examination for his diplomatic career than had his brother in
office in Rotterdam. I thought I might take up studying the representatives
of our diplomatic service overseas. I had seen so many American consuls
in the movies and in musical comedies like *Madame Butterfly*. Having a
rare opportunity to do so, I thought it might be a good idea to learn
whether the movie-makers have again lied, as they mostly, not to say
always, do.

I had to wait the whole morning. Nor did my turn come in the afternoon. The class I belong to always has to wait and wait, stand long nights
and days in long files to get a cup of coffee and a slice of bread. Everybody
in the world, official or boss, takes it for granted that our sort of people
have ages of time to waste. It is different with those who have money.
They can arrange everything with money. Therefore they never have to
wait. We who cannot pay with cold cash have to pay with our time instead. Suppose you get sore at the official who lets you wait and wait, and
you say something about the citizen's right—it won't help you a bit. He
then lets you wait ten times longer, and you never do it again. He is the
king. Do not forget that. Don't ever believe that kings were done with
when the fathers of the country made a revolution.

The waiting-room was crowded with people, with plain people like
me. Some of them had already been sitting there four days. Others had
been there scores of times. First a certain paper had been missing, then a

certain certificate was not complete, then some record was not sufficient, and blanks had been filled in fifty times, and fifty times torn up and thrown into the waste-basket and done over again. The whole thing was no longer an affair of human beings; it had become an affair of papers, blanks, affidavits, certificates, photographs, stamps, seals, files, height-measuring, and quarreling about the correct color of the eyes and the hair. The human being himself was out and forgotten. A piece of merchandise would not have been treated so.

The good old flag spread all over the wall. A picture of the man who had said something about the country being created by the Lord to be the land of the free and for the hunted. Another picture of another man who had said great things about the right of human beings even Negroes, to unrestricted freedom.

A huge map was there also. It was the map of a country great and large enough to give some space to an extra fifty million human beings eager to work and to find happiness on earth. I looked at the map and I was pleased to see that good old Sconsin was still on it.

I was still looking around when a lady came in like a clap of thunder. Short, unbelievably fat. In this room where everyone awaiting his turn had a lean and hungry figure, this lady had the effect of a loathsome insult.

The fat lady had curly, bluish-black, oily hair, done up in the manner affected by street-girls when they want to go with their men to the chauffeurs' ball. She had a pronounced hooked nose, thick lips, brightly painted, brown dreamy eyes that were larger than the holes they were set in and looked as if they might pop out any moment. The fat lady was dressed in the most elegant masterpiece of a French dressmaker. Looking at how she tried to walk like a human being on her immensely high heels, one had the impression that in a minute she would collapse under the weight of her heavy pearl necklace and the heavy platinum bracelets around her wrists. Her fingers were ridiculously short and thick. On all fingers, save on the thumb, she wore diamond rings; on some fingers she carried two and even three rings. It seemed that the finger-rings were necessary to keep her thick fingers from bursting open.

Hardly had she opened the door when she cried: "For God's sake, I have lost my passport." (She pronounced it "pacepot".) "Where is that consul? He has to receive me immediately. I must have another pacepot. I take the Oriental Express in the evening."

I had been made to believe that only sailors can lose their papers. Now I see that even well-dressed people can be without passports. Hello, Fanny, I can tell you that Mr. Consul is going to say something very interesting to you about lost passports. I feel some sympathy for that fat lady. The sympathy of the galley-slave for his fellow.

The clerk jumped to his feet, all devotion. He bowed and said in a soft and very polite voice: "Of course, madame. I will announce you right away to the consul. It will be a pleasure. Just one moment, please."

He ran and brought a chair and begged the fat lady to be seated. He did not say: "Sit down!" Just: "Will you be seated, madame? Thank you."

He helped the lady to fill in all the blanks. The hungry and lean people who had been waiting for weeks had to do this by themselves, and when it was not satisfactorily written they had to do it over and over again. The lady perhaps could not write. So of course the clerk had to help her. Or she was so great a personage that she did not need to write. At home she probably had a social secretary who did all the writing for her and told her all the gossip.

No sooner had the clerk filled out the applications than he took up the forms, ran to one of the doors, behind which the death-sentences were passed out, knocked softly, and went in. In less than half a minute he returned, ran up to the lady, bowed, and said: "Mr. Grgrgrgrs wishes to see you, madame. I am certain you have the three photographs with you."

"Here they are," the fat lady said, and handed the photographs to the clerk. Then the clerk sprang to the door, opened it with a bow, and let her in.

The lady was not long in the holy chamber. When she came out, she closed her hand-bag with an energetic gesture which announced better than her speech ever could: "Thank heaven, we have money. And we do not mind paying for quick and good service. A consul cannot live by his salary alone. Live and let live." Then she walked across the room wagging her hips like a dog that is pleased with itself.

The clerk rose from his chair and invited her to be seated again. The fat lady sat down, using only half of the chair, thinking this would indicate best how much of a hurry she was in. She went fishing in the depths of her hand-bag, took out a powder-puff, and began to powder her thick nose. She had taken out not only her powder, but something which distinctly crinkled in her hands. She pushed the crisp affair among papers lying on the table. As she did so, she gave the clerk a glance, which he caught all right. However, he made believe he did not know what the glance meant. When the lady had whitened her nose, she shut her hand-bag with the same energetic snap she had used on coming out of the holy chamber.

The hungry men and women waiting in the room had never been in God's country before. They merely wanted to go there and partake of the riches of the world. So they were still innocent and did not understand the universal language of snapping hand-bags. Since they did not know how to use this sort of language, and since they had no means of using it in the right way, no one offered them a chair, and they had to wait until their turn came.

"If it would please you, madame, will you call for your passport in half an hour, or do you wish us to send it to your hotel?"

"Never mind, mister," the fat lady said. "I shall drop in myself in an hour on my way to the station. I have signed the passport already, in the consul's office. Good afternoon."

The fat lady returned in an hour. She received her passport with a bow from the clerk and with: "Always a great pleasure to be at your service, madame."

I was still sitting and awaiting my turn.

I apologized mentally for my unjustified bad opinion of American consuls. They are not so bad as I thought. It was nothing but national jealousy, what Belgian, Dutch, and French policemen had told me about American consuls being the worth of all bureaucrats alive. Here, at this consulate, I certainly would obtain the passport that would help me get a ship to go back home and be an honest worker ever after. I would settle down somewhere in the West, get married, and do my bit to populate my country and make the kids bigger and better citizens.

I was asked to "come in." All the other people waiting here had to go, when their number was called, through a different door from the one I used. I passed through the same door through which the fat lady had passed. So I was, after all, to see Mr. Grgrgrgrs, or whatever his name was. Exactly the gent I was most eager to see. A person so kind as to give a lady in need, in so short a time, a new passport would understand my troubles better than anybody else.

The gentleman I met was short, lean, and rather sad or worried about something. He was dried up to the bones. He looked as though he had been working in an office before he had reached fourteen. I had the impression that, should it ever happen that he could no longer go to an office at a certain hour in the morning and work there or sit there until a certain hour in the afternoon, he would die inside of six weeks, believing himself a failure.

"Sit down. What can I do for you?"

"I would like to have a passport."

"Lost your passport?"

"Not my passport. Only my sailor's identification card."

"Oh, then you are a sailor?"

When I said: "Yes, sir," he changed the expression on his face, and his voice took another tone. He narrowed his eyes, and from then on he looked at me with suspicion written all over his face.

"You see, sir, I missed my ship."

"Drunk, eh?"

"I never drink, sir. Not a drop. I believe in prohibition."

"But you did tell me you are a sailor?"

"Exactly. My ship got under weigh three hours before the time we were supposed to sail. I had presumed that we would go out with high water. As we had no cargo and were going home in ballast, the skipper didn't have to wait for high water to come in, and so he ordered the ship to make off early in the night."

"Your papers were left aboard, I suppose?"

"Right, sir."

"I might have known this before. Do you remember the register number of your sailor's card?"

"No, sir. I am sorry."

"So am I. Where was the card issued? By what shippipng board?"

"I don't remember where it was. You see, I have shipped in coast traffic, Boston, New York, Philly, New Orleans, Galveston, and all along the Mexican Gulf. You see, sir, a sailor does not look every day at his card. In fact, I have never looked at all at what it said. Often it is not even asked for by the skipper when he signs you on. He takes it for granted that a guy has his card. More important to the skipper is what ship you have been on before, and under which master, and what you know about the job."

"I know. You don't have to tell me."

"Yes, sir."

"Naturalized?"

"No, sir. Native-born!"

"Birth registered?"

"I do not know, sir. When this happened, I was too small to remember exactly if it was done or not."

"Then your birth has not been registered."

"I said I do not know, sir."

"But I do know."

"Well, sir, if you know everything beforehand, why do you ask me?"

"Now, don't you get excited here. No reason for that. Was your mother married to your father?"

"I never asked my mother. I thought it her own business, and that it concerns nobody else."

"Right. Excuse me. I was only thinking that the marriage license might be found somewhere. Your father was also a sailor, like you?"

"Yes, sir."

"I thought so. Never came home again I suppose?"

"I do not know, sir."

"Any relatives alive?"

"I do not know, sir. Never knew any."

"Know somebody in the States who has known you since you were a boy?"

"I think there ought to be lots of people who ought to know me."

He took up a pencil and got ready to write down names and addresses. "Will you, please, name any of these people who have known you for a long time—let us say fifteen years or so?"

"How could I recall any of them, sir? They all are people of no importance. Just plain people. Working folks. Changing places whenever their work calls for it. I would not know their full names or even their real names, only the names we knew them by or called them."

"Have you a permanent address back home?"

"No, sir. I could not pay for one. You see, I live on my ships, like most sailors do. When laid off for a while I stay in a sailors' home or just in any cheap boarding-house near the waterfront."

"Your mother still alive?"

"I think so. But I do not know for sure."

"You do not know for sure?"

"How can I know for sure, sir? While I was away, she changed her address several times. Perhaps she's married to somebody whose name I do not know. You see, sir, with us working people and sailors everything cannot be done as fine and smooth as with the rich guys that have an elegant house of their own and a swell bank-account and a telephone and a lot of servants. We have to look out first for a job, and afterwards we worry about other things. The job means eating. Without a job we are just like a farmer without a farm."

"Ever gone to the polls to vote in any state election?"

"No, sir. I never had any time to mix with politics."

"You are a pacifist?"

"A what, sir?"

"Well, I mean you are communist. You do not want to fight for the country."

"I did not say so, sir. I think that as a sailor who works hard I am fighting every day for the greatness of my country. Our country would not be a great country if there were no sailors and no working-men."

"Didn't you say you shipped in New Orleans?"

"Yes, sir, that's right."

"Then, of course, you are a member of the—now, what is the name? Yes, of the Industrial Workers of the World. Syndicalism and such things?"

"No, sir, never heard of it."

"But you said you shipped in New Orleans?"

"Yes, sir."

"Never in Los Angeles?"

"No, sir."

For a long while he looks at me with dull eyes. He does not know what more to ask. He drums the desk with his pencil. Then he says: "Well, I cannot give you a passport, and that is all there is to it. Sorry."

"But why, sir?"

"Upon what proofs? Your statement that you claim American citizenship is no proof. Personally, I believe that you are American. However, the Department of Labor in Washington, to which I am responsible for making out passports and other identifications, does not wish to know what I believe and what I do not believe. This office in Washington accepts only unquestionable evidence and no mere belief of a consul abroad. If you bring proper evidence, it will be my obligation to issue a passport to you. How can you prove that you are American, that I am obliged to spend my time on your case?"

"You can hear that, sir."

"How? By your language? That is no proof."

"Of course it is. It is the best proof."

"Here in France there live thousands of Russians who speak better French than the average Frenchman does. That does not make a Russian a Frenchman, does it? In New Orleans, on the other hand, there are several thousand people who speak only French and very little if any English. Nevertheless they are as true Americans as I am. Texas and southern California are full of people who speak Mexican and Spanish, but they are Americans in spite of their foreign language. So what proof is the language you are speaking?"

"I was born in the States."

"Prove that and I will give you a passport within two days. But even if you were born in the States, I would still have the right to question your citizenship, because it might have happened that your father, before you were of age, certified on your behalf for another citizenship. I would not go that far, of course. Just prove to me that you were born in the States. Or name me a few persons who will testify that you are native-born."

"How can I ever prove anything, then, since my birth was not registered?"

"That is not my fault, is it?"

"It looks, sir, as though you would even doubt the fact that I was born at all?"

"Right, my man. Think it silly or not. I doubt your birth as long as you have no certificate of your birth. The fact that you are sitting in front of me is no proof of your birth. Officially it is no proof. The law or the Department of Labor may or may not accept my word that I have seen you and that, as I have seen you, you must have been born. I know this is silly, it is nonsense. But I did not make the law. Do you know that I might get fired or discharged from public service for having given you a passport without any other evidence than your word and your presence in person? Frankly, in your case I do not know what to do."

He pressed a button. In came the clerk. The consul writes my name on a scrap of paper, asking me how I spell it. "Look up this name, please, Gerard Gales, last residence New Orleans, sailor, *Tuscaloosa*."

The clerk leaves the door partly open. I see him going into a small room where all the files are located. I know what he is looking for: the deported, the undesirables, the criminals, the anarchists, the communists, the pacifists and all the other trouble-makers whom the government is anxious to refuse re-entry into the country.

The clerk returned. The consul had been standing at the window in the meantime, looking out into the street, where life went on as busy as ever, papers or no papers.

The consul asked: "Well?"

"Not on file. No records."

"You gave your right name, did you?" the consul asked. "I mean the name you were living by in the home country?"

"Yes, sir. I never had any trouble back home."

The clerk left the room and I was again alone with the consul.

There was silence for a long time. I looked at the pictures on the wall. All faces familiar since I was a kid. All great men. All lovers and supporters of freedom, of the rights of human beings, builders of a great country, where men may and shall be free to pursue their happiness.

The consul rose and left the room.

After five minutes he came back. A new question had occurred to him: "You might be—I do not insinuate you are—an escaped convict. You might be wanted by the police at home, or in any other country."

"You are quite right, sir. I might. I see now that I have come in vain to my consul, who is paid to help Americans in need. I see it is hopeless. Thank you for your trouble, sir."

"I am very sorry, but in your case I simply do not see any way I could do anything for you. I am only an official. I have strict regulations by which I have to work. You should have been more careful with your papers. In times like these nobody can afford to lose his passport or similar important papers. We are no longer living in those carefree prewar times when practically no papers were asked for."

"Would you, please, and if you don't mind, tell me one thing, sir?" I asked.

"Yes?"

"There was here, yesterday afternoon, a very fat lady, with a dozen heavy diamond rings on her fingers and a pearl necklace around her fat neck which might have cost ten thousand dollars at least. Well, that lady had lost her passport just as I have. She got a new passport here in less than an hour."

"I see, you are referring to Mrs. Sally Marcus from New York. Surely, you have heard the name before. That big banking firm of New York." This the consul said with a gesture and a modulation of his voice as though he had wanted to say: "My good man, don't you know, this was His Royal Highness the Prince of Wales and not just a drunken sailor without a ship."

He must have noticed by the expression on my face that I had not taken the information as he had expected I would. So he added hastily: "The well-known banking firm, you know, in New York."

I still did not satisfy his hope of seeing me turn pale when such a great personage was mentioned in my presence.

But Wall Street, the house of Morgan, the richness of the Rockefellers, a seat on the stock-exchange has never made any, not even the slightest, impression upon me. It all leaves me as unimpressed as a cold potato.

So I said to the consul: "I do not believe that this lady is an American. I would think her born somewhere in Bucharest."

"How did you guess?" the consul opened his eyes wide and almost lost his breath. "Sure, she was born in Bucharest, in Roumania. But she is an American citizen."

"Did she carry along her naturalization papers?"

"Of course not. Why?"

"Then how could you tell that she is an American citizen? She has not even learned to speak the American language. Her lingo is not even East Side. I bet it is not even accepted at Whitechapel."

"Now get me right. In the case of that lady I do not need any evidence. Her husband, Mr. Reuben Marcus, is one of the best-known bankers of New York. Mrs. Marcus crossed in the most expensive stateroom on the *Majestic.* I saw her name on the list."

"Yes, I understand. You said it, Mr. Consul. I crossed only as a plain deck-hand in the forecastle bunk of a freighter. That, I see, makes all the difference. Not the papers. Not the birth-certificate. A big banking firm is the only evidence needed to prove a man a citizen. Thank you, sir. That's exactly what I wanted to know. Thank you, sir."

"Now, look here, mister sailor. Let's talk this over and get it straight. I do not wish you to leave here with the wrong impression about me. I have told you that, under the circumstances, I have no power whatever to do anything for you. I am not to blame. It is the system of which I am a slave. If I had the power—let us say if I were going to leave office anyway during the year to retire—I promise you, upon my word, I would be pleased to give you any paper you need. But I cannot do it. My hands are bound. Entirely. Frankly, I believe your story. It sounds true. I have had cases similar to yours. The same result. Could do nothing. I believe you are American. I almost think you are a better American than certain bankers ever will be. You belong with us. You are the right blood. But I tell you just as frankly: should it happen that the French police bring you here before me, to recognize you, I would deny vehemently your claim to American citizenship. I might say, as a man, I would do it with a bleeding heart, but I would do it, because I have to, as a soldier in war has to kill even his friend when he meets him on the battle-field clad in the uniform of the enemy."

"Which means, in fewer words, that I may go to hell."

"I did not say that. But since we have become frank with each other, I might as well admit, yes, it means exactly that. I have no other choice. I might, of course, write to Washington and present your case. Suppose you could produce the names and addresses of people back home who know you. It would nevertheless be from four to eight months before your citizenship would be established satisfactorily. Have you got the means to stay that long in Paris to wait for the final decision of Washington?"

"How could I, sir? I am a sailor. I have to look for a ship. There are no ships in Paris. I am a high-sea sailor, not a sailor of vegetable boats on the river Seine."

"I knew that. You cannot wait here in Paris for months and months.

We have no funds to provide for your staying here. By the way, would you like to have a ticket for three days' board and lodging? When it expires you may drop in again to have another one."

"No, thank you just the same. I'll get along all right."

"I suppose you would rather have a railroad ticket to a port where you might pick a ship sailing under another flag, or you may have the good luck to find a master of an American ship who knows you."

"No, many thanks. I shall find my own way."

He sighed. For a while he went to the window looking out again. Nothing new seemed to come into his mind. It would have been a rare thing anyhow for an official to come upon an idea that is not provided for in the regulations.

So there was nothing left for him to say but: "I am so sorry. Well, then, good-by and all the luck!"

After all, there is a great difference between American officials in general and European officials in general. The office hours ended at four, or even at three. When I was out in the street again I noticed that it was five. But at no time during my conversation with the consul did he show any sign of impatience or make me think that he was in a hurry and had to go home or to the golf links. Not all American officials are like that, yet there are still some. In Europe, however, I have never met any official who did not, fifteen minutes before his working hours terminated, start showing me my way out regardless of how important my business might be.

Now I had really lost my ship.

Good-by, my sunny New Orleans! Good-by and good luck to you.

Well, honey, you'd better stick up with somebody else now. Don't wait any longer on Jackson Square or at the Levee. Your boy is not coming home any more. The sea has swallowed him. I could fight gales and waves, be it with fists or with the paint-brush. But I have lost out in my fight against the almighty papers and certificates. Get another boy, sweetheart, before it is too late, and ere all your blossoms have fallen off in the autumn winds. Don't waste the roses of your sweet youth waiting for the guy who no longer has a country, for the man who was not born.

Damn the skirt! Ship ahoy! Fresh wind coming up! All hands, hear, get all the canvas spread! Sheet home! And all of it! Up and high! A fresh wind is coming up!

The Archer-Shee Case

Alexander Woollcott

FROM TIME to time, since the turn of the century, there has issued from the press of a publishing house in London and Edinburgh a series of volumes called the *Notable British Trials,* each volume dedicated to some case in the criminal annals of England or Scotland. Each would contain not only the testimony of witnesses, the photographs of exhibits, the arguments of counsel, the dicta from the bench, and the verdict of the jury, but also an introductory essay nicely calculated to enthrall those readers who collect such instances of human violence, much as other madmen collect coins or autographs or stamps.

The cases thus made available range all the way from the trials of the mutineers aboard the *Bounty* to the libel action which, in the twilight of the Victorian era, grew out of a charge of cheating during a card game at a place called Tranby Croft, a gaudy lawsuit which agitated the entire Empire because it dragged into the witness box no less a personage, a bit ruffled and breathing heavily, than H. R. H. the Prince of Wales, who was later to rule and consolidate that Empire as Edward VII. But for the most part, of course, the cases thus edited have had their origin in murder most foul, and they constitute not only an indispensable part of every law library but a tempting pastime to all of us whose telltale interest in poison and throat-cutting is revealed in no other aspects of our humdrum, blameless lives.

Now, as an avid subscriber to the series, I have long been both exasperated and puzzled by the fact that it contained no transcript of that trial which, more and more in recent years, has taken definite shape in my own mind as one of the most notable and certainly the most British of them all. Nowhere in England or America is there available in any library a record of the Archer-Shee case. The student eager to master its details must depend on such scattered odds and ends as he can dredge up from contemporary memoirs and from the woefully incomplete reports in newspaper files which already moulder to dust at the touch.

But within recent months, by a series of curious chances too fantastic to have been foreseen, a complete private record of the entire case has come into my possession, and it is my present plan, before another year has passed, to put it into print for the use of anyone who needs it as a light or craves it as a tonic. For the Archer-Shee case is a short, sharp, illuminating chapter in the long history of human liberty, and a study of it might, it seems to me, stiffen the purpose of all those who in our own day are freshly resolved that that liberty shall not perish from the earth.

In the fall of 1908, Mr. Martin Archer-Shee, a bank manager in Liverpool, received word, through the commandant of the Royal Naval College at Osborne, that the Lords Commissioners of the Admiralty had decided to dismiss his thirteen-year-old son George, who had been proudly entered as a cadet only a few months before. It seems that a five-shilling postal order had been stolen from the locker of one of the boys—stolen, forged, and cashed—and, after a sifting of all the available evidence, the authorities felt unable to escape the conclusion that young Archer-Shee was the culprit. Out of such damaged and unpromising material the Admiralty could scarcely be expected to fashion an officer for His Majesty's Navy. "My Lords deeply regret," the letter went on to say, "that they must therefore request you to withdraw your son from the College." This devastating and puzzling news brought the family hurrying to Osborne. Was it true? No, Father. Then why did the authorities accuse him? What had made them think him guilty? The bewildered boy had no idea. "Well," said the father in effect, "we'll have to see about this," little guessing then, as he was to learn through many a bitter and discouraging month, that that would be easier said than done.

What had made them think the boy a thief? The offish captain could only refer him to the admiralty, and the Lords of the Admiralty—by not answering letters, evading direct questions, and all the familiar technique of bureaucratic delay—retired behind the tradition that the Navy must be the sole judge of material suitable for the making of a British officer. If once they allowed their dismissal of a cadet to be reviewed by an inevitably outraged family, they would be establishing a costly and regrettable precedent.

What the elder Archer-Shee found blocking the path was no personal devil, no vindictive enemy of his son, no malignant spirit. But he was faced with an opponent as maddening, as cruel, and as destructive. He was entering the lists against the massive, complacent inertia of a government department which is not used to being questioned and does not like to be bothered. He was girding his loins for the kind of combat that takes all the courage and patience and will power a man can summon to his aid. He was challenging a bureaucracy to battle.

At a dozen points in the ensuing struggle, in which he was backed up every day by his first-born, who was a Major and an M.P. and a D. S. O., a less resolute fighter might have been willing to give up, and one of smaller means would have had to. After all, the boy's former teachers and classmates at Stonyhurst, the Catholic college where he was prepared for Osborne, had welcomed him back with open arms, and, as allusions to the episode began to find their way into print, there were plenty of comfortable old men in clubs who opined loudly that this man Archer-Shee was making a bloody nuisance of himself. But you may also be sure that there were those among the neighbors who implied by their manner that the Navy must know what it was doing, that where there was so much smoke there must be some fire, that if the whole story could be told, and so forth and so forth. I think the father knew in his heart, as surely as anyone can know anything in this world, that his son was innocent. While there was a breath left in his body and a pound in his bank account, he could not let the youngster go out into the world with that stain on his name. He would not give up. Probably he was strengthened by his memory of how bitterly his little boy had wept on the day they took him away from Osborne. The father lived—by no more than a few months—to see the fight through.

The first great step was the retaining of Sir Edward Carson, then at the zenith of his incomparable reputation as an advocate. In his day, Carson was to hold high office—Attorney-General, Solicitor-General—to assume political leadership in the Ulster crisis—leader of the Irish Unionists in the House—to be rewarded with a peerage. It was part of the manifold irony of that crowded and stormy life, which ended in his death at eighty-one in 1935, that probably he will be longest remembered because of that hour of merciless cross-examination, in a libel suit at the Old Bailey, which brought down in ruins the towering and shaky edifice known as Oscar Wilde. But some there are who, when all is forgotten, will rather hold Carson in highest honor for the good turn he once did to a small boy in trouble. He put all his tremendous power and implacable persistence and passionate hatred of tyranny at the service of Master Archer-Shee.

It was only after he had heard the boy's own story (and raked him with such a bracketing fire of questions as he was famous for directing against a witness) that he agreed to take the case at all. From that interview he rose, saying in effect, "This boy did not steal that postal order. Now, let's get at the facts."

This took a bit of doing. It was the nub of the difficulty that the small embryo officer had, by becoming a cadet, lost the rights of an ordinary citizen without yet reaching that status which would have entitled him to a court-martial. To be sure, the Admiralty by this time had resentfully bestirred itself to make several supplementary inquiries, but these were all *ex parte* proceedings, with the boy unrepresented by counsel, the witnesses unsubjected to the often clarifying fire of cross-examination. Even when the badgered authorities went so far as to submit their findings to the Judge Advocate general for review, they still kept the Archer-Shees cooling their heels in the anteroom.

I am commanded by the Lords Commissioners of the Admiralty to acknowledge receipt of your letter relative to the case of George Archer-Shee, and my
Lords desire me to say that the further enquiry is not one at which a representative of your side in the sense in which you use the word would be appropriate.

Well, even at the horrid risk of following a procedure which might
be described as "inappropriate," Carson was determined to get the case
into court, to make those witnesses tell their story not to a biased and
perhaps comatose representative of the Admiralty but to a jury of ordinary
men—above all, to tell it with the public listening. Resisting him in this
was Sir Rufus Isaacs, later to become, as Lord Reading, Chief Justice of
England, but then—in 1909 and 1910, this was—Solicitor-General and,
unbecoming as was the posture into which it threw him, mysteriously
compelled by professional tradition to defend the Admiralty's action at
every step.

How to get the case into court? Carson finally had recourse to an
antique and long-neglected device known as the Petition of Right. First
he had to establish the notion that there had been a violation of contract—
a failure of the Crown to keep its part of the bargain implied when, at
some considerable expense to his folks and with a binding agreement on
his own part to serve as an officer in the Navy once he had been trained
for the job, the boy matriculated. But, contract or no contract, a subject
may sue the King only under certain circumstances. If he approach the
throne with a Petition of Right and the King consent to write across it
"Let right be done," His Majesty can, in that instance and on that issue,
be sued like any commoner.

Instead of welcoming such a course as the quickest way of settling the
original controversy and even of finding out what really had happened
to that fateful postal order, the Admiralty, perhaps from sheer force of
habit, resorted to legal technicalities as a means of delay. Indeed, it was
only the human impatience of the justices, to whom a demurrer was carried on appeal, that finally cut through the red tape. They would eventually
have to decide whether or not a Petition of Right was the suitable remedy,
but in the meantime, they asked, why not let them have the facts? Why
not, indeed? It was all Carson was contending for. It was all the Archer-
Shees had ever asked for. Later in the House of Commons, where he was
to hear the intervention of the demurrer denounced as a tragic error, Sir
Rufus took considerable credit to himself for having bowed to this call
for the facts, but he was making a virtue of something that had been very
like necessity.

Anyway, the trial was ordered. So at long last, on a hot day in July
1910—nearly two years after the postal order was stolen and too late for
any hope of finding out who really had stolen it—the case came before a
jury in the King's Bench Division, and the witnesses whose stories in the
first place had convinced the Osborne authorities that young Archer-Shee

was a thief must, with Sir Rufus vigilant to protect them, submit themselves to cross-examination by the most alarming advocate of the English Bar.

By this time the case had ceased to be a local squabble, reported as a matter of professional interest in various service journals but showing up in the ordinary newspapers only in an occasional paragraph. Now it was being treated by the press, column after column, as a *cause célèbre,* and all the Empire was following it with bated breath. Carson was on his feet in open court speaking for the Suppliant:

His son was branded as a thief and as a forger, a boy thirteen years old was labeled and ticketed, and has been since labeled and ticketed for all his future life, as a thief and a forger, and in such investigation as led to that disastrous result, neither his father nor any friend was ever there to hear what was said against a boy of thirteen, who by that one letter, and by that one determination was absolutely deprived of the possibility of any future career either in His Majesty's Service, or indeed in any other Service. Gentlemen, I protest against the injustice to a little boy, a child thirteen years of age, without communication with his parents, without his case ever being put, or an opportunity of its ever being put forward by those on his behalf—I protest against that boy at that early stage, a boy of that character, being branded for the rest of his life by that one act, an irretrievable act that I venture to think could never be got over. That little boy from that day, and from the day that he was first charged, up to this moment, whether it was in the ordeal of being called in before his Commander and his Captain, or whether it was under the softer influences of the persuasion of his own loving parents, has never faltered in the statement that he is an innocent boy.

But these reverberant words had overtones which all Englishmen could hear. Now the case was being followed with painful attention by plain men and women slowly come to the realization that here was no minor rumpus over the discipline and punctilio of the service, indeed no mere matter of a five-shilling theft and a youngster's reputation, but a microcosm in which was summoned up all the long history of British liberty. Here in the small visible compass of one boy's fate was the entire issue of the inviolable sovereignty of the individual.

The Archer-Shees had as their advantageous starting point the inherent improbability of the boy's guilt. There seemed no good reason why he *should* steal five shillings when he was in ample funds on which he could lay his hands at will by the simple process of writing a chit. But if, for good measure or out of sheer deviltry, he *had* stolen his classmate's postal order, it seemed odd that instead of cashing it furtively he would not only openly get permission to go to the post office, which was out of bounds, but first loiter about for some time in an effort to get a schoolmate to go along with him for company. But this inherent improbability, so visible from this distance, quite escaped the attention of the college authorities who, by the sheer momentum of prosecution, had hastily reached their own conclusion by another route.

When young Terence Back dolefully reported to the Cadet Gunner that the postal order which had arrived that very morning as a present from some doting relative was missing from his locker, the Chief Petty Officer at once telephoned the post office to find out if it had already been cashed. It had. Oh!

There followed a rush of officialdom to the post office and much questioning of the chief clerk, Miss Anna Clara Tucker, first there and later at the college by Commander Cotton, the officer in charge of the investigation. Now, Miss Tucker, had there been any cadets at the post office that day? Yes, two—one to buy a 15s. 6d. postal order, the other to buy two totaling 14s. 9d. And was it one of them who had cashed the stolen order? Yes, it was. Would the postmistress be able to pick him out? No. They all looked so alike, in their uniforms, that she wouldn't know one from the other. But this she could tell, this she *did* remember—the stolen order was cashed by the boy who had bought the postal order for fifteen and six. And which one was that? Well, her records could answer that question. It was Cadet Archer-Shee. (He had needed that order, by the way, to send for a model engine on which his heart was set, and to purchase the order he had that morning drawn sixteen shillings from his funds on deposit with the Chief Petty Officer, a sum which would not only buy the order but pay for the necessary postage and leave in his pocket some small change for emergencies.)

Thus to Commander Cotton—Richard Greville Arthur Wellington Stapleton Cotton, who, oddly enough, was later to command H. M. S. *Terrible*—thus to Commander Cotton, who reported accordingly to the Captain, and he, through Portsmouth, to the Admiralty, it seemed satisfactorily evident that the postmistress was ineluctably identifying Archer-Shee as the thief, or at least as the villain who had converted the stolen goods into cash.

On her testimony the authorities acted—innocently, if you like, and not without later taking the precaution to support it by the dubious opinion of a handwriting expert. But so muddle-headed was this investigation, and such is the momentum of prosecution the world around, that the very first *précis* of that testimony filed with the Admiralty was careful to omit, as perhaps weakening the evidence against the boy—so swiftly do departmental investigators change from men seeking the truth into men trying to prove a hasty conclusion—was careful to omit the crucial fact that at the college next morning, when six or seven of the cadets were herded past her for inspection, the postmistress had been unable, either by the look of his face or by the sound of his voice, to pick out Archer-Shee. This failure became patently crucial when, two years later on that sweltering July day, Carson, with artfully deceptive gentleness, took over Miss Tucker for cross-examination.

The cashing of the stolen order and the issuing of the order for fifteen and six had taken place at the same time? Well, one transaction after the other. Her records showed that? No, but she remembered. The two took place within what space of time? Well, there might have been interruptions. After all, she was in sole charge of the office at the time? Yes. There was the telephone to answer, telegrams to take down as they came over the wire? Yes, and the mail to sort. These matters often took her away from the window? Yes. Even into the back room? Sometimes. So sometimes, if one cadet should go away from the window and another step into his place during any one of the interruptions, she might not notice the exchange? That was true. And, since they all looked alike to her, one cadet in this very instance *could* have taken the place of another without her realizing, when she returned to the window, that she had not been dealing throughout with the same boy? Possibly. So that now she couldn't say it was Archer-Shee who had cashed the stolen order? She had never said that exactly. Nor could she even be sure, now that she came to think of it, that the stolen order had, in fact, been cashed by the same cadet who bought the order for fifteen and six? Not absolutely sure. That, in effect— here oversimplified in condensation, but in effect—was her testimony.

Well, there it was—a gap in her story wide enough to drive a coach through. As soon as he saw it—it would strike a mere onlooking layman that the Admiralty might well have asked these same questions two years before—Sir Rufus knew the jig was up. Wherefore, when court opened on the fourth day, he was soon on his feet announcing that he no longer wished to proceed with any question of fact. It takes no great feat of imagination to guess at the breathlessness in that courtroom as the Solicitor-General came to the point:

As a result of the evidence that has been given during the trial that has been going on now for some days, and the investigation that has taken place, I say now, on behalf of the Admiralty, that I accept the statement of George Archer-Shee that he did not write the name on the postal order, and did not cash it, and consequently that he is innocent of the charge. I say further, in order that there may be no misapprehension about it, that I make that statement without any reserve of any description, intending that it shall be a complete justification of the statement of the boy and the evidence he has given before the Court.

In return—perhaps a fair exchange haggled for behind the scenes— Carson went on record as holding the belief that the responsible persons at Osborne and at the Admiralty had acted in good faith and that not even the disastrous Miss Tucker had been wanting in honesty. He had merely sought to show that she was mistaken.

Then, while the jury swarmed out of the box to shake hands with Carson and with the boy's father, the exhausted advocate turned to congratulate the boy himself, only to find that he wasn't even in court. Indeed, the case was over and court had adjourned before he got the news. When, blushing and grinning from ear to ear and falling all over himself, he went to Carson's room in the Law Courts to thank him, the great advocate ventured to ask how in his hour of triumph the boy had happened to be missing. Well, sir, he got up late. It seems he went to the theater the night before and so had overslept. Overslept! For weeks Carson himself had hardly been able to get any sleep. Overslept! Good God! Hadn't he even been anxious? Oh, no, sir. He had known all along that once the case got into court the truth would come out. Carson mopped his brow. Then he laughed. Perhaps that *was* the best way to take such things.

Thereafter, of course, the boy's was not the only attention that wandered. All England may have been watching, but, after all, other current topics were not without their elements of public interest. For one thing, a new King was on the throne. The Edward who had written "Let right be done" across the Archer-Shee petition now lay in his tomb at Windsor, and his son George was only just beginning the reign which was to prove so unforeseeably eventful. Then, even as the case came to an end, another was ready to overshadow it. Indeed, on the very day when, on behalf of the Admiralty, Sir Rufus acknowledged the boy's innocence, Inspector Dew arrived in Quebec to wait for the incoming *Montrose* and arrest two of her passengers, a fugitive medico named Crippen and his dream-girl, Ethel Le Neve. Even so, thanks to the sounding board known as the House of Commons, neither the public nor the Admiralty was allowed to forget the Archer-Shee case. Indeed, news of its conclusion had hardly reached the House when several members were on their feet giving notice—due notice that England would expect some specific assurance that the lesson had been learned, that never again would a boy be thus cavalierly dismissed from Osborne without notice to his folks or a chance for adequate defense.

In this instance, of course, it was too late for anything but apology and indemnification. "This," one speaker said with apparently unconscious humor, "could be left to the generosity of the Admiralty." Another speaker—the honorable member for the Universities of Glasgow and Aberdeen—put it this way: "I am quite sure the Admiralty will do all in their power to redress the very terrible and almost irreparable wrong done to the boy, on such a wrong being brought to their knowledge." But this confidence proved to be naïve. Month followed month with no word of apology, no word even of regret, and, as for indemnification, no offer to pay more than a fraction of what the boy's father had already spent in his defense. Indeed, in the fitful discussion on this point, the Admiralty had even introduced the pretty suggestion that the nipping of young Archer-Shee's naval career in the bud had not been so very injurious, because he was not a promising student anyway. It looks, at this distance, like a bad case of bureaucratic sulks.

So in March and April of the following year the attack was renewed. By the quaint but familiar device of moving that the salary of the First Lord of the Admiralty (Mr. Reginald McKenna) be reduced by one hundred pounds, the honorable member for Kingston (Mr. Cave) started the ball rolling. Although the honorable member for Leicester, Mr. Ramsay MacDonald, was so far out of key as to call the motion an attempt to blackmail the Treasury (cries of "Shame! Shame!"), the resulting debate went to the heart of the matter and put in memorable and satisfying words just what many decent and inarticulate men had been wanting to have said about the case all along.

The relative passages in *Hansard* make good reading to this day, because all those who moved to the attack spoke as if nothing in the world could matter more than the question of justice to one small unimportant boy. The wretched legalism of the Admiralty's evasions received its just meed of contempt, with the wits of Sir Rufus Isaacs matched (and a bit more) by the same F. E. Smith who was later to become Lord Birkenhead and who, by the way, was at the time fresh from the defense of Ethel Le Neve at the Old Bailey. These members, together with Lord Charles Beresford and others, firmly jockeyed the unhappy First Lord into the position where he not only gave assurance that thereafter no boy at Osborne would ever be so dealt with—this he had come prepared to do —but went on record, at long reluctant last, as expressing in this case his unqualified regrets. He even consented to pay to the boy's father whatever sum a committee of three (including Carson himself) should deem proper. This ended in a payment of £7120, and with that payment the case may be said to have come to an end.

The case—but not the story. That has an epilogue. The characters? Most of them are gone. I don't know whatever became of poor Miss Tucker, but the elder Archer-Shee is gone, and Isaacs and Carson. Even Osborne is gone—Osborne where Victoria walked with Albert and one day plucked the primroses for Disraeli. At least its Naval College has gone out of existence, swallowed up in Dartmouth.

And the boy himself? Well, when it came to him, the author of the epilogue dipped his pen in irony. To say that much is tantamount to a synopsis. If you will remember that the boy was thirteen when they threw him out of Osborne and fifteen when his good name was re-established, you will realize that when the Great War began he was old enough to die for King and Country. And did he? Of course. As a soldier, mind you. The lost two years had rather discouraged his ambitions with regard to the Navy. August 1914 found him in America, working in the Wall Street firm of Fisk & Robinson. Somehow he managed to get back to England, join up with the Second Battalion of the South Staffordshire Regiment, win a commission as Second Lieutenant, and get over to France in time to be killed—at Ypres—in the first October of the War.

So that is the story of Archer-Shee, whose years in the land, all told, were nineteen. To me his has always been a deeply moving story, and more and more, as the years have gone by, a significant one. Indeed, I should like to go up and down our own land telling it to young people not yet born when Archer-Shee kept his rendezvous with death. You see, I know no easier way of saying something that is much on my mind. For this can be said about the Archer-Shee case: that it could not happen in any totalitarian state. It is so peculiarly English, this story of a whole people getting worked up about a little matter of principle; above all, the story of the foremost men of the land taking up the cudgels—taking up the cudgels against the state, mind you—because a youngster had been unfairly treated. It would have been difficult to imagine it in the Germany of Bismarck and the Wilhelms. It is impossible to imagine it in the Germany of Adolf Hitler.

"Justice Is That Which Serves Our Purpose"

Erika Mann

IN THE local university of our city Professor Habermann occupied the chair of criminal law. Habermann—the picture of the "Germanic" type, fat, blond, with several dueling scars on his face, and a clean-shaven bull neck, pink and shiny like a ham—was forty years old when Hitler came to power. Until that time he had not risen higher than the rank of assistant tutor at various second-rate universities, a circumstance due less to lack of knowledge and ability than to an essential attitude of indifference toward his own career. Dr. Habermann, German-Nationalist to the marrow of his bones, had anything but a liking for the German Republic. He preferred to hide himself in some small town, spending his free time with his books, or meeting with his friends over a glass of wine to run down the regime, rather than to seek fame in the capital, obligating himself thereby to the leaders of Republican Germany.

Then, early in 1935, Habermann was appointed full-fledged professor at our university. A half-Jewish colleague in the profession was dismissed to make room for him, and Habermann was quite content to have it so. The students found that, everything being considered, the appointment was not as bad as it might have been.

The university was situated just beyond the maze of streets which sur-

From *The Lights Go Down*, by Erika Mann, translated by Maurice Samuel. Copyright, 1940, by Rinehart & Co., and reprinted with their permission.

rounded the market place. The fountains on the campus could be heard in every classroom which gave on it, even when the windows were closed. It was a soporific sound, but without it, the interminable repetition of the monotonous, unvarying basic principles of the Nazi "life philosophy" sufficed to put large numbers of students to sleep. Professor Habermann was one of the few teachers who, during every lesson, always kept one or two surprises up his sleeve, so that students found it worth while to stay awake and pay attention.

"Gentleman," he would say, "I submit the following case." Then he would describe a murder which had been committed under such and such circumstances. These and these were the facts, on the basis of which those and those persons were suspected of the crime. No one had been caught *in flagrante delicto*. The evidence was circumstantial. But the circumstantial evidence did not constitute proof beyond a reasonable doubt.

"The prosecuting attorney demands the death penalty for the suspect charged with the crime, one Lissauer. Lissauer is a Jew; he lives not far from the place where the crime was committed. He is unable to produce an ironclad alibi. Now, gentlemen, would you, under oath, justify conviction of murder and the pronouncement of the death penalty?"

The students thought hard. Habermann had raised his voice. Even those whom the fountains outside had put to sleep, had awakened. They did not have to answer; this was a lecture, not a seminar. It was up to Habermann himself to give the answer.

"Gentlemen!" he said, and two angry sparks glittered in his pale eyes, which he drew together so that he looked like a Kalmuck, and not at all like a regulation Germanic graduate of a students' dueling corps: "Gentlemen! In a case of this kind—and I wish you to take note that cases of this kind are thoroughly typical in our legal world—in such a case, it is perfectly idiotic—you understand?—it is perfectly idiotic, it is futile and therefore illegal, to ask for more than circumstantial evidence. For what is it we are concerned with in such a case?"

Here the professor fixed his eyes on a student in the front row, who, with head lowered, was drawing figures on his pad. "We are concerned with nothing more nor less than what is called 'the healthy folk instinct.' It is to this, and to this alone, that the prosecuting attorney makes his appeal. And is not the solution of the case obvious at a glance? A murder has been committed. Someone who committed it must be found; the law must make an example. A Jew who happens to be involved is unable to prove his innocence. The ancient Roman dictum that where there is doubt the benefit goes to the accused, has lost its validity. The new German law knows no clemency when the defense of the national wholeness is involved. Gentlemen, you have been inducted into a superbly constructed system of laws in harmony with the right life philosophy, penetrated with the emotional power and significance of the National Socialist concept of justice. It will be very simple for you, it *must* be very simple for you, to defend the verdict of 'guilty.' Your plea, gentlemen, must be such that

every member of the jury would be *ashamed* to pronounce Lissauer innocent. Every member of the jury must consider it dangerous—dangerous
for himself and for his family—to dismiss the charge against Lissauer!"

The young man in the front row put his pencil down on the desk with
a clatter. Dr. Habermann looked at him, and saw on his lips a half-
suppressed smile of agreement. Then the student threw back his head and
gave vent to a short but distinctly audible laugh. The class stamped with
its feet. That was the traditional student expression of agreement and
applause. It was quite clear; Habermann had spoken against the Nazis,
and the class was at one with him.

"Gentlemen," continued Professor Habermann, "you must clear your
minds of all preconceptions and idle notions regarding 'objective justice'
and 'natural justice.' Only recently our minister of justice, Dr. Frank,
gave us a striking formulation of the new truth: 'The spirit which must
dominate our courts, and radiate from them,' he said, 'must be that of
the nation's fanatical will to survival and self-vindication.' Some of you
may be tempted to object. You may ask: 'But how does one expect the
nation to know exactly what will serve its will to survival?' That, gentlemen, would be a thoroughly stupid question, and I am glad to say that
the minister of justice has spared me the trouble of stooping to answer it.
'It is for the National Socialist party,' he declares, 'to determine what is
due to the German people. In the matter of law and justice, as in everything else, the decisions and opinions of the National Socialist party provide the source for the authentically German system of juristic ideas. The
foundation of our legal system must be consistently envisaged under the
aspect of our world philosophy; we must repress excessive objectivization!'

"You see, then, gentlemen," exclaimed Habermann, and glanced at his
friend, the young man in the front row, "you see how right I was to warn
you against outmoded and un-German conceptions of 'natural justice.'
As between 'excessive objectivization' and 'our world philosophy' there is
simply no choice, because everyone here knows that it is our world philosophy which rules, whatever the claims of so-called 'objective justice.'
But I notice"— the professor interrupted himself, and looked long and
earnestly into some of the faces before him, as if trying to read the thoughts
they concealed—"I notice a fresh uncertainty in your eyes, as though you
wanted to ask: 'But how on earth are we to accept as the basis of our legal
system a world philosophy which is subject to frequent change, and which
shifts its ground in accordance with political need and political developments? Does not the fanatical will to survival of the nation *demand* that
this world philosophy adapt itself to whatever the Führer considers advantageous and useful and *just* at every given moment?'

"Gentlemen, I congratulate you on the question," cried Professor
Habermann, as if the members of his class had really formulated it. "A
logical and penetrating question! But in this case too the state has anticipated every difficulty, and once again I am spared the trouble of formu-
lating an answer. In the life of the state there *is* one immutable principle

to which all other principles must adapt themselves; and that is the principle of *power*. I refer once more to the address of our minister of justice. 'The pitiful condition of the juridical ideal in the domain of world politics is demonstrated by the fact that an appeal to international justice is meaningless unless that appeal is backed by the determination and the practical means to give it effect.' The demand for justice, then, is a demand —any kind of demand—which is backed by the power to enforce it. That does, of course, make the study of law more difficult than it has been hitherto. Pedants and bookworms, who derive their knowledge of law from the writing of specialists without having studied the 'healthy folk instinct' are not going to get very far in our new Germany.

"I think it proper to remind you, gentlemen, that my superior, the minister of justice, proceeds with the utmost energy against the suggestion that the Nazi state 'can delegate to any scholar or specialist the right to delimit the powers of the Führer or of the Nazi party in the domain of law.' Nothing, in fact, can be so defined as to constitute a fixed opinion, for the concepts and emotions which feed our system of legal ideas are themselves too fluid. Since 'justice it that which is useful to the German people,' and since that which is useful today may no longer be useful tomorrow, it follows that today's justice may be tomorrow's injustice. Furthermore, since a just demand is one that is backed by the will and the means to enforce it, the same demand ceases to be just, in fact, it becomes null and void, when the power to enforce it ceases to exist or passes into other hands. Have I made myself clear, gentlemen? Has everyone understood me?"

The class stamped. The young man in the front row thought: By God! He nearly took me in once or twice. He sounded so serious when he talked about the "pedants and bookworms." But he's actually attacking the system! Only he's doing it in a new way. The man means business, no mistake about it.

On Habermann's face reappeared fleetingly the crooked grin which had distorted it when he had "proved" the guilt of the Jew Lissauer. Then he turned to a thick volume which lay before him on the reading desk.

"In spite of the warning issued by the ministers of justice," said Professor Habermann, "I find that a man calling himself 'a scholar or specialist' has dared to delimit or at least to define the powers of the party and the Führer in the domain of law, and to provide them with some sort of form. This production, dealing though it does with the law, is not properly part of our curriculum today. However, it provides in its own way so many valuable hints, that I shall introduce it into my lecture."

Does he actually mean that, thought the young man in the front row, and felt a shiver of fear.

"I am speaking of this book," continued Professor Habermann, and he held the volume before him between the forefinger and thumb of his right hand, as if he were in contact with some evil-smelling object. "It is called

The Constitutional Law of the Greater German Reich, published recently by the Hanseatische Verlagsanstalt; its author is Ernst Rudolph Huber, professor of law at Leipzig University. Gentlemen, I cannot recommend this brilliant work too highly. It is an astounding achievement—the more so if you bear in mind, as you should, under what difficulties the author labored in its production. Among these difficulties, by far the greatest, especially for a jurist, is the fact that the highest law, higher than so-called truth, is the decision of the Führer, which in turn is dictated by the afore-mentioned 'fanatical will to survival' of the nation. To give you a foretaste of the pleasure and profit which awaits you in the reading of it, gentlemen, I shall permit myself the following brief characterization of Ernst Rudolph Huber's masterpiece."

Opinion was divided in the class. Many of the students believed that Habermann genuinely admired the book that he praised in such glowing terms. They would have to read it, for it would undoubtedly be referred to in the examination papers. There was no point in listening to the professor now, he was done with joking. Others, and among them was the student in the front row, had been more attentive; they had understood thoroughly Habermann's sly but devastating condemnation of the book which he pretended to extol as a masterpiece. By God! breathed the student in the front row, then added under his breath: How's he going to pull this off?

Habermann turned the pages rapidly. "The thesis of the learned professor," he said, "may be summarized as follows:

"(1) The juridical tradition which Germany helped to found in the nineteenth century is pitched overboard, lock, stock and barrel. The 'sovereignty of the people,' with a great German, Johannes Althusius, once rescribed as 'inalienable,' goes overboard with it. The state, as you know, is all-powerful, and is vested with the authority to give effect to its demands 'totaliter' in every domain of life. The author, to whom all 'excessive objectivization' is obviously revolting, asserts (2) that the state is nothing but 'the personification of the will of the people.' 'The essential character and idea of the people,' he writes, 'are the fundamental data for the political and juridical being of the Reich. . . . Folk unity implies a unity of political life philosophy which possesses unique and exclusive validity.' You will find that passage on Page 158. Hence there is neither 'freedom of religious conscience' as such—Page 495—nor 'individual rights of liberty as against the power of the state'—Page 361. The right to liberty, he tells us, 'cannot be reconciled with the principle of the people's Reich.'

"And now, gentlemen," exclaimed Professor Habermann, raising his voice. "May I ask for a little co-operation from those of you who are showing an inclination to drop off to sleep? I must warn you that in marking the examination papers I shall have no mercy for such of you as have not learned by heart the following passage from *The Constitutional Law of the Greater German Reich*: *'There is no individual liberty antecedent to the state, or standing outside the state, which the state is bound to re-*

spect.' Mark those words, gentlemen, you who are the future administrators of the law in Germany. The German people will be delivered into your hands and into the hands of those in whose name you will interpret the law. This situation is referred to by Professor Huber as 'the Principle of Wholeness,' a principle which demands that a 'unity of political outlook' shall extend to all human activities and enterprises 'as a universal, all-embracing and all-penetrating phenomenon.' "

Professor Habermann paused and his blue eyes, which had narrowed down to two slits, ranged over the silent class.

"I need hardly tell you," he added, "what are the conclusions which must flow naturally and indeed inevitably from the work under discussion. For you know these conclusions. Nor do I believe that any fellow student of yours, to whatever faculty he belongs whether it be the mathematical or the political-economical, can escape them. As the author puts it: 'In the Folk as a political entity, only one supreme carrier of political power can be effective. That is the Führer, from whom all political power and all political authority flows.'

"Yes, yes, gentlemen," exclaimed Professor Habermann, joining in the laughter. "This is no easy profession which you have chosen, and the state will do everything in its power to see that you carry your choice through to the end. The secretary to the ministry of Justice, Dr. Roland Freisler, has expressed himself emphatically on this point. 'Above everything else,' he says, 'the jurist must be a real he-man' (Ein ganzer Kerl). Gentlemen, I am absolutely of the same opinion; the expression used by Dr. Freisler covers perfectly my hopes and wishes. 'A real he-man!' There is, naturally, room for discussion on the question of what constitutes 'a real he-man,' and I am sorry that time does not permit me to enter into a more detailed analysis of Dr. Freisler's conception of the same."

The students glanced at their wrist watches. This was a two-hour lecture and the first hour had not yet passed. Lack of time was hardly the explanation of the Professor's failure to pursue the subject of the Freislerian 'he-man.'

"However," continued Professor Habermann, "it may be pointed out that, according to the secretary of the Reich ministry of justice, 'for every kind of promotion, it is a man's effective activity, in the world war, or in the battle of the Nazi movement, or in military service, or in his capacity as family man, which must be the ultimate measure of his merit.' Dr. Freisler then adds: 'National political considerations make it desirable that when the abilities and achievements of two men are fairly even, the advantages should be given to the one with more children.' Gentlemen, you understand what that means: 'When the abilities and achievements of the two men are *fairly* even . . .' (bei gewisser Eignungs-und Leistungsgleichheit) So when one judge is a little inferior to another who has fewer children, it is the inferior one who is to be promoted 'because of national political consideration!'

"But nowadays it is not a simple matter for our leaders to discover who is 'superior' and who 'inferior.' Dr. Freisler, however, offers a valuable contribution toward the solution of the problem in listing the qualities which must be considered in estimating the 'effective activity' of a jurist: First, in the world war; second, in the battle of the Nazi movement; third, in the army; fourth—and last—as a family man. It cannot have escaped your observation that a man's 'effective activity' in a court of justice does not enter into the picture at all."

Habermann swung the pamphlet, *Deutsche Justiz,* from which he was quoting, aloft in the air as if it were a flag. The pages opened, and the professor held them for a moment before his eyes, then continued with the lecture:

"Dr. Freisler, after having made the student's readiness to contact an early marriage one of the basic requirements of the legal profession, adds the following remark: 'The new politics of personality must cancel much of the old, traditional body of thought; it must overcome many ingrained habits *in order that the new work may be imperiled.'* "

At this point Habermann raised his voice. "The emphasis on that last clause is mine, but the words are those of Secretary Freisler, and I feel it my duty to warn you specifically against misunderstanding them. We all know, of course, that the secretary means the exact opposite of what he is saying. But the German language is not an easy one, and not all 'he-men' possess the requisite skill in the handling of it." Here Professor Habermann grinned boyishly.

A handful of students laughed out loud. The young man in the front row frowned agonizingly and shook his head, unaware of what he was doing. Watch it! flashed through his mind. For God's sake, don't overdo it! That was going a bit too far!

Habermann, however, seemed to have nothing whatsoever on his conscience. He put down the pamphlet and drew from his pocket a folded newspaper, which he now opened.

"Yes," he repeated, "the German language is not an easy one, and many of our law students seem to have declared open war on it. The state legal board has been following this war with increasing concern, and we shall do well to devote a little attention to it. The head of the state legal board, Dr. Palandt, makes the following report from the field of battle: 'Not infrequently the crucial part of theses submitted by the legal examinees is so unintelligibly expressed that close study fails to elicit any meaning. It is quite clear that the examinee finds the greatest difficulty in producing a plain, readable document. It does not testify to a very high standard of intelligence among the legal examinees that they should be using the verbs "to claim," "to establish," "to cite," "to object," etc., without any distinction of meaning. They should have learned this much during the three preliminary years. In the majority of cases the students fail completely to make use of the evidence submitted by their own witnesses. The students, faced with the task of explaining and justifying a legal decision, are completely helpless. This absence of ability to establish or demolish a case is utterly incomprehensible.' "

Habermann, who had put considerable energy and feeling into the quotation, let the newspaper fall.

"How true!" he exclaimed. "How accurate! Here too, however, I would like to anticipate a possible misunderstanding." He placed his hands on the reading desk, leaned forward, and scrutinized earnestly the young student in the front row.

"It is quite easy to imagine that a student capable of distinguishing between the verbs 'to claim,' 'to establish,' 'to cite,' and 'to object,' might find himself utterly incapable of establishing the validity of decisions with which he is sometimes confronted. We must, in other words, liberate ourselves from the old and outlived concepts of what constitutes the 'validity of a decision.' Gentlemen, I come back to the thesis with which this lecture began: 'Justice is that which serves our purpose.' "

The one thing that could not be said about Professor Habermann's lecture was that it lacked variety and color. Indeed, a superficial listener might have accused the learned jurist of jumping from subject to subject without rhyme or reason. But here, suddenly, he had swung the lecture back to the main thesis. It was perhaps this peculiarity of method and mentality, this diversity and discontinuity, which explained his indifference to "career" before the coming of Hitler. Now that a career had been opened to him he seemed to care little about pursuing it. Sooner or later his behavior would come to the attention of the authorities, and then neither his one hundred per cent Germanic character nor his popularity among his students would save him from the abyss on the edge of which he carried on his dangerous game.

The second hour period of the lecture now began, and Habermann brought up the subject of youthful criminality. He spoke slowly and impressively. He seemed to be enjoying what he said:

"It must be clear to everyone that the continuous unemployment that raged during the frightful years of Germany's decline, and the demoralization of the youth that resulted therefrom, was bound to result in an appalling increase in youthful criminality. To us, students of the legal code, it had always been an undoubted fact that only a small minority of criminals—and among youthful criminals only the smallest minority—enter upon a career of crime in response to a criminal impulse. It is much rather, as you are aware, opportunity which makes the thief. Despair, too, produces thieves. But, above all, it is bad example which breeds crime. It is therefore not to be wondered at that in the late republic, large numbers of youthful criminals were constantly being prosecuted. Unfortunately, however, we are confronted in National Socialist Germany with a strange and extremely disturbing phenomenon. Gentleman, not only has youthful criminality not *declined;* on the contrary, the numbers of youthful criminals have grown to threatening proportions during these last years. I submit some comparative figures:

CRIMES OF A GENERAL CHARACTER

Berlin . . . . . . 1934: 948 cases; 1936: 1,485 cases
Hamburg . . . . 1934: 566 cases; 1936:   979 cases
Cologne . . . . . 1934: 328 cases; 1936:   549 cases

SEX CRIMES

Berlin . . . . 1934: 22 cases; 1936:   72 cases
Hamburg . . . . . . 1934: 26 cases; 1936: 107 cases
Mannheim . . . . . 1934: 10 cases; 1936:   48 cases

CRIMES OF PHYSICAL VIOLENCE

Berlin . . . . 1934: 30 cases; 1936: 75 cases
Hamburg . . . . 1934: 21 cases; 1936: 47 cases
Breslau . . . . 1934: 1 case; 1936: 47 cases

"You see, then, gentlemen, the number of convictions of youthful criminals has, during these last years, practically doubled in the big cities. Particularly disturbing, however, is the fact that physical crimes, crimes of sex, cases of assault and battery, have on the average risen threefold. You may observe, gentlemen, in passing, that in the city of Breslau the increase has been *forty-seven-fold!* In connection with this extremely interesting subject I recommend for reading an essay which appeared in *Jung Deutschland,* where you will find the figures I have cited reproduced, as they have been, indeed, in scores of legal periodicals. This particular article, however, makes the observation that unemployment 'has ceased to be a significant factor within Germany in the demoralization of the youthful population.' "

Professor Habermann, his face screwed up again into a Mongolian grimace, now launched a series of rhetorical questions at his class:

"Should we not have thought that the new order in our national life, the new moral inspiration flowing from our Führer, the high ideals of our Führer, and the admirable and thoroughly German means which he invokes for their attainment, would have resulted in a cleansing of the country? Instead, wherever we turn our gaze, filth and decay, an appalling relapse into criminality, a criminality of such shamelessness as not even the Germany of the decline would have tolerated. What explanation can we offer, gentlemen, for this degrading phenomenon, for this cancer on the body of the German people?"

The professor paused. The student in the front row now definitely expected that the lecturer, in his incredible boldness, would supply the rhetorical answer in the stereotyped phrases of Nazi propaganda: "Foreign influence!" or "The shame of the Versailles peace"—which would, in this case, produce the effect of irresistible parody. The young man felt his skin crawl. There's going to be a scandal, he thought. One way or another, it will come to a scandal. Either someone will denounce our clever Habermann, or else there'll be such a demonstration here in the class, such a stamping of applause, that the dean will be sent in; and then we'll be questioned and have to tell. God almighty, what will happen then?

Habermann, the narrowed eyes still fixed on the student, remained silent. There was a deathly stillness in the classroom. Tense, expectant, the young people waited to hear their teacher burst into a denunciation, a passionate, raging denunciation of the regime and its guardians. Every one of them had formed his resolution in those seconds, which endured like an eternity. What will I do? everyone asked himself. And almost everyone was thinking: It would be a relief. We all *know* what he can say, what he ought to say. But it would be relief to hear it uttered, to hear it ringing out loud and clear in this auditorium of our old university, a vindication of our dignity which has been compromised by so many servile lies.

A short, loud rap at the door dissolved the tension. Two young men in storm troop uniforms strode in. ""Heil, Hitler!" they called, and the class rose reluctantly to the greeting. The ceremony over, the storm troopers marched forward toward Habermann and the lecture desk.

The professor lowered his head between his shoulders. He looked now like a bull facing a red flag. What had happened? Had they heard him from behind the door, these guardians of the National Socialist order? Had one of the students sneaked out during the lecture and reported him? If there was such a one, woe to him! The other students would teach him a lesson he would never forget. One of the storm troopers mounted the platform. He stood facing the class, with his back to Habermann, and concealing him. The student in the front row had sprung to his feet. His handsome, angry face was turned half toward the class and half, with a threatening side glance, toward the storm trooper, who cleared his throat and began to speak.

"Comrades and friends," said the storm trooper, "in this hour of destiny of our fatherland—"

The student thought: What? The hour of destiny again? Are we never going to get away from that hour of destiny? What does he want now, the Nazi?

"In this hour of destiny I turn to you, my party comrades, and to you, too, who serve our Führer without as yet belonging to the party—"

At this point, the student in the front row resumed his seat noisily.

The storm trooper continued: "I stand before you"—his voice began to soar—"as the representative and local administrator of the Reich food department, and as such—"

The student in the front row clapped his hands, not just once, but continuously, insistently, a furious, wholly unstudentlike kind of applause, for it was not the custom among students to applaud by clapping.

The storm trooper came to a startled halt. Then he continued, trying to drown out the applause.

"Gentlemen," he shrieked, "the harvest duty calls—" but the class had taken up the applause. Half the students were clapping. Professor Habermann, too, behind the storm trooper, and of shorter stature, and therefore almost hidden from the class, was applauding like a madman. He lifted up his hands, he clapped them together above his head. He was, in fact, a kind of conductor, leading the class in an extraordinary concert. Swifter and swifter the hands came together, and by now there was not a single student who had not joined in the wild applause. Their faces—this was the most startling aspect of it all—wore an expression of deadly earnest. More exactly, it was one of angry and obstinate defiance. They were grimly determined not to let this uniformed intruder, this official of the Reich food department, have his say. No! *He was not going to speak,* not if the whole class was to be sentenced the next morning to the concentration camp.

The storm trooper, helpless in the face of this spontaneously organized resistance, yelled at the top of his voice: "I thank you, gentlemen, for this expression of agreement, and I know that there isn't one of you who will fail to volunteer, during the coming vacation months, for the harvest service."

Scarcely a word broke through the tempest of applause; the sound of the messenger's voice was swallowed up. "East Prussia!" he screamed, as if these were magic syllables by which he sought to allay the uproar. "East Prussia! You will be sent to East Prussia, party comrades—in this hour of the destiny of our fatherland. . . ."

He was as crimson as a lobster. The swollen veins on his forehead threatened to burst. Professor Habermann, who was still clapping his hands in a rapid rhythm above his head, began to slow down the tempo. The rhythm died down in the class, too. Finally, behind the back of the storm trooper, the professor conductor gave the signal to stop the applause. The storm trooper, overtaken by the unexpected silence, bellowed senselessly at the top of his voice: "Our organic and intimate relationships to the agricultural spirit of Germany . . ." His voice filled the auditorium like the howl of a beast of prey. He stopped abruptly, and looked around the room like a man bereft of his senses. Peering out from behind the brown shirt, Habermann's face was screwed up in its slyest expression. The pale eyes laughed.

The storm trooper was silent. But now it was the turn of the student in the front row, who sprang up to his feet, and with a correct, almost elegant bow, directed half toward the trooper and half toward the class, took the floor.

"On behalf of this student body, I wish to thank the representative of the Reich food department for his illuminating observations. The representative of the Reich food department does not need my reassurances; he can judge from the applause how *fully* we stand behind him and our Führer. If, as a result of our enthusiastic, our irrepressible demonstration" —the class laughed—"certain decisive remarks may have failed to reach us, the Reich food department may be all the more certain that we are blind, and deaf, and dumb, in our devotion to its orders, and we do not even pause to ask what, in this or that or the other hour of destiny, is expected of us."

He bowed once more and resumed his seat. The storm trooper, utterly incapable of grasping the content of this neat, ironical address, flung his arm into the air.

"Heil Hitler!" he called.

"Heil Hitler!" responded his companion—his sole contribution to the incident. The class did not answer. Professor Habermann conducted the two uniformed men to the door, and dismissed them with a gracious bow. Then he turned back and, as if nothing had intervened, mounted his lecture desk and resumed his lesson.

"We were speaking," he said, and his quiet glance measured the class, through which there ran a scarcely perceptible shudder, "we were discussing, if I remember rightly, the difficulties which may arise for our new, authoritarian state from acts of sabotage which issue, not from individuals, but from organized groups."

Once more there was deathly stillness in the class. The young man in the front row stared full into the lecturer's face. His brown eyes were filled with the luster which is born of admiration and love. But his friends, too, the young people near him and behind him on the rising tiers of the amphitheater, were all listening with almost religious absorption. All of them knew quite well that their professor did not "remember rightly;" in fact, he was "remembering wrongly." The subject he had been discussing had had nothing whatsoever to do with organized acts of sabotage. But they had been witnesses, they had been witnesses of, and participants in, such an act, and there was something magnificent in the fact that this man, their wordless leader in the act, now dared to define it and call it by its right name, to describe it in the sober language of the lecture hall.

"We students of the criminal law of the Third Reich," said Habermann, "can know of nothing which can become as dangerous to the state as the passive resistance of the masses, or even the passive resistance of small and determined groups."

He interrupted himself, looked at his watch, and made his concluding remarks in a very casual tone of voice: "In accordance with instructions, I would like to ask those gentlemen who intend to volunteer for the harvest service in East Prussia, to rise."

There was neither sound nor motion in the auditorium. The young man in the first row, as if seized with sudden panic, looked round at the remainder of the class. But no one moved.

Professor Habermann, after lingering deliberately and pleasurably two or three seconds over the silence, made a brief gesture.

"I thank you, gentlemen," he said, and in that conventional phrase there rang, unmistakable, the immeasurable volume of his pride, triumph and gratitude. Nothing was heard beside the sleepy music of the fountains in the campus as the professor, holding himself very erect, very tense, withdrew from the classroom.

The Confession of N. S. Rubashov

Arthur Koestler

IN THE *words of the author, "The life of the man N. S. Rubashov is a synthesis of the lives of a number of men who were victims of the so-called Moscow Trials." The following excerpt from the remarkable novel* DARKNESS AT NOON *begins at what is very nearly the end of a series of preliminary examinations extending over weeks.*—Editor.

T HE QUESTION of motive is the last,' said Gletkin. 'When you have signed that, we will have finished with one another.'
The lamp radiated a sharper light than it had for a long time. Rubashov was forced to blink.
'. . . And then you will be able to rest,' said Gletkin.
Rubashov passed his hand over his temples, but the coolness of the snow was gone. The word 'rest,' with which Gletkin had ended his sentence, remained suspended in the silence. Rest and sleep. Let us choose a captain and return into the land of Egypt. . . . He blinked sharply through his pince-nez at Gletkin:
'You know my motives as well as I do,' he said. 'You know that I acted neither out of a "counter-revolutionary mentality," nor was I in the service of a foreign Power. What I thought and what I did, I thought and did according to my own conviction and conscience.'
Gletkin had pulled a dossier out of his drawer. He went through it, pulled out a sheet and read in his monotonous voice.

' ". . . For us the question of subjective good faith is of no interest. He who is in the wrong must pay; he who is in the right will be absolved. That was our law. . . ." You wrote that in your diary shortly after your arrest.'

Rubashov felt behind his eye-lids the familiar flickering of the light. In Gletkin's mouth the sentence he had thought and written acquired a peculiarly naked sound—as though a confession, intended only for the anonymous priest, had been registered on a gramophone record, which now was repeating it in its cracked voice.

Gletkin had taken another page out of the dossier, but read only one sentence from it, with his expressionless gaze fixed on Rubashov:

' "Honour is: to serve without vanity, and unto the last consequence." '

Rubashov tried to withstand his gaze.

'I don't see,' he said, 'how it can serve the Party that her members have to grovel in the dust before all the world. I have signed everything you wanted me to sign. I have pleaded guilty to having pursued a false and objectively harmful policy. Isn't that enough for you?'

He put on his pince-nez, blinked helplessly past the lamp, and ended in a tired, hoarse voice:

'After all, the name N. S. Rubashov is itself a piece of Party history. By dragging it in dirt, you besmirch the history of the Revolution.'

Gletkin looked through the dossier.

'To that I can also reply with a citation from your own writings. You wrote:

' "It is necessary to hammer every sentence into the masses by repetition and simplification. What is presented as right must shine like gold; what is presented as wrong must be black as pitch. For consumption by the masses, the political processes must be coloured like ginger-bread figures at a fair." '

Rubashov was silent. Then he said:

'So that is what you are aiming at: I am to play the Devil in your Punch and Judy show—howl, grind my teeth and put out my tongue—and voluntarily, too. Danton and his friends were spared that, at least.'

Gletkin shut the cover of the dossier. He bent forward a bit and settled his cuffs.

'Your testimony at the trial will be the last service you can do the Party.'

Rubashov did not answer. He kept his eyes shut and relaxed under the rays of the lamp like a tired sleeper in the sun; but there was no escape from Gletkin's voice.

'Your Danton and the Convention,' said the voice, 'were just a gallant play compared to what is at stake here. I have read books about it: those people wore powdered pigtails and declaimed about their personal honour. To them, it only mattered to die with a noble gesture, regardless of whether this gesture did good or harm.'

Rubashov said nothing. There was a buzzing and humming in his

ears; Gletkin's voice was above him; it came from every side of him; it
hammered mercilessly on his aching skull.

'You know what is at stake here,' Gletkin went on. 'For the first time
in history, a revolution has not only conquered power, but also kept it. We
have made our country a bastion of the new era. It covers a sixth of the
world and contains a tenth of the world's population.'

Gletkin's voice now sounded at Rubashov's back. He had risen and
was walking up and down the room. It was the first time this had happened. His boots creaked at every step, his starched uniform crackled and
a sourish smell of sweat and leather became noticeable.

'When our Revolution had succeeded in our country, we believed that
the rest of the earth would follow suit. Instead, came a wave of reaction,
which threatened to swamp us. There were two currents in the Party.
One consisted of adventurers, who wanted to risk what we had won to
promote the revolution abroad. You belonged to them. We recognized
this current to be dangerous, and have liquidated it.'

Rubashov wanted to raise his head and say something. Gletkin's steps
resounded in his skull. He was too tired. He let himself fall back, and
kept his eyes shut.

'The leader of the Party,' Gletkin's voice went on, 'had the wider perspective and the more tenacious tactics. He realized that everything depended on surviving the period of world reaction and keeping the bastion. He had realized that it might last ten, perhaps twenty, perhaps fifty
years, until the world was ripe for a fresh wave of revolution. Until then
we stand alone. Until then we have only one duty: not to perish.'

A sentence swam vaguely in Rubashov's memory: 'It is the Revolu-
tionary's duty to preserve his own life.' Who had said that? He, himself?
Ivanov? It was in the name of that principle that he had sacrificed Arlova.
And where had it led him?

'. . . Not to perish,' sounded Gletkin's voice. 'The bulwark must be
held, at any price and with any sacrifice. The leader of the Party recognized this principle with unrivalled clearsightedness, and has consistently
applied it. The policy of the International had to be subordinated to our
national policy. Whoever did not understand this necessity had to be destroyed. Whole sets of our best functionaries in Europe had to be physically liquidated. We did not recoil from crushing our own organizations
abroad when the interests of the Bastion required it. We did not recoil
from co-operation with the police of reactionary countries in order to suppress revolutionary movements which came at the wrong moment. We
did not recoil from betraying our friends and compromising with our
enemies, in order to preserve the Bastion. That was the task which history had given us, the representatives of the first victorious revolution.
The shortsighted, the æsthetes, the moralists did not understand. But the
leader of the Revolution understood that all depended on one thing: to be
the better stayer.'

Gletkin interrupted his pacing through the room. He stopped behind

Rubashov's chair. The scar on his shaven skull shone sweatily. He panted, wiped his skull with his handkerchief, and seemed embarrassed at having broken his customary reserve. He sat down again behind the desk and settled his cuffs. He turned down the light a little, and continued in his usual expressionless voice:

'The Party's line was sharply defined. Its tactics were determined by the principle that the end justifies the means—all means, without exception. In the spirit of this principle, the Public Prosecutor will demand your life, Citizen Rubashov.

'Your faction, Citizen Rubashov, is beaten and destroyed. You wanted to split the Party, although you must have known that a split in the Party meant civil war. You know of the dissatisfaction amongst the peasantry, which has not yet learnt to understand the sense of the sacrifices imposed on it. In a war which may be only a few months away, such currents can lead to a catastrophe. Hence the imperious necessity for the Party to be united. It must be as if cast from one mould—filled with blind discipline and absolute trust. You and your friends, Citizen Rubashov, have made a rent in the Party. If your repentance is real, then you must help us to heal this rent. I have told you, it is the last service the Party will ask of you.

'Your task is simple. You have set it yourself: to gild the Right, to blacken the Wrong. The policy of the opposition is wrong. Your task is therefore to make the opposition contemptible; to make the masses understand that opposition is a crime and that the leaders of the opposition are criminals. That is the simple language which the masses understand. If you begin to talk of your complicated motives, you will only create confusion amongst them. Your task, Citizen Rubashov, is to avoid awakening sympathy and pity. Sympathy and pity for the opposition are a danger to the country.

'Comrade Rubashov, I hope that you have understood the task which the Party has set you.'

It was the first time since their acquaintance that Gletkin called Rubashov 'Comrade.' Rubashov raised his head quickly. He felt a hot wave rising in him, against which he was helpless. His chin shook slightly while he was putting on his pince-nez.

'I understand.'

'Observe,' Gletkin went on, 'that the Party holds out to you no prospect of reward. Some of the accused have been made amenable by physical pressure. Others, by the promise to save their heads—or the heads of their relatives who had fallen into our hands as hostages. To you, Comrade Rubashov, we propose no bargain and we promise nothing.'

'I understand,' Rubashov repeated.

Gletkin glanced at the dossier.

'There is a passage in your journal which impressed me,' he went on. 'You wrote: "I have thought and acted as I had to. If I was right, I have nothing to repent of; if wrong, I shall pay." '

He looked up from the dossier and looked Rubashov fully in the face:

'You were wrong, and you will pay, Comrade Rubashov. The Party promises only one thing: after the victory, one day when it can do no more harm, the material of the secret archives will be published. Then the world will learn what was in the background of this Punch and Judy show—as you called it—which we had to act to them according to history's text-book. . . .'

He hesitated a few seconds, settled his cuffs and ended rather awkwardly, while the scar on his skull reddened:

'And then you, and some of your friends of the older generation, will be given the sympathy and pity which are denied to you to-day.'

While he was speaking, he had pushed the prepared statement over to Rubashov, and laid his fountain-pen beside it. Rubashov stood up and said with a strained smile:

'I have always wondered what it was like when the Neanderthalers became sentimental. Now I know.'

'I do not understand,' said Gletkin, who had also stood up.

Rubashov signed the statement, in which he confessed to having committed his crimes through counter-revolutionary motives and in the service of a foreign Power. As he raised his head, his gaze fell on the portrait of No. 1 hanging on the wall, and once again he recognized the expression of knowing irony with which years ago No. 1 had taken leave of him—that melancholy cynicism which stared down on humanity from the omnipresent portrait.

'It does not matter if you don't understand,' said Rubashov. 'There are things which only that older generation, the Ivanovs, Rubashovs and Kieffers have understood. That is over now.'

'I will give order that you are not to be troubled until the trial,' said Gletkin after a short pause, again stiff and precise. Rubashov's smiling irritated him. 'Have you any other particular wish?'

'To sleep,' said Rubashov. He stood in the open door, beside the giant warder, small, elderly and insignificant with his pince-nez and beard.

'I will give orders that your sleep must not be disturbed,' said Gletkin.

When the door had shut behind Rubashov, he went back to his desk. For a few seconds he sat still. Then he rang for his secretary.

She sat down in her usual place in the corner. 'I congratulate you on your success, Comrade Gletkin,' she said.

Gletkin turned the lamp down to normal.

'That,' he said with a glance at the lamp, 'plus lack of sleep and physical exhaustion. It is all a matter of constitution.'

'Asked whether he pleaded guilty, the accused Rubashov answered "Yes" in a clear voice. To a further question of the Public Prosecutor as to whether the accused has acted as an agent of the counter-revolution, he again answered "Yes" in a lower voice. . . .'

The porter Wassilij's daughter read slowly, each syllable separately. She had spread the newspaper on the table and followed the lines with her finger; from time to time she smoothed her flowered head-kerchief.

'. . . Asked whether he wanted an advocate for his defence, the accused declared he would forgo that right. The court then proceeded to the reading of the accusation. . . .'

The porter Wassilij was lying on the bed with his face turned to the wall. Vera Wassiljovna never quite knew whether the old man listened to her reading or slept. Sometimes he mumbled to himself. She had learnt not to pay any attention to that, and had made a habit of reading the paper aloud every evening, 'for educational reasons'—even when after work at the factory she had to go to a meeting of her cell and returned home late.

'. . . The Definition of the Charge states that the accused Rubashov is proved guilty on all points contained in the accusation, by documentary evidence and his own confession in the preliminary investigation. In answer to a question of the President of the Court as to whether he had any complaint to make against the conduct of the preliminary investigation, the accused answered in the negative, and added that he had made his confession of his own free will, in sincere repentance of his counter-revolutionary crimes. . . .'

The porter Wassilij did not move. Above the bed, directly over his head, hung the portrait of No. 1. Next to it a rusty nail stuck out of the wall: until a short time ago the photograph of Rubashov as Partisan-commander had hung there. Wassilij's hand felt automatically for the hole in his mattress in which he used to hide his greasy Bible from the daughter; but shortly after Rubashov's arrest the daughter had found it and thrown it away, for educational reasons.

'. . . At the Prosecutor's request, the accused Rubashov now proceeded to describe his evolution from an opponent of the Party line to a counter-revolutionary and traitor to the Fatherland. In the presence of a tense audience, the accused began his statement as follows: "Citizen Judges, I will explain what led me to capitulate before the investigating magistrate and before you, the representatives of justice in our country. My story will demonstrate to you how the slightest deflection from the line of the Party must inevitably end in counter-revolutionary banditry. The necessary result of our oppositional struggle was that we were pushed further and further down into the morass. I will describe to you my fall, that it may be a warning to those who in this decisive hour still waver, and have hidden doubts in the leadership of the Party and the rightness of the Party line. Covered with shame, trampled in the dust, about to die, I will describe to you the sad progress of a traitor, that it may serve as a lesson and terrifying example to the millions of our country. . . ." '

The porter Wassilij had turned round on the bed and pressed his face into the mattress. Before his eyes was the picture of the bearded Partisan-commander Rubashov, who in the worst sort of mess knew how to swear in such a pleasant way that it was a joy to God and man. 'Trampled in the dust, about to die. . . .' Wassilij groaned. The Bible was gone, but he knew many passages by heart.

'. . . At this point the Public Prosecutor interrupted the accused's narrative to ask a few questions concerning the fate of Rubashov's former secretary, Citizen Arlova, who had been executed on the charge of treasonable activities. From the answers of the accused Rubashov, it appears that the latter, driven into a corner at that time by the watchfulness of the Party, had laid the responsibility of his own crimes to Arlova's charge, so as to save his head and be able to continue his disgraceful activities. N. S. Rubashov confesses to this monstrous crime with un-ashamed and cynical openness. To the Citizen Prosecutor's remark: "You are apparently quite without any moral sense," the accused answers with a sarcastic smile: "Apparently." His behaviour provoked the audience to repeated spontaneous demonstrations of anger and contempt, which were, however, quickly suppressed by the Citizen President of the Court. On one occasion these expressions of the revolutionary sense of justice gave place to a wave of merriment—namely, when the accused interrupted the description of his crimes with the request that the proceedings might be suspended for a few minutes, as he was suffering from "intolerable toothache." It is typical of the correct procedure of revolutionary justice that the President immediately granted this wish and, with a shrug of contempt, gave the order for the hearing to be interrupted for five minutes.'

The porter Wassilij lay on his back and thought of the time when Rubashov had been conducted in triumph through the meetings, after his rescue from the foreigners; and of how he had stood leaning on his crutches up on the platform under the red flags and decorations, and, smiling, had rubbed his glasses on his sleeve, while the cheerings and shoutings never ceased.

'*And the soldiers led him away, into the hall called Prætorium; and they called together the whole band. And they clothed him with purple and they smote him on the head with a reed and did spit upon him; and bowing their knees worshipped him.*'

'What are you mumbling to yourself?' asked the daughter.

'Never mind,' said old Wassilij, and turned to the wall. He felt with his hand in the hole in the mattress, but it was empty. The hook hanging over his head was also empty. When the daughter had taken the portrait of Rubashov from the wall and thrown it in the dust-bin, he had not protested—he was now too old to stand the shame of prison.

The daughter had interrupted her reading and put the Primus stove on the table to prepare tea. A sharp smell of petrol spread over the porter's lodge. 'Were you listening to my reading?' asked the daughter.

Wassilij obediently turned his head towards her. 'I heard it all,' he said.

'So now you see,' said Vera Wassiljovna, pumping petrol into the hissing apparatus. 'He says himself that he is a traitor. If it weren't true, he wouldn't say so himself. In the meeting at our factory we have already carried a resolution which all have to sign.'

'A lot you understand about it,' sighed Wassilij.

Vera Wassiljovna threw him a quick glance which had the effect of making him turn his head to the wall again. Each time she gave him that peculiar glance, Wassilij was reminded that he was in Vera Wassiljovna's way, who wanted to have the porter's lodge for herself. Three weeks ago, she and a junior mechanic at her factory had put their names down together in the marriage register, but the pair had no home; the boy shared a room with two colleagues and nowadays it often was many years before one was assigned a flat by the housing trust.

The Primus was at last alight. Vera Wassiljovna put the kettle on it.

'The cell secretary read us the resolution. In it is written that we demand that the traitors be mercilessly exterminated. Whoever shows pity to them is himself a traitor and must be denounced,' she explained in a purposely matter-of-fact voice. 'The workers must be watchful. We have each received a copy of the resolution in order to collect signatures for it.'

Vera Wassiljovna took a slightly crushed sheet of paper out of her blouse and flattened it out on the table. Wassilij now lay on his back; the rusty nail stuck out of the wall straight above his head. He squinted over to the paper, which lay spread next to the Primus stove. Then he turned his head away quickly.

'*And he said: I tell thee, Peter, the cock shall not crow this day before that thou shalt thrice deny that thou knowest me. . . .?*'

The water in the kettle began to hum. Old Wassilij put on a cunning expression:

'Must also those sign who were in the Civil War?'

The daughter stood bent over the kettle, in her flowered head-kerchief. 'Nobody has to,' she said with the same peculiar glance as before. 'In the factory they know, of course, that he lived in this house. The cell secretary asked me after the meeting whether you were friends until the end, and whether you had spoken much together.'

Old Wassilij sat up on the mattress with a jump. The effort made him cough, and the veins swelled on his thin, scrofulous neck.

The daughter put two glasses on the edge of the table and scattered some tea-leaf dust into each out of a paper bag. 'What are you mumbling again?' she asked.

'Give me that damned paper,' said old Wassilij.

The daughter passed it to him. 'Shall I read it to you, so that you know exactly what is in it?'

'No,' said the old man, writing his name on it. 'I don't want to know. Now give me some tea.'

The daughter passed him the glass. Wassilij's lips were moving; he mumbled to himself while drinking the pale yellow liquid in small sips.

After they had drunk their tea, the daughter went on reading from the newspaper. The trial of the accused Rubashov and Kieffer was nearing its end. The debate on the charge of the planned assassination of the leader of the Party had released storms of indignation amongst the audience; shouts of 'Shoot the mad dogs!' were heard repeatedly. To the Public Prosecutor's concluding question, concerning the motive of his actions, the accused Rubashov, who seemed to have broken down, answered in a tired, dragging voice:

'I can only say that we, the opposition, having once made it our criminal aim to remove the Government of the Fatherland of the Revolution, used methods which seemed proper to our purpose, and which were just as low and vile as that purpose.'

Vera Wassiljovna pushed back her chair. 'That is disgusting,' she said. 'It makes you sick the way he crawls on his belly.'

She put aside the newspaper and began noisily to clear away Primus and glasses. Wassilij watched her. The hot tea had given him courage. He sat up in bed.

'Don't you imagine that you understand,' he said. 'God knows what was in his mind when he said that. The Party has taught you all to be cunning, and whoever becomes too cunning loses all decency. It's no good shrugging your shoulders,' he went on angrily. 'It's come to this in the world now that cleverness and decency are at loggerheads, and whoever sides with one must do without the other. It's not good for a man to work things out too much. That's why it is written: "Let your communication be, Yea, yea; Nay, nay; for whatever is more than these cometh of evil." '

He let himself sink back on the mattress and turned away his head, so as not to see the face his daughter would make. He had not contradicted her so bravely for a long time. Anything might come of it, once she had it in her mind that she wanted the room for herself and her husband. One had to be cunning in this life, after all—else one might in one's old age go to prison or have to sleep under the bridges in the cold. There one had it: either one behaved cleverly or one behaved decently: the two did not go together.

'I will now read you the end,' announced the daughter.

The Public Prosecutor had finished his cross-examination of Rubashov. Following it, the accused Kieffer was examined once more; he repeated his preceding statement on the attempted assassination in full detail. '. . . Asked by the President whether he desired to put any questions to Kieffer, which he would be entitled to do, the accused Rubashov answered that he would forgo this right. This concluded the hearing of evidence and the Court was adjourned. After the re-opening of the sitting, the Citizen Public Prosecutor begins his summing-up. . . .'

Old Wassilij was not listening to the Prosecutor's speech. He had turned to the wall and gone to sleep. He did not know afterwards how long he had slept, how often the daughter had refilled the lamp with oil, nor how often her forefinger had reached the bottom of the page and started on a new column. He only woke up when the Public Prosecutor, summing up his speech, demanded the death sentence. Perhaps the daughter had changed her tone of voice towards the end, perhaps she had made a pause; in any case, Wassilij was awake again when she came to the last sentence of the Public Prosecutor's speech, printed in heavy black type:

'I demand that all these mad dogs be shot.'

Then the accused were allowed to say their last words.

'. . . The accused Kieffer turned to the judges and begged that, in consideration of his youth, his life be spared. He admitted once again the baseness of his crime and tried to attribute the whole responsibility for it to the instigator Rubashov. In so doing, he started to stammer agitatedly, thus provoking the mirth of the spectators, which was, however, rapidly suppressed by the Citizen President. Then Rubashov was allowed to speak. . . .'

The newspaper reporter here vividly depicted how the accused Rubashov 'examined the audience with eager eyes and, finding not a single sympathetic face, let his head sink despairingly.'

Rubashov's final speech was short. It intensified the unpleasant impression which his behaviour in court had already made.

'Citizen President,' the accused Rubashov declared, 'I speak here for the last time in my life. The opposition is beaten and destroyed. If I ask myself to-day, "For what am I dying?" I am confronted by absolute nothingness. There is nothing for which one could die, if one died without having repented and unreconciled with the Party and the Movement. Therefore, on the threshold of my last hour, I bend my knees to the country, to the masses and to the whole people. The political masquerade, the mummery of discussions and conspiracy are over. We were politically dead long before the Citizen Prosecutor demanded our heads. Woe unto the defeated, whom history treads into the dust. I have only one justification before you, Citizen Judges: that I did not make it easy for myself. Vanity and the last remains of pride whispered to me: Die in silence, say nothing; or die with a noble gesture, with a moving swan-song on your lips; pour out your heart and challenge your accusers. That would have been easier for an old rebel, but I overcame the temptation. With that my task is ended. I have paid; my account with history is settled. To ask you for mercy would be derision. I have nothing more to say.'

'. . . After a short deliberation, the President read the sentence. The Council of the Supreme Revolutionary Court of Justice sentenced the accused in every case to the maximum penalty: death by shooting and the confiscation of all their personal property.'

The old man Wassilij stared at the rusty hook above his head. He murmured: 'Thy will be done. Amen,' and turned to the wall.

PART TWO
MORALS

One of the Seven [wise men of Greece] was wont to say: That laws were like cobwebs, where the small flies were caught and the great brake through.

BACON, APOTHEGMS NEW AND OLD, *no. 181 (1625).*

Susanna and the Elders

THERE dwelt a man in Babylon, called Joacim: and he took a wife, whose name was Susanna, the daughter of Chelcias, a very fair woman, and one that feared the Lord. Her parents also were righteous, and taught their daughter according to the law of Moses.

Now Joacim was a great rich man, and had a fair garden joining unto his house: and to him resorted the Jews; because he was more honourable than all others.

The same year were appointed two of the ancients of the people to be judges, such as the Lord spoke of, that wickedness came from Babylon from ancient judges, who seemed to govern the people. These kept much at Joacim's house: and all that had any suits in law came unto them.

Now when the people departed away at noon, Susanna went into her husband's garden to walk. And the two elders saw her going in every day, and walking; so that their lust was inflamed toward her. And they perverted their own mind, and turned away their eyes, that they might not look unto heaven, nor remember just judgments.

And albeit they both were wounded with her love, yet durst not one show another his grief. For they were ashamed to declare their lust, that they desired to have to do with her. Yet they watched diligently from day to day to see her. And the one said to the other, "Let us now go home: for it is dinner time."

So when they were gone out, they parted the one from the other, and turning back again they came to the same place; and after they had asked one another the cause, they acknowledged their lust: then appointed they a time both together, when they might find her alone.

And it fell out, as they watched a fit time, she went in as before with two maids only, and she was desirous to wash herself in the garden: for it was hot. And there was nobody there save the two elders, that had hid themselves, and watched her.

Then she said to her maids, "Bring me oil and washing balls, and shut the garden doors, that I may wash me."

And they did as she bade them, and shut the garden doors, and went

From *The Apocrypha*.

out themselves at privy doors to fetch the things that she had commanded them: but they saw not the elders, because they were hid.

Now when the maids were gone forth, the two elders rose up, and ran unto her, saying "Behold, the garden doors are shut, that no man can see us, and we are in love with thee; therefore consent unto us, and lie with us. If thou wilt not, we will bear witness against thee, that a young man was with thee: and therefore thou didst send away thy maids from thee."

Then Susanna sighed, and said, "I am straitened on every side: for if I do this thing, it is death unto me: and if I do it not, I cannot escape your hands. It is better for me to fall into your hands, and not do it, than to sin in the sight of the Lord."

With that Susanna cried with a loud voice: and the two elders cried out against her. Then ran the one, and opened the garden door.

So when the servants of the house heard the cry in the garden, they rushed in at a privy door, to see what was done unto her. But when the elders had declared their matter, the servants were greatly ashamed: for there was never such a report made of Susanna.

And it came to pass the next day, when the people were assembled to her husband Joacim, the two elders came also full of mischievous imagination against Susanna to put her to death; and said before the people, "Send for Susanna, the daughter of Chelcias, Joacim's wife."

And so they sent. So she came with her father and mother, her children, and all her kindred. Now Susanna was a very delicate woman, and beauteous to behold. And these wicked men commanded to uncover her face (for she was covered), that they might be filled with her beauty. Therefore her friends and all that saw her wept.

Then the two elders stood up in the midst of the people, and laid their hands upon her head. And she weeping looked up toward heaven: for her heart trusted in the Lord. And the elders said, "As we walked in the garden alone, this woman came in with two maids, and shut the garden doors, and sent the maids away. Then a young man, who there was hid, came unto her, and lay with her. Then we that stood in a corner of the garden, seeing this wickedness, ran unto them. And when we saw them together, the man we could not hold: for he was stronger than we, and opened the door, and leaped out. But having taken this woman, we asked who the young man was, but she would not tell us: these things do we testify."

Then the assembly believed them, as those that were the elders and judges of the people: so they condemned her to death.

Then Susanna cried out with a loud voice, and said, "O everlasting God, that knowest the secrets, and knowest all things before they be: thou knowest that they have borne false witness against me, and, behold I must die; whereas I never did such things as these men have maliciously invented against me."

And the Lord heard her voice.

Therefore when she was led to be put to death, the Lord raised up the holy spirit of a young youth, whose name was Daniel: who cried with a loud voice, "I am clear from the blood of this woman."

Then all the people turned them toward him, and said, "What mean these words that thou hast spoken?"

So he standing in the midst of them said, "Are ye such fools, ye sons of Israel, that without examination or knowledge of the truth ye have condemned a daughter of Israel? Return again to the place of judgment: for they have borne false witness against her."

Wherefore all the people turned again in haste, and the elders said unto him, "Come, sit down among us, and show it us, seeing God hath given thee the honour of an elder."

Then said Daniel unto them, "Put these two aside one far from another, and I will examine them."

So when they were put asunder one from another, he called one of them, and said unto him, "O thou that are waxed old in wickedness, now thy sins which thou hast committed aforetime are come to light: for thou hast pronounced false judgment, and hast condemned the innocent, and hast let the guilty go free: albeit the Lord saith, 'The innocent and righteous shalt thou not slay.' Now then, if thou hast seen her, tell me under what tree sawest thou them companying together?"

Who answered, "Under the mastic tree."

And Daniel said, "Very well; thou hast lied against thine own head; for even now the angel of God hath received the sentence of God to cut thee in two."

So he put him aside, and commanded to bring the other, and said unto him, "O thou seed of Chanaan, and not of Juda, beauty hath deceived thee, and lust hath perverted thine heart. Thus have ye dealt with the daughters of Israel, and they for fear companied with you: but the daughter of Juda would not abide your wickedness. Now therefore tell me under what tree didst thou take them companying together?"

Who aswered, "Under a holm tree."

Then said Daniel unto him, "Well; thou hast also lied against thine own head: for the angel of God waiteth with the sword to cut thee in two, that he may destroy you."

With that all the assembly cried out with a loud voice, and praised God, who saveth them that trust in him. And they arose against the two elders, for Daniel had convicted them of false witness by their own mouth: and according to the law of Moses they did unto them in such sort as they maliciously intended to do to their neighbour: and they put them to death. Thus the innocent blood was saved the same day.

Therefore Chelcias and his wife praised God for their daughter Susanna, with Joacim her husband, and all the kindred, because there was no dishonesty found in her.

Madam Filippa Is Accused
of Wronging Her Husband

Giovanni Boccaccio

S CALZA'S argument to prove nobility of the Baronci having made them all very merry, the queen turned to Filostrato, who began in this manner:—It is a good thing, most worthy ladies, to be able to speak well, and to the purpose; but I hold it best of all to know how to do it when need requires, as was the case with a lady of whom I am going to treat, who escaped an ignominous death by this means, as you shall hear.

In the territory of Prato there was formerly a most severe law, which, without distinction, condemned all such women to be burnt as were detected by their husbands in adultery. Whilst this law was in force, it chanced that a beautiful young lady, named Filippa, was surprised by her husband with her gallant, a young gentleman of the same city, in her own chamber. Rinaldo de' Pugliesi, for that was the husband's name, was so provoked at this, that he could scarcely refrain from putting them both to death, and forbore it only out of regard to his own life; but yet he resolved that the law should effect what he durst not accomplish with his own hand—the death, namely, of his wife. Having, therefore sufficient testimony to prove the fact, he had her summoned before the court. The lady, who was of an undaunted spirit, resolved to make her appearance, contrary to the advice of her friends, choosing rather to die by a resolute confession of the truth, than abscond and live basely in exile, or, by denying the fact, show herself unworthy of the lover with whom she had this intrigue. Being brought, then, before the lord-provost, attended by a great number of friends of both sexes, and encouraged all the way to deny it, she asked him, with a firm voice and steady countenance, what he had to say to her. The provost, seeing her beauty, her noble deportment, and greatness of spirit, began to pity her, fearing lest she should confess something which would force him, for the sake of his honour, to condemn her to death. Being constrained, however, to interrogate her

From *The Decameron*.

upon the charge preferred before him, he said to her, "Madam, here is Rinaldo, your husband, who affirms that he has taken you in adultery, and insists that I pronounce sentence of death upon you, according to the law in that case; but this I cannot do, unless you yourself confess it; therefore take care what answers you make, and tell me if this accusation of his be true." The lady, without showing the least concern, replied: "My lord, it is true, that Rinaldo is my husband, and that he found me in the arms of Lazzarino, where I have been many a time, for the great love I bear him, nor will I ever deny it; but you must know, at the same time, that laws ought to be alike for all, and made with the consent of those persons whom they concern. Now, in this law of yours it is quite otherwise; for it is binding only on us poor women, who are much better able than men to satisfy many, and moreover none of us ever consented to, or were even consulted about the making of it. I call it, therefore, a most iniquitous law. If you are disposed to take away my life for the breach of it, why of course you may; but, before you pass sentence, I entreat one little favour of you, that is, that you would ask my husband whether, at all times, and as often as he pleased, I have not yielded myself fully to his desires, without ever saying him nay." Rinaldo, without waiting to be questioned by the provost, declared at once, that the lady had never failed to respond to his wishes in that respect. "Well, then, master provost," said the lady, "if he has always had from me as much as he wanted and wished, what, I ask, was I to do with what was left? Should I throw it to the dogs? Is it not much better to gratify with it a man who loves me more than himself, than to let it be lost or spoiled?" All the principal people of the city were present to hear this process, and after laughing heartily at this humorous question, they cried out, as with one voice, "The lady says well; she is quite right!" Before they broke up, the law, by the interposition of the lord-provost, was moderated so far as to apply only to such women as wronged their husbands for the sake of money. So Rinaldo departed from the court, covered with shame and confusion, whilst the lady, snatched as it were out of the fire, returned victorious to her own house.

Malefactors in Plymouth

William Bradford

Anno. Dom: 1630

THIS YEAR John Billinton the elder (one that came over with the first) was arrained, and both by grand and petie jurie found guilty of willfull murder, by plaine and notorious evidence. And was for the same accordingly executed. This, as it was the first execution amongst them, so was it a mater of great sadnes unto them. They used all due means about his triall, and tooke the advice of Mr. Winthrop and other the ablest gentle-men in the Bay of Massachusets, that were then new-ly come over, who concured with them that he ought to dye, and the land to be purged from blood. He and some of his had been often punished for miscariags before, being one of the profanest families amongst them. They came from London, and I know not by what freinds shufled into their company. His facte was, that he way-laid a yong-man, one John New-comin, (about a former quarell,) and shote him with a gune, wherof he dyed.

Anno Dom: 1638

This year Mr. Thomas Prence was chosen Gov.ʳ

Amongst other enormities that fell out amongst them, this year 3. men were (after due triall) executed for robery and murder which they had committed; their names were these, Arthur Peach, Thomas Jackson, and Richard Stinnings; ther was a 4., Daniel Crose, who was also guilty, but he escaped away, and could not be found. This Arthur Peach was the cheefe of them, and the ring leader of all the rest. He was a lustie and a desperate yonge man, and had been one of the souldiers in the Pequente warr, and had done as good servise as the most ther, and one of the forwardest in any attempte. And being now of means, and loath to worke, and falling to idle courses and company, he intended to goe to the Dutch

From *The History of Plymouth Plantation*.

plantation; and had alured these 3., being other mens servants and apprentices, to goe with him. But another cause ther was allso of his secret
going away in this maner; he was not only rune into debte, but he had
gott a maid with child, (which was not known till after his death,) a
mans servante in the towne, and fear of punishmente made him gett
away. The other 3. complotting with him, ranne away from their maisters
in the night, and could not be heard of, for they went not the ordinarie
way, but shaped such a course as they thought to avoyd the pursute of
any. But falling into the way that lyeth betweene the Bay of Massachusetts
and the Narrigansets, and being disposed to rest them selves, struck fire,
and took tobaco, a litle out of the way, by the way side. At length ther
came a Narigansett Indean by, who had been in the Bay a trading, and
had both cloth and beads aboute him. (They had meett him the day before, and he was now returning.) Peach called him to drinke tobaco with
them, and he came and sate downe with them. Peach tould the other he
would kill him, and take what he had from him. But they were some
thing afraid; but he said, Hang him, rougue, he had killed many of them.
So they let him alone to doe as he would; and when he saw his time, he
tooke a rapier and rane him through the body once or twise, and tooke
from him 5. fathume of wampan, and 3. coats of cloath, and wente their
way, leaving him for dead. But he scrabled away, when they were gone,
and made shift to gett home, (but dyed within a few days after,) by which
means they were discovered; and by subtilty the Indeans tooke them. For
they desiring a canow to sett them over a water, (not thinking their facte
had been known,) by the sachems command they were carried to Aquidnett Iland, and ther accused of the murder, and were examend and co-
mitted upon it by the English ther. The Indeans sent for Mr. Williams,[1]
and made a greeveous complainte; his freinds and kinred were ready to
rise in armes, and provock the rest therunto, some conceiving they should
now find the Pequents words trew: that the English would fall upon
them. But Mr. Williams pacified them, and tould them they should see
justice done upon the offenders; and wente to the man, and tooke Mr.
James, a phisition, with him. The man tould him who did it, and in
what maner it was done; but the phisition found his wounds mortall, and
that he could not live, (as he after testified upon othe, before the jurie
in oppen courte,) and so he dyed shortly after, as both Mr. Williams, Mr.
James, and some Indeans testified in courte. The Gov^rt in the Bay were
aquented with it, but refferrd it hither, because it was done in this jurisdiction; but pressed by all means that justice might be done in it; or els
the countrie must rise and see justice done, otherwise it would raise a
warr. Yet some of the rude and ignorante sorte murmured that any English should be put to death for the Indeans. So at last they of the iland
brought them hither, and being often examened, and the evidence pro-
dused, they all in the end freely confessed in effect all that the Indean

---

[1] Roger Williams, always trusted by the Narragansetts.

accused them of, and that they had done it, in the maner afforesaid; and so, upon the forementioned evidence, were cast by the jurie, and condemned, and executed for the same. And some of the Narigansett Indeans, and of the parties freinds, were presente when it was done, which gave them and all the countrie good satisfaction. But it was a matter of much sadnes to them hear, and was the 2. execution which they had since they came; being both for wilfull murder, as hath bene before related. Thus much of this mater.

Anno Dom: 1642

Marvilous it may be to see and consider how some kind of wickednes did grow and breake forth here, in a land wher the same was so much witnessed against, and so narrowly looked unto, and severly punished when it was knowne; as in no place more, or so much, that I have known or heard of; insomuch as they have been somewhat censured, even by moderate and good men, for their severitie in punishments. And yet all this could not suppress the breaking out of sundrie notorious sins, (as this year, besids other, gives us too many sad presidents and instances,) espetially drunkennes and unclainnes; not only incontinencie betweene persons unmaried, for which many both men and women have been punished sharply enough, but some maried persons allso. But that which is worse, even sodomie and bugerie, (things fearfull to name,) have broak forth in this land, oftener then once. I say it may justly be marveled at, and cause us to fear and tremble at the consideration of our corrupte natures, which are so hardly bridled, subdued, and mortified; nay, cannot by any other means but the powerfull worke and grace of Gods spirite. But (besids this) one reason may be, that the Divell may carrie a greater spite against the churches of Christ and the gospell hear, by how much the more they indeaour to preserve holynes and puritie amongst them, and strictly punisheth the contrary when it ariseth either in church or comone wealth; that he might cast a blemishe and staine upon them in the eyes of ⌈the⌉ world, who use to be rash in judgmente. I would rather thinke thus, then that Satane hath more power in these heathen lands, as som have thought, then in more Christian nations, espetially over Gods servants in them.

2. An other reason may be, that it may be in this case as it is with waters when their streames are stopped or dammed up, when they gett passage they flow with more violence, and make more noys and disturbance, then when they are suffered to rune quietly in their owne chanels. So wikedness being here more stopped by strict laws, and the same more nerly looked unto, so as it cannot rune in a comone road of liberty as it would, and is inclined, it searches every wher, and at last breaks out wher it getts vente.

3. A third reason may be, hear (as I am verily perswaded) is not more evills in this kind, nor nothing nere so many by proportion, as in other places; but they are here more discoverd and seen, and made publick by

due serch, inquisition, and due punishment; for the churches looke narrowly to their members, and the magistrats over all, more strictly then in other places. Besids, here the people are but few in comparison of other places, which are full and populous, and lye hid, as it were, in a wood or thickett, and many horrible evills by that means are never seen nor knowne; wheras hear, they are, as it were, brought into the light, and set in the plaine feeld, or rather on a hill, made conspicuous to the veiw of all.

But to proceede; ther came a letter from the Govr in the Bay to them here, touching matters of the forementioned nature, which because it may be usefull I shall hear relate it, and the passages ther aboute.

Sr: Having an opportunitie to signifie the desires of our Generall Court in toow things of spetiall importance, I willingly take this occasion to imparte them to you, that you may imparte them to the rest of your magistrats, and also to your Elders, for counsell; and give us your advise in them. The first is cancerning heinous offences in point of uncleannes; the perticuler cases, with the circomstances, and the questions ther upon, you have hear inclosed. The 2. thing is concerning the Ilanders at Aquidnett;[1] that seeing the cheefest of them are gone from us, in offences, either to churches, or commone welth, or both; others are dependants on them, and the best sorte are such as close with them in all their rejections of us. Neither is it only in a faction that they are devided from us, but in very deed they rend them selves from all the true churches of Christ, and, many of them, from all the powers of majestracie. We have had some experience hereof by some of their underworkers, or emissaries, who have latly come amongst us, and have made publick defiance against magistracie, ministrie, churches, and church covenants, etc. as antichristian; secretly also sowing the seeds of Familisme,[2] and Anabaptistrie to the infection of some, and danger of others; so that we are not willing to joyne with them in any league or confederacie at all, but rather that you would consider and advise with us how we may avoyd them, and keep ours from being infected by them. Another thing I should mention to you, for the maintenance of the trad of beaver; if ther be not a company to order it in every jurisdition among the English, which companies should agree in generall of their way in trade, I supose that the trade will be overthrowne, and the Indeans will abuse us. For this cause we have latly put it into order amongst us, hoping of incouragmente from you (as we have had) that we may continue the same. Thus not further to trouble you, I rest, with my loving remembrance to your selfe, etc.

Your loving friend,

Boston, 28. (1.) 1642.   Ri: Bellingham.[3]

---

[1] The settlers on the island of Rhode Island.

[2] The Familists were a sect existing in Holland and England in the sixteenth century, called the Family of Love, because of the love they professed for all human beings, however wicked. They and the Anabaptists were regarded with great horror by the orthodox Puritans.

[3] Bellingham had been elected governor of Massachusetts June 2, 1641, and was governor one year. The date of this letter may be presumed to be March 28, 1642.

The note inclosed follows on the other side.[1]

Worthy and beloved Sr:

Your letter (with the questions inclosed) I have comunicated with our Assistants, and we have refered the answer of them to such Reve[nd] Elders as are amongst us, some of whose answers thertoo we have here sent you inclosed, under their owne hands; from the rest we have not yet received any. Our farr distance hath bene the reason of this long delay, as also that they could not conferr their counsells togeather.

For our selves, (you know our breedings and abilities,) we rather desire light from your selves, and others, whom God hath better inabled, then to presume to give our judgments in cases so difficulte and of so high a nature. Yet under correction, and submission to better judgments, we propose this one thing to your prudent considerations. As it seems to us, in the case even of wilifull murder, that though a man did smite or wound an other, with a full pourpose or desire to kill him, (which is murder in a high degree, before God,) yet if he did not dye, the magistrate was not to take away the others life.[2] So by proportion in other grosse and foule sines, though high attempts and nere approaches to the same be made, and such as in the sight and account of God may be as ill as the accomplishment of the foulest acts of that sine, yet we doute whether it may be safe for the magistrate to proceed to death; we thinke, upon the former grounds, rather he may not. . . . Yet we confess foulnes of circomstances, and frequencie in the same, doth make us remaine in the darke, and desire further light from you, or any, as God shall give.

As for the 2. thing, concerning the Ilanders? we have no conversing with them, nor desire to have, furder then necessitie or humanity may require.

And as for trade? we have as farr as we could ever therin held an orderly course, and have been sory to see the spoyle therof by others, and fear it will hardly be recovered. But in these, or any other things which may concerne the commone good, we shall be willing to advise and concure with you in what we may. Thus with my love remembered to your selfe, and the rest of our worthy friends, your Assistants, I take leave, and rest,

Your loving friend,

Plim: 17. 3. month, 1642.	W. B.[3]

But it may be demanded how came it to pass that so many wicked persons and profane people should so quickly come over into this land, and mix them selves amongst them? seeing it was religious men that begane the work, and they came for religions sake. I confess this may be marveilled at, at least in time to come, when the reasons therof should not be knowne; and the more because here was so many hardships and wants mett withall. I shall therfore indeavor to give some answer here-

---

[1] A leaf is here wanting in the original manuscript, it having been cut out before Prince's time, as is shown by a note in his handwriting.

[2] "Exod: 21. 22. Deu: 19. 11. Num: 35. 16. 18." (Br.)

[3] Here follow clerical opinions, of Reynor, Partridge and Chauncy, which it has been deemed proper to omit, together with a page or two ensuing.

unto. And first, according to that in the gospell, it is ever to be remem-
bred that wher the Lord begins to sow good seed, ther the envious man
will endeavore to sow tares. 2. Men being to come over into a wildernes,
in which much labour and servise was to be done aboute building and
planting, etc., such as wanted help in that respecte, when they could not
have such as they would, were glad to take such as they could; and so,
many untoward servants, sundry of them proved, that were thus brought
over, both men and women kind; who, when their times were expired,
became families of them selves, which gave increase hereunto. 3. An other
and a maine reason hearof was, that men, finding so many godly disposed persons willing to come into these parts, some begane to make a
trade of it, to transeport passengers and their goods, and hired ships for
that end; and then, to make up their fraight and advance their profite,
cared not who the persons were, so they had money to pay them. And by
this means the cuntrie became pestered with many unworthy persons,
who, being come over, crept into one place or other. 4. Againe, the Lords
blesing usually following his people, as well in outward as spirituall
things, (though afflictions be mixed withall,) doe make many to adhear
to the people of God, as many followed Christ, for the loaves sake, John
6. 26. and a mixed multitud came into the willdernes with the people of
God out of Eagipte of old, Exod. 12. 38; so allso ther were sente by their
freinds some under hope that they would be made better; others that they
might be eased of such burthens, and they kept from shame at home that
would necessarily follow their dissolute courses. And thus, by one means
or other, in 20. years time, it is a question whether the greater part be not
growne the worser.

Bardell against Pickwick

Charles Dickens

1.

MR. PICKWICK's apartments in Goswell Street, although on a limited scale, were not only of a very neat and comfortable description, but peculiarly adapted for the residence of a man of his genius and observation. His sitting-room was the first floor front, his bed-room the second floor front; and thus, whether he were sitting at his desk in the parlour, or standing before the dressing-glass in his dormitory, he had an equal opportunity of contemplating human nature in all the numerous phases it exhibits, in that not more populous than popular thoroughfare. His landlady, Mrs. Bardell—the relict and sole executrix of a deceased custom-house officer—was a comely woman of bustling manners and agreeable appearance, with a natural genius for cooking, improved by study and long practice into an exquisite talent. There were no children, no servants, no fowls. The only other inmates of the house were a large man, and a small boy; the first a lodger, the second a production of Mrs. Bardell's. The large man was always home precisely at ten o'clock at night, at which hour he regularly condensed himself into the limits of a dwarfish French bedstead in the back parlour; and the infantine sports and gymnastic exercises of Master Bardell were exclusively confined to the neighbouring pavements and gutters. Cleanliness and quiet reigned throughout the house; and in it Mr. Pickwick's will was law.

To any one acquainted with these points of the domestic economy of the establishment, and conversant with the admirable regulation of Mr. Pickwick's mind, his appearance and behaviour on the morning previous to that which had been fixed upon for the journey to Eatanswill, would have been most mysterious and unaccountable. He paced the room to and fro with hurried steps, popped his head out of the window at intervals of about three minutes each, constantly referred to his watch, and exhibited

From *The Pickwick Papers*.

many other manifestations of impatience, very unusual with him. It was evident that something of great importance was in contemplation, but what that something was not even Mrs. Bardell herself had been enabled to discover.

"Mrs. Bardell," said Mr. Pickwick, at last, as that amiable female approached the termination of a prolonged dusting of the apartment—

"Sir," said Mrs. Bardell.

"Your little boy is a very long time gone."

"Why it's a good long way to the Borough, sir," remonstrated Mrs. Bardell.

"Ah," said Mr. Pickwick, "very true; so it is."

Mr. Pickwick relapsed into silence, and Mrs. Bardell resumed her dusting.

"Mrs. Bardell," said Mr. Pickwick, at the expiration of a few minutes.

"Sir," said Mrs. Bardell again.

"Do you think it's a much greater expense to keep two people, than to keep one?"

"La, Mr. Pickwick," said Mrs. Bardell, colouring up to the very border of her cap, as she fancied she observed a species of matrimonial twinkle in the eyes of her lodger; "La, Mr. Pickwick, what a question!"

"Well, but *do* you?" inquired Mr. Pickwick.

"That depends—" said Mrs. Bardell, approaching the duster very near to Mr. Pickwick's elbow, which was planted on the table—"that depends a good deal upon the person, you know, Mr. Pickwick; and whether it's a saving and careful person, sir."

"That's very true," said Mr. Pickwick, "but the person I have in my eye (here he looked very hard at Mrs. Bardell) I think possesses these qualities; and has, moreover, a considerable knowledge of the world, and a great deal of sharpness, Mrs. Bardell; which may be of material use to me."

"La, Mr. Pickwick," said Mrs. Bardell; the crimson rising to her cap-border again.

"I do," said Mr. Pickwick, growing energetic, as was his wont in speaking of a subject which interested him, "I do, indeed; and to tell you the truth, Mrs. Bardell, I have made up my mind."

"Dear me, sir," exclaimed Mrs. Bardell.

"You'll think it very strange now," said the amiable Mr. Pickwick, with a good-humoured glance at his companion, "that I never consulted you about this matter, and never even mentioned it, till I sent your little boy out this morning—eh?"

Mrs. Bardell could only reply by a look. She had long worshipped Mr. Pickwick at a distance, but here she was, all at once, raised to a pinnacle to which her wildest and most extravagant hopes had never dared to aspire. Mr. Pickwick was going to propose—a deliberate plan, too—sent her little boy to the Borough, to get him out of the way—how thoughtful —how considerate!

"Well," said Mr. Pickwick, "What do you think?"

"Oh, Mr. Pickwick," said Mrs. Bardell, trembling with agitation, "you're very kind, sir."

"It'll save you a good deal of trouble, won't it?" said Mr. Pickwick.

"Oh, I never thought anything of the trouble, sir," replied Mrs. Bardell; "and of course, I should take more trouble to please you then, than ever; but it is so kind of you, Mr. Pickwick, to have so much consideration for my loneliness."

"Ah, to be sure," said Mr. Pickwick; "I never thought of that. When I am in town, you'll always have somebody to sit with you. To be sure, so you will."

"I'm sure I ought to be a very happy woman," said Mrs. Bardell.

"And your little boy—" said Mr. Pickwick.

"Bless his heart," interposed Mrs. Bardell with a maternal sob.

"He, too, will have a companion," resumed Mr. Pickwick, "a lively one, who'll teach him, I'll be bound, more tricks in a week than he would ever learn in a year." And Mr. Pickwick smiled placidly.

"Oh you dear—" said Mrs. Bardell.

Mr. Pickwick started.

"Oh you kind, good, playful dear," said Mrs. Bardell; and without more ado, she rose from her chair, and flung her arms round Mr. Pickwick's neck, with a cataract of tears and a chorus of sobs.

"Bless my soul," cried the astonished Mr. Pickwick—"Mrs. Bardell my good woman—dear me, what a situation—pray consider.—Mrs. Bardell, don't—if anybody should come—"

"Oh, let them come," exclaimed Mrs. Bardell, frantically, "I'll never leave you—dear, kind, good, soul;" and with these words Mrs. Bardell clung the tighter.

"Mercy upon me," said Mr. Pickwick, struggling violently, "I hear somebody coming up the stairs. Don't, don't, there's a good creature, don't." But entreaty and remonstrance were alike unavailing: for Mrs. Bardell had fainted in Mr. Pickwick's arms; and before he could gain time to deposit her on a chair, Master Bardell entered the room, ushering in Mr. Tupman, Mr. Winkle, and Mr. Snodgrass.

Mr. Pickwick was struck motionless and speechless. He stood with his lovely burden in his arms, gazing vacantly on the countenances of his friends, without the slightest attempt at recognition or explanation. They, in their turn, stared at him; and Master Bardell, in his turn, stared at everybody.

The astonishment of the Pickwickians was so absorbing, and the perplexity of Mr. Pickwick was so extreme, that they might have remained in exactly the same relative situations until the suspended animation of the lady was restored, had it not been for a most beautiful and touching expression of filial affection on the part of her youthful son. Clad in a tight suit of corduroy, spangled with brass buttons of a very considerable size, he at first stood at the door astounded and uncertain; but by degrees, the impression that his mother must have suffered some personal damage, pervaded his partially developed mind, and considering Mr. Pickwick as the aggressor, he set up an appalling and semi-earthly kind of howling, and butting forward with his head, commenced assailing that immortal gentleman about the back and legs, with such blows and pinches as the strength of his arm, and the violence of his excitement, allowed.

"Take this little villain away," said the agonised Mr. Pickwick, "he's mad."

"What *is* the matter?" said the three tongue-tied Pickwickians.

"I don't know," replied Mr. Pickwick, pettishly. "Take away the boy," —(here Mr. Winkle carried the interesting boy, screaming and struggling, to the further end of the apartment)—"Now, help me, lead this woman down stairs."

"Oh, I am better now," said Mrs. Bardell, faintly.

"Let me lead you down stairs," said the ever gallant Mr. Tupman.

"Thank you, sir—thank you;" exclaimed Mrs. Bardell, hysterically. And down stairs she was led accordingly, accompanied by her affectionate son.

"I cannot conceive—" said Mr. Pickwick, when his friend returned—"I cannot conceive what has been the matter with that woman. I had merely announced to her my intention of keeping a man servant, when she fell into the extraordinary paroxysm in which you found her. Very extraordinary thing."

"Very," said his three friends.

"Placed me in such an extremely awkward situation," continued Mr. Pickwick.

"Very," was the reply of his followers, as they coughed slightly, and looked dubiously at each other.

This behaviour was not lost upon Mr. Pickwick. He remarked their incredulity. They evidently suspected him.

"There is a man in the passage now," said Mr. Tupman.

"It's the man I spoke to you about," said Mr. Pickwick. "I sent for him to the Borough this morning. Have the goodness to call him up, Snodgrass."

Mr. Snodgrass did as he was desired; and Mr. Samuel Weller forthwith presented himself.

"Oh—you remember me, I suppose?" said Mr. Pickwick.

"I should think so," replied Sam, with a patronising wink. "Queer start that 'ere, but he was one too many for you, warn't he? Up to snuff and a pinch or two over—eh?"

"Never mind that matter now," said Mr. Pickwick, hastily, "I want to speak to you about something else. Sit down."

"Thank'ee, sir," said Sam. And down he sat without further bidding, having previously deposited his old white hat on the landing outside the door. "Ta'nt a werry good 'un to look at," said Sam, "but it's an astonishin' 'un to wear; and afore the brim went, it was a werry handsome tile.

Hows'ever it's lighter without it, that's one thing, and every hole lets in some air, that's another—wentilation gossamer I calls it." On the delivery of this sentiment, Mr. Weller smiled agreeably upon the assembled Pickwickians.

"Now, with regard to the matter on which I, with the concurrence of these gentlemen, sent for you," said Mr. Pickwick.

"That's the pint, sir," interposed Sam; "out vith it, as the father said to the child, wen he swallowed a farden."

"We want to know, in the first place," said Mr. Pickwick, "whether **you** have any reason to be discontented with your present situation."

"Afore I answers that 'ere question, gen'lm'n," replied Mr. Weller, "*I* should like to know, in the first place, whether you're a goin' to purwide me with a better."

A sunbeam of placid benevolence played on Mr. Pickwick's features as he said, "I have half made up my mind to engage you myself."

"Have you, though?" said Sam."

Mr. Pickwick nodded in the affirmative.

"Wages?" inquired Sam.

"Twelve pounds a year," replied Mr. Pickwick.

"Clothes?"

"Two suits."

"Work?"

"To attend upon me; and travel about with me and these gentlemen here."

"Take the bill down," said Sam, emphatically. "I'm let to a single gentleman, and the terms is agreed upon."

"You accept the situation?" inquired Mr. Pickwick.

"Cert'nly," replied Sam. "If the clothes fits me half as well as the place, they'll do."

"You can get a character of course?" said Mr. Pickwick.

"Ask the landlady o' the White Hart about that, sir," replied Sam.

"Can you come this evening?"

"I'll get into the clothes this minute, if they're here," said Sam with great alacrity.

"Call at eight this evening," said Mr. Pickwick; "and if the inquiries are satisfactory, they shall be provided."

With the single exception of one amiable indiscretion, in which an assistant housemaid had equally participated, the history of Mr. Weller's conduct was so very blameless, that Mr. Pickwick felt fully justified in closing the engagement that very evening. With the promptness and energy which characterised not only the public proceedings, but all the private actions of this extraordinary man, he at once led his new attendant to one of those convenient emporiums where gentlemen's new and second-hand clothes are provided, and the troublesome and inconvenient formality of measurement dispensed with; and before night had closed in, Mr. Weller was furnished with a grey coat with the 'P. C.' button, a black hat with a cockade to it, a pink striped waistcoat, light breeches and gaiters, and a variety of other necessaries, too numerous to recapitulate.

"Well," said that suddenly-transformed individual, as he took his seat on the outside of the Eatanswill coach next morning; "I wonder whether I'm meant to be a footman, or a groom, or a gamekeeper, or a seedsman. I looks like a sort of compo of every one on 'em. Never mind; there's change of air, plenty to see, and little to do; and all this suits my complaint uncommon; so long life to the Pickwicks, says I!"

2.

"I, too, have had something of an adventure," said Mr. Winkle, with a smile; and at the request of Mr. Pickwick, he detailed the malicious libel of the Eatanswill Independent, and the consequent excitement of their friend, the editor.

Mr. Pickwick's brow darkened during the recital. His friends observed it, and, when Mr. Winkle had concluded, maintained a profound silence. Mr. Pickwick struck the table emphatically with his clenched fist, and spoke as follows:

"Is it not a wonderful circumstance," said Mr. Pickwick, "that we seem destined to enter no man's house, without involving him in some degree of trouble? Does it not, I ask, bespeak the indiscretion, or, worse than that, the blackness of heart—that I should say so!—of my followers, that beneath whatever roof they locate, they disturb the peace of mind and happiness of some confiding female? Is it not, I say—"

Mr. Pickwick would in all probability have gone on for some time, had not the entrance of Sam, with a letter, caused him to break off in his eloquent discourse. He passed his handkerchief across his forehead, took off his spectacles, wiped them, and put them on again; and his voice had recovered its wonted softness of tone, when he said,

"What have you there, Sam?"

"Called at the Post-office just now, and found this here letter, as has laid there for two days," replied Mr. Weller. "It's sealed with a vafer, and directed in round hand."

"I don't know this hand," said Mr. Pickwick, opening the letter. "Mercy on us! what's this? It must be a jest; it—it—can't be true."

"What's the matter?" was the general inquiry.

"Nobody dead, is there?" said Wardle, alarmed at the horror in Mr. Pickwick's countenance.

Mr. Pickwick made no reply, but, pushing the letter across the table, and desiring Mr. Tupman to read it aloud, fell back in his chair with a look of vacant astonishment quite alarming to behold.

Mr. Tupman, with a trembling voice, read the letter, of which the following is a copy:—

Freeman's Court, Cornhill,
August 28th, 1830.

Bardell against Pickwick.

Sir,

Having been instructed by Mrs. Bardell, to commence an action
against you, for a breach of promise of marriage, for which the plaintiff
lays her damages at fifteen hundred pounds, we beg to inform you that
a writ has been issued against you in this suit, in the Court of Common
Pleas; and request to know, by return of post, the name of your attorney
in London, who will accept service thereof.

We are, Sir,
Your obedient servants,
Dodson and Fogg.

Mr. Samuel Pickwick.

There was something so impressive in the mute astonishment with
which each man regarded his neighbour, and every man regarded Mr.
Pickwick, that all seemed afraid to speak. The silence was at length
broken by Mr. Tupman.

"Dodson and Fogg," he repeated mechanically.

"Bardell and Pickwick," said Mr. Snodgrass, musing.

"Peace of mind and happiness of confiding females," murmured Mr.
Winkle with an air of abstraction.

"It's a conspiracy," said Mr. Pickwick, at length recovering the power
of speech; "a base conspiracy between these two grasping attorneys, Dodson and Fogg. Mrs. Bardell would never do it;—she hasn't the heart to
do it;—she hasn't the case to do it. Ridiculous—ridiculous."

"Of her heart," said Wardle, with a smile, "you should certainly be
the best judge. I don't wish to discourage you, but I should certainly say
that, of her case Dodson and Fogg are far better judges than any of us
can be."

"It's a vile attempt to extort money," said Mr. Pickwick.

"I hope it is," said Wardle, with a short dry cough.

"Who ever heard me address her in any way but that in which a
lodger would address his landlady?" continued Mr. Pickwick, with great
vehemence. "Who ever saw me with her? Not even my friends here—"

"Except on one occasion," said Mr. Tupman.

Mr. Pickwick changed colour.

"Ah," said Wardle. "Well, that's important. There was nothing suspicious then, I suppose?"

Mr. Tupman glanced timidly at his leader. "Why," he said, "there was
nothing suspicious; but—I don't know how it happened, mind—she certainly was reclining in his arms."

"Gracious powers!" ejaculated Mr. Pickwick, as the recollection of the
scene in question struck forcibly upon him; "what a dreadful instance of
the force of circumstances! So she was—so she was."

"And our friend was soothing her anguish," said Mr. Winkle, rather maliciously.

"So I was," said Mr. Pickwick. "I won't deny it. So I was."

"Hallo!" said Wardle; "for a case in which there's nothing suspicious, this looks rather queer—eh, Pickwick? Ah, sly dog—sly dog!" and he laughed till the glasses on the sideboard rang again.

"What a dreadful conjunction of appearances!" exclaimed Mr. Pickwick, resting his chin upon his hands. "Winkle—Tupman—I beg your pardon for the observations I made just now. We are all the victims of circumstances, and I the greatest." With this apology, Mr. Pickwick buried his head in his hands, and ruminated; while Wardle measured out a regular circle of nods and winks, addressed to the other members of the company.

"I'll have it explained, though," said Mr. Pickwick, raising his head, and hammering the table. "I'll see this Dodson and Fogg! I'll go to London to-morrow."

"Not to-morrow," said Wardle; "you're too lame."

"Well then, next day."

"Next day is the first of September, and you're pledged to ride out with us as far as Sir Geoffrey Manning's grounds, at all events, and to meet us at lunch, if you don't take the field."

"Well then, the day after," said Mr. Pickwick; "Thursday.—Sam!"

"Sir," replied Mr. Weller.

"Take two places outside to London, on Thursday morning, for yourself and me."

"Wery well, sir."

Mr. Weller left the room, and departed slowly on his errand, with his hands in his pockets, and his eyes fixed on the ground.

"Rum feller, the hemperor," said Mr. Weller, as he walked slowly up the street. "Think o' his making up to that ere Mrs. Bardell—vith a little boy, too! Always the vay vith these here old 'uns hows'ever, as is such steady goers to look at. I didn't think he'd ha' done it, though—I didn't think he'd ha' done it!" And moralising in this strain, Mr. Samuel Weller bent his steps towards the booking-office.

3.

In the ground-floor of a dingy house, at the very furthest end of Freeman's Court, Cornhill, sat the four clerks of Messrs. Dodson and Fogg, two of his Majesty's Attorneys of the Courts of King's Bench and Common Pleas at Westminster, and solicitors of the High Court of Chancery: the aforesaid clerks catching as favourable glimpses of Heaven's light and Heaven's sun, in the course of their daily labours, as a man might hope to do, were he placed at the bottom of a reasonably deep well; and without the opportunity of perceiving the stars in the day-time, which the latter secluded situation affords.

The clerks' office of Messrs. Dodson and Fogg was a dark, mouldy, earthy-smelling room, with a high wainscotted partition to screen the clerks from the vulgar gaze: a couple of old wooden chairs: a very loud-ticking clock: an almanack, an umbrella-stand, a row of hat pegs, and a few shelves, on which were deposited several ticketed bundles of dirty papers, some old deal boxes with paper labels, and sundry decayed stone ink bottles of various shapes and sizes. There was a glass door leading into the passage which formed the entrance to the court, and on the outer side of this glass door, Mr. Pickwick, closely followed by Sam Weller, presented himself on the Friday morning succeeding the occurrence, of which a faithful narration is given in the last chapter.

"Come in, can't you!" cried a voice from behind the partition, in reply to Mr. Pickwick's gentle tap at the door. And Mr. Pickwick and Sam entered accordingly.

"Mr. Dodson or Mr. Fogg at home, sir?" inquired Mr. Pickwick, gently advancing, hat in hand, towards the partition.

"Mr. Dodson ain't at home, and Mr. Fogg's particularly engaged," replied the voice; and at the same time the head to which the voice belonged, with a pen behind its ear, looked over the partition, and at Mr. Pickwick.

It was a ragged head, the sandy hair of which, scrupulously parted on one side, and flattened down with pomatum, was twisted into little semi-circular tails round a flat face ornamented with a pair of small eyes, and garnished with a very dirty shirt collar, and a rusty black stock.

"Mr. Dodson ain't at home, and Mr. Fogg's particularly engaged," said the man to whom the head belonged.

"When will Mr. Dodson be back, sir?" inquired Mr. Pickwick.

"Can't say."

"Will it be long before Mr. Fogg is disengaged, sir?"

"Don't know."

Here the man proceeded to mend his pen with great deliberation, while another clerk, who was mixing a Seidlitz powder, under cover of the lid of his desk, laughed approvingly.

"I think I'll wait," said Mr. Pickwick. There was no reply, so Mr. Pickwick sat down unbidden, and listened to the loud ticking of the clock and the murmured conversation of the clerks.

"That was a game, wasn't it?" said one of the gentlemen, in a brown coat and brass buttons, inky drabs, and bluchers, at the conclusion of some inaudible relation of his previous evening's adventures.

"Devilish good—devilish good," said the Seidlitz-powder man.

"Tom Cummins was in the chair," said the man with the brown coat; "It was half-past four when I got to Somers Town, and then I was so uncommon lushy that I couldn't find the place where the latch-key went in, and was obliged to knock up the old 'ooman. I say, I wonder what old Fogg 'ud say, if he knew it. I should get the sack, I s'pose—eh?"

At this humorous notion, all the clerks laughed in concert.

"There was such a game with Fogg here, this mornin'," said the man in the brown coat, "while Jack was up stairs sorting the papers, and you two were gone to the stamp-office. Fogg was down here, opening the letters, when that chap as we issued the writ against at Camberwell, you know, came in—what's his name again?"

"Ramsey," said the clerk who had spoken to Mr. Pickwick.

"Ah, Ramsey—a precious seedy-looking customer. 'Well, sir,' says old Fogg, looking at him very fierce—you know his way—'well, sir, have you come to settle?' 'Yes, I have, sir,' said Ramsey, putting his hand in his pocket, and bringing out the money, 'the debt's two pound ten, and the costs three pound five, and here it is, sir;' and he sighed like bricks, as he lugged out the money, done up in a bit of blotting-paper. Old Fogg looked first at the money, and then at him, and then he coughed in his rum way, so that I knew something was coming. 'You don't know there's a declaration filed, which increases the costs materially, I suppose?' said Fogg. 'You don't say that, sir,' said Ramsey, starting back; 'the time was only out, last night, sir.' 'I do say it, though,' said Fogg, 'my clerk's just gone to file it. Hasn't Mr. Jackson gone to file that declaration in Bullman and Ramsey, Mr. Wicks?' Of course I said yes, and then Fogg coughed again, and looked at Ramsey. 'My God!' said Ramsey; 'and here have I nearly driven myself mad, scraping this money together, and all to no purpose.' 'None at all,' said Fogg, coolly; 'so you had better go back and scrape some more together, and bring it here in time.' 'I can't get it, by God,' said Ramsey, striking the desk with his fist. 'Don't bully me, sir,' said Fogg, getting into a passion on purpose. 'I am not bullying you, sir,' said Ramsey. 'You are,' said Fogg; 'get out, sir; get out of this office, sir, and come back, sir, when you know how to behave yourself.' Well, Ramsey tried to speak, but Fogg wouldn't let him, so he put the money in his pocket, and sneaked out. The door was scarcely shut, when old Fogg turned round to me, with a sweet smile on his face, and drew the declaration out of his coat pocket. 'Here, Wicks,' says Fogg, 'take a cab, and go down to the Temple as quick as you can, and file that. The costs are quite safe, for he's a steady man with a large family, at a salary of five-and-twenty shillings a week, and if he gives us a warrant of attorney, as he must in the end, I know his employers will see it paid; so we may as well get all we can out of him, Mr. Wicks; it's a Christian act to do it, Mr. Wicks, for with his large family and small income, he'll be all the better for a good lesson against getting into debt,—won't he, Mr. Wicks, won't he?'—and he smiled so goodnaturedly as he went away, that it was delightful to see him. He is a capital man of business," said Wicks, in a tone of deepest admiration, "capital, isn't he?"

The other three cordially subscribed to this opinion, and the anecdote afforded the most unlimited satisfaction.

"Nice men these here, sir," whispered Mr. Weller to his master; "wery nice notion of fun they has, sir."

Mr. Pickwick nodded assent, and coughed to attract the attention of the young gentlemen behind the partition, who, having now relaxed their minds by a little conversation among themselves, condescended to take some notice of the stranger.

"I wonder whether Fogg's disengaged now?" said Jackson.

"I'll see," said Wicks, dismounting leisurely from his stool. "What name shall I tell Mr. Fogg?"

"Pickwick," replied the illustrious subject of these memoirs.

Mr. Jackson departed up stairs on his errand, and immediately returned with a message that Mr. Fogg would see Mr. Pickwick in five minutes; and having delivered it, returned again to his desk.

"What did he say his name was?" whispered Wicks.

"Pickwick," replied Jackson; "it's the defendant in Bardell and Pick-wick."

A sudden scraping of feet, mingled with the sound of suppressed laughter, was heard from behind the partition.

"They're a twiggin' of you, sir," whispered Mr. Weller.

"Twigging of me, Sam!" replied Mr. Pickwick; "what do you mean by twigging me?"

Mr. Weller replied by pointing with his thumb over his shoulder, and Mr. Pickwick, on looking up, became sensible of the pleasing fact, that all the four clerks, with countenances expressive of the utmost amusement, and with their heads thrust over the wooden screen, were minutely inspecting the figure and general appearance of the supposed trifler with female hearts, and disturber of female happiness. On his looking up, the row of heads suddenly disappeared, and the sound of pens travelling at a furious rate over paper, immediately succeeded.

A sudden ring at the bell which hung in the office, summoned Mr. Jackson to the apartment of Fogg, from whence he came back to say that he (Fogg) was ready to see Mr. Pickwick if he would step up stairs.

Up stairs Mr. Pickwick did step accordingly, leaving Sam Weller below. The room door of the one-pair back, bore inscribed in legible characters the imposing words "Mr. Fogg;" and, having tapped thereat, and been desired to come in, Jackson ushered Mr. Pickwick into the presence.

"Is Mr. Dodson in?" inquired Mr. Fogg.

"Just come in, sir," replied Jackson.

"Ask him to step here."

"Yes, sir." Exit Jackson.

"Take a seat, sir," said Fogg; "there is the paper, sir; my partner will be here directly, and we can converse about this matter, sir."

Mr. Pickwick took a seat and the paper, but instead of reading the latter, peeped over the top of it, and took a survey of the man of business, who was an elderly pimply-faced, vegetable-diet sort of man, in a black coat, dark mixture trousers, and small black gaiters: a kind of being who seemed to be an essential part of the desk at which he was writing, and to have as much thought or sentiment.

After a few minutes' silence, Mr. Dodson, a plump, portly, stern-looking man, with a loud voice, appeared; and the conversation commenced.

"This is Mr. Pickwick," said Fogg.

"Ah! You are the defendant, sir, in Bardell and Pickwick?" said Dodson.

"I am, sir," replied Mr. Pickwick.

"Well, sir," said Dodson, "and what do you propose?"

"Ah!" said Fogg, thrusting his hands into his trousers' pockets, and throwing himself back in his chair, "what do you propose, Mr. Pickwick?"

"Hush, Fogg," said Dodson, "let me hear what Mr. Pickwick has to say."

"I came, gentlemen," replied Mr. Pickwick,—gazing placidly on the two partners,—"I came here, gentlemen, to express the surprise with which I received your letter of the other day, and to inquire what grounds of action you can have against me."

"Grounds of—" Fogg had ejaculated thus much, when he was stopped by Dodson.

"Mr. Fogg," said Dodson, "I am going to speak."

"I beg your pardon, Mr. Dodson," said Fogg.

"For the grounds of action, sir," continued Dodson, with moral elevation in his air, "you will consult your own conscience and your own feelings. We, sir, we are guided entirely by the statement of our client. That statement, sir, may be true, or it may be false; it may be credible, or it may be incredible; but, if it be true, and if it be credible, I do not hesitate to say, sir, that our grounds of action, sir, are strong, and not to be shaken. You may be an unfortunate man, sir, or you may be a designing one; but if I were called upon, as a juryman upon my oath, sir, to express an opinion of your conduct, sir, I do not hesitate to assert that I should have but one opinion about it." Here Dodson drew himself up with an air of offended virtue, and looked at Fogg, who thrust his hands further in his pockets, and nodding his head sagely, said in a tone of the fullest concurrence, "Most certainly."

"Well, sir," said Mr. Pickwick, with considerable pain depicted in his countenance, "you will permit me to assure you, that I am a most unfortunate man, so far as this case is concerned."

"I hope you are, sir," replied Dodson; "I trust you may be, sir. If you are really innocent of what is laid to your charge, you are more unfortunate than I had believed any man could possibly be. What do *you* say, Mr. Fogg?"

"I say precisely what you say," replied Fogg, with a smile of incredulity.

"The writ, sir, which commences the action," continued Dodson, "was issued regularly. Mr. Fogg, where is the *praecipe* book?"

"Here it is," said Fogg, handing over a square book, with a parchment cover.

"Here is the entry," resumed Dodson. " 'Middlesex, Capias *Martha Bardell, widow, v. Samuel Pickwick*. Damages £1500. Dodson and Fogg for the plaintiff, Aug. 28, 1830.' All regular, sir; perfectly." Dodson coughed and looked at Fogg, who said "Perfectly," also. And then they both looked at Mr. Pickwick.

"I am to understand, then," said Mr. Pickwick, "that it really is your intention to proceed with this action?"

"Understand, sir?—that you certainly may," replied Dodson, with something as near a smile as his importance would allow.

"And that the damages are actually laid at fifteen hundred pounds?" said Mr. Picwick.

"To which understanding you may add my assurance, that if we could have prevailed upon our client, they would have been laid at treble the amount, sir;" replied Dodson.

"I believe Mrs. Bardell specially said, however," observed Fogg, glancing at Dodson, "that she would not compromise for a farthing less."

"Unquestionably," replied Dodson, sternly. For the action was only just begun; and it wouldn't have done to let Mr. Pickwick compromise it then, even if he had been so disposed.

"As you offer no terms, sir," said Dodson, displaying a slip of parchment in his right hand, and affectionately pressing a paper copy of it on Mr. Pickwick with his left, "I had better serve you with a copy of this writ, sir. Here is the original, sir."

"Very well, gentlemen, very well," said Mr. Pickwick, rising in person and wrath at the same time; "you shall hear from my solicitor, gentlemen."

"We shall be very happy to do so," said Fogg, rubbing his hands.

"Very," said Dodson, opening the door.

"And before I go, gentlemen," said the excited Mr. Pickwick, turning round on the landing, "permit me to say, that of all the disgraceful and rascally proceedings—"

"Stay, sir, stay," interposed Dodson, with great politeness. "Mr. Jackson! Mr. Wicks!"

"Sir," said the two clerks, appearing at the bottom of the stairs.

"I merely want you to hear what this gentleman says," replied Dodson. "Pray go on, sir—disgraceful and rascally proceedings, I think you said?"

"I did," said Mr. Pickwick, thoroughly roused. "I said, sir, that of all the disgraceful and rascally proceedings that ever were attempted, this is the most so. I repeat it, sir."

"You hear that, Mr. Wicks?" said Dodson.

"You won't forget these expressions, Mr. Jackson?" said Fogg.

"Perhaps you would like to call us swindlers, sir," said Dodson. "Pray do, sir, if you feel disposed—now pray do, sir."

"I do," said Mr. Pickwick. "You *are* swindlers."

"Very good," said Dodson. "You can hear down there, I hope, Mr. Wicks?"

"Oh yes, sir," said Wicks.

"You had better come up a step or two higher, if you can't," added Mr. Fogg. "Go on, sir; do go on. You had better call us thieves, sir; or perhaps you would like to assault one of us. Pray do it, sir, if you would; we will not make the smallest resistance. Pray do it, sir."

As Fogg put himself very temptingly within the reach of Mr. Pickwick's clenched fist, there is little doubt that that gentleman would have complied with his earnest entreaty, but for the interposition of Sam, who, hearing the dispute, emerged from the office, mounted the steps, and seized his master by the arm.

"You just come avay," said Mr. Weller. "Battledore and shuttlecock's a wery good game, vhen you a'n't the shuttlecock and two lawyers the battledores, in wich case it gets too excitin' to be pleasant. Come avay, sir. If you want to ease your mind by blowing up somebody, come out into the court and blow up me; but it's rayther too expensive work to be carried on here."

And without the slightest ceremony, Mr. Weller hauled his master down the stairs, and down the court, and having safely deposited him in Cornhill, fell behind, prepared to follow whithersoever he should lead.

Mr. Pickwick walked on abstractedly, crossed opposite the Mansion House, and bent his steps up Cheapside. Sam began to wonder where they were going, when his master turned round, and said:

"Sam, I will go immediately to Mr. Perker's."

"That's just exactly the wery place vere you ought to have gone last night, sir," replied Mr. Weller.

"I think it is, Sam," said Mr. Pickwick.

"I *know* it is," said Mr. Weller.

4.

Having accomplished the main end and object of his journey, by the exposure of Jingle, Mr. Pickwick resolved on immediately returning to London, with the view of becoming acquainted with the proceedings which had been taken against him, in the mean time, by Messrs. Dodson and Fogg. Acting upon this resolution with all the energy and decision of his character, he mounted to the back seat of the first coach which left Ipswich on the morning after the memorable occurrences detailed at length in the two preceding chapters; and accompanied by his three friends, and Mr. Samuel Weller, arrived in the metropolis, in perfect health and safety, the same evening.

Here, the friends, for a short time, separated. Messrs. Tupman, Winkle, and Snodgrass repaired to their several homes to make such preparations as might be requisite for their forthcoming visit to Dingley Dell; and Mr. Pickwick and Sam took up their present abode in very good, old-fashioned, and comfortable quarters: to wit, the George and Vulture Tavern and Hotel, George Yard, Lombard Street.

Mr. Pickwick had dined, finished his second pint of particular port, pulled his silk handkerchief over his head, put his feet on the fender, and thrown himself back in an easy chair, when the entrance of Mr. Weller with his carpet bag, aroused him from his tranquil meditations.

"Sam," said Mr. Pickwick.

"Sir," said Mr. Weller.

"I have just been thinking, Sam," said Mr. Pickwick, "that having left a good many things at Mrs. Bardell's, in Goswell Street, I ought to arrange for taking them away before I leave town again."

"Wery good, sir," replied Mr. Weller.

"I could send them to Mr. Tupman's, for the present, Sam," continued Mr. Pickwick, "but, before we take them away, it is necessary that they should be looked up, and put together. I wish you would step up to Goswell Street, Sam, and arrange about it."

"At once, sir?" inquired Mr. Weller.

"At once," replied Mr. Pickwick. "And stay, Sam," added Mr. Pickwick, pulling out his purse, "there is some rent to pay. The quarter is not due till Christmas, but you may pay it, and have done with it. A month's notice terminates my tenancy. Here it is, written out. Give it, and tell Mrs. Bardell she may put a bill up as soon as she likes."

"Wery good, sir," replied Mr. Weller; "anythin' more, sir?"

"Nothing more, Sam."

Mr. Weller stepped slowly to the door, as if he expected something more; slowly opened it, slowly stepped out, and had slowly closed it within a couple of inches, when Mr. Pickwick called out,

"Sam."

"Sir," said Mr. Weller, stepping quickly back, and closing the door behind him.

"I have no objection, Sam, to your endeavouring to ascertain how Mrs. Bardell herself seems disposed towards me, and whether it is really probable that this vile and groundless action is to be carried to extremity. I say I do not object to your doing this, if you wish it, Sam," said Mr. Pickwick.

Sam gave a short nod of intelligence, and left the room. Mr. Pickwick drew the silk handkerchief once more over his head, and composed himself for a nap. Mr. Weller promptly walked forth, to execute his commission.

It was nearly nine o'clock when he reached Goswell Street. A couple of candles were burning in the little front parlour, and a couple of caps were reflected on the window-blind. Mrs. Bardell had got company.

Mr. Weller knocked at the door, and after a pretty long interval— occupied by the party without in whistling a tune, and by a party within, in persuading a refractory flat candle to allow itself to be lighted— a pair of small boots pattered over the floor-cloth, and Master Bardell presented himself.

"Well, young township," said Sam, "how's mother?"

"She's pretty well," replied Master Bardell, "so am I."

"Well, that's a mercy," said Sam; "tell her I want to speak to her, will you, my hinfant fernomenon?"

Master Bardell, thus adjured, placed the refractory flat candle on the bottom stair, and vanished into the front parlour with his message.

The two caps, reflected on the window-blind, were the respective head-dresses of a couple of Mrs. Bardell's most particular acquaintance, who had just stepped in to have a quiet cup of tea, and a little warm supper of a couple of sets of pettitoes and some toasted cheese. The cheese was simmering and browning away, most delightfully, in a little Dutch oven before the fire; and the pettitoes were getting on deliciously in a little tin saucepan on the hob; and Mrs. Bardell and her two friends were getting on very well, also, in a little quiet conversation about and concerning all their particular friends and acquaintance; when Master Bardell came back from answering the door, and delivered the message intrusted to him by Mr. Samuel Weller.

"Mr. Pickwick's servant!" said Mrs. Bardell, turning pale.

"Bless my soul!" said Mrs. Cluppins.

"Well, I raly would *not* ha' believed it, unless I had ha' happened to ha' been here!" said Mrs. Sanders.

Mrs. Cluppins was a little, brisk, busy-looking woman; and Mrs. Sanders was a big, fat, heavy-faced personage; and the two were the company.

Mrs. Bardell felt it proper to be agitated; and as none of the three exactly knew whether, under existing circumstances, any communication, otherwise than through Dodson and Fogg, ought to be held with Mr. Pickwick's servant, they were all rather taken by surprise. In this state of indecision, obviously the first thing to be done, was to thump the boy for finding Mr. Weller at the door. So his mother thumped him, and he cried melodiously.

"Hold your noise—do—you naughty creetur!" said Mrs. Bardell.

"Yes; don't worrit your poor mother," said Mrs. Sanders.

"She's quite enough to worrit her, as it is, without you, Tommy," said Mrs. Cluppins, with sympathising resignation.

"Ah! worse luck, poor lamb!" said Mrs. Sanders.

At all which moral reflections, Master Bardell howled the louder.

"Now, what *shall* I do?" said Mrs. Bardell to Mrs. Cluppins.

"*I* think you ought to see him," replied Mrs. Cluppins. "But on no account without a witness."

"*I* think two witnesses would be more lawful," said Mrs. Sanders, who, like the other friend, was bursting with curiosity.

"Perhaps he'd better come in here," said Mrs. Bardell.

"To be sure," replied Mrs. Cluppins, eagerly catching at the idea. "Walk in, young man; and shut the street-door first, please."

Mr. Weller immediately took the hint; and presenting himself in the parlour, explained his business to Mrs. Bardell, thus:

"Wery sorry to 'casion any personal inconwenience, ma'am, as the housebreaker said to the old lady when he put her on the fire; but as me and my governor's only jest come to town, and is jest going away agin, it can't be helped you see."

"Of course, the young man can't help the faults of his master," said

Mrs. Cluppins, much struck by Mr. Weller's appearance and conversation.

"Certainly not," chimed in Mrs. Sanders, who, from certain wistful glances at the little tin saucepan, seemed to be engaged in a mental calculation of the probable extent of the pettitoes, in the event of Sam's being asked to stop supper.

"So all I've come about, is just this here," said Sam, disregarding the interruption; "First, to give my governor's notice—there it is. Secondly, to pay the rent—here it is. Thirdly, to say as all his things is to be put together, and give to anybody as we sends for 'em. Fourthly, that you may let the place as soon as you like—and that's all."

"Whatever has happened," said Mrs. Bardell, "I always have said, and always will say, that in every respect but one, Mr. Pickwick has always behaved himself like a perfect gentleman. His money always was as good as the bank: always."

As Mrs. Bardell said this, she applied her handkerchief to her eyes, and went out of the room to get the receipt.

Sam well knew that he had only to remain quiet, and the women were sure to talk; so he looked alternately at the tin saucepan, the toasted cheese, the wall, and the ceiling, in profound silence.

"Poor dear!" said Mrs. Cluppins.

"Ah, poor thing!" replied Mrs. Sanders.

Sam said nothing. He saw they were coming to the subject.

"I raly cannot contain myself," said Mrs. Cluppins, "when I think of such perjury. I don't wish to say anything to make you uncomfortable, young man, but your master's an old brute, and I wish I had him here to tell him so."

"I wish you had," said Sam.

"To see how dreadful she takes on, going moping about, and taking no pleasure in nothing, except when her friends comes in, out of charity, to sit with her, and make her comfortable," resumed Mrs. Cluppins, glancing at the tin saucepan and the Dutch oven, "it's shocking!"

"Barbareous," said Mrs. Sanders.

"And your master, young man! A gentleman with money, as could never feel the expense of a wife, no more than nothing," continued Mrs. Cluppins, with great volubility, "why there ain't the faintest shade of an excuse for his behaviour! Why don't he marry her?"

"Ah," said Sam, "to be sure; that's the question."

"Question, indeed," retorted Mrs. Cluppins; "she'd question him, if she'd my spirit. Hows'ever, there *is* law for us women, mis-rable creeturs as they'd make us, if they could; and that your master will find out, young man, to his cost, afore he's six months older."

At this consolatory reflection, Mrs. Cluppins bridled up and smiled at Mrs. Sanders, who smiled back again.

"The action's going on, and no mistake," thought Sam, as Mrs. Bardell re-entered with the receipt.

"Here's the receipt, Mr. Weller," said Mrs. Bardell, "and here's the change, and I hope you'll take a little drop of something to keep the cold out, if it's only for old acquaintance sake, Mr. Weller."

Sam saw the advantage he should gain, and at once acquiesced; whereupon Mrs. Bardell produced, from a small closet, a black bottle and a wine glass; and so great was her abstraction, in her deep mental affliction, that, after filling Mr. Weller's glass, she brought out three more wine glasses, and filled them too.

"Lauk, Mrs. Bardell," said Mrs. Cluppins, "see what you've been and done!"

"Well, that is a good one!" ejaculated Mrs. Sanders.

"Ah, my poor head!" said Mrs. Bardell, with a faint smile.

Sam understood all this, of course, so he said at once, that he never could drink before supper, unless a lady drank with him. A great deal of laughing ensued, and Mrs. Sanders volunteered to humour him, so she took a slight sip out of her glass. Then, Sam said it must go all round, so they all took a slight sip. Then, little Mrs. Cluppins proposed as a toast, "Success to Bardell against Pickwick;" and then the ladies emptied their glasses in honour of the sentiment, and got very talkative directly.

"I suppose you've heard what's going forward, Mr. Weller?" said Mrs. Bardell.

"I've heerd somethin' on it," replied Sam.

"It's a terrible thing to be dragged before the public, in that way, Mr. Weller," said Mrs. Bardell; "but I see now, that it's the only thing I ought to do, and my lawyers, Mr. Dodson and Fogg, tell me, that with the evidence as we shall call, we must succeed. I don't know what I should do, Mr. Weller, if I didn't."

The mere idea of Mrs. Bardell's failing in her action, affected Mrs. Sanders so deeply, that she was under the necessity of re-filling and re-emptying her glass immediately; feeling, as she said afterwards, that if she hadn't had the presence of mind to have done so, she must have dropped.

"Ven is it expected to come on?" inquired Sam.

"Either in February or March," replied Mrs. Bardell.

"What a number of witnesses there'll be, won't there?" said Mrs. Cluppins.

"Ah, won't there!" replied Mrs. Sanders.

"And won't Mr. Dodson and Fogg be wild if the plaintiff shouldn't get it?" added Mrs. Cluppins, "when they do it all on speculation!"

"Ah! won't they!" said Mrs. Sanders.

"But the plaintiff must get it," resumed Mrs. Cluppins.

"I hope so," said Mrs. Bardell.

"Oh, there can't be any doubt about it," rejoined Mrs. Sanders.

"Vell," said Sam, rising and setting down his glass. "All I can say is, that I wish you *may* get it."

"Thank'ee, Mr. Weller," said Mrs. Bardell, fervently.

"And of them Dodson and Fogg, as does these sorts o' things on spec," continued Mr. Weller, "as well as for the other kind and gen'rous people o' the same purfession, as sets people by the ears, free gratis for nothin', and sets their clerks to work to find out little disputes among their neighbours and acquaintance as vants settlin' by means o' law-suits—all I can say o' them, is, that I vish they had the revard I'd give 'em."

"Ah, I wish they had the reward that every kind and generous heart would be inclined to bestow upon them!" said the gratified Mrs. Bardell.

"Amen to that," replied Sam, "and a fat and happy livin' they'd get out of it! Wish you good night, ladies."

To the great relief of Mrs. Sanders, Sam was allowed to depart, without any reference, on the part of the hostess, to the pettitoes and toasted cheese: to which the ladies, with such juvenile assistance as Master Bardell could afford, soon afterwards rendered the amplest justice—indeed they wholly vanished, before their strenuous exertions.

Mr. Weller went his way back to the George and Vulture, and faithfully recounted to his master, such indications of the sharp practice of Dodson and Fogg, as he had contrived to pick up, in his visit to Mrs. Bardell's. An interview with Mr. Perker, next day, more than confirmed Mr. Weller's statement; and Mr. Pickwick was fain to prepare for his Christmas visit to Dingley Dell, with the pleasant anticipation that some two or three months afterwards, an action brought against him for damages sustained by reason of a breach of promise of marriage, would be publicly tried in the Court of Common Pleas: the plaintiff having all the advantages derivable, not only from the force of circumstances, but from the sharp practice of Dodson and Fogg to boot.

5.

Scattered about in various holes and corners of the Temple, are certain dark and dirty chambers, in and out of which, all the morning in Vacation, and half the evening too in Term time, there may be seen constantly hurrying with bundles of papers under their arms, and protruding from their pockets, an almost uninterrupted succession of Lawyers' Clerks. There are several grades of Lawyers' Clerks. There is the Articled Clerk, who has paid a premium, and is an attorney in perspective, who runs a tailor's bill, receives invitations to parties, knows a family in Gower Street, and another in Tavistock Square: who goes out of town every Long Vacation to see his father, who keeps live horses innumerable; and who is, in short, the very aristocrat of clerks. There is the salaried clerk—out of door, or in door, as the case may be—who devotes the major part of his thirty shillings a week to his personal pleasure and adornment, repairs half-price to the Adelphia Theatre at least three times a week, dissipates majestically at the cider cellars afterwards, and is a dirty caricature of the fashion which expired six months ago. There is the middle-aged copying clerk, with a large family, who is always shabby, and often drunk. And there are the office lads in their first surtouts, who feel a befitting contempt for boys at day-schools: club as they go home at night, for saveloys and porter: and think there's nothing like "life." There are varieties of the genus, too numerous to recapitulate, but however numerous they may be, they are all to be seen at certain regulated business hours, hurrying to and from the places we have just mentioned.

These sequestered nooks are the public offices of the legal profession, where writs are issued, judgments signed, declarations filed, and numerous other ingenious little machines put in motion for the torture and torment of His Majesty's liege subjects, and the comfort and emolument of the practitioners of the law. They are, for the most part, low-roofed, mouldy rooms, where innumerable rolls of parchment, which have been perspiring in secret for the last century, send forth an agreeable odour, which is mingled by day with the scent of the dry rot, and by night with the various exhalations which arise from damp cloaks, festering umbrellas, and the coarsest tallow candles.

About half past seven o'clock in the evening, some ten days or a fortnight after Mr. Pickwick and his friends returned to London, there hurried into one of these offices, an individual in a brown coat and brass buttons, whose long hair was scrupulously twisted round the rim of his napless hat, and whose soiled drab trousers were so tightly strapped over his Blucher boots, that his knees threatened every moment to start from their concealment. He produced from his coat pockets a long and narrow strip of parchment, on which the presiding functionary impressed an illegible black stamp. He then drew forth four scraps of paper, of similar dimensions, each containing a printed copy of the strip of parchment with blanks for a name; and having filled up the blanks, put all the five documents in his pocket, and hurried away.

The man in the brown coat, with the cabalistic documents in his pocket, was no other than our old acquaintance Mr. Jackson, of the house of Dodson and Fogg, Freeman's Court, Cornhill. Instead of returning to the office from whence he came, however, he bent his steps direct to Sun Court, and walking straight into the George and Vulture, demanded to know whether one Mr. Pickwick was within.

"Call Mr. Pickwick's servant, Tom," said the barmaid of the George and Vulture.

"Don't trouble yourself," said Mr. Jackson, "I've come on business. If you'll show me Mr. Pickwick's room, I'll step up myself."

"What name, sir?" said the waiter.

"Jackson," replied the clerk.

The waiter stepped up stairs to announce Mr. Jackson; but Mr. Jackson saved him the trouble by following close at his heels, and walking into the apartment before he could articulate a syllable.

Mr. Pickwick had, that day, invited his three friends to dinner; they were all seated round the fire, drinking their wine, when Mr. Jackson presented himself, as above described.

"How de do, sir?" said Mr. Jackson, nodding to Mr. Pickwick.

That gentleman bowed, and looked somewhat surprised, for the physiognomy of Mr. Jackson dwelt not in his recollection.

"I have called from Dodson and Fogg's," said Mr. Jackson, in an explanatory tone.

Mr. Pickwick roused at the name. "I refer you to my attorney, sir: Mr. Perker, of Gray's Inn," said he. "Waiter, show this gentleman out."

"Beg your pardon, Mr. Pickwick," said Jackson, deliberately depositing his hat on the floor, and drawing from his pocket the strip of parchment. "But personal service, by clerk or agent, in these cases, you know, Mr. Pickwick—nothing like caution, sir, in all legal forms?"

Here Mr. Jackson cast his eye on the parchment; and, resting his hands on the table, and looking round with a winning and persuasive smile, said, "Now come; don't let's have no words about such a little matter as this. Which of you gentlemen's name's Snodgrass?"

At this inquiry, Mr. Snodgrass gave such a very undisguised and palpable start, that no further reply was needed.

"Ah! I thought so," said Mr. Jackson, more affably than before. "I've got a little something to trouble you with, sir."

"Me!" exclaimed Mr. Snodgrass.

"It's only a *subpoena* in Bardell and Pickwick on behalf of the plaintiff," replied Jackson, singling out one of the slips of paper, and producing a shilling from his waistcoat-pocket. "It'll come on, in the settens after Term; fourteenth of Febooary, we expect; we've marked it a special jury cause, and it's only ten down the paper. That's yours, Mr. Snodgrass." As Jackson said this, he presented the parchment before the eyes of Mr. Snodgrass, and slipped the paper and the shilling into his hand.

Mr. Tupman had witnessed this process in silent astonishment, when Jackson, turning sharply upon him, said:

"I think I ain't mistaken when I say your name's Tupman, am I?"

Mr. Tupman looked at Mr. Pickwick; but, perceiving no encouragement in that gentleman's widely-opened eyes to deny his name, said:

"Yes, my name *is* Tupman, sir."

"And that other gentleman's Mr. Winkle, I think," said Jackson.

Mr. Winkle faltered out a reply in the affirmative; and both gentlemen were forthwith invested with a slip of paper, and a shilling each, by the dexterous Mr. Jackson.

"Now," said Jackson, "I'm afraid you'll think me rather troublesome, but I want somebody else, if it ain't inconvenient. I *have* Samuel Weller's name here, Mr. Pickwick."

"Send my servant here, waiter," said Mr. Pickwick. The waiter retired, considerably astonished, and Mr. Pickwick motioned Jackson to a seat.

There was a painful pause, which was at length broken by the innocent defendant.

"I suppose, sir," said Mr. Pickwick, his indignation rising while he spoke; "I suppose, sir, that it is the intention of your employers to seek to criminate me, upon the testimony of my own friends?"

Mr. Jackson struck his fore-finger several times against the left side of his nose, to intimate that he was not there to disclose the secrets of the prison-house, and playfully rejoined,

"Not knowin', can't say."

"For what other reason, sir," pursued Mr. Pickwick, "are these sub-poenas served upon them, if not for this?"

"Very good plant, Mr. Pickwick," replied Jackson, slowly shaking his head. "But it won't do. No harm in trying, but there's little to be got out of me."

Here Mr. Jackson smiled once more upon the company; and, applying his left thumb to the tip of his nose, worked a visionary coffee-mill with his right hand: thereby performing a very graceful piece of pantomime (then much in vogue, but now, unhappily, almost obsolete) which was familiarly denominated "taking a grinder."

"No, no, Mr. Pickwick," said Jackson, in conclusion; "Perker's people must guess what we've served these subpoenas for. If they can't, they must wait till the action comes on, and then they'll find out."

Mr. Pickwick bestowed a look of excessive disgust on his unwelcome visitor, and would probably have hurled some tremendous anathema at the heads of Messrs. Dodson and Fogg, had not Sam's entrance at the instant interrupted him.

"Samuel Weller?" said Mr. Jackson, inquiringly.

"Vun o' the truest things as you've said for many a long year," replied Sam, in a most composed manner.

"Here's a subpoena for you, Mr. Weller," said Jackson.

"What's that in English?" inquired Sam.

"Here's the original," said Jackson, declining the required explanation.

"Which?" said Sam.

"This," replied Jackson, shaking the parchment.

"Oh, that's the 'rig'nal, is it?" said Sam. "Well, I'm wery glad I've seen the 'rig'nal, 'cos it's a gratifyin' sort o' thing, and eases vun's mind so much."

"And here's the shilling," said Jackson. "It's from Dodson and Fogg's."

"And it's uncommon handsome o' Dodson and Fogg, as knows so little of me, to come down vith a present," said Sam. "I feel it as a wery high compliment, sir; it's a wery hon'rable thing to them, as they knows how to reward merit werever they meets it. Besides wich, it's affectin' to one's feelin's."

As Mr. Weller said this, he inflicted a little friction on his right eye-lid, with the sleeve of his coat, after the most approved manner of actors when they are in domestic pathetics.

Mr. Jackson seemed rather puzzled by Sam's proceedings; but, as he had served the subpoenas, and had nothing more to say, he made a feint of putting on the one glove which he usually carried in his hand, for the sake of appearances; and returned to the office to report progress.

Mr. Pickwick slept little that night; his memory had received a very disagreeable refresher on the subject of Mrs. Bardell's action. He breakfasted betimes next morning; and, desiring Sam to accompany him, set forth towards Gray's Inn Square.

"Sam!" said Mr. Pickwick, looking round, when they got to the end of Cheapside.

"Sir?" said Sam, stepping up to his master.

"Which way?"

"Up Newgate Street."

Mr. Pickwick did not turn round immediately, but looked vacantly in Sam's face for a few seconds, and heaved a deep sigh.

"What's the matter, sir?" inquired Sam.

"This action, Sam," said Mr. Pickwick, "is expected to come on, on the fourteenth of next month."

"Remarkable coinci*dence* that 'ere, sir," replied Sam.

"Why remarkable, Sam?" inquired Mr. Pickwick.

"Walentine's day, sir," responded Sam; "reg'lar good day for a breach o' promise trial."

Mr. Weller's smile awakened no gleam of mirth in his master's countenance. Mr. Pickwick turned abruptly round, and led the way in silence.

They had walked some distance: Mr. Pickwick trotting on before, plunged in profound meditation, and Sam following behind, with a countenance expressive of the most enviable and easy defiance of everything and everybody: when the latter, who was always especially anxious to impart to his master any exclusive information he possessed, quickened his pace until he was close at Mr. Pickwick's heels; and, pointing up at a house they were passing, said,

"Wery nice pork-shop that 'ere, sir."

"Yes, it seems so," said Mr. Pickwick.

"Celebrated Sassage factory," said Sam.

"Is it?" said Mr. Pickwick.

"Is it!" reiterated Sam with some indignation; "I should rayther think it was. Why sir, bless your innocent eyebrows, that's where the mysterious disappearance of a 'spectable tradesman took place, four years ago."

"You don't mean to say he was burked, Sam?" said Mr. Pickwick, looking hastily round.

"No I don't indeed, sir," replied Mr. Weller, "I wish I did; far worse than that. He was the master o' that 'ere shop, sir, and the inwenter o' that patent-never-leavin-off sassage steam ingine, as ud swaller up a pavin' stone if you put it too near, and grind it into sassages as easy as if it was a tender young babby. Wery proud o' that machine he was, as it was nat'ral he should be; and he'd stand down in the celler a lookin' at it, wen it was in full play, till he got quite melancholy with joy. A wery happy man he'd ha' been, sir, in the procession o' that 'ere ingine and two more lovely hinfants besides, if it hadn't been for his wife, who was a most ow-dacious wixin. She was always a follerin' him about, and din-nin' in his ears, 'till at last he couldn't stand it no longer. 'I'll tell you what it is, my dear,' he says one day; 'if you persewere in this here sort of amusement,' he says, 'I'm blessed if I don't go away to 'Merriker; and that's all about it.' 'You're a idle willin',' says she, 'and I wish the 'Merri-kins joy for their bargin.' Arter wich she keeps on abusin' of him for half an hour, and then runs into the little parlour behind the shop, sets to a screamin', says he'll be the death of her, and falls in a fit, which lasts for three good hours—one o' them fits wich is all screamin' and kickin'. Well, next mornin', the husband was missin'. He hadn't taken nothin' from the till,—hadn't even put on his great-coat—so it was quite clear he warn't gone to 'Merriker. Didn't come back next day; didn't come back next week; Missis had bills printed, sayin' that, if he'd come back, he should be forgiven everythin', (which was very liberal, seein' that he hadn't done nothin' at all,) all the canals was dragged, and for two months artervards whenever a body turned up, it was carried, as a reg'lar thing, straight off to the sassage shop. Hows'ever none on 'em answered, so they gave out that he'd run avay, and she kept on the bis'ness. One Saturday night, a little thin old gen'l'm'n comes into the shop in a great passion and says, 'Are you the missis o' this here shop?' 'Yes I am,' says she. 'Well ma'am,' says he, 'then I've just looked in to say, that me and my family ain't a goin' to be choaked for nothin'; and more than that, ma'am,' he says, 'you'll allow me to observe, that as you don't use the primest parts of the meat in the manafacter o' sassages, I think you'd find beef come nearly as cheap as buttons.' 'As buttons, sir!' says she. 'Buttons, ma'am,' says the little old gentleman, unfolding a bit of paper, and shewin' twenty or thirty halves o' buttons. 'Nice seasonin' for sassages, is trousers' buttons, ma'am.' 'They're my husband's but-tons!' say the widder, beginnin' to faint. 'What!' screams the little old gen'l'm'n, turnin' wery pale. 'I see it all,' says the widder; 'in a fit of tem-porary insanity he rashly converted his-self into sassages!' And so he had, sir," said Mr. Weller, looking steadily into Mr. Pickwick's horror-stricken countenance, "or else he'd been draw'd into the ingine; but how-ever that might ha' been, the little old gen'l'm'n, who had been remark-ably partial to sassages all his life, rushed out o' the shop in a wild state, and was never heerd on, artervards!"

The relation of this affecting incident of private life, brought master and man to Mr. Perker's chambers. Lowten, holding the door half open, was in conversation with a rustily-clad, miserable looking man, in boots without toes, and gloves without fingers. There were traces of pri-vation and suffering—almost of despair—in his lank and careworn countenance; he felt his poverty, for he shrunk to the dark side of the staircase as Mr. Pickwick approached.

"It's very unfortunate," said the stranger, with a sigh.

"Very," said Lowten, scribbling his name on the door post with his pen and rubbing it out again with the feather. "Will you leave a message for him?"

"When do you think he'll be back?" inquired the stranger.

"Quite uncertain," replied Lowten, winking at Mr. Pickwick, as the stranger cast his eyes towards the ground.

"You don't think it would be of any use my waiting for him?" said the stranger, looking wistfuly into the office.

"Oh no, I'm sure it wouldn't," replied the clerk, moving a little more into the centre of the doorway. "He's certain not to be back this week, and it's a chance whether he will, next; for when Perker once gets out of town, he's never in a hurry to come back again."

"Out of town!" said Mr. Pickwick; "dear me, how unfortunate!"

"Don't go away, Mr. Pickwick," said Lowten, "I've got a letter for you." The stranger seeming to hesitate, once more looked towards the ground, and the clerk winked slily at Mr. Pickwick, as if to intimate that some exquisite piece of humour was going forward; though what it was, Mr. Pickwick could not, for the life of him, divine.

"Step in, Mr. Pickwick," said Lowten. "Well, will you leave a message, Mr. Watty, or will you call again?"

"Ask him to be so kind as to leave out word what has been done in my business," said the man; "for God's sake don't neglect it, Mr. Lowten."

"No, no; I won't forget it," replied the clerk. "Walk in, Mr. Pickwick. Good morning, Mr. Watty; it's a fine day for walking, isn't it?" Seeing that the stranger still lingered, he beckoned Sam Weller to follow his master in, and shut the door in his face.

"There never was such a pestering bankrupt as that, since the world began, I do believe!" said Lowten, throwing down his pen with the air of an injured man. "His affairs haven't been in chancery quite four years yet, and I'm d—d if he don't come worrying here twice a-week. Step this way, Mr. Pickwick. Perker *is* in, and he'll see you, I know. Devilish cold," he added pettishly, "standing at that door, wasting one's time with such seedy vagabonds!" Having very vehemently stirred a particularly large fire with a particularly small poker, the clerk led the way to his principal's private room, and announced Mr. Pickwick.

"Ah, my dear sir," said little Mr. Perker, bustling up from his chair; "Well, my dear sir, and what's the news about your matter—eh? Anything more about our friends in Freeman's-court? They've not been sleeping, *I* know that. Ah, they're very smart fellows—very smart, indeed."

As the little man concluded, he took an emphatic pinch of snuff, as a tribute to the smartness of Messrs. Dodson and Fogg.

"They are great scoundrels," said Mr. Pickwick.

"Aye, aye," said the little man; "that's a matter of opinion, you know, and we won't dispute about terms, because of course you can't be expected to view these subjects with a professional eye. Well, we've done everything that's necessary. I have retained Serjeant Snubbin."

"Is he a good man?" inquired Mr. Pickwick.

"Good man!" replied Perker; "bless your heart and soul, my dear sir, Serjeant Snubbin is at the very top of his profession. Gets treble the business of any man in court—engaged in every case. You needn't mention it abroad; but we say—we of the profession—that Serjeant Snubbin leads the court by the nose."

The little man took another pinch of snuff as he made this communication, and nodded mysteriously to Mr. Pickwick.

"They have subpoena'd my three friends," said Mr. Pickwick.

"Ah! of course they would," replied Perker. "Important witnesses; saw you in a delicate situation."

"But she fainted of her own accord," said Mr. Pickwick. "She threw herself into my arms."

"Very likely, my dear sir," replied Perker; "very likely and very natural. Nothing more so, my dear sir—nothing. But who's to prove it?"

"They have subpoena'd my servant too," said Mr. Pickwick, quitting the other point; for there Mr. Perker's question had somewhat staggered him.

"Sam?" said Perker.

Mr. Pickwick replied in the affirmative.

"Of course, my dear sir; of course. I knew they would; I could have told *you* that, a month ago. You know, my dear sir if you *will* take the management of your affairs into your own hands after intrusting them to your solicitor, you must also take the consequences." Here Mr. Perker drew himself up with conscious dignity, and brushed some stray grains of snuff from his shirt frill.

"And what do they want him to prove?" asked Mr. Pickwick, after two or three minutes' silence.

"That you sent him up to the plaintiff's to make some offer of a compromise, I suppose," replied Perker. "It don't matter much, though; I don't think many counsel could get a great deal out of *him.*"

"I don't think they could," said Mr. Pickwick; smiling, despite his vexation, at the idea of Sam's appearance as a witness. "What course do we pursue?"

"We have only one to adopt, my dear sir," replied Perker, "cross-examine the witnesses; trust to Snubbin's eloquence; throw dust in the eyes of the judge; and ourselves on the jury."

"And suppose the verdict is against me?" said Mr. Pickwick.

Mr. Perker smiled, took a very long pinch of snuff, stirred the fire, shrugged his shoulders, and remained expressively silent.

"You mean that in that case I must pay the damages?" said Mr. Pickwick, who had watched this telegraphic answer with considerable sternness.

Perker gave the fire another very unnecessary poke, and said, "I am afraid so."

"Then I beg to announce to you, my unalterable determination to pay no damages whatever," said Mr. Pickwick, most emphatically. "None, Perker. Not a pound, not a penny, of my money, shall find its way into the pockets of Dodson and Fogg. That is my deliberate and irrevocable determination." Mr. Pickwick gave a heavy blow on the table before him, in confirmation of the irrevocability of his intention.

"Very well, my dear sir, very well," said Perker. "You know best, of course."

"Of course," replied Mr. Pickwick hastily. "Where does Serjeant Snubbin live?"

"In Lincoln's Inn Old Square," replied Perker.

"I should like to see him," said Mr. Pickwick.

"See Serjeant Snubbin, my dear sir!" rejoined Perker, in utter amazement. "Pooh, pooh, my dear sir, impossible. See Serjeant Snubbin! Bless you, my dear sir, such a thing was never heard of, without a consultation fee being previously paid, and a consultation fixed. It couldn't be done, my dear sir; it couldn't be done."

Mr. Pickwick, however, had made up his mind not only that it could be done, but that it should be done; and the consequence was, that within ten minutes after he had received the assurance that the thing was impossible, he was conducted by his solicitor into the outer office of the great Serjeant Snubbin himself.

It was an uncarpeted room of tolerable dimensions, with a large writing-table drawn up near the fire: the baize top of which had long since lost all claim to its original hue of green, and had gradually grown grey with dust and age, except where all traces of its natural colour were obliterated by ink-stains. Upon the table, were numerous little bundles of papers tied with red tape; and behind it, sat an elderly clerk, whose sleek appearance, and heavy gold watch-chain, presented imposing indications of the extensive and lucrative practice of Mr. Serjeant Snubbin.

"Is the Serjeant in his room, Mr. Mallard?" inquired Perker, offering his box with all imaginable courtesy.

"Yes he is," was the reply, "but he's very busy. Look here, not an opinion given yet, on any one of these cases; and an expedition fee paid with all of 'em." The clerk smiled as he said this, and inhaled the pinch of snuff with a zest which seemed to be compounded of a fondness for snuff and a relish for fees.

"Something like practice that," said Perker.

"Yes," said the barrister's clerk, producing his own box and offering it with the greatest cordiality; "and the best of it is, that as nobody alive except myself can read the Serjeant's writing, they are obliged to wait for the opinions, when he has given them, till I have copied 'em, ha—ha—ha!"

"Which makes good for we know who, besides the Serjeant, and draws a little more out of the clients, eh?" said Perker; "Ha, ha, ha!" At this the Serjeant's clerk laughed again—not a noisy boisterous laugh, but a silent internal chuckle, which Mr. Pickwick disliked to hear. When a man bleeds inwardly, it is a dangerous thing for himself; but when he laughs inwardly, it bodes no good to other people.

"You haven't made me out that little list of the fees that I'm in your debt, have you?" said Perker.

"No, I have not," replied the clerk.

"I wish you would," said Perker. "Let me have them, and I'll send you a cheque. But I suppose you're too busy pocketing the ready money, to think of the debtors, eh? ha, ha, ha!" This sally seemed to tickle the clerk amazingly, and he once more enjoyed a little quiet laugh to himself.

"But, Mr. Mallard, my dear friend," said Perker, suddenly recovering his gravity, and drawing the great man's great man into a corner, by the lapel of his coat; "you must persuade the Serjeant to see me, and my client here."

"Come, come," said the clerk, "that's not bad, either. See the Serjeant! come, that's too absurd." Notwithstanding the absurdity of the proposal, however, the clerk allowed himself to be gently drawn beyond the hearing of Mr. Pickwick; and after a short conversation conducted in whispers, walked softly down a little dark passage, and disappeared into the legal luminary's sanctum: whence he shortly returned on tiptoe, and informed Mr. Perker and Mr. Pickwick that the Serjeant had been prevailed upon, in violation of all established rules and customs, to admit them at once.

Mr. Serjeant Snubbin was a lantern-faced, sallow-complexioned man, of about five-and-forty, or—as the novels say—he might be fifty. He had that dull-looking boiled eye which is so often to be seen in the heads of people who have applied themselves during many years to a weary and laborious course of study; and which would have been sufficient, without the additional eye-glass which dangled from a broad black riband round his neck, to warn a stranger that he was very near-sighted. His hair was thin and weak, which was partly attributable to his having never devoted much time to its arrangement, and partly to his having worn for five-and-twenty years the forensic wig which hung on a block beside him. The marks of hair-powder on his coat-collar, and the ill-washed and worse-tied white neckerchief round his throat, showed that he had not found leisure since he left the court to make any alteration in his dress: while the slovenly style of the remainder of his costume warranted the inference that his personal appearance would not have been very much improved if he had. Books of practice, heaps of papers, and opened letters, were scattered over the table, without any attempt at order or arrangement; the furniture of the room was old and ricketty; the doors of the book-case were rotting in their hinges; the dust flew out from the carpet in little clouds at every step; the blinds were yellow with age and dirt; and the state of everything in the room showed, with a clearness not to be mistaken, that Mr. Serjeant Snubbin was far too much occupied with his professional pursuits to take any great heed or regard of his personal comforts.

The Serjeant was writing when his clients entered; he bowed abstractedly when Mr. Pickwick was introduced by his solicitor; and then, motioning them to a seat, put his pen carefully in the inkstand, nursed his left leg, and waited to be spoken to.

"Mr. Pickwick is the defendant in Bardell and Pickwick, Serjeant Snubbin," said Perker.

"I am retained in that, am I?" said the Serjeant.

"You are, sir," replied Perker.

The Serjeant nodded his head, and waited for something else.

"Mr. Pickwick was anxious to call upon you, Serjeant Snubbin," said Perker, "to state to you, before you entered upon the case, that he denies there being any ground or pretence whatever for the action against him; and that unless he came into court with clean hands, and without the most conscientious conviction that he was right in resisting the plaintiff's demand, he would not be there at all. I believe I state your views correctly; do I not, my dear sir?" said the little man, turning to Mr. Pickwick.

"Quite so," replied that gentleman.

Mr. Serjeant Snubbin unfolded his glasses, raised them to his eyes; and, after looking at Mr. Pickwick for a few seconds with great curiosity, turned to Mr. Perker, and said, smiling slightly as he spoke:

"Has Mr. Pickwick a strong case?"

The attorney shrugged his shoulders.

"Do you purpose calling witnesses?"

"No."

The smile on the Serjeant's countenance became more defined; he rocked his leg with increased violence; and, throwing himself back in his easy-chair, coughed dubiously.

These tokens of the Serjeant's presentiments on the subject, slight as they were, were not lost on Mr. Pickwick. He settled the spectacles, through which he had attentively regarded such demonstrations of the barrister's feeling as he had permitted himself to exhibit, more firmly on his nose: and said with great energy, and in utter disregard of all Mr. Perker's admonitory winkings and frownings:

"My wishing to wait upon you, for such a purpose as this, sir, appears, I have no doubt, to a gentleman who sees so much of these matters as you must necessarily do, a very extraordinary circumstance."

The Serjeant tried to look gravely at the fire, but the smile came back again.

"Gentlemen of your profession, sir," continued Mr. Pickwick, "see the worst side of human nature—all its disputes, all its ill-will and bad blood, rise up before you. You know from your experience of juries (I mean no disparagement to you, or them) how much depends upon *effect* and you are apt to attribute to others, a desire to use, for purposes of deception and self-interest, the very instruments which you, in pure honesty and honour of purpose, and with a laudable desire to do your utmost for your client, know the temper and worth of so well, from constantly employing them yourselves. I really believe that to this circumstance may be attributed the vulgar but very general notion of your being, as a body, suspicious, distrustful, and over-cautious. Conscious as I am, sir, of the disadvantage of making such a declaration to you, under such circumstances, I have come here, because I wish you distinctly to understand, as my friend Mr. Perker has said, that I am innocent of the falsehood laid to my charge; and although I am very well aware of the inestimable value of your assistance, sir, I must beg to add, that unless you sincerely believe this, I would rather be deprived of the aid of your talents than have the advantage of them."

Long before the close of this address, which we are bound to say was of a very prosy character for Mr. Pickwick, the Serjeant had relapsed into a state of abstraction. After some minutes, however, during which he had re-assumed his pen, he appeared to be again aware of the presence of his clients; and, raising his head from the paper, said, rather snappishly,

"Who's with me in this case?"

"Mr. Phunky, Serjeant Snubbin," replied the attorney.

"Phunky, Phunky," said the Serjeant; "I never heard the name before. He must be a very young man."

"Yes, he is a very young man," replied the attorney. "He was only called the other day. Let me see—he has not been at the Bar eight years yet."

"Ah, I thought not," said the Serjeant, in that sort of pitying tone in which ordinary folks would speak of a very helpless little child. "Mr. Mallard, send round to Mr.—Mr.—."

"Phunky's—Holborn Court, Gray's Inn," interposed Perker. (Holborn Court, by the bye, is South Square now). "Mr. Phunky, and say I should be glad if he'd step here, a moment."

Mr. Mallard departed to execute his commission; and Serjeant Snubbin relapsed into abstraction until Mr. Phunky himself was introduced.

Although an infant barrister, he was a full-grown man. He had a very nervous manner, and a painful hesitation in his speech; it did not appear to be a natural defect, but seemed rather the result of timidity, arising from the consciousness of being "kept down" by want of means, or interest, or connexion, or impudence, as the case might be. He was overawed by the Serjeant, and profoundly courteous to the attorney.

"I have not had the pleasure of seeing you before, Mr. Phunky," said Serjeant Snubbin, with haughty condescension.

Mr. Phunky bowed. He *had* had the pleasure of seeing the Serjeant, and of envying him too, with all a poor man's envy, for eight years and a quarter.

"You are with me in this case, I understand?" said the Serjeant.

If Mr. Phunky had been a rich man, he would have instantly sent for his clerk to remind him; if he had been a wise one, he would have applied his fore-finger to his forehead, and endeavoured to recollect, whether, in the multiplicity of his engagements he had undertaken this one, or not; but as he was neither rich nor wise (in this sense at all events) he turned red, and bowed.

"Have you read the papers, Mr. Phunky?" inquired the Serjeant.

Here again, Mr. Phunky should have professed to have forgotten all about the merits of the case; but as he had read such papers as had been laid before him in the course of the action, and had thought of nothing else, waking or sleeping, throughout the two months during which he had been retained as Mr. Serjeant Snubbin's junior, he turned a deeper red, and bowed again.

"This is Mr. Pickwick," said the Serjeant, waving his pen in the direction in which that gentleman was standing.

Mr. Phunky bowed to Mr. Pickwick with the reverence which a first client must ever awaken; and again inclined his head towards his leader.

"Perhaps you will take Mr. Pickwick away," said the Serjeant, "and—and—and—hear anything Mr. Pickwick may wish to communicate. We shall have a consultation, of course." With this hint that he had been interrupted quite long enough, Mr. Serjeant Snubbin, who had been gradually growing more and more abstracted, applied his glass to his eyes for an instant, bowed slightly round, and was once more deeply immersed in the case before him: which arose out of an interminable lawsuit, originating in the act of an individual, deceased a century or so ago, who had stopped up a pathway leading from some place which nobody ever came from, to some other place which nobody ever went to.

Mr. Phunky would not hear of passing through any door until Mr. Pickwick and his solicitor had passed through before him, so it was some time before they got into the Square; and when they did reach it, they walked up and down, and held a long conference, the result of which was, that it was a very difficult matter to say how the verdict would go; that nobody could presume to calculate on the issue of an action; that it was very lucky they had prevented the other party from getting Serjeant Snubbin; and other topics of doubt and consolation, common in such a position of affairs.

Mr. Weller was then roused by his master from a sweet sleep of an hour's duration; and, bidding adieu to Lowten, they returned to the City.

6.

"I WONDER what the foreman of the jury, whoever he'll be, has got for breakfast," said Mr. Snodgrass, by way of keeping up a conversation on the eventful morning of the fourteenth of February.

"Ah!" said Perker, "I hope he's got a good one."

"Why so?" inquired Mr. Pickwick.

"Highly important; very important, my dear sir," replied Perker. "A good, contented, well-breakfasted juryman, is a capital thing to get hold of. Discontented or hungry jurymen, my dear sir, always find for the plaintiff."

"Bless my heart," said Mr. Pickwick, looking very blank; "what do they do that for?"

"Why, I don't know," replied the little man, coolly; "saves time, I suppose. If it's near dinner-time, the foreman takes out his watch when the jury have retired, and says, 'Dear me, gentlemen, ten minutes to five, I declare! I dine at five, gentlemen.' 'So do I,' says every body else, except two men who ought to have dined at three, and seem more than half disposed to stand out in consequence. The foreman smiles, and puts up his watch:—'Well, gentlemen, what do we say? plaintiff or defendant, gentlemen? I rather think, so far as I am concerned, gentleman,—I say, I rather think,—but don't let that influence you—I *rather* think the plaintiff's the man.' Upon this, two or three other men are sure to say that they think so too—as of course they do; and then they get on very unanimously and comfortably. Ten minutes past nine!" said the little man, looking at his watch. "Time we were off, my dear sir; breach of promise trial—court is generally full in such cases. You had better ring for a coach, my dear sir, or we shall be rather late."

Mr. Pickwick immediately rang the bell; and a coach having been procured, the four Pickwickians and Mr. Perker ensconced themselves therein, and drove to Guildhall: Sam Weller, Mr. Lowten, and the blue bag, following in a cab.

"Lowten," said Perker, when they reached the outer hall of the court, "put Mr. Pickwick's friends in the students' box; Mr. Pickwick himself had better sit by me. This way, my dear sir, this way." Taking Mr. Pickwick by the coat-sleeve, the the little man led him to the low seat just beneath the desks of the King's Counsel, which is constructed for the convenience of attorneys, who from that spot can whisper into the ear of the leading counsel in the case, any instructions that may be necessary during the progress of the trial. The occupants of this seat are invisible to the great body of spectators, inasmuch as they sit on a much lower level than either the barristers or the audience, whose seats are raised above the floor. Of course they have their backs to both, and their faces towards the judge.

"That's the witness-box, I suppose?" said Mr. Pickwick, pointing to a kind of pulpit, with a brass rail, on his left hand.

"That's the witness-box, my dear sir," replied Perker, disinterring a quantity of papers from the blue bag, which Lowten had just deposited at his feet.

"And that," said Mr. Pickwick, pointing to a couple of enclosed seats on his right, "that's where the jurymen sit, is it not?"

"The identical place, my dear sir," replied Perker, tapping the lid of his snuff-box.

Mr. Pickwick stood up in a state of great agitation, and took a glance at the court. There were already a pretty large sprinkling of spectators in the gallery, and a numerous muster of gentlemen in wigs, in the barristers' seats: who presented, as a body, all that pleasing and extensive variety of nose and whisker for which the bar of England is so justly celebrated. Such of the gentlemen as had a brief to carry, carried it in as conspicuous a manner as possible, and occasionally scratched their noses therewith, to impress the fact more strongly on the observation of the spectators. Other gentlemen, who had no briefs to show, carried under their arms goodly octavos, with a red label behind, and that under-done-pie-crust-coloured cover, which is technically known as "law calf." Others, who had neither briefs nor books, thrust their hands into their pockets, and looked as wise as they conveniently could; others, again, moved here and there with great restlessness and earnestness of manner, content to awaken thereby the admiration and astonishment of the uninitiated strangers. The whole, to the great wonderment of Mr. Pickwick, were divided into little groups, who were chatting and discussing the news of the day in the most unfeeling manner possible,—just as if no trial at all were coming on.

A bow from Mr. Phunky, as he entered, and took his seat behind the row appropriated to the King's Counsel, attracted Mr. Pickwick's attention; and he had scarcely returned it, when Mr. Serjeant Snubbin appeared, followed by Mr. Mallard, who half hid the Serjeant behind a large crimson bag, which he placed on his table, and, after shaking hands with Perker, withdrew. Then there entered two or three more Serjeants: and among them, one with a fat body and a red face, who nodded in a friendly manner to Mr. Serjeant Snubbin, and said it was a fine morning.

"Who's that red-faced man, who said it was a fine morning, and nodded to our counsel?" whispered Mr. Pickwick.

"Mr. Serjeant Buzfuz," replied Perker. "He's opposed to us; he leads on the other side. That gentleman behind him is Mr. Skimpin, his junior."

Mr. Pickwick was on the point of inquiring, with great abhorrence of the man's cold-blooded villany, how Mr. Serjeant Buzfuz, who was counsel for the opposite party, dared to presume to tell Mr. Serjeant Snubbin, who was counsel for him, that it was a fine morning, when he was interrupted by a general rising of the barristers, and a loud cry of

"Silence!" from the officers of the court. Looking round, he found that this was caused by the entrance of the judge.

Mr. Justice Stareleigh (who sat in the absence of the Chief Justice, occasioned by indisposition,) was a most particularly short man, and so fat, that he seemed all face and waistcoat. He rolled in, upon two little turned legs, and having bobbed gravely to the bar, who bobbed gravely to him, put his little legs underneath his table, and his little three-cornored hat upon it; and when Mr. Justice Stareleigh had done this, all you could see of him was two queer little eyes, one broad pink face, and somewhere about half of a big and very comical-looking wig.

The judge had no sooner taken his seat, than the officer on the floor of the court called out "Silence!" in a commanding tone, upon which another officer in the gallery cried "Silence!" in an angry manner, whereupon three or four more ushers shouted "Silence!" in a voice of indignant remonstrance. This being done, a gentleman in black, who sat below the judge, proceeded to call over the names of the jury; and, after a great deal of bawling, it was discovered that only ten special jurymen were present. Upon this, Mr. Serjeant Buzfuz prayed a *tales;* the gentleman in black then proceeded to press into the special jury, two of the common jurymen; and a green-grocer and a chemist were caught directly.

"Answer to your names, gentlemen, that you may be sworn," said the gentleman in black. "Richard Upwitch."

"Here," said the green-grocer.

"Thomas Groffin."

"Here," said the chemist.

"Take the book, gentlemen. You shall well and truly try—"

"I beg this court's pardon," said the chemist, who was a tall, thin, yellow-visaged man, "but I hope this court will excuse my attendance."

"On what grounds, sir?" said Mr. Justice Stareleigh.

"I have no assistant, my Lord," said the chemist.

"I can't help that, sir," replied Mr. Justice Stareleigh. "You should hire one."

"I can't afford it, my Lord," rejoined the chemist.

"Then you ought to be able to afford it, sir," said the judge, reddening; for Mr. Justice Stareleigh's temper bordered on the irritable, and brooked not contradiction.

"I know I *ought* to do, if I got on as well as I deserved, but I don't, my Lord," answered the chemist.

"Swear the gentleman," said the judge, peremptorily.

The officer had got no further than the "You shall well and truly try," when he was again interrupted by the chemist.

"I am to be sworn, my Lord, am I?" said the chemist.

"Certainly, sir," replied the testy little judge.

"Very well, my Lord," replied the chemist, in a resigned manner. "Then there'll be murder before this trial's over; that's all. Swear me, if you please, sir;" and sworn the chemist was, before the judge could find words to utter.

"I merely wanted to observe, my Lord," said the chemist, taking his seat with great deliberation, "that I've left nobody but an errand boy in my shop. He is a very nice boy, my Lord, but he is not acquainted with drugs; and I know that the prevailing impression on his mind is, that Epsom salts means oxalic acid; and syrup of senna, laudanum. That's all, my Lord." With this, the tall chemist composed himself into a comfortable attitude, and, assuming a pleasant expression of countenance, appeared to have prepared himself for the worst.

Mr. Pickwick was regarding the chemist with feelings of the deepest horror, when a slight sensation was perceptible in the body of the court; and immediately afterwards Mrs. Bardell, supported by Mrs. Cluppins, was led in, and placed, in a drooping state, at the other end of the seat on which Mr. Pickwick sat. An extra-sized umbrella was then handed in by Mr. Dodson, and a pair of pattens by Mr. Fogg, each of whom had prepared a most sympathising and melancholy face for the occasion. Mrs. Sanders then appeared, leading in Master Bardell. At sight of her child, Mrs. Bardell started; suddenly recollecting herself, she kissed him in a frantic manner; then relapsing into a state of hysterical imbecility, the good lady requested to be informed where she was. In reply to this, Mrs. Cluppins and Mrs. Sanders turned their heads away and wept, while Messrs. Dodson and Fogg intreated the plaintiff to compose herself. Serjeant Buzfuz rubbed his eyes very hard with a large white handkerchief, and gave an appealing look towards the jury, while the judge was visibly affected, and several of the beholders tried to cough down their emotions.

"Very good notion that, indeed," whispered Perker to Mr. Pickwick. "Capital fellows those Dodson and Fogg; excellent ideas of effect, my dear sir, excellent."

As Perker spoke, Mrs. Bardell began to recover by slow degrees, while Mrs. Cluppins, after a careful survey of Master Bardell's buttons and the button-holes to which they severally belonged, placed him on the floor of the court in front of his mother,—a commanding position in which he could not fail to awaken the full commiseration and sympathy of both judge and jury. This was not done without considerable opposition, and many tears, on the part of the young gentleman himself, who had certain inward misgivings that the placing him within the full glare of the judge's eye was only a formal prelude to his being immediately ordered away for instant execution, or for transportation beyond the seas, during the whole term of his natural life, at the very least.

"Bardell and Pickwick," cried the gentleman in black, calling on the case, which stood first on the list.

"I am for the plaintiff, my Lord," said Mr. Serjeant Buzfuz.

"Who is with you, brother Buzfuz?" said the judge. Mr. Skimpin bowed, to intimate that he was.

"I appear for the defendant, my Lord," said Mr. Serjeant Snubbin.

"Anybody with you, brother Snubbin?" inquired the court.

"Mr. Phunky, my Lord," replied Serjeant Snubbin.

"Serjeant Buzfuz and Mr. Skimpin for the plaintiff," said the judge, writing down the names in his note-book, and reading as he wrote; "for the defendant, Serjeant Snubbin and Mr. Monkey."

"Beg your Lordship's pardon, Phunky."

"Oh, very good," said the judge; "I never had the pleasure of hearing the gentleman's name before." Here Mr. Phunky bowed and smiled, and the judge bowed and smiled too, and then Mr. Phunky, blushing into the very whites of his eyes, tried to look as if he didn't know that everybody was gazing at him: a thing which no man ever succeeded in doing yet, or in all reasonable probability, ever will.

"Go on," said the judge.

The ushers again called silence, and Mr. Skimpin proceeded to "open the case;" and the case appeared to have very little inside it when he had opened it, for he kept such particulars as he knew, completely to himself, and sat down, after a lapse of three minutes, leaving the jury in precisely the same advanced stage of wisdom as they were in before.

Serjeant Buzfuz then rose with all the majesty and dignity which the grave nature of the proceedings demanded, and having whispered to Dodson, and conferred briefly with Fogg, pulled his gown over his shoulders, settled his wig, and addressed the jury.

Serjeant Buzfuz began by saying, that never, in the whole course of his professional experience—never, from the very first moment of his applying himself to the study and practice of the law—had he approached a case with feelings of such deep emotion, or with such a heavy sense of the responsibility imposed upon him—a responsibility, he would say, which he could never have supported, were he not buoyed up and sustained by a conviction so strong, that it amounted to positive certainty that the cause of truth and justice, or, in other words, the cause of his much-injured and most oppressed client, must prevail with the high-minded and intelligent dozen of men whom he now saw in that box before him.

Counsel always begin in this way, because it puts the jury on the very best terms with themselves, and makes them think what sharp fellows they must be. A visible effect was produced immediately; several jury-men beginning to take voluminous notes with the utmost eagerness.

"You have heard from my learned friend, gentlemen," continued Serjeant Buzfuz, well knowing that, from the learned friend alluded to, the gentlemen of the jury had heard just nothing at all—"you have heard from my learned friend, gentlemen, that this is an action for a breach of promise of marriage, in which the damages are laid at 1500*l*. But you have not heard from my learned friend, inasmuch as it did not come within my learned friend's province to tell you, what are the facts and circumstances of the case. Those facts and circumstances, gentlemen, you shall hear detailed by me, and proved by the unimpeachable female whom I will place in that box before you."

Here Mr. Serjeant Buzfuz, with a tremendous emphasis on the word "box," smote his table with a mighty sound, and glanced at Dodson and Fogg, who nodded admiration of the serjeant, and indignant defiance of the defendant.

"The plaintiff, gentlemen," continued Serjeant Buzfuz, in a soft and melancholy voice, "the plaintiff is a widow; yes, gentlemen, a widow. The late Mr. Bardell, after enjoying, for many years, the esteem and confidence of his sovereign, as one of the guardians of his royal revenues, glided almost inperceptibly from the world, to seek elsewhere for that repose and peace which a custom-house can never afford."

At this pathetic description of the decease of Mr. Bardell, who had been knocked on the head with a quart-pot in a public-house cellar, the learned serjeant's voice faltered, and he proceeded with emotion:

"Some time before his death, he had stamped his likeness upon a little boy. With this little boy, the only pledge of her departed exciseman, Mrs. Bardell shrunk from the world, and courted the retirement and tranquillity of Goswell-street; and here she placed in her front parlour-window a written placard, bearing this inscription—'Apartments furnished for a single gentleman. Inquire within.'" Here Serjeant Busfuz paused, while several gentlemen of the jury took a note of the document.

"There is no date to that, is there, sir?" inquired a juror.

"There is no date, gentlemen," replied Serjeant Buzfuz; "but I am instructed to say that it was put in the plaintiff's parlour-window just this time three years. I entreat the attention of the jury to the wording of this document—'Apartments furnished for a single gentleman!' Mrs. Bardell's opinions of the opposite sex, gentlemen, were derived from a long contemplation of the inestimable qualities of her lost husband. She had no fear—she had no distrust—she had no suspicion—all was confidence and reliance. 'Mr. Bardell,' said the widow; 'Mr. Bardell was a man of honour —Mr. Bardell was a man of his word—Mr. Bardell was no deceiver—Mr. Bardell was once a single gentleman himself; *to* single gentlemen I look for protection, for assistance, for comfort, and for consolation—*in* single gentlemen I shall perpetually see something to remind me of what Mr. Bardell was, when he first won my young and untried affections; to a single gentleman then shall my lodgings be let.' Actuated by this beautiful and touching impulse, (among the best impulses of our imperfect nature, gentlemen,) the lonely and desolate widow dried her tears, furnished her first floor, caught her innocent boy to her maternal bosom, and put the bill up in her parlour-window. Did it remain there long? No. The serpent was on the watch, the train was laid, the mine was preparing, the sapper and miner was at work. Before the bill had been in the parlour-window three days—three days, gentlemen—a Being, erect upon two legs, and bearing all the outward semblance of a man, and not of a monster, knocked at the door of Mrs. Bardell's house. He inquired within; he took the lodgings; and on the very next day he entered into possession of them. This man was Pickwick—Pickwick the defendant."

Serjeant Buzfuz who had proceeded with such volubility that his face was perfectly crimson, here paused for breath. The silence awoke Mr. Justice Stareleigh, who immediately wrote down something with a pen without any ink in it, and looked unusually profound, to impress the jury with the belief that he always thought most deeply with his eyes shut, Serjeant Buzfuz proceeded.

"Of this man Pickwick I will say little; the subject presents but few attractions; and I, gentlemen, am not the man, nor are you, gentlemen, the men to delight in the contemplation of revolting heartlessness, and of systematic villany."

Here Mr. Pickwick, who had been writhing in silence for some time, gave a violent start, as if some vague idea of assaulting Serjeant Buzfuz, in the august presence of justice and law, suggested itself to his mind. An admonitory gesture from Perker restrained him, and he listened to the learned gentleman's continuation with a look of indignation, which contrasted forcibly with the admiring faces of Mrs. Cluppins and Mrs. Sanders.

"I say systematic villany, gentlemen," said Serjeant Buzfuz, looking through Mr. Pickwick, and talking *at* him; "and when I say systematic villany, let me tell the defendant Pickwick if he be in court, as I am informed he is, that it would have been more decent in him, more becoming, in better judgment, and in better taste, if he had stopped away. Let me tell him, gentlemen, that any gestures of dissent or disapprobation in which he may indulge in this court will not go down with you; that you will know how to value and how to appreciate them; and let me tell him further, as my lord will tell you, gentlemen, that a counsel, in the discharge of his duty to his client, is neither to be intimidated nor bullied, nor put down; and that any attempt to do either the one or the other, or the first, or the last, will recoil on the head of the attempter, be he plaintiff or be he defendant, be his name Pickwick, or Noakes, or Stoakes, or Stiles, or Brown, or Thompson."

This little divergence from the subject in hand, had of course the intended effect of turning all eyes to Mr. Pickwick. Serjeant Buzfuz, having partially recovered from the state of moral elevation into which he had lashed himself, resumed:

"I shall show you, gentlemen, that for two years Pickwick continued to reside constantly, and without interruption or intermission, at Mrs. Bardell's house. I shall show you that Mrs. Bardell, during the whole of that time, waited on him, attended to his comforts, cooked his meals, looked out his linen for the washerwoman when it went abroad, darned, aired, and prepared it for wear, when it came home, and, in short, enjoyed his fullest trust and confidence. I shall show you that, on many occasions, he gave halfpence, and on some occasions even sixpences, to her little boy; and I shall prove to you, by a witness whose testimony it will be impossible for my learned friend to weaken or controvert, that on one occasion he patted the boy on the head, and, after inquiring whether he had won any *alley tors* or *commoneys* lately (both of which I understand to be a particular species of marbles much prized by the youth of this town), made use of this remarkable expression—'How should you like to have another father?' I shall prove to you, gentlemen, that about a year ago, Pickwick suddenly began to absent himself from home, during long intervals, as if with the intention of gradually breaking off from my client; but I shall show you also, that his resolution was not at that time sufficiently strong, or that his better feelings conquered, if better feelings he has, or that the charms and accomplishments of my client prevailed against his unmanly intentions; by proving to you, that on one occasion, when he returned from the country, he distinctly and in terms, offered her marriage: previously however, taking special care that there should be no witnesses to their solemn contract; and I am in a situation to prove to you, on the testimony of three of his own friends—most unwilling witnesses, gentlemen— most unwilling witnesses—that on the morning he was discovered by them holding the plaintiff in his arms, and soothing her agitation by his caresses and endearments."

A visible impression was produced upon the auditors by this part of the learned serjeant's address. Drawing forth two very small scraps of paper, he proceeded—

"And now, gentlemen, but one word more. Two letters have passed between these parties, letters which are admitted to be in the hand-writing of the defendant, and which speak volumes indeed. These letters, too, bespeak the character of the man. They are not open, fervent, eloquent epistles, breathing nothing but the language of affectionate attachment. They are covert, sly, underhanded communications, but, fortunately, far more conclusive than if couched in the most glowing language and the most poetic imagery—letters that must be viewed with a cautious and suspicious eye—letters that were evidently intended at the time, by Pickwick, to mislead and delude any third parties into whose hands they might fall. Let me read the first:—'Garraway's, twelve o'clock. Dear Mrs. B.— Chops and Tomata sauce. Yours, PICKWICK.' Gentlemen, what does this mean? Chops and Tomata sauce. Yours, Pickwick! Chops! Gracious heavens! and Tomata sauce! Gentlemen, is the happiness of a sensitive and confiding female to be trifled away, by such shallow artifices as these? The next has no date whatever, which is in itself suspicious.—'Dear Mrs. B., I shall not be at home till to-morrow. Slow coach.' And then follows this very very remarkable expression—'Don't trouble yourself about the warming-pan.' The warming-pan! Why, gentlemen, who *does* trouble himself about a warming-pan? When was the peace of mind of man or woman broken or disturbed by a warming-pan, which is in itself a harmless, a useful, and I will add, gentlemen, a comforting article of domestic furniture? Why is Mrs. Bardell so earnestly entreated not to agitate herself about this warming-pan, unless (as is no doubt the case) it is a mere cover for hidden fire—a mere substitute for some endearing word or promise, agreeably to a preconcerted system of correspondence, artfully contrived by Pickwick with a view to his contemplated desertion, and which I am not in a condition to explain? And what does this allusion to the slow coach mean? For naught I know, it may be a reference to Pickwick himself, who has most unquestionably been a criminally slow coach during the whole of this transaction, but whose speed will now be very unexpectedly accelerated, and whose wheels, gentlemen, as he will find to his cost, will very soon be greased by you!"

Mr. Serjeant Buzfuz paused in this place, to see whether the jury smiled at his joke; but as nobody took it but the green-grocer, whose sensitiveness on the subject was very probably occasioned by his having subjected a chaise-cart to the process in question on that identical morning, the learned serjeant considered it advisable to undergo a slight relapse into the dismals before he concluded.

"But enough of this, gentlemen," said Mr. Serjeant Buzfuz, "it is difficult to smile with an aching heart; it is ill jesting when our deepest sympathies are awakened. My client's hopes and prospects are ruined, and it is no figure of speech to say that her occupation is gone indeed. The bill is down—but there is no tenant. Eligible single gentlemen pass and repass —but there is no invitation for them to inquire within or without. All is gloom and silence in the house; even the voice of the child is hushed; his infant sports are disregarded when his mother weeps; his 'alley tors' and his 'commoneys' are alike neglected; he forgets the long familiar cry of 'knuckle down,' and at tip-cheese, or odd and even, his hand is out. But Pickwick, gentlemen, Pickwick, the ruthless destroyer of this domestic oasis in the desert of Goswell Street—Pickwick, who has choked up the well, and thrown ashes on the sward—Pickwick, who comes before you to-day with his heartless Tomata sauce and warming-pans—Pickwick still rears his head with unblushing effrontery, and gazes without a sigh on the ruin he has made. Damages, gentlemen—heavy damages is the only punishment with which you can visit him; the only recompence you can award to my client. And for those damages she now appeals to an enlightened, a high-minded, a right-feeling, a conscientious, a dispassionate, a sympathising, a contemplative jury of her civilised countrymen." With this beautiful peroration, Mr. Serjeant Buzfuz sat down, and Mr. Justice Stareleigh woke up.

"Call Elizabeth Cluppins," said Serjeant Buzfuz, rising a minute afterwards, with renewed vigour.

The nearest usher called for Elizabeth Tuppins; another one, at a little distance off, demanded Elizabeth Jupkins; and a third rushed in a breathless state into King-Street, and screamed for Elizabeth Muffins till he was hoarse.

Meanwhile Mrs. Cluppins, with the combined assistance of Mrs. Bardell, Mrs. Sanders, Mr. Dodson, and Mr. Fogg, was hoisted into the witness-box; and when she was safely perched on the top step, Mrs. Bardell stood on the bottom one, with the pocket-handkerchief and pattens in one hand, and a glass bottle that might hold about a quarter of a pint of smelling salts in the other, ready for any emergency. Mrs. Sanders, whose eyes were intently fixed on the judge's face, planted herself close by, with the large umbrella: keeping her right thumb pressed on the spring with an earnest countenance, as if she were fully prepared to put it up at a moment's notice.

"Mrs. Cluppins," said Serjeant Buzfuz, "pray compose yourself, ma'am." Of course, directly Mrs. Cluppins was desired to compose herself she sobbed with increased vehemence, and gave divers alarming manifestations of an approaching fainting fit, or, as she afterwards said, of her feelings being too many for her.

"Do you recollect, Mrs. Cluppins?" said Serjeant Buzfuz, after a few unimportant questions, "do you recollect being in Mrs. Bardell's back one pair of stairs, on one particular morning in July last, when she was dusting Pickwick's apartment?"

"Yes, my Lord and Jury, I do," replied Mrs. Cluppins.

"Mr. Pickwick's sitting-room was the first-floor front, I believe?"

"Yes, it were, sir," replied Mrs. Cluppins.

"What were you doing in the back room, ma'am?" inquired the little judge.

"My Lord and Jury," said Mrs. Cluppins, with interesting agitation, "I will not deceive you."

"You had better not, ma'am," said the little judge.

"I was there," resumed Mrs. Cluppins, "unbeknown to Mrs. Bardell; I had been out with a little basket, gentlemen, to buy three pounds of red kidney purtaties, which was three pound tuppense ha'penny, when I see Mrs. Bardell's street door on the jar."

"On the what?" exclaimed the little judge.

"Partly open, my Lord," said Serjeant Snubbin.

"She *said* on the jar," said the little judge, with a cunning look.

"It's all the same, my Lord," said Serjeant Snubbin. The little judge looked doubtful, and said he'd make a note of it. Mrs. Cluppins then resumed:

"I walked in, gentlemen, just to say good mornin', and went, in a permiscuous manner, up stairs, and into the back room. Gentlemen, there was the sound of voices in the front room, and—"

"And you listened, I believe, Mrs. Cluppins?" said Serjeant Buzfuz.

"Beggin' your pardon, sir," replied Mrs. Cluppins, in a majestic manner, "I would scorn the haction. The voices was very loud, sir, and forced themselves upon my ear."

"Well, Mrs. Cluppins, you were not listening, but you heard the voices. Was one of those voices, Pickwick's?"

"Yes, it were, sir."

And Mrs. Cluppins, after distinctly stating that Mr. Pickwick addressed himself to Mrs. Bardell, repeated, by slow degrees, and by dint of many questions, the conversation with which our readers are already acquainted.

The jury looked suspicious, and Mr. Serjeant Buzfuz smiled and sat down. They looked positively awful when Serjeant Snubbin intimated that he should not cross-examine the witness, for Mr. Pickwick wished it to be distinctly stated that it was due to her to say, that her account was in substance correct.

Mrs. Cluppins, having once broken the ice, thought it a favourable opportunity for entering into a short dissertation on her own domestic affairs; so, she straightway proceeded to inform the court that she was the mother of eight children at that present speaking, and that she entertained confident expectations of presenting Mr. Cluppins with a ninth, somewhere about that day six months. At this interesting point, the little judge interposed most irascibly; and the effect of the interposition was, that both the worthy lady and Mrs. Sanders were politely taken out of court, under the escort of Mr. Jackson, without further parley.

"Nathaniel Winkle!" said Mr. Skimpin.

"Here!" replied a feeble voice. Mr. Winkle entered the witness-box, and having been duly sworn, bowed to the judge with considerable deference.

"Don't look at me, sir," said the judge, sharply, in acknowledgement of the salute; "look at the jury."

Mr. Winkle obeyed the mandate, and looked at the place where he thought it most probable the jury might be; for seeing any thing in his then state of intellectual complication was wholly out of the question.

Mr. Winkle was then examined by Mr. Skimpin, who, being a promising young man of two or three and forty, was of course anxious to confuse a witness who was notoriously predisposed in favour of the other side, as much as he could.

"Now, sir," said Mr. Skimpin, "have the goodness to let his Lordship and the jury know what your name is, will you?" And Mr. Skimpin inclined his head on one side to listen with great sharpness to the answer, and glanced at the jury meanwhile, as if to imply that he rather expected Mr. Winkle's natural taste for perjury would induce him to give some name which did not belong to him.

"Winkle," replied the witness.

"What's your Christian name, sir?" angrily inquired the little judge.

"Nathaniel, sir."

"Daniel—any other name?"

"Nathaniel, Sir—my Lord, I mean."

"Nathaniel Daniel, or Daniel Nathaniel?"

"No, my Lord, only Nathaniel—not Daniel at all."

"What did you tell me it was Daniel for then, sir?" inquired the judge.

"I didn't, my Lord," replied Mr. Winkle.

"You did, sir," replied the judge, with a severe frown. "How could I have got Daniel on my notes, unless you told me so, sir?"

This argument was, of course, unanswerable.

"Mr. Winkle has rather a short memory, my Lord," interposed Mr. Skimpin, with another glance at the jury. "We shall find means to refresh it before we have quite done with him, I dare say."

"You had better be careful, sir," said the little judge, with a sinister look at the witness.

Poor Mr. Winkle bowed, and endeavoured to feign an easiness of manner, which, in his then state of confusion, gave him rather the air of a disconcerted pickpocket.

"Now, Mr. Winkle," said Mr. Skimpin, "attend to me, if you please, sir; and let me recommend you, for your own sake, to bear in mind his Lordship's injunctions to be careful. I believe you are a particular friend of Pickwick, the defendant, are you not?"

"I have known Mr. Pickwick now, as well as I recollect at this moment, nearly—"

"Pray, Mr. Winkle, do not evade the question. Are you, or are you not, a particular friend of the defendant's?"

"I was just about to say, that—"

"Will you, or will you not, answer my question, sir?"

"If you don't answer the question, you'll be committed, sir," interposed the little judge, looking over his note-book.

"Come, sir," said Mr. Skimpin, "yes or no, if you please."

"Yes, I am," replied Mr. Winkle.

"Yes, you are. And why couldn't you say that at once, sir? Perhaps you know the plaintiff too—eh, Mr. Winkle?"

"I don't know her; I've seen her."

"Oh, you don't know her, but you've seen her? Now, have the goodness to tell the gentlemen of the jury what you mean by *that*, Mr. Winkle."

"I mean that I am not intimate with her, but that I have seen her when I went to call on Mr. Pickwick, in Goswell Street."

"How often have you seen her, sir?"

"How often?"

"Yes, Mr. Winkle, how often? I'll repeat the question for you a dozen times, if you require it, sir." And the learned gentleman, with a firm and steady frown, placed his hands on his hips, and smiled suspiciously at the jury.

On this question there arose the edifying brow-beating, customary on such points. First of all, Mr. Winkle said it was quite impossible for him to say how many times he had seen Mrs. Bardell. Then he was asked if he had seen her twenty times, to which he replied, "Certainly,—more than that." Then he was asked whether he hadn't seen her a hundred times—whether he couldn't swear that he had seen her more than fifty times—whether he didn't know that he had seen her at least seventy-five times—and so forth; the satisfactory conclusion which was arrived at, at last, being, that he had better take care of himself, and mind what he was about. The witness having been by these means reduced to the requisite ebb of nervous perplexity, the examination was continued as follows:

"Pray, Mr. Winkle, do you remember calling on the defendant Pickwick at these apartments in the plaintiff's house in Goswell Street, on one particular morning, in the month of July last?"

"Yes, I do."

"Were you accompanied on that occasion by a friend of the name of Tupman, and another of the name of Snodgrass?"

"Yes, I was."

"Are they here?"

"Yes, they are," replied Mr. Winkle, looking very earnestly towards the spot where his friends were stationed.

"Pray attend to me, Mr. Winkle, and never mind your friends," said Mr. Skimpin, with another expressive look at the jury. "They must tell their stories without any previous consultation with you, if none has yet taken place (another look at the jury). Now, sir, tell the gentlemen of the jury what you saw on entering the defendant's room, on this particular morning. Come; out with it, sir; we must have it, sooner or later."

"The defendant, Mr. Pickwick, was holding the plaintiff in his arms, with his hands clasping her waist," replied Mr. Winkle, with natural hesitation, "and the plaintiff appeared to have fainted away."

"Did you hear the defendant say anything?"

"I heard him call Mrs. Bardell a good creature, and I heard him ask her to compose herself, for what a situation it was, if anybody should come, or words to that effect."

"Now, Mr. Winkle, I have only one more question to ask you, and I beg you to bear in mind his lordship's caution. Will you undertake to swear that Pickwick, the defendant, did not say on the occasion in question, 'My dear Mrs. Bardell, you're a good creature; compose yourself to this situation, for to this situation you must come,' or words to *that* effect?"

"I—I didn't understand him so, certainly," said Mr. Winkle, astounded at this ingenious dove-tailing of the few words he had heard. "I was on the staircase, and couldn't hear distinctly; the impression on my mind is—"

"The gentlemen of the jury want none of the impressions on your mind, Mr. Winkle, which I fear would be of little service to honest, straight-forward men," interposed Mr. Skimpin. "You were on the staircase, and didn't distinctly hear; but you will not swear that Pickwick did not make use of the expressions I have quoted? Do I understand that?"

"No I will not," replied Mr. Winkle; and down sat Mr. Skimpin with a triumphant countenance.

Mr. Pickwick's case had not gone off in so particularly happy a manner up to this point, that it could very well afford to have any additional suspicion cast upon it. But as it could afford to be placed in a rather better light, if possible, Mr. Phunky rose for the purpose of getting something important out of Mr. Winkle in cross-examination. Whether he did get anything important out of him, will immediately appear.

"I believe, Mr. Winkle," said Mr. Phunky, "that Mr. Pickwick is not a young man?"

"Oh no," replied Mr. Winkle; "old enough to be my father."

"You have told my learned friend that you have known Mr. Pickwick a long time. Had you ever any reason to suppose or believe that he was about to be married?"

"Oh no; certainly not;" replied Mr. Winkle with so much eagerness, that Mr. Phunky ought to have got him out of the box with all possible dispatch. Lawyers hold that there are two kinds of particularly bad witnesses: a reluctant witness, and a too-willing witness; it was Mr. Winkle's fate to figure in both characters.

"I will even go further than this, Mr. Winkle," continued Mr. Phunky in a most smooth and complacent manner. "Did you ever see anything in Mr. Pickwick's manner and conduct towards the opposite sex, to induce you to believe that he ever contemplated matrimony of late years, in any case?"

"Oh no; certainly not," replied Mr. Winkle.

"Has his behaviour, when females have been in the case, always been that of a man, who, having attained a pretty advanced period of life, content with his own occupations and amusements, treats them only as a father might his daughters?"

"Not the least doubt of it," replied Mr. Winkle, in the fulness of his heart. "That is—yes—oh yes—certainly."

"You have never known anything in his behaviour towards Mrs. Bardell, or any other female, in the least degree suspicious?" said Mr. Phunky, preparing to sit down; for Serjeant Snubbin was winking at him.

"N—n—no," replied Mr. Winkle, "except on one trifling occasion, which, I have no doubt, might be easily explained."

Now, if the unfortunate Mr. Phunky had sat down when Serjeant Snubbin winked at him, or if Serjeant Buzfuz had stopped this irregular cross-examination at the outset (which he knew better than to do; observing Mr. Winkle's anxiety, and well knowing it would, in all probability, lead to something serviceable to him), this unfortunate admission would not have been elicited. The moment the words fell from Mr. Winkle's lips, Mr. Phunky sat down, and Serjeant Snubbin rather hastily told him he might leave the box, which Mr. Winkle prepared to do with great readiness, when Serjeant Buzfuz stopped him.

"Stay, Mr. Winkle—stay!" said Serjeant Buzfuz; "will your Lordship have the goodness to ask him, what this one instance of suspicious behaviour towards females on the part of this gentleman, who is old enough to be his father, was?"

"You hear what the learned counsel says, sir," observed the judge, turning to the miserable and agonised Mr. Winkle. "Describe the occasion to which you refer."

"My Lord," said Mr. Winkle, trembling with anxiety, "I—I'd rather not."

"Perhaps so," said the little judge; "but you must."

Amid the profound silence of the whole court, Mr. Winkle faltered out, that the trifling circumstance of suspicion was Mr. Pickwick's being found in a lady's sleeping apartment at midnight; which had terminated, he believed, in the breaking off of the projected marriage of the lady in question, and had led, he knew, to the whole party being forcibly carried before George Nupkins, Esq., magistrate and justice of the peace, for the borough of Ipswich.

"You may leave the box, sir," said Serjeant Snubbin. Mr. Winkle *did* leave the box, and rushed with delirious haste to the George and Vulture, where he was discovered some hours after, by the waiter, groaning in a hollow and dismal manner, with his head buried beneath the sofa cushions.

Tracy Tupman, and Augustus Snodgrass, were severally called into the box; both corroborated the testimony of their unhappy friend; and each was driven to the verge of desperation by excessive badgering.

Susannah Sanders was then called, and examined by Serjeant Buzfuz, and cross-examined by Serjeant Snubbin. Had always said and believed that Pickwick would marry Mrs. Bardell; knew that Mrs. Bardell's being engaged to Pickwick was the current topic of conversation in the neighbourhood, after the fainting in July; had been told it herself by Mrs. Mudberry which kept a mangle, and Mrs. Bunkin which clear-starched, but did not see either Mrs. Mudberry or Mrs. Bunkin in court. Had heard Pickwick ask the little boy how he should like to have another father. Did not know that Mrs. Bardell was at that time keeping company with the baker, but did know that the baker was then a single man and is now married. Couldn't swear that Mrs. Bardell was not very fond of the baker, but should think that the baker was not very fond of Mrs. Bardell, or he wouldn't have married somebody else. Thought Mrs. Bardell fainted away on the morning in July, because Pickwick asked her to name the day; knew that she (witness) fainted away stone dead when Mr. Sanders asked *her* to name the day, and believed that everybody as called herself a lady would do the same, under similar circumstances. Heard Pickwick ask the boy the question about the marbles, but upon her oath did not know the difference between an alley tor and a commoney.

By the COURT.—During the period of her keeping company with Mr. Sanders had received love letters, like other ladies. In the course of their correspondence Mr. Sanders had often called her a "duck," but never "chops" nor yet "tomata sauce." He was particularly fond of ducks. Perhaps if he had been as fond of chops and tomata sauce, he might have called her that, as a term of affection.

Sergeant Buzfuz now rose with more importance than he had yet exhibited, if that were possible, and vociferated "Call Samuel Weller."

It was quite unnecessary to call Samuel Weller; for Samuel Weller stepped briskly into the box the instant his name was pronounced; and placing his hat on the floor, and his arms on the rail, took a bird's-eye view of the bar, and a comprehensive survey of the bench with a remarkably cheerful and lively aspect.

"What's your name sir?" inquired the judge.

"Sam Weller, my Lord," replied that gentleman.

"Do you spell it with a 'V' or a 'W?' " inquired the judge.

"That depends upon the taste and fancy of the speller, my Lord," replied Sam, "I never had occasion to spell it more than once or twice in my life, but I spells it with a 'V.' "

Here a voice in the gallery exclaimed aloud, "Quite right too, Samivel; quite right. Put it down a we, my Lord, put it down a we."

"Who is that, who dares to address the court?" said the little judge, looking up. "Usher."

"Yes, my Lord."

"Bring that person here instantly."

"Yes, my Lord."

But as the usher didn't find the person, he didn't bring him; and, after a great commotion, all the people who had got up to look for the culprit, sat down again. The little judge turned to the witness as soon as his indignation would allow him to speak, and said,

"Do you know who that was, sir?"

"I rayther suspect it was my father, my Lord," replied Sam.

"Do you see him here now?" said the judge.

"No, I don't, my Lord," replied Sam, staring right up into the lantern in the roof of the court.

"If you could have pointed him out, I would have committed him instantly," said the judge.

Sam bowed his acknowledgements and turned, with unimpaired cheerfulness of countenance, towards Serjeant Buzfuz.

"Now, Mr. Weller," said Serjeant Buzfuz.

"Now, sir," replied Sam.

"I believe you are in the service of Mr. Pickwick, the defendant in this case. Speak up, if you please, Mr. Weller."

"I mean to speak up, sir," replied Sam, "I am in the service o' that 'ere gen'l'man, and a wery good service it is."

"Little to do, and plenty to get, I suppose?" said Serjeant Buzfuz, with jocularity.

"Oh, quite enough to get, sir, as the soldier said ven they ordered him three hundred and fifty lashes," replied Sam.

"You must not tell us what the soldier, or any other man, said, sir," interposed the judge, "it's not evidence."

"Wery good, my Lord," replied Sam.

"Do you recollect anything particular happening on the morning when you were first engaged by the defendant; eh, Mr. Weller?" said Serjeant Buzfuz.

"Yes I do, sir," replied Sam.

"Have the goodness to tell the jury what it was."

"I had a reg'lar new fit out o' clothes that mornin,' gen'l'men of the jury," said Sam, "and that was a wery partickler and uncommon circumstance vith me in those days."

Hereupon there was a general laugh; and the little judge, looking with an angry countenance over his desk, said, "You had better be careful, sir."

"So Mr. Pickwick said at the time, my Lord," replied Sam, "and I was wery careful o' that 'ere suit o' clothes; wery careful indeed, my lord."

The judge looked sternly at Sam for full two minutes, but Sam's features were so perfectly calm and serene that the judge said nothing, and motioned Serjeant Buzfuz to proceed.

"Do you mean to tell me, Mr. Weller," said Serjeant Buzfuz, folding his arms emphatically, and turning half round to the jury, as if in mute assurance that he would bother the witness yet—"Do you mean to tell me, Mr. Weller, that you saw nothing of this fainting on the part of the plaintiff in the arms of the defendant, which you have heard described by the witnesses?"

"Certainly not," replied Sam, "I was in the passage 'till they called me up, and then the old lady was not there."

"Now, attend, Mr. Weller," said Serjeant Buzfuz, dipping a large pen into the inkstand before him, for the purpose of frightening Sam with a show of taking down his answer. "You were in the passage and yet saw nothing of what was going forward. Have you a pair of eyes, Mr. Weller?"

"Yes, I have a pair of eyes," replied Sam, "and that's just it. If they wos a pair o' patent double million magnifyin' gas microscopes of hextra power, p'raps I might be able to see through a flight o' stairs and a deal door; but bein' only eyes you see, my wision's limited."

At this answer, which was delivered without the slightest appearance of irritation, and with the most complete simplicity and equanimity of manner, the spectators tittered, the little judge smiled, and Serjeant Buzfuz looked particularly foolish. After a short consultation with Dodson and Fogg, the learned Serjeant again turned towards Sam, and said, with a painful effort to conceal his vexation, "Now, Mr. Weller, I'll ask you a question on another point, if you please."

"If you please, sir," rejoined Sam, with the utmost good-humour.

"Do you remember going up to Mrs. Bardell's house, one night in November last?"

"Oh yes, wery well."

"Oh, you *do* remember that, Mr. Weller," said Serjeant Buzfuz, recovering his spirits, "I thought we should get at something at last."

"I rayther thought that, too, sir," replied Sam; and at this the spectators tittered again.

"Well; I suppose you went up to have a little talk about this trial—eh, Mr. Weller?" said Serjeant Buzfuz, looking knowingly at the jury.

"I went up to pay the rent; but we *did* get a talkin' about the trial," replied Sam.

"Oh, you did get a talking about the trial," said Serjeant Buzfus, brightening up with the anticipation of some important discovery. "Now what passed about the trial; will you have the goodness to tell us, Mr. Weller?"

"Vith all the pleasure in life, sir," replied Sam. "Arter a few unimportant observations from the two wirtuous females as has been examined here to-day, the ladies gets into a wery great state o' admiration at the honourable conduct of Mr. Dodson and Fogg—them two gen'l'men as is settin' near you now." This, of course, drew general attention to Dodson and Fogg, who looked as virtuous as possible.

"The attornies for the plaintiff," said Mr. Serjeant Buzfuz, "well, they spoke in high praise of the honourable conduct of Messrs. Dodson and Fogg, the attornies for the plaintiff, did they?"

"Yes," said Sam, "they said what a wery gen'rous thing it was o' them to have taken up the case on spec, and to charge nothin' at all for costs, unless they got 'em out of Mr. Pickwick."

At this very unexpected reply, the spectators tittered again, and Dodson and Fogg, turning very red, leant over to Serjeant Buzfuz, and in a hurried manner whispered something in his ear.

"You are quite right," said Serjeant Buzfus aloud, with affected composure. "It's perfectly useless, my Lord, attempting to get at any evidence through the impenetrable stupidity of this witness. I will not trouble the court by asking him any more questions. Stand down, sir."

"Would any other gen'l'man like to ask me anythin'?" inquired Sam, taking up his hat, and looking round most deliberately.

"Not I, Mr. Weller, thank you," said Serjeant Snubbin, laughing.

"You may go down, sir," said Serjeant Buzfuz, waving his hand impatiently. Sam went down accordingly, after doing Messrs. Dodson and Fogg's case as much harm as he conveniently could, and saying just as little respecting Mr. Pickwick as might be, which was precisely the object he had had in view all along.

"I have no objection to admit, my Lord," said Serjeant Snubbin, "if it will save the examination of another witness, that Mr. Pickwick has retired from business, and is a gentleman of considerable independent property."

"Very well," said Serjeant Buzfuz, putting in the two letters to be read. "Then that's my case, my Lord."

Serjeant Snubbin then addressed the jury on behalf of the defendant; and a very long and a very emphatic address he delivered, in which he bestowed the highest possible eulogiums on the conduct and character of Mr. Pickwick; but inasmuch as our readers are far better able to form a correct estimate of that gentleman's merits and deserts, than Serjeant Snubbin could possibly be, we do not feel called upon to enter at any length into the learned gentleman's observations. He attempted to show that the letters which had been exhibited, merely related to Mr. Pickwick's dinner, or to the preparations for receiving him in his apartments on his return from some country excursion. It is sufficient to add in general terms, that he did the best he could for Mr. Pickwick; and the best, as every body knows, on the infallible authority of the old adage, could do no more.

Mr. Justice Stareleigh summed up, in the old-established and most approved form. He read as much of his notes to the jury as he could decipher on so short a notice, and made running comments on the evidence as he went along. If Mrs. Bardell were right, it was perfectly clear Mr. Pickwick was wrong, and if they thought the evidence of Mrs. Cluppins worthy of credence they would believe it, and, if they didn't, why they wouldn't. If they were satisfied that a breach of promise of marriage had been committed, they would find for the plaintiff with such damages as they thought proper; and if, on the other hand, it appeared to them that no promise of marriage had even been given, they would find for the defendant with no damages at all. The jury then retired to their private room to talk the matter over, and the judge retired to *his* private room, to refresh himself with a mutton chop and a glass of sherry.

An anxious quarter of an hour elapsed; the jury came back; and the judge was fetched in. Mr. Pickwick put on his spectacles, and gazed at the foreman with an agitated countenance and a quickly beating heart.

"Gentlemen," said the individual in black, "are you all agreed upon your verdict?"

"We are," replied the foreman.

"Do you find for the plaintiff, gentlemen, or for the defendant?"

"For the plaintiff."

"With what damages, gentlemen?"

"Seven hundred and fifty pounds."

Mr. Pickwick took off his spectacles, carefully wiped the glasses, folded them into their case, and put them in his pocket: and then having drawn on his gloves with great nicety, and stared at the foreman all the while, he mechanically followed Mr. Perker and the blue bag out of court.

They stopped in a side room while Perker paid the court-fees; and here Mr. Pickwick was joined by his friends. Here, too, he encountered Messrs. Dodson and Fogg, rubbing their hands with every token of outward satisfaction.

"Well, gentlemen," said Mr. Pickwick.

"Well, sir," said Dodson: for self and partner.

"You imagine you'll get your costs, don't you, gentlemen?" said Mr. Pickwick.

Fogg said they thought it rather probable. Dodson smiled, and said they'd try.

"You may try, and try, and try again, Messrs. Dodson and Fogg," said Mr. Pickwick, vehemently, "but not one farthing of costs or damages do you ever get from me, if I spend the rest of my existence in a debtor's prison."

"Ha, ha!" laughed Dodson. "You'll think better of that before next term, Mr. Pickwick."

"He, he, he! we'll soon see about that, Mr. Pickwick," grinned Fogg.

Speechless with indignation, Mr. Pickwick allowed himself to be led by his solicitor and friends to the door, and there assisted into a hackney-coach, which had been fetched for the purpose by the ever watchful Sam Weller.

Sam had put up the steps, and was preparing to jump upon the box, when he felt himself gently touched on the shoulder, and, looking round, his father stood before him. The old gentleman's countenance wore a mournful expression, as he shook his head gravely, and said, in warning accents,

"I'd know'd what'ud come o' this here mode o' doin' bisness. Oh Sammy, Sammy, vy worn' there a alleybi!"

Judge Priest Comes Back

Irvin S. Cobb

F ROM TIME to time persons of an inquiring turn of mind have been moved audibly to speculate—I might even say to ponder—regarding the enigma underlying the continued presence in the halls of our National Congress of the Honourable Dabney Prentiss. All were as one in agreeing that he had a magnificent delivery, but in this same connection it has repeatedly been pointed out that he so rarely had anything to deliver. Some few among this puzzled contingent, knowing,

From *Old Judge Priest*, by Irvin S. Cobb. Copyright, 1916, by George H. Doran Company. Copyright renewed. Used by permission of Mrs. Irvin S. Cobb.

as they did, the habits and customs of the people down in our country, could understand that in a corner of the land where the gift of tongue is still highly revered and the golden chimings of a full-jewelled throat are not yet entirely lost in the click of cash registers and the whir of looms, how the Honourable Dabney within his limitations might have been oratorically conspicuous and politically useful, not alone to himself but to others. But as a constructive statesman sent up to Washington, District of Columbia, and there engaged in shaping loose ends of legislation into the welded and the tempered law, they could not seem to see him at all. It was such a one, an editorial writer upon a metropolitan daily, who once referred to Representative Prentiss as The Human Voice. The title stuck, a fact patently testifying to its aptness. That which follows here in this chapter is an attempt to explain the mystery of this gentleman's elevation to the high places which he recently adorned.

To go back to the very start of things we must first review briefly the case of old Mr. Lysander John Curd, even though he be but an incidental figure in the narrative. He was born to be incidental, I reckon, heredity, breeding and the chance of life all conspiring together to fit him for that inconsequential rôle. He was born to be a background. The one thing he ever did in all his span on earth to bring him for a moment into the front of the picture was that, having reached middle age, he took unto himself a young wife. But since he kept her only long enough to lose her, even this circumstance did not serve to focus the attention of the community upon his uncoloured personality for any considerable period of time.

Considering him in all his aspects—as a volunteer soldier in the Great War, as a district school-teacher, as a merchant in our town, as a bachelor of long standing, as a husband for a fleeting space, and as a grass widower for the rest of his days—I have gleaned that he never did anything ignoble or anything conspicuous. Indeed, I myself, who knew him as a half-grown boy may know a middle-aged man, find it hard after the lapse of years to describe him physically for you. I seem to recall that he was neither tall nor short, neither thick nor thin. He had the customary number of limbs and the customary number of features arranged in the customary way—I know that, of course. It strikes me that his eyes were mild and gentle, that he was, as the saying runs, soft-spoken and that his whiskers were straggly and thin, like young second growth in a new clearing; also that he wore his winter overcoat until the hot suns of springtime scorched it, and that he clung to his summer alpaca and his stray hat until the frosts of autumn came along and nipped them with the sweet-gum and the dogwood. That lets me out. Excusing these things, he abides merely as a blur in my memory.

On a certain morning of a certain year, the month being April, Judge Priest sat at his desk in his chamber, so-called, on the right-hand side of the long hall in the old courthouse, as you came in from the Jefferson Street door. He was shoulders deep down in his big chair, with both his plump legs outstretched and one crossed over the other, and he was reading a paper-bound volume dealing in the main with certain inspiring episodes in the spectacular life of a Western person known as Trigger Sam. On his way downtown from home that morning he had stopped by Wilcox & Powell's bookstore and purchased this work at the price of five cents; it was the latest production of the facile pen of a popular and indefatigable author of an earlier day than this, the late Ned Buntline. In his hours of leisure and seclusion the judge dearly loved a good nickel library, especially one with a lot of shooting and some thrilling rescues in it. Now he was in the middle of one of the most exciting chapters when there came a mild rap at the outer door. Judge Priest slid the Trigger Sam book into a half-open drawer and called out:

"Come right on in, whoever 'tis."

The door opened and old Mr. Lysander John Curd entered, in his overcoat, with his head upon his chest.

"Good morning, Judge Priest," he said in his gentle halting drawl; "could I speak with you in private a minute? It's sort of a personal matter and I wouldn't care to have anybody maybe overhearing."

"You most certainly could," said Judge Priest. He glanced through the adjoining room at the back, where Circuit Clerk Milam and Sheriff Giles Birdsong, heads together, were busy over the clerical details of the forthcoming term of circuit court. Arising laboriously from his comfortable place he waddled across and kicked the open door between the two rooms shut with a thrust of a foot clad in a box-toed, low-quartered shoe. On his way back to his desk he brushed an accumulation of old papers out of a cane-bottomed chair. "Set down here, Lysandy," he said in that high whiny voice of his, "and let's hear whut's on your mind. Nice weather, ain't it?"

An eavesdropper trained, mayhap, in the psychology of tone and gesture might have divined from these small acts and this small utterance that Judge Priest had reasons for suspecting what was on his caller's mind; as though this visit was not entirely unexpected, even though he had had no warning of it. There was in the judge's words an intangible inflection of understanding, say, or sympathy; no, call it compassion—that would be nearer to it. The two old men—neither of them would ever see sixty-five again—lowered themselves into the two chairs and sat facing each other across the top of the judge's piled and dusty desk. Through his steel-rimmed glasses the judge fixed a pair of kindly, but none-the-less keen, blue eyes on Mr. Lysander Curd's sagged and slumped figure. There was despondency and there was embarrassment in all the drooping lines of that elderly frame. Judge Priest's lips drew up tightly, and unconsciously he nodded—the brief nod that a surgeon might employ on privately confirming a private diagnosis.

The other did not detect these things—neither the puckering of the lips nor the small forward bend of the judge's head. His own chin was in his collar and his own averted eyes were on the floor. One of his hands— a gnarly, rather withered hand it must have been—reached forth absently and fumbled at a week-old copy of the *Daily Evening News* that rested upon a corner of the desk. The twining fingers tore a little strip loose from the margin of a page and rolled it up in a tiny wad.

For perhaps half a minute there was nothing said. Then Judge Priest bent forward suddenly and touched the nearermost sleeve of Mr. Curd with a gentle little half-pat.

"Well, Lysandy?" he prompted.

"Well, Judge." The words were the first the visitor had uttered since his opening speech, and they came from him reluctantly. "Well, sir, it would seem like I hardly know how to start. This is a mighty personal matter that I've come to see you in regards to—and it's just a little bit hard to speak about it even to somebody that I've known most of my life, same as I've always known you. But things in my home have finally come to a head, and before the issue reaches you in an official capacity as the judge on the bench I sort of felt like it might help some—might make the whole thing pass off easier for all concerned—if I could have a few words with you privately, as a friend and as a former comrade in arms on the field of battle."

"Yes, Lysandy, go ahead. I'm listenin'," stated Judge Priest, as the other halted.

Old Mr. Curd raised his face and in his faded eyes there was at once a bewildered appeal and a fixed and definite resolution. He spoke on very slowly and carefully, choosing his words as he went, but without faltering:

"I don't know as you know about it, Judge Priest—the chances are you naturally wouldn't—but in a domestic way things haven't been going very smoothly with me—with us, I should say—for quite a spell back. I reckon after all it's a mistake on the part of a man after he's reached middle age and got set in his ways to be taking a young wife, more especially if he can't take care of her in the way she's been used to, or anyhow in the way she'd like to be taken care of. I suppose it's only human nature for a young woman to hanker after considerable many things that a man like me can't always give her—jewelry and pretty things, and social life, and running around and seeing people, and such as that. And Luella— well, Luella really ain't much more than a girl herself yet, is she?"

The question remained unanswered. It was plain, too, that Mr. Curd had expected no answer to it, for he went straight on:

"So I feel as if the blame for what's happened is most of it mine. I reckon I was too old to be thinking about getting married in the first place. And I wasn't very well off then either—not well enough off to have the money I should've had if I expected to make Luella contented. Still, all that part of it's got nothing to do with the matter as it stands— I'm just telling it to you, Judge, as a friend."

"I understand, Lysandy," said Judge Priest almost in the tone which he might have used to an unhappy child. "This is all a strict confidence between us two and this is all the further it'll ever go, so fur ez I'm concerned, without you authorise me to speak of it."

He waited for what would come next. It came in slow, steady sentences, with the regularity of a statement painfully rehearsed beforehand:

"Judge Priest, I've never been a believer in divorce as a general thing. It seemed to me there was too much of that sort of thing going on round this country. That's always been my own private doctrine, more or less. But in my own case I've changed my mind. We've been talking it over back and forth and we've decided—Luella and me have—that under the circumstances a divorce is the best thing for both of us; in fact we've decided that it's the only thing. I want that Luella should be happy and I think maybe I'll feel easier in my own mind when it's all over and done with and settled up according to law. I'm aiming to do what's best for both parties—and I want that Luella should be happy. I want that she should be free to live her own life in her own way without me hampering her. She's young and she's got her whole life before her—that's what I'm thinking of."

He paused and with his tongue he moistened his lips, which seemed dry.

"I don't mind telling you I didn't feel this way about it first-off. It was a pretty tolerably hard jolt to me—the way the proposition first came up. I've spent a good many sleepless nights thinking it over. At least I couldn't sleep very much for thinking of it," he amended with the literal impulse of a literal mind to state things exactly and without exaggeration. "And then finally I saw my way clear to come to this decision. And so—"

"Lysandy Curd," broke in Judge Priest, "I don't aim to give you any advice. In the first place, you ain't asked fur it; and in the second place, even ef you had asked, I'd hesitate to advise any man about his own private family affairs. But I jest want to ask you one thing right here: It wasn't you, was it, that first proposed the idea of this here divorce?"

"Well, no, Judge, I don't believe 'twas," confessed the old man whose misery-reddened eyes looked into Judge Priest's from across the littered desk. "I can't say as it was me that first suggested it. But that's neither here nor there. The point I'm trying to get at is just this:

"The papers have all been drawn up and they'll be bringing them in here sometime to-day to be filed—the lawyers in the case will be, Bigger & Quigley. Naturally, with me and Luella agreeing as to everything, there's not going to be any fight made in your court. And after it's all over I'm aiming to sell out my feed store—it seems like I haven't been able to make it pay these last few months, the same as it used to pay, and debts have sort of piled up on me some way. I reckon the fellow that said two could live as cheap as one didn't figure on one of them being a young woman—pretty herself and wanting pretty things to wear and have round the house. But I shouldn't say that—I've come to see how it's mainly my fault, and I'm figuring on how to spare Luella in every way that it's possible to spare her. So as I was saying, I'm figuring, when it's all over, on selling out my interests here, such as they are, and going back to live on that little farm I own out yonder in the Lone Elm district. It's got a mortgage on it that I put on it here some months back, but I judge I can lift that and get the place clear again, if I'm given a fair amount of time to do it in.

"And now that everything's been made clear to you, I want to ask you, Judge, to do all in your power to make things as easy as you can for Luella. I'd a heap rather there wouldn't be any fuss made over this case in the newspapers. It's just a straight, simple divorce suit, and after all it's just between me and my present wife, and it's more our business than 'tis anybody else's. So, seeing as the case is not going to be defended, I'd take it as a mighty big favour on your part if you'd shove it up on the docket for the coming term of court, starting next Monday, so as we could get it done and over with just as soon as possible. That's my personal wish, and I know it's Luella's wish too. In fact she's right anxious on that particular point. And here's one more thing: I reckon that young Rawlings boy, that's taken a job reporting news items for the *Daily Evening News,* will be round here in the course of the day, won't he?"

"He likely will," said Judge Priest; "he comes every day—purty near it. Why?"

"Well," said Mr. Curd, "I don't know him myself except by sight, and I don't feel as if I was in a position to be asking him to do anything for me. But I thought, maybe, if you spoke to him yourself when he came, and put it on the grounds of a favour to you, maybe he'd not put any more than just a little short piece in the paper saying suit had been filed —Curd against Curd—for a plain divorce, or maybe he might leave it out of his paper altogether. I'd like to see Luella shielded from any newspaper talk. It's not as if there was a scandal in it or a fight was going to be made." He bent forward in his eagerness. "Do you reckon you could do that much for me, Judge Priest—for old times' sake?"

"Ah-hah," assented Judge Priest. "I reckin part of it kin be arranged anyway. I kin have Lishy Milam set the case forward on the docket at the head of the list of uncontested actions. And I'll mention the matter to that there young Rawlings ef you want me to. Speaking personally, I should think jest a line or two ought to satisfy the readers of the *Daily Evenin' News.* Of course him bein' a reporter and all that, he'll probably want to know whut the facts are ez set forth in your petition—whut allegations are made in—"

He stopped in mid-speech, seeing how the other had flinched at this last. Mr. Curd parted his lips to interrupt, but the old judge, having no wish to flick wounds already raw, hurried on:

"Don't you worry, Lysandy, I'll be glad to speak to young Rawlings. I jedge you've got no call to feel uneasy about whut's goin' to be said in print. You was sayin' jest now that the papers would be filed sometime to-day?"

"They'll be filed to-day sure."

"And no defence is to be made?" continued Judge Priest, tallying off the points on his fingers. "And you've retained Bigger & Quigley to represent you—that's right, ain't it?"

"Hold on a minute, Judge," Mr. Curd was shaking his white-grey head in dissent. "I've taken up a lot of your valuable time already, and still it would seem like I haven't succeeded in getting this affair all straight in your mind. Bigger & Quigley are not going to represent me. They're going to represent Luella."

He spoke as one stating an accepted and easily understood fact, yet at the words Judge reared back as far as his chair would let him go and his ruddy cheeks swelled out with the breath of amazement.

"Do you mean to tell me," he demanded, "that you ain't the plaintiff here?"

"Why, Judge Priest," answered Mr. Curd, "you didn't think for a minute, did you, that I'd come into court seeking to blacken my wife's good name? She's been thoughtless, maybe, but I know she don't mean any harm by it, and besides look how young she is. It's her, of course, that's asking for this divorce—I thought you understood about that from the beginning."

Still in his posture of astonishment, Judge Priest put another question and put it briskly: "Might it be proper fur me to ask on what grounds this lady is suin' you fur a divorce?"

A wave of dull red ran up old Mr. Curd's throat and flooded his shamed face to the hair line.

"On two grounds," he said—"non-support and drunkenness."

"Non-support?"

"Yes; I haven't been able to take care of her lately as I should like to, on account of my business difficulties and all."

"But look here, Lysandy Curd—you ain't no drunkard. You never was one. Don't tell me that!"

"Well, now, Judge Priest," argued Mr. Curd, "you don't know about my private habits, and even if I haven't been drinking in public up to now, that's no sign I'm not fixing to start in doing so. Besides which my keeping silent shows that I admit to everything, don't it? Well, then?" He stood up. "Well, I reckon that's all. I won't be detaining you any longer. I'm much obliged to you, Judge, and I wish you good-day, sir."

For once Judge Priest forgot his manners. He uttered not a syllable, but only stared through his spectacles in stunned and stricken silence while Mr. Curd passed out into the hallway, gently closing the door behind him. Then Judge Priest vented his emotions in a series of snorts.

In modern drama what is technically known as the stage aside has gone out of vogue; it is called old-fashioned. Had a latter-day playwright been there then, he would have resented the judge's thoughtlessness in addressing empty space. Nevertheless that was exactly what the judge did.

"Under the strict letter of the law I ought to throw that case out of court, I s'pose. But I'm teetotally dam' ef I do any sech thing! . . . That old man's heart is broke now, and there ain't no earthly reason that I kin think of why that she-devil should be allowed to tromp on the pieces. And that's jest exactly whut she'll do, shore ez shootin', unless she's let free mighty soon to go her own gait. . . . Their feet take hold on hell. . . . I'll bet in the Kingdom there'll be many a man that was called a simple-minded fool on this earth that'll wear the biggest, shiniest halo old Peter kin find in stock."

He reached for the Trigger Sam book, but put it back again in the drawer. He reached into a gaping side pocket of his coat for his corncob pipe, but forgot to charge the fire-blackened bowl from the tobacco cannister that stood handily upon his desk. Chewing hard upon the discoloured cane stem of his pipe, he projected himself toward the back room and opened the door, to find Mr. Milam, the circuit clerk, and Mr. Birdsong, the sheriff, still engaged together in official duties there.

"Lishy," he said from the doorway, "young Rawlings generally gits round here about two o'clock in the evenin', don't he?"

"Generally about two or two-thirty," said Mr. Milam.

"I thought so. Well, to-day when he comes tell him, please, I want to see him a minute in my chambers."

"What if you're not here? Couldn't I give him the message?"

"I'll be here," promised the judge. "And there's one thing more: Bigger & Quigley will file a divorce petition to-day—Curd versus Curd is the title of the suit. Put it at the head of the list of undefended actions, please, Lishy, ez near the top of the docket ez you kin."

"Curd? Is it the Lysander Curds, Judge?" asked Mr. Milan.

"You guessed right the very first pop—it's the Lysandy Curds," said Judge Priest grimly.

"Well, for one I'm not surprised," said Mr. Milam. "If poor old Lysander hadn't stayed blind for about two years after the rest of this town got its eyes wide open this suit would have been filed long before now."

But Judge Priest didn't hear him. He had closed the door.

Mr. Milam looked meaningly at Mr. Birdsong. Mr. Birdsong felt in his pocket for his plug and helped himself to a copious chew, meanwhile looking meaningly back at Mr. Milam. With the cud properly bestowed in his right jaw Mr. Birdsong gave vent to what for him was a speech of considerable length:

"Jedge said Bigger & Quigley, didn't he? Well, they're a good smart team of lawyers, but ef I was in Lysander John Curd's shoes I think I'd intrust my interests in this matter to a different firm than them."

"Who's that?" inquired Mr. Milam.

"It's a Yankee firm up North," answered Mr. Birdsong, masticating slowly. "One named Smith and the other'n named Wesson."

It will be noted that our worthy sheriff fell plump into the same error over which Judge Priest's feet had stumbled a few minutes earlier—he assumed offhand, Sheriff Birdsong did, that in this cause of Curd against

Curd the husband was to play the rôle of the party aggrieved. Indeed, we may feel safe in assuming that at first blush almost everybody in our town would have been guilty of that same mistake. The real truth in this regard, coming out, as it very shortly did—before sunset of that day, in fact—gave the community a profound shock. From house to house, from street to street and from civic ward to civic ward the tale travelled, growing as it went. The *Daily Evening News* carried merely the barest of bare statements, coupled with the style of the action and the names of the attorneys for the plaintiff; but with spicy added details, pieced out from surmise and common rumour, the amazing tidings percolated across narrow roads and through the panels of partition fences with a rapidity which went far toward proving that the tongue is mightier than the printed line, or at least is speedier.

When you see a woman hasten forth from her house with eyes that burn and hear her hail her neighbour next door; when you see their two heads meet above the intervening pickets and observe that one is doing the talking and the other is doing the listening, sucking her breath in, gaspingly, at frequent intervals; and when on top of this you take note that, having presently parted company with the first, the second woman speeds hot-foot to call her neighbour upon the other side, all men may know by these things alone that a really delectable scandal has been loosed upon the air. Not once but many times this scene was enacted in our town that night, between the going-down of the sun and the coming-up of the moon. Also that magnificent adjunct of modern civilisation, the telephone, helped out tremendously in spreading the word.

Hard upon the heels of the first jolting disclosure correlated incidents eventuated, and these, as the saying goes, supplied fuel to the flames. Just before supper-time old Mr. Lysander Curd went with dragging feet and downcast head to Mrs. Teenie Morrill's boarding house, carrying in one hand a rusty valise, and from Mrs. Morrill he straightaway engaged board and lodging for an indefinite period. And in the early dusk of the evening Mrs. Lysander Curd drove out in the smart top-phaeton that her husband had given her on her most recent birthday—she sitting very erect and handling the ribbons on her little spirited bay mare very prettily, and seemingly all oblivious to the hostile eyes which stared at her from sidewalks and porch fronts. About dark she halted at the corner of Clay and Contest, where a row of maples, new fledged with young leaves, made a thick shadow across the road.

Exactly there, as it chanced, State Senator Horace K. Maydew happened to be loitering about, enjoying the cooling breeze of the spring night, and he lifted his somewhat bulky but athletic forty-year-old form into the phaeton alongside of the lady. In close conversation they were seen to drive out Contest and to turn into the Towhead Road; and—if we may believe what that willing witness, old Mrs. Whitridge, who lived at the corner of Clay and Contest, had to say upon the subject—it was ten minutes of eleven o'clock before they got back again to that corner. Mrs.

Whitridge knew the exact hour, because she stayed up in her front room to watch, with one eye out of the bay window and the other on the mantel clock. To be sure, this had happened probably a hundred times before—this meeting of the pair in the shadows of the water maples, this riding in company over quiet country roads until all hours—but by reason of the day's sensational developments it now took on an enhanced significance. Mrs. Whitridge could hardly wait until morning to call up, one by one, the members of her circle of intimate friends. I judge the telephone company never made much money off of Mrs. Whitridge even in ordinary times; she rented her telephone by the month and she used it by the hour.

As we are following the course of things with some regard for their chronological sequence, perhaps I should state here that on the next day but one the Lysander John Curd hay and feed store was closed on executions sworn out by a coterie of panic-stricken creditors. It is a mistake, I think, to assume that rats always leave a sinking ship. It has been my limited observation that, if they are commercial rats, they stay aboard and nibble more holes in the hull. However, that is neither here nor there.

In less than no time at all following this—in less than two weeks thereafter, to be exact—the coils which united Mr. Lysander Curd and Luella his wife in the bonds of matrimony were by due process of the statutory law unloosed and slackened off. Being free, the ex-husband promptly gathered together such meagre belongings as he might call his own and betook himself to that little mortgage-covered farm of his out Lone Elm way. Being free also, the ex-wife with equal celerity became the bride of State Senator Horace K. Maydew, with a handy justice of the peace to officiate at the ceremony. It was characteristic of State Senator Maydew that he should move briskly in consummating this, the paramount romance of his life. For he was certainly an up-and-coming man.

There was no holding him down, it seemed. Undoubtedly he was a rising light, and the lady who now bore his name was bound and determined that she rise with him. She might have made one matrimonial mistake, but this time she had hitched her wagon to a star—a star which soared amain and cast its radiance afar. Soon she was driving her own car—and a seven-passenger car at that. They sent to Chicago for an architect to design their new home on Flournoy Boulevard and to Louisville for a decorator to decorate it. It wasn't the largest house in town, but it was by long odds the smartest.

The Senator willed that she should have the best of everything, and she had it. For himself he likewise desired much. His was an uneasy ambition, which ate into him like a canker and gave him no peace. Indeed, peace was not of his craving. He watered his desire with the waters of self-appreciation and mulched it with constant energy, and behold it grew like the gourd and bourgeoned like the bay. He had been mayor; at this time he was state senator; presently it was to transpire that he would admire to be more than that.

Always his handclasp had been ardent and clinging. Now the inner flames that burned its owner made it feverish to the touch. His smile was as warming as a grate fire and almost as wide. Shoulders were made for him to slap, and children had been created into the world to the end that he might inquire regarding their general health and well doing. Wherefore parents—and particularly young parents—were greatly drawn to him. If there was a lodge he joined it; if there was a church fair he went to it; if there was an oration to be made he made it. His figure broadened and took on a genial dignity. Likewise in the accumulation of worldly goods he waxed amazingly well. His manner was paternal where it was not fraternal. His eye, though, remained as before—a sharp, greedy, appraising eye. There is no alibi for a bad eye. Still, a lot of people never look as high as the eyes. They stop at the diamond in the scarfpin.

When a vacancy occurred in the district chairmanship it seemed quite in keeping with the trend of the political impulses of the times that Senator Maydew should slip into the hole. Always a clever organiser, he excelled his past record in building up and strengthening the district organisation. It wasn't long before he had his fences as they should be— hog-tight, horse-high and bull-strong.

Yet in the midst of manifold activities he found time to be an attentive and indulgent husband. If the new Mrs. Maydew did not enjoy the aloof society of those whom we fondly call down our way The Old Families, at least she had her fine new home, and her seven-passenger car, and her generous and loving husband. And she was content; you could tell that by her air and her expression at all times. Some thought there was just a trace of defiance in her bearing.

It was just about a year after her marriage to him that the Senator, in response to the demands of a host of friends and admirers—so ran the language of his column-long paid-for card in the *Daily Evening News* and other papers—announced himself as a candidate for the Democratic nomination for congressman. Considering conditions and everything, the occasion appeared to be propitious for such action on his part. The incumbent, old Major J. C. C. Guest, had been congressman a long, long time—entirely too long a time, some were beginning to say. He had never been a particularly exciting personage, even back yonder in those remote dim days of his entry into public life. At the beginning his principal asset and his heaviest claim upon the support of his fellow-citizens had been an empty trouser-leg.

In eighty-four, a cross-roads wag had said he didn't believe Major Guest ever lost that leg in battle—it was his private opinion that the Maje wore it off running for office. At the time this quip was thought almost to border upon the sacrilegious, and nobody had laughed at it except the utterer thereof. But fully sixteen lagging years had dragged by since then; and for the old-soldier element the times were out of joint. Maybe that was because there weren't so very many of the old soldier element left. A mouse-coloured sleeve without an arm inside of it, no longer had the appeal upon the popular fancy that once it had, and the same was true of the one-time sentimental and vote-catching combination of a pair of hickory crutches and an amputation at the hip joint.

Nevertheless, Major Guest was by no means ready to give up and quit. With those who considered him ripe for retirement he disagreed violently. As between resting on his laurels and dying in the harness he infinitely preferred the chafe of the leather to the questionable softness of the laurel-bed. So the campaign shaped itself to be a regular campaign. Except for these two—Maydew and Guest—there were no openly avowed candidates, though Dabney Prentiss, who dearly loved a flirtation with reluctant Destiny, was known to have his ear to the ground, ready to qualify as the dark horse in the event a deadlock should develop and a cry go forth for a compromising nominee. Possibly it was because Dabney Prentiss generally kept his ear to the ground that he had several times been most painfully trampled upon. From head to foot he was one big mental bruise.

Since he held the levers of the district machinery in the hollows of his two itching hands, Senator Maydew very naturally and very propertly elected to direct his own canvass. Judge Priest, quitting the bench temporarily, came forth to act as manager for his friend, Major Guest. At this there was rejoicing in the camp of the clan of Maydew. To Maydew and his lieutenants it appeared that providence had dealt the good cards into their laps. Undeniably the judge was old and, moreover, he was avowedly old-fashioned. It stood to reason he would conduct the affairs of his candidate along old-fashioned lines. To be sure, he had his following; so much was admitted. Nobody could beat Judge Priest for his own job; at least nobody ever had. But controlling his own job and his own country was one thing. Engineering a district-wide canvass in behalf of an aging and uninspiring incumbent was another. And if over the bent shoulders of Major Guest they might strike a blow at Judge Priest, why, so much the better for Maydew now, and so much the worse for Priest thereafter. Thus to their own satisfaction the Maydew men figured it out.

The campaign went forward briskly and not without some passing show of bitterness. In a measure, Judge Priest justified the predictions of the other side by employing certain time-hallowed expedients for enlisting the votes of his fellow Democrats for Major Guest. He appealed, as it were, to the musty traditions of a still mustier past. He sent the Major over the district to make speeches. He organised schoolhouse rallies and brush-arbour ratifications. He himself was mighty in argument and opulent in the use of homely oratory.

Very different was the way of State Senator Maydew. The speeches that he made were few as to number and brief as to their length, but they were not bad speeches. He was a ready and frequent purchaser of newspaper space; and he shook hands and slapped shoulders and inquired after babies without cessation. But most of all he kept both of his eyes and all of his ten nimble fingers upon the machine, triggering it and thimbling it and pulling at secret wires by day and by night. It was, perhaps, a tribute to his talents in this direction that the method that he inaugurated was beginning to be called Maydewism—by the opposition, of course—before the canvass was a month old. In an unusually vociferous outburst of indignation at a meeting in the Independent Order of Odd Fellows' hall at Settleville, Major Guest referred to it as "the fell blight of Maydewism." When a physician discovers a new and especially malignant disease his school of practice compliments him by naming the malady after him; when a political leader develops a political system of his own, his opponents, although actuated by different motives, do the same thing, which may be taken as an absolute sign that the person in question has made some sincere enemies at least. But if Maydew made enemies he made friends too; at any rate he made followers. As the campaign drew near to its crackling finish it was plain that he would carry most of the towns; Major Guest's strength apparently was in the country—among the farmers and the dwellers in the small villages.

County conventions to name delegates to the district conventions which, in turn, would name the congressional nominee were held simultaneously in the nine counties composing the district at two P. M. of the first Tuesday after the first Monday in August. A week before, Senator Maydew, having cannily provided that his successor should be a man after his own heart, resigned as district chairman. Although he had thrown overboard most of the party precedents, it seemed to him hardly ethical that he should call to order and conduct the preliminary proceedings of the body that he counted upon to nominate him as its standard bearer—standard bearer being the somewhat ornamental phrase customarily used among us on these occasions. He was entirely confident of the final outcome. The cheering reports of his aides in the field made him feel quite sure that the main convention would take but one ballot. They allowed, one and all, it would be a walk-over.

Howsoever, these optimists, as it developed, had reckoned without one factor: they had reckoned without a certain undercurrent of disfavour for Maydew which, though it remained for the most part inarticulate during the campaign, was to manifest itself in the county conventions. Personalities, strictly speaking, had not been imported into the fight. Neither candidate had seen fit to attack the private life of his opponent, but at the last moment there came to the surface an unexpected and, in the main, a silent antagonism against the Senator which could hardly be accounted for on the ground of any act of his official and public career.

So, late in the afternoon of the first Tuesday after the first Monday, when the smoke cleared away and the shouting and the tumult died, the complete returns showed that of the nine counties totalling one hundred and twenty delegate votes, Maydew had four counties and fifty-seven votes. Guest had carried four counties also, with fifty-one votes, while Bryce County, the lowermost county of the district, had failed to instruct its twelve delegates for either Maydew or Guest, which, to anybody who knew anything at all about politics, was proof positive that in the main convention Bryce County would hold the balance of power. It wouldn't be a walkover; that much was certain, anyhow. Maydew's jaunty smile lost some of its jauntiness, and anxious puckers made little seams at the corners of those greedy eyes of his, when the news from Bryce County came. As for Judge Priest, he displayed every outward sign of being well content as he ran over the completed figures. Bryce was an old-fashioned county, mainly populated by a people who clung to old-fashioned notions. Old soldiers were notably thick in Bryce, too. There was a good chance yet for his man. It all depended on those twelve votes of Bryce county.

To Marshallville, second largest town in the district, befell the honour that year of having the district convention held in its hospitable midst; and, as the *Daily Evening News* smartly phrased it, to Marshallville on a Thursday All Roads Ran. In accordance with the rote of fifty years it had been ordained that the convention should meet in the Marshallville courthouse, but in the week previous a fire of mysterious origin destroyed a large segment of the shingled roof of that historic structure. A darky was on trial for hog stealing upon the day of the fire, and it may have been that sparks from the fiery oratory of the prosecuting attorney, as he pleaded with the jury for a conviction, went upward and lodged among the rafters. As to that I am not in a position to say. I only know this explanation for the catastrophe was advanced by divers ribald-minded individuals who attended the trial.

In this emergency the local committee on arrangements secured for the convention the use of the new Marshallville opera house, which was the pride of Marshallville—a compact but ornate structure having on its first floor no less than one hundred and fifty of those regular theatre chairs magnificently upholstered in hot red plush, and above, at the back, a balcony, and to crown all, two orthodox stage boxes of stucco, liberally embossed with gold paint, which clung, like gilded mud-dauber's nests, at either side of the proscenium arch, overhanging the stage below.

In one of these boxes, as the delegates gathered that very warm August afternoon, a lady sat in solitary state. To the delegates were assigned the plush-enveloped grandeurs of the main floor. The spectators, including a large number of the male citizens of Marshallville with a sprinkling of their women-folk, packed the balcony to the stifling point, but this lady had a whole box to herself. She seemed fairly well pleased with herself as she sat there. Certainly she had no cause to complain of a lack of public interest in her and her costume. To begin with, there was a much be-plumed hat, indubitably a thing of great cost and of augmented size, which effectively shaded and set off her plump face. No such hat had been seen in Marshallville before that day.

The gown she wore was likewise of a fashion new to the dazzled gaze of her more plainly habited sisters in the balcony. I believe in the favoured land where they originated they call them princesse gowns. Be its name what it may, this garment ran in long, well-nigh unwrinkled lines from the throat of its wearer to her ankles. It was of some clinging white stuff, modelled seemingly with an intent to expose rather than to hide the curves of the rounded figure which it covered. It was close at the neck, snug at the bust, snugger still at the hips, and from there it flowed on tightly yet smoothly to where it ended, above a pair of high-heeled, big-buckled slippers of an amazing shininess. The uninitiated might well have marvelled how the lady ever got in her gown unless she had been melted and poured into it; but there was no mystery concerning the manner in which she had fastened it, once she was inside of it, for, when she turned away from the audience, a wondrously decorative finishing touch was to be seen: straight down the middle of her back coursed a close row of big, shiny black jet buttons, and when she shifted her shoulders these buttons undulated glisteningly along the line of her spinal column. The effect was snaky but striking.

The lady, plainly, was not exactly displeased with herself. Even a rear view of her revealed this. There was assurance in the poise of her head; assuredly there was a beaming as of confidence in her eyes. Indeed, she had reasons other than the satisfaction inspired by the possession of a modish and becoming garb for feeling happy. Things promised to go well with her and what was hers that afternoon. Perhaps I should have stated sooner that the lady in question was Mrs. Senator Maydew, present to witness and to glorify the triumph of her distinguished husband.

For a fact, triumph did seem near at hand now—nearer than it had been any time these past forty-eight hours. A quarter of an hour earlier an exultant messenger had come from her husband to bring to her most splendid and auspicious tidings. Luck had swung his way, and no mistake about it: of the doubtful delegates from Bryce County only two had arrived. The other ten had not arrived. Moreover there was no apparent possibility that they would arrive before the following day, and by then, if the Senator's new-born scheme succeeded, it would be all over but the shouting. A Heaven-sent freshet in Little River was the cause. Sitting there now in her stage box, Mrs. Senator Maydew silently blessed the name of Little River.

Ordinarily Little River is a stream not calculated to attract the attention of historians or geographers—a torpid, saffron-coloured thread of water meandering between flat yellow banks, and owing its chief distinction to the fact that it cuts off three-quarters of Bryce County from the remaining quarter and from the adjoining counties on its north. But it has its moods and its passions. It is temperamental, that river. Suddenly and enormously swollen by torrential summer rains in the hills where it has its rise, it went, the night before, on a rampage, overflooding its banks, washing away fences and doing all manner of minor damages in the low grounds.

At dawn the big bridge which spanned the river at the gravel road had gone out, and at breakfast time Ferris' Ford, a safe enough crossing place in times of low water, was fifteen feet deep under a hissing brown flood. Two of Bryce County's delegates, who chanced to live in the upper corner of the county, had driven through hub-deep mud to the junction and there caught the train for Marshallville; but their ten compatriots were even now somewhere on the far bank, cut off absolutely from all prospect of attending the convention until the roiled and angry waters should subside.

Senator Maydew, always fertile in expedient, meant to ride to victory, as it were, on the providential high tide in Little River. Immediately on hearing what had happened, he divined how the mishap of the washed-out bridge and the flooded ford might be made to serve his ends and better his fortunes. He was keeping the plan secret for the moment; for it was a very precious plan. And this, in effect, was the word that his emissary brought to his wife just before the convention met. He could not bring it himself; custom forbade that a candidate show himself upon the floor in the early stages, but she was told to wait and watch for what would presently ensue, and meanwhile be of good cheer. Which, verily, she was.

She did not have so very long to wait. The convention assembled on the hour—a block of ten vacant seats in the second aisle showing where the missing ten of Bryce should have been—and was called to order by the new district chairman. Up rose Judge Priest from his place in the middle of the house, flanking the centre aisle, and addressed the chair. He had just learned, he stated, that a considerable quota of the number of duly chosen delegates had not yet reached Marshallville. It appeared that the elements were in conspiracy against the extreme lower end of the district. In justice to the sovereign voters of the sovereign County of Bryce he moved that a recess of twenty-four hours be taken. The situation which had arisen was unforeseen and extraordinary, and time should be granted for considering it in all its aspects. And so on and so forth for five minutes or more, in Judge Priest's best ungrammatical style. The chairman, who, as will be recalled, was Maydew's man, ruled the motion out of order.

I shall pass over as briefly as possible the proceedings of the next half hour. To go fully into those details would be to burden this narrative with technicalities and tiresomeness. For our purposes it is sufficient, I think, to say that the Maydew machine, operating after the fashion of a well-lubricated, well-steered and high-powered steam roller, ran over all obstacles with the utmost despatch. These painful crunching operations began early and continued briskly. On the first roll call of the counties, as the County of Bryce—second on our list after Bland—was reached, one of those two lone delegates from the upper side of Little River stood up and, holding his own credentials and the credentials of his team-mate, demanded the right to cast the votes of the whole Bryce County delegation—twelve in all.

The district chairman, acting with a promptness that bespoke priming beforehand for just such a contingency, held that the matter should be referred to the committee on credentials. As floor leader and spokesman for the Guest faction, old Judge appealed from the ruling of the chair. A vote was taken. The chairman was sustained by fifty-seven to fifty-one, the two indignant delegates from Bryce not being permitted, under a ruling from the chair, to cast any votes whatsoever, seeing as their own status in the convention was the question at issue. Disorder ensued; in the absence of a sergeant-at-arms the services of volunteer peacemakers were required to separate a Maydew delegate from Bland County and a Guest delegate from Mims County.

Dripping with perspiration, his broad old face one big pinky-red flare, his nasal whine rising to heights of incredible whininess under the stress of his earnestness, the judge led the fight for the minority. The steam roller went out of its way to flatten him. Not once, but twice and thrice it jounced over him, each time leaving him figuratively squashed but entirely undismayed. He was fighting a losing but a valiant fight for time.

A committee on resolutions was named and went forth to an ante-room to draw up a platform. Nobody cared much about that. A set of resolutions pointing with pride to everything that was Democratic and viewing with alarm everything even remotely Republican in aspect would be presently forthcoming, as was customary. It was the committee on credentials upon which everything depended. Being chosen, it likewise retired, returning in a miraculously short space of time with its completed report.

And this in brief was what the majority of the committee on credentials —all reliable Maydew men—had to report:

There being no contests, it was recommended that the sitting delegates from the eight counties fully represented upon the floor be recognised as properly accredited delegates. But in respect to the ninth county, namely Bryce, an unprecedented situation had arisen. Two of Bryce's delegates were present, bearing credentials properly attested by their county chairman; unfortunately ten others were absent, through no fault of their own or of the convention. As a majority of the credentials committee viewed the matter, it would be a manifest injustice to deprive these two delegates of their right to take a hand in the deliberations; on the other hand, the committee held it to be equally unfair that those two should be permitted to cast the ballots of their ten associates, inasmuch as they could have no way of knowing what the personal preferences of the absentees might be. However, to meet the peculiar condition the committee now made the following recommendation, to wit as follows: That the secretary of the convention be instructed to prepare an alphabetical list of such delegates as were present in person, and that only such delegates as answered to their own names upon roll call—and no others whatsoever—be permitted to vote upon any question or questions subsequently arising in this convention. Respectfully submitted.

For a period of time to be measured by split seconds there was silence.

Then a whirlwind of sound whipped round and round that packed little martin-box of an opera house and, spiraling upward, threatened the integrity of its tin roof. Senator Maydew had delivered his king-stroke, and the purport of it stood clearly betrayed to the understanding of all. With Bryce's voting strength reduced from twelve votes to two, and with all possibility of voting by proxy removed, the senator was bound to win the nomination on the first ballot. The Maydew men foresaw the inevitable result, once the nomination of the committee had prevailed and they reared up in their places and threw their hats aloft and yelled. The Guest forces saw it, and they howled their disapprobation until they were hoarse.

The tumult stilled down to a ground breeze of mutterings as Judge Priest got upon his feet. To him in this dire emergency the Guest forces, now neck-deep in the last ditch, looked hopefully for a counterfire that might yet save them from the defeat looming so imminent. There and then, for once in his life the judge failed to justify the hopes and the faith of his followers. He seemed strangely unable to find language in which effectively to combat the proposition before the house. He floundered about, making no headway, pushing no points home. He practically admitted he knew of nothing in party usage or in parliamentary law that might serve as a bar to the adoption of the proposed rule. He proposed to vote against it, he said, but in the event that it be adopted he now moved that immediately thereafter the convention take an adjournment, thus giving the secretary time and opportunity in which to prepare the alphabetical list. With that he broke off suddenly and quit and sat down; and then the heart went out of the collective body of the Guest adherents and they quit, too, waiting in sullen, bewildered, disappointed silence for the inevitable.

After this it was felt that any further opposition to the Maydew programme would be but perfunctory opposition. The majority report of the committee on credentials was adopted by fifty-seven to fifty-three, the two Bryce delegates voting in the negative, as was to be expected. Even so, Maydew had a lead of four votes. which was not very many—but enough. To the accompaniment of a few scattered and spiritless *Nays* the convention took a recess of one hour. This meant a mighty busy hour for the secretary, but Maydew, from his temporary abiding place in the wings, sent orders to his floor managers to permit no more than an hour's delay at most. He was famishing for the taste of his accomplished triumph. Besides, there was no trusting so mercurial a stream as Little River. It might go down with the same rapidity that had marked its coming up. So an hour it was.

The delegates flowed out of the Marshallville opera house into the public square of Marshallville, and half of them, or a little more than half, were openly jubilant; and half of them, or a little less than half, were downcast, wearing the look upon their faces of men who were licked and who knew it, good and well. Moving along through the crowded aisle, a despondent delegate from Mims, a distant kinsman of Major Guest, found himself touching shoulders with Sergeant Jimmy Bagby, who was a delegate from our own county.

The Mims County man, with a contemptuous flirt of his thumb, indicated the broad back of Judge Priest as the judge ambled deliberately along toward the door.

"I knowed it," he said in the tones of bitter recapitulation; "I knowed it frum the start and I told 'em so; but no, they wouldn't listen to me. I knowed old Priest yonder was too old to be tryin' to run a campaign ag'inst a smart feller like Maydew, dern his slick hide! When the real test come, whut did your Jedge Priest do? Why, he jest natchelly curled up and laid flat down—that's whut he done. I reckin they'll listen to me next time."

For once in his life, and once only, Sergeant Jimmy Bagby teetered just the least bit in his unquestioning allegiance to his life-long friend.

"Well, I don't know," he said, shaking his head; "I don't know. You might be right in what you say, and then ag'in you might be wrong. It shore did look like he slipped a little, awhile ago, but you can't jest always tell whut's on Jedge Priest's mind," he added, pluckily renewing his loyalty.

The Mims County man grunted his disgust.

"Don't be foolin' yourself," he stated morosely. "You take it frum me —when old men start goin' they don't never come back. And your old Jedge is plumb gone. A baby could 'a' seen that frum the way he acted jest now."

The object of this criticism ploughed his slow way outdoors, all the while shaking his head with the air of one who has abandoned hope. In the street he gently but firmly disengaged himself from those who would have speech with him, and with obvious gloom in his manner made a way across the square to the Mansard House, where he and Major Guest had adjoining rooms on the second floor. His gait briskened, though, as soon as he had passed through the lobby of the Mansard House and was hidden from the eyes of friend and enemy alike.

From the privacy of his room he sent out for certain men. With Cap'n Buck Owings, a small, greyish, resolute gentleman, and with Sheriff Giles Birdsong, a large, reddish, equally resolute gentleman, he was closeted perhaps ten minutes. They went away saying nothing to any one, for the gift of silence was an attribute that these two shared in common. Then the judge had brief audience with Major Guest, who emerged from the conference a crushed and diminished figure. Finally he asked to speak with Sergeant Bagby. The sergeant found him sitting in his shirt-sleeves, with his feet on a window ledge, looking out into the square and gently agitating a palm-leaf fan.

"Jimmy," he said, "I want you to run an errand fur me. Will you go find Dabney Prentiss—I seen him down there on the street a minute ago —and tell him I say to git a speech ready?"

"Whut kind of a speech?" inquired Sergeant Bagby.

"Jimmy Bagby," reproved Judge Priest, "ain't you knowed Dab Prentiss long enough to know that you don't have to tell him whut kind of a speech he's to make? He's got all kinds of speeches in stock at all times. I'll confide this much to you though—it'll be the kind of a speech that he would 'specially prefer to make. Jest tell him I say be ready to speak out and utter a .few burnin' words when the proper time comes, ef it does come, which I certainly hope and trust it may."

Not greatly informed in his mind by this somewhat cryptic explanation, the Sergeant withdrew, and Judge Priest, getting up on his feet, actually began humming a little wordless, tuneless tune which was a favourite of his. However, a thought of the melancholy interview that he had just had with Major Guest must have recurred to him almost immediately, for when he appeared in the open a bit later on his return to the opera house his head was bent and his form was shrunken and his gait was slow. He seemed a man weighed down with vain repinings and vainer regrets.

It would appear that the secretary in the interim had completed his appointed task, for no sooner had the convention reassembled than the chairman mounted to the stage and took his place alongside a small table behind the footlights and announced that nominations would now be in order; which statement was a cue for Attorney-at-Law Augustus Tate, of the County of Emmett, to get gracefully upon his feet and toss back his imposing sable mane and address the assemblage.

Attorney Tate was an orator of parts, as he now proceeded to prove beyond the slightest peradventure of a doubt. He was known as the Black Eagle of Emmett, for it had been said of him that he had an eye like that noble bird, the eagle. He had a chin like one, too; but that, of course, had no bearing upon his talents as displayed upon the stump, on the platform and in the forum, and in truth only a few malicious detractors had ever felt called upon to direct attention to the fact. In flowing and sonorous periods he placed in nomination the name of the Honourable Horace K. Maydew, concluding in a burst of verbal pin wheels and metaphorical skyrockets, whereat there was a great display of enthusiasm from floor and balcony.

When quiet had been restored Judge Priest got slowly up from where he sat and took an action which was not entirely unexpected, inasmuch as rumours of it had been in active circulation for half an hour or more. In twenty words he withdrew the name of the Honourable J. C. C. Guest as a candidate before the convention.

Only a rustle of bodies succeeded this announcement—that and an exhalation of breath from a few delegations, which attained to the volume of a deep joint sigh.

The chairman glanced over the house with a brightening eye. It was almost time to begin the jubilation. As a matter of fact several ardent souls among the Maydewites could hardly hold themselves in until the few remaining formalities had been complied with. They poised themselves upon the edges of their chairs, with throats tuned to lead in the yelling.

"Are there any other nominations?" asked the chairman, turning this way and that. He asked it as a matter of form merely. "If not, the nominations will be closed and the secretary will—"

"Mister Cheerman, one minute, ef you please."

The interrupting voice was the high-piped voice of Judge Priest, and the chairman straightened on his heels to find Judge Priest still upon his feet.

"The chair recognises Judge Priest again," said the chairman blandly. He assumed the judge meant to accept his beating gracefully and, in the interest of party harmony, to move the nomination of Maydew by acclamation. On his part that would have been a fair enough presumption, but the first utterances that came now from the old judge jerked open the eyes and gaped the mouth of the presiding officer. However, he was not alone there; nearly everybody was stunned.

"It was my painful duty a minute ago to withdraw the candidate that I had been privileged to foller in this campaign," said Judge Priest in his weedy notes. "It is now my pleasure to offer in his stead the name of another man as a suitable and a fittin' representative of this district in the National Halls of Congress." He glanced about him as though enjoying the surprised hush that had fallen upon the place, and for just a fraction of a second his eyes focused upon the lone occupant of the right-hand stage box, almost above his head. Then he went on, deliberately prolonging his syllables:

"The man whom I would nominate has never so fur as I know been active in politics. So fur as I know he has never aspired to or sought fur public office at the hands of his feller-citizens; in fact, he does not now seek this office. In presentin' his name for your consideration I am doin' so solely upon my own responsibility and without consultin' any one on this earth.

"My present candidate is not an orator. He is not a mixer or an organiser. I am constrained to admit that, measured by the standards of commerce, he is not even a successful man. He is poor in this world's goods. He is leadin' at this moment a life of retirement upon a little barren hillside farm, where the gulleys furrow his tobacco patch and the sassafras sprouts are takin' his cornfield, and the shadder of a mortgage rests heavy upon his lonely roof tree.

"But he is an honest man and a God-fearin' man. Ez a soldier under the stars and bars he done his duty to the sorrowful end. Ez a citizen he has never wilfully harmed his feller-man. He never invaded the sanctity of any man's home, and he never brought sorrow to any hearthstone. Ef he has his faults—and who amongst us is without them?—he has been the sole sufferer by them. I believe it has been charged that he drank some, but I never seen him under the influence of licker, and I don't believe anybody else ever did either.

"I nominate—" His voice took on the shrillness of a fife and his right fist, pudgy and clenched, came up at arm's length above his head—"I nominate—and on that nomination, in accordance with a rule but newly framed by this body, I call here and now fur an alphabetical roll call of each and every delegate—I offer as a candidate fur Congress ag'inst the Honourable Horace K. Maydew the name of my friend, my neighbour and my former comrade, Lysandy John Curd, of the voting precinct of Lone Ellum and the County of Red Gravel."

There was no applause. Not a ripple of approbation went up, nor a ripple of hostility either. But a gasp went up—a mighty gasp, deep and sincere and tremendously significant.

Of those upon the stage it was the chairman, I think, who got his wits back first. He was naturally quick-witted, else his sponsor would never have chosen him for chairman. In a mute plea for guidance he turned his head toward the wing of the stage where he knew that sponsor should be, and abruptly, at a distance from him to be measured by inches rather than by feet, his gaze encountered the hypnotising stare of Cap'n Buck Owings, who had magically materialised from nowhere in particular and was now at his elbow.

"Stay right where you are," counselled Cap'n Buck in a half whisper. "We've had plenty of these here recesses—these proceedin's are goin' right on."

Daunted and bewildered, the chairman hesitated, his gavel trembling in his temporarily palsied hand. In that same moment Sheriff Giles Birdsong had got upon the stage, too; only he deemed his proper place to be directly alongside the desk of the secretary, and into the startled ear of the secretary he now spoke.

"Start your roll call, buddy," was what Mr. Birdsong said, saying it softly, in lullaby tones, yet imparting a profound meaning to his crooning and gentle accents. "And be shore to call off the names in alphabetical order—don't furgit that part!"

Inward voices of prudence dictated the value of prompt obedience in the brain of that secretary. Quaveringly he called the first name on the list of the first county, and the county was Bland and the name was Homer H. Agnew.

Down in the Bland County delegation, seated directly in front of the stage, an old man stood up—the Rev. Homer H. Agnew, an itinerant Baptist preacher.

"My county convention," he explained, "instructed us for Maydew. But under the law of this convention I vote now as an individual. As between the two candidates presented I can vote only one way. I vote for Curd."

Having voted, he remained standing. There were no cheers and no hisses. Everybody waited. In a silence so heavy that it hurt, they waited. And the secretary was constrained to call the second name on the Bland County list: "Patrick J. Burke!"

Now Patrick J. Burke, as one might guess from his name, belonged to a race that has been called sentimental and emotional. Likewise he was a communicant of a faith which long ago set its face like a flint against the practice of divorce.

"I vote for Curd," said Patrick J. Burke, and likewise he stood up, a belligerent, defiant, stumpy, red-haired man.

"Rufus Barnett!"

This was the first convention Rufus Burnett had ever attended in an official capacity. In order that she might see how well he acquitted himself, he had brought his wife with him and put her in the balcony. We may figure Mrs. Burnett as a strong-minded lady, for before he answered to his name Mr. Burnett, as though seeking higher guidance, cocked a pestered eye aloft to where the lady sat, and she, saying nothing, merely pointed a finger toward the spot where old Judge Priest was stationed. Rufus knew.

"Curd," he said clearly and distinctly. Somebody yelled then, and other voices took up the yell.

There were eleven names on the Bland County list. The secretary had reached the eighth and had heard eight voices speak the same word, when an interruption occurred—perhaps I should say two interruptions occurred.

The Black Eagle of Emmett darted out from the wings, bounded over the footlights and split a path for himself to the seat of Judge Priest. For once he forgot to be oratorical. "We'll quit, Judge," he panted, "we're ready to quit. Maydew will withdraw—I've just come from him. He can't stand for this to go on; he'll withdraw if you'll take Curd's name down too. Any compromise candidate will do. Only, for heaven's sake, withdraw Curd before this goes any further!"

"All right, son," said Judge Priest, raising his voice to be heard, for by now the secretary had called the ninth name and the cheering was increasing in volume; "that suits me first rate. But you withdraw your man first, and then I'll tell you who the nominee of this here convention is goin' to be."

Turning, he put a hand upon Sergeant Bagby's arm and shook him until the sergeant broke a whoop in two and hearkened.

"Jimmy," said Judge Priest with a little chuckle, "step down the aisle, will you, and tell Dabney Prentiss to uncork himse'f and git his speech of acceptance all ready. He don't know it yit, but he's goin' to move up to Washington, D. C., after the next general election."

Just as the sergeant started on his mission the other interruption occurred. A lady fainted. She was conspicuously established in the stage box on the right-hand side, and under the circumstances and with so many harshly appraisive eyes fixed upon her there was really nothing else for her to do, as a lady, except faint. She slipped out of her chair and fell

backward upon the floor. It must have been a genuine faint, for certainly
no person who was even partially conscious, let alone a tenderly nurtured
lady, could have endured to lie flat upon the hard planks, as this lady did,
with all those big, knobby jet buttons grinding right into her spine.

Although I may have wandered far from the main path and taken
the patient reader into devious byways, I feel I have accomplished what
I set out to do in the beginning: I have explained how Dabney Prentiss
came to be our representative in the Lower House of the National Congress. The task is done, yet I feel that I should not conclude the chapter
until I have repeated a short passage of words between Sergeant Jimmy
Bagby and that delegate from Mims County who was a distant kinsman
of Major Guest. It happened just after the convention, having finished its
work, had adjourned, and while the delegates and the spectators were
emerging from the Marshallville opera house.

All jubilant and excited now, the Mims County man came charging
up and slapped Sergeant Bagby upon the shoulder.

"Well, suh," he clarioned, "the old jedge did come back, didn't he?"

"Buddy," said Sergeant Bagby, "you was wrong before and you're
wrong ag'in. He didn't have to come back, because he ain't never been
gone nowheres."

Judge Rumford Bland

Thomas Wolfe

GEORGE SAT by the window and watched the stifled land stroke past
him. It was unseasonably hot for September, there had been no
rain for weeks, and all afternoon the contours of the eastern seaboard faded away into the weary hazes of the heat. The soil was
parched and dusty, and under a glazed and burning sky coarse yellow
grasses and the withered stalks of weeds simmered and flashed beside the
tracks. The whole continent seemed to be gasping for its breath. In the

hot green depths of the train a powder of fine cinders beat in through the meshes of the screens, and during the pauses at stations the little fans at both ends of the car hummed monotonously, with a sound that seemed to be the voice of the heat itself. During these intervals when the train stood still, enormous engines steamed slowly by on adjacent tracks, or stood panting, passive as great cats, and their engineers wiped wads of blackened waste across their grimy faces, while the passengers fanned feebly with sheaves of languid paper or sat in soaked and sweltering dejection.

For a long time George sat alone beside his window. The great train pounded down across New Jersey, across Pennsylvania, across the tip of Delaware, and into Maryland. The unfolding panorama of the land was itself like a sequence on the scroll of time. . . .

At Baltimore, when the train slowed to a stop in the gloom beneath the station, he caught a momentary glimpse of a face on the platform as it slid past his window. All that he could see was a blur of thin, white features and a sunken mouth, but at the corners of the mouth he thought he also caught the shadow of a smile—faint, evil, ghostly—and at sight of it a sudden and unreasoning terror seized him. Could that be Judge Rumford Bland?

As the train started up again and passed through the tunnel on the other side of the city, a blind man appeared at the rear of the car. The other people were talking, reading, or dozing, and the blind man came in so quietly that none of them noticed him enter. He took the first seat at the end and sat down. When the train emerged into the waning sunlight of this September day, George looked around and saw him sitting there. He just sat quietly, gripping a heavy walnut walking stick with a frail hand, the sightless eyes fixed in vacancy, the thin and sunken face listening with that terrible intent stillness that only the blind know, and around the mouth hovered that faint suggestion of a smile, which, hardly perceptible though it was, had in it a kind of terrible vitality and the mercurial attractiveness of a ruined angel. It *was* Judge Rumford Bland!

George had not seen him in fifteen years. At that time he was not blind, but already his eyes were beginning to fail. George remembered him as he was then, and remembered, too, how the sight of the man, frequently to be seen prowling the empty streets of the night when all other life was sleeping and the town was dead, had struck a nameless terror into his boy's heart. Even then, before blindness had come upon him, some nocturnal urge had made him seek deserted pavements beneath the blank and sterile corner lights, past windows that were always dark, past doors that were forever locked.

He came from an old and distinguished family, and, like all his male ancestors for one hundred years or more, he had been trained in the profession of the law. For a single term he had been a police court magistrate, and from then on was known as "Judge" Bland. But he had fallen grievously from the high estate his family held. During the period of George Webber's boyhood he still professed to be a lawyer. He had a shabby office in a disreputable old building which he owned, and his name was on the door as an attorney, but his living was earned by other and more devious means. Indeed, his legal skill and knowledge had been used more for the purpose of circumventing the law and defeating justice than in maintaining them. Practically all his "business" was derived from the Negro population of the town, and of this business the principal item was usury.

On the Square, in his ramshackle two-story building of rusty brick, was "the store." It was a second-hand furniture store, and it occupied the ground floor and basement of the building. It was, of course, nothing but a blind for his illegal transactions with the Negroes. A hasty and appalled inspection of the mountainous heap of ill-smelling junk which it contained would have been enough to convince one that if the owner had to depend on the sale of his stock he would have to close his doors within a month. It was incredible. In the dirty window was a pool table, taken as brutal tribute from some Negro billiard parlor. But what a pool table! Surely it had not a fellow in all the relics in the land. Its surface was full of lumps and dents and ridges. Not a pocket remained without a hole in the bottom big enough to drop a baseball through. The green cloth covering had worn through or become unfixed in a dozen places. The edges of the table and the cloth itself were seared and burnt with the marks of innumerable cigarettes. Yet this dilapidated object was by all odds the most grandiose adornment of the whole store.

As one peered back into the gloom of the interior he became aware of the most fantastic collection of nigger junk that was ever brought together in one place. On the street floor as well as in the basement it was piled up to the ceiling, and all jumbled together as if some gigantic steamshovel had opened its jaws and dumped everything just as it was. There were broken-down rocking chairs, bureaus with cracked mirrors and no bottoms in the drawers, tables with one, two, or three of their legs missing, rusty old kitchen stoves with burnt-out grates and elbows of sooty pipe, blackened frying pans encased in the grease of years, flat irons, chipped plates and bowls and pitchers, washtubs, chamber pots, and a thousand other objects, all worn out, cracked, and broken.

What, then, was the purpose of this store, since it was filled with objects of so little value that even the poorest Negroes could get slight use from them? The purpose, and the way Judge Rumford Bland used it, was quite simple:

A Negro in trouble, in immediate need of money to pay a police court fine, a doctor's bill, or some urgent debt, would come to see Judge Bland. Sometimes he needed as little as five or ten dollars, occasionally as much as fifty dollars, but usually it was less than that. Judge Bland would then demand to know what security he had. The Negro, of course, had none, save perhaps a few personal possessions and some wretched little furniture —a bed, a chair, a table, a kitchen stove. Judge Bland would send his collector, bulldog, and chief lieutenant—a ferret-faced man named Clyde Beals—to inspect these miserable possessions, and if he thought the junk important enough to its owner to justify the loan, he would advance the money, extracting from it, however, the first installment of his interest.

From this point on, the game was plainly and flagrantly usurious. The interest was payable weekly, every Saturday night. On a ten-dollar loan Judge Bland extracted interest of fifty cents a week; on a twenty-dollar loan, interest of a dollar a week; and so on. That is why the amount of the loans was rarely as much as fifty dollars. Not only were the contents of most Negro shacks worth less than that, but to pay two dollars and a half in weekly interest was beyond the capacity of most Negroes, whose wage, if they were men, might not be more than five or six dollars a week, and if they were women—cooks or house-servants in the town—might be only three or four dollars. Enough had to be left them for a bare existence or it was no game. The purpose and skill of the game came in lending the Negro a sum of money somewhat greater than his weekly wage and his consequent ability to pay back, but also a sum whose weekly interest was within the range of his small income.

Judge Bland had on his books the names of Negroes who had paid him fifty cents or a dollar a week over a period of years, on an original loan of ten or twenty dollars. Many of these poor and ignorant people were unable to comprehend what had happened to them. They could only feel mournfully, dumbly, with the slavelike submissiveness of their whole training and conditioning, that at some time in the distant past they had got their money, spent it, and had their fling, and that now they must pay perpetual tribute for that privilege. Such men and women as these would come to that dim-lit place of filth and misery on Saturday night, and there the Judge himself, black-frocked, white-shirted, beneath one dingy, fly-specked bulb, would hold his private court:

"What's wrong, Carrie? You're two weeks behind in your payments. Is fifty cents all you got this week?"

"It doan seem lak it was three weeks. Musta slipped up somewheres in my countin'."

"You didn't slip up. It's three weeks. You owe a dollar fifty. Is this all you got?"

With sullen apology: "Yassuh."

"When will you have the rest of it?"

"Dey's a fellah who say he gonna give me—"

"Never mind about that. Are you going to keep up your payments after this or not?"

"Dat's whut Ah wuz sayin'. Jus' as soon as Monday come, an' dat fellah—"

Harshly: "Who you working for now?"

"Doctah Hollandah—"

"You cooking for him?"

Sullenly, with unfathomable Negro mournfulness: "Yassuh."

"How much is he paying you?"

"Three dollahs."

"And you mean you can't keep up? You can't pay fifty cents a week?"

Still sullen, dark, and mournful, as doubtful and confused as jungle depths of Africa: "Doan know. . . . Seems lak a long time since Ah started payin' up—"

Harshly, cold as poison, quick as a striking snake: "You've never started paying up. You've paid nothing. You're only paying interest, and behind in that."

And still doubtfully, in black confusion, fumbling and fingering and bringing forth at last a wad of greasy little receipts from the battered purse: "Doan know, seems lak Ah got enough of dese to've paid dat ten dollars up long ago. How much longer does Ah have to keep on payin'?"

"Till you've got ten dollars. . . . All right, Carrie: here's your receipt. You bring that extra dollar in next week."

Others, a little more intelligent than Carrie, would comprehend more clearly what had happened to them, but would continue to pay because they were unable to get together at one time enough money to release them from their bondage. A few would have energy and power enough to save their pennies until at last they were able to buy back their freedom. Still others, after paying week by week and month by month, would just give up in despair and would pay no more. Then, of course, Clyde Beals was on them like a vulture. He nagged, he wheedled, and he threatened; and if, finally, he saw that he could get no more money from them, he took their household furniture. Hence the chaotic pile of malodorous junk which filled the shop.

Why, it may be asked, in a practice that was so flagrantly, nakedly, and unashamedly usurious as this, did Judge Rumford Bland not come into collision with the law? Did the police not know from what sources, and in what ways, his income was derived?

They knew perfectly. The very store in which this miserable business was carried on was within twenty yards of the City Hall, and within fifty feet of the side entrance to the town calaboose, up whose stone steps many of these same Negroes had time and again been hauled and mauled and hurled into a cell. The practice, criminal though it was, was a common one, winked at by the local authorities, and but one of many similar practices by which unscrupulous white men all over the South feathered their own nests at the expense of an oppressed and ignorant people. The fact that such usury was practiced chiefly against a "bunch of niggers" to a large degree condoned and pardoned it in the eyes of the law.

Moreover, Judge Rumford Bland knew that the people with whom he dealt would not inform on him. He knew that the Negro stood in awe of the complex mystery of the law, of which he understood little or nothing, or in terror of its brutal force. The law for him was largely a matter of the police, and the police was a white man in a uniform, who had the power and authority to arrest him, to beat him with his fist or with a club, to shoot him with a gun, and to lock him up in a small, dark cell. It was not likely, therefore, that any Negro would take his troubles to the police. He was not aware that he had any rights as a citizen, and that Judge Rumford Bland had violated those rights; or, if he was aware of rights, however vaguely, he was not likely to ask for their protection by a group of men at whose hands he had known only assault, arrest, and imprisonment.

Above the shambles of the nigger junk, upon the second floor, were Judge Bland's offices. A wooden stairway, worn by the tread of clay-booted time, and a hand rail, loose as an old tooth, smooth, besweated by the touch of many a black palm, led up to a dark hallway. Here, in Stygian gloom, one heard the punctual monotone of a single and regularly repeated small drop of water dripping somewhere in the rear, and caught the overpowering smell of the tin urinal. Opening off this hallway was the glazed glass of the office door, which bore the legend in black paint, partly flaked off:

RUMFORD BLAND
ATTORNEY AT LAW

Within, the front room was furnished with such lumber as lawyers use. The floor was bare, there were two roll-top desks, black with age, two bookcases with glass doors, filled with battered volumes of old pigskin brown, a spittoon, brass-bodied and capacious, swimming with tobacco juice, a couple of ancient swivel chairs, and a few other nondescript straight-backed chairs for visitors to sit and creak in. On the walls were several faded diplomas—Pine Rock College, Bachelor of Arts; The University of Old Catawba, Doctor of Laws; and a certificate of The Old Catawba Bar Association. Behind was another room with nothing in it but some more bookcases full of heavy tomes in musty calf bindings, a few chairs, and against the wall a plush sofa—the room, it was whispered, "where Bland took his women." Out front, in the windows that looked on the Square, their glass unwashed and specked with the ghosts of flies that died when Gettysburgh was young, were two old, frayed, mottled-yellow window shades, themselves as old as Garfield, and still faintly marked with the distinguished names of "Kennedy and Bland." The Kennedy of that old law firm had been the father of Baxter Kennedy, the Mayor, and his partner, old General Bland, had been Rumford's father. Both had been dead for years, but no one had bothered to change the lettering.

Such were the premises of Judge Rumford Bland as George Webber remembered them. Judge Rumford Bland—"bondsman," "furniture dealer," usurious lender to the blacks. Judge Rumford Bland—son of a brigadier of infantry, C.S.A., member of the bar, wearer of immaculate white and broadcloth black.

What happened to this man that had so corrupted and perverted his life from its true and honorable direction? No one knew. There was no question that he possessed remarkable gifts. In his boyhood George had heard the more reputable attorneys of the town admit that few of them would have been Judge Bland's match in skill and ability had he chosen to use his talents in an honest way.

But he was stained with evil. There was something genuinely old and corrupt at the sources of his life and spirit. It had got into his blood, his bone, his flesh. It was palpable in the touch of his thin, frail hand when he greeted you, it was present in the deadly weariness of his tone of voice, in the dead-white texture of his emaciated face, in his lank and lusterless auburn hair, and, most of all, in his sunken mouth, around which there hovered constantly the ghost of a smile. It could only be called the ghost of a smile, and yet, really, it was no smile at all. It was, if anything, only a shadow at the corners of the mouth. When one looked closely, it was gone. But one knew that it was always there—lewd, evil, mocking, horribly corrupt, and suggesting a limitless vitality akin to the humor of death, which welled up from some secret spring in his dark soul.

In his early manhood Judge Bland had married a beautiful but dissolute woman, whom he shortly divorced. The utter cynicism that marked has attitude toward women was perhaps partly traceable to this source. Ever since his divorce he had lived alone with his mother, a stately, white-haired lady to whom he rendered at all times a faithful, solicitous, exquisitely kind and gentle duty. Some people suspected that this filial devotion was tinged with irony and contemptuous resignation, but certainly the old lady herself had no cause to think so. She occupied a pleasant old house, surrounded with every comfort, and if she ever guessed by what dark means her luxuries had been assured, she never spoke of it to her son. As for women generally, Judge Bland divided them brutally into two groups—the mothers and the prostitutes—and, aside from the single exception in his own home, his sole interest was in the second division.

He had begun to go blind several years before George left Libya Hill, and the thin, white face, with its shadowy smile, had been given a sinister enhancement by the dark spectacles which he then wore. He was under treatment at the Johns Hopkins Hospital in Baltimore, and made trips there at intervals of six weeks, but his vision was growing steadily worse, and the doctors had already told him that his condition was practically hopeless. The malady that was destroying his sight had been brought on by a loathsome disease which he thought had been checked long since, and which he frankly admitted had been engendered in his eyes.

In spite of all these sinister and revolting facts of character, of spirit, and of person, Judge Bland, astonishing as it may seem, had always been an enormously attractive figure. Everyone who met him knew at once that the man was bad. No, "bad" is not the word for it. Everyone knew that he was evil—genuinely, unfathomably evil—and evil of this sort has a grandeur about it not unlike the grandeur of supreme goodness. And indeed, there was goodness in him that had never altogether died. In his single term upon the bench as a police court magistrate, it was universally agreed that Judge Bland had been fair and wise in his disposal of swift justice. Whatever it was that had made this fact possible—no one pretended to understand it—the aura of it still clung to him. And it was for just this reason that people who met him were instantly, even if they fought against it, captivated, drawn close to him, somehow made to like him. At the very moment that they met him, and felt the force of death and evil working in him, they also felt—oh, call it the phantom, the radiance, the lost soul, of an enormous virtue. And with the recognition of that quality came the sudden stab of overwhelming regret, the feeling of "What a loss! What a shame!" And yet no one could say why.

An Allegation in Lavender

Gene Fowler

THOMAS MOTT OSBORNE, stormy penologist, was born in Auburn, New York, September 23, 1859. His father was a figure in the so-called Harvester Trust; his mother a leader of the women's suffrage movement. The Osbornes lived in an ivy-covered mansion of the roomy Cambridge type, with a brickwalk approach, bordered by boxwood hedges and tall poplar trees. The South Street house was not far from Auburn State Prison. It was inevitable that Osborne become interested in prison affairs.

Tom Osborne attended Hobart College, and later was graduated from Harvard. He was tall and athletic. He was interested in art and music and could play the piano well. Sometimes he gave recitals. Mr. Osborne was married once, his wife dying in 1886. They had four sons.

Like another Harvard product, Big Bill Thompson of Chicago, Osborne reveled in the dramatic and the spectacular. Unlike Big-Bill-the-Builder, Osborne was cultured and articulate, and never even thought of "busting King George on the snoot." It is reasonable to assume that King George, barred from Chicago, might have come safely to Auburn at any time, and that Mr. Osborne himself would have captained the reception committee—perhaps carrying His Majesty's crown and scepter. Of course it would not have been advisable for the King to visit Auburn during a prison riot. Nobody's snoot is safe at such a time.

On graduating from Harvard, Osborne entered his father's reaper-works, eventually succeeding to the presidency of a concern employing 3,500 men. He proved a splendid organizer, a humane employer, and his men spoke well of him. Osborne, however, had a penchant for public service. He became Commissioner of the Board of Education. He enjoyed a close friendship with President Eliot of Harvard, sending many indigent boys to that University, paying all their expenses. Another friend and admirer was Dean George S. Kirchwey of Columbia Law School.

Osborne began his political life as a Democrat and subsequently became a leader up-state. He was unstable in his party affiliations, however, bolting the ticket that supported William Jennings Bryan in '96. Later he returned to the fold, in which the Grapejuice Commoner was silverplating his followers.

Osborne decided to run for mayor of Auburn. He organized an overall brigade and campaigned among the lunchbuckets of the workingmen. He was elected then, as well as a second time, in a community that hitherto had produced a Republican majority of 2,500. He was defeated a third time out.

Osborne's speeches were rip-roarers. His attacks were vigorous. He did not, at any time, however, dip into the gutter for political syllables.

Together with Henry George, Jr., and William Randolph Hearst, the publicist, Osborne became interested in the George Junior Republic. This was a self-governing institution for city boys—usually street waifs. The republic was at Freeville, New York, thirty miles south of Auburn. Osborne eventually became president of the association controlling the republic. He took many of the boys into his employ and sent some of them to Harvard. Before long he had differences with Mr. Hearst. He charged that the publicist sought to use his connection with the boys' institution as advertising promotion for his newspapers. This breach widened later in political conventions.

Osborne organized a Beethoven Orchestra in Auburn and frequently took the baton himself. He was not without critics in his home town. There were charges that Tom Osborne was "conceited" and "too smart." Certain of his detractors held it "a pity he should waste his father's money on his personal vanity." He had plenty of money, and just whose business it was what he did with it is not clear. As mayor he refused to accept a salary. Although gubernatorial sparks crackled in the Osborne skull, it is certain that he was charitable and no grafter.

He was fond of motoring. He toured Europe with his four sons in a machine called "The Green Dragon." This led him to turn literary, and he wrote a travel-book entitled "The Green Dragon."

Osborne hoped to be candidate for governor in the Democratic convention of 1906 that nominated the then Congressman William Randolph Hearst. He was outspoken against the publicist at the Buffalo conclave. He denounced the methods of State Chairman "Fingey" Connors, politician and Buffalo newspaper proprietor; also Tammany leader Charles Murphy. Osborne claimed these men favored and forced the Hearst nomination through ulterior motives.

State Chairman "Fingey" Connors was quite a boy. As a politician he was cagey and picturesque. His newspaper training was a bit ragged, but he made a go of his properties. Certain functions of newspaper-making were Greek to "Fingey." For example, he never could grasp the reason for an exchange editor. In case you don't know, an exchange editor sits at a paper-littered desk, reading public prints from other cities, clipping for fillers such whimsies as "When to Move Bees" and "Three-legged Donkey Born in the Bahamas."

"Fingey" passed the exchange editor's desk, day after day, and finally could stand the sight no longer.

"Who the hell is *that* guy?" he asked the managing editor.

"It's the exchange editor," was the reply.

"Well," said Mr. Connors, " '*It's*' goin' to be fired."

"Fired?"

"You heard me."

"O. K., Mr. Connors, but may I ask on what grounds?"

"Fire him," repeated Fingey. "I've seen him every day for a month, and all he ever does is *read newspapers!*"

Osborne bolted the Democratic ticket on account of the Hearst nomination. He turned whole-heartedly to prison affairs. He commenced an intensive study of penal conditions, and his opinions began to be quoted widely.

In 1913, Thomas Mott Osborne—as special investigator—voluntarily served a "sentence" at Auburn Prison. He was there a week. Warden Rattigan—an old friend—and one or two members of the prison board were the only persons supposed to know that the new "convict," Tom Brown, Number 33,333, was Thomas Mott Osborne.

Osborne, as Tom Brown, was placed at his request in the prison basket-shop. There had been complaints by convicts regarding the inferior grade of rattan rods. The rattans were too thick, they said, and too hard. Sore fingers became infected. Prison officers steamed the rods and otherwise treated them, but they were admittedly not up to standard.

On October 3, 1913, Tom Brown worked a short time on the afternoon shift. He put down a half-completed basket and nodded to Officer Otto Stitt, the basket-shop guard. Then he went to the toilet.

When Tom Brown returned, Officer Stitt said: "Whatcha go away for without askin'?"

"Why, officer," said Brown, "I looked toward you, and I thought I saw you nod that it was all right."

OFFICER: Well, I didn't see you, and I didn't nod.

BROWN: Oh, well, officer, it makes no difference. These rattans are too thick, and they hurt my fingers.

OFFICER: The hell they do! Well, you're the biggest guy here, and if the rest can work 'em, you ought to. Now let's not have none of your lip. Get busy, see!

BROWN: No, Mr. Stitt, I'm not going to work with these rattans any more.

OFFICER: Don't "Mr. Stitt" me, and cut out puttin' on airs. Remember, you're just a con, and you'll do as you're told, see?

BROWN: I'm through for today.

OFFICER: Do you mean you won't work no more?

BROWN: Precisely.

OFFICER: Oho! So you're pullin' big words on me, hey? "Precisely," hey? So that's it? Well, take your "precisely" over to that bench, and do it God damn quick, see?

BROWN: You mean you'll strike me if I refuse?

OFFICER: You fresh bastard! Get your hat and coat and come to the P. K.'s office. You fresh bastard, you!

BROWN: I'll go anywhere except back to the bench. Is that clear?

OFFICER: I ought to push in your face. Come on. You'll get yours!

Tom Brown got his gray coat and prison cap. Officer Stitt took him to the quarters of the Principal Keeper. There he repeated his refusal to work.

PRINCIPAL KEEPER: Then you'll have to go to the dungeons.

BROWN: Just as you say, sir.

KEEPER: I don't like to do it. You look like a sensible man.

BROWN: I won't work with those inferior rattans.

KEEPER: You use pretty good language for a con. I'll give you one more chance to comply, Brown. What say?

BROWN: My mind is made up.

OFFICER: He's settin' a bad example for the others.

BROWN: I'm thinking of the others when I choose to quit. Conditions are intolerable.

OFFICER: Who the hell do you think *you* are? Maybe you have a pull with the Gov'nor.

BROWN: That may be, too.

OFFICER: Haw! Haw! Give the Govvie my regards when you see him.

BROWN: I shall be delighted to do so, officer.

KEEPER: Well, how about you, Brown? Will it be back to work, or solitary confinement? It's no picnic in the dungeon.

BROWN: It's no picnic anywhere here, sir.

OFFICER: He's a philosopher. That's how he got to be a bunkie of His Knobs, the Gov'nor.

KEEPER: I've no alternative, Brown. (To officer) Take him to the dungeon. No convict can run this prison.

BROWN: Some day the convicts *will* have a voice.

OFFICER: He's screwy. Come on, Brown. It's nice and dark where you're goin'.

BROWN: Wouldn't you be surprised to wake up and find you'd made a mistake, officer?

OFFICER: Wouldn't you be surprised if I took a good swift kick at your pratt?

The guards stripped Tom Brown at 3 o'clock in the afternoon. "He's built like a horse," said Guard Raymond to Guard Cummings.

"What's he in for?" asked Cummings.

"Damned if I know. Somethin' desp'rate. I hear he tried to kill Stitt."

"Yeah. They say he smuggled in a gun or somethin'."

A special suit without pockets or metal fittings was put on Brown. Everything, including his pocket handkerchief, was taken away. They thrust him into a dungeon-cell. He had five neighbors, whom he could hear but could not see. The place smelled like a cabbage-cellar. Two of the five others were mental cases. There was neither bed nor chair. Brown lay on the floor, but he had to get to his feet when a rat and wife wanted to share his stone bed. He was nauseated.

Three gills of water and three slices of coarse-grained bread, cut thin, were put in his cell. "What time is it?" Brown asked the guard who placed the rations on the cell-floor.

"Shut your mouth," the guard said. "And keep it shut."

"Then you won't even tell me the time?"

"If you want the strait-jacket, just keep on crackin'."

The two feeble-minded prisoners began to gibber obscenely. When it became quiet again, the rats started to fight for Tom Brown's neglected bread. He kicked them away, knocking over his water. His throat was dry all night long. He had no way of knowing when dawn came, but at 6 o'clock there was a noise outside his cell. A guard with a flash-lamp told him to come along. Tom Brown returned to his regular cell. He was pale and dazed. His big body shook. He flopped on his cell-cot and lay face downward.

At 7 o'clock a keeper said: "Get up from there, Brown. The warden wants to see you."

When Warden Rattigan and Tom Brown were alone in the main office, Rattigan said: "Well, Tom, how about you? Don't you think you've had enough of this?"

"I have got what I came after," said Tom.

"The newspapers have got wind of it. Some of the boys are waiting to see you. Well?"

"I notified the newspapers myself, but I didn't know I'd be so upset. Tell them I'll give out a statement later."

At chapel the Rev. Arthur Copeland announced that Convict Tom Brown would make a speech. In his address, Tom Brown revealed himself as Thomas Mott Osborne. He received an ovation when he said he had undergone convict-treatment to familiarize himself with the problems of prisoners. He promised to work unceasingly for the betterment of convicts. When he left chapel, he was solicited by several separate guards, all of whom hoped their jobs were not jeopardized by their handling of him as Tom Brown.

"Don't worry," he said to each one individually, "it's not your fault. It's the fault of a barbarous system. You did your duty as you saw it."

"He's O. K.," said one "screw."

"He's batty," said another. "This ain't no kindy-garden."

Brown had a light lunch with the warden. On his way to the prison gate and to freedom, he was stopped by newspaper men. "I'll publish my findings later, boys. Right now I am too thrilled—in a horrible way, of course—by my recent experience in solitary. I am more confirmed than ever that the prison system is singularly unintelligent. It is a form of slavery."

Osborne's electric automobile was awaiting him at the gate. He drove to his home in South Street. The first thing he did was to eat a good meal. Then he began writing his book: "Within Prison Walls." In it, he described the prison system as "the organized lunacy of the people."

One passage read: "An aching, overwhelming sense of the hideous cruelty of the whole barbaric, brutal business sweeps over me; the feeling of moral, physical and mental outrage; the monumental imbecility of it all; the horrible darkness, the cruel iron walls at our backs; the nerve-racking routine; the whirring dynamo through the other wall; the filth, the vermin, the bad air; the insufficient food, the denial of water and the overpowering, sickening sense of accumulated misery—of madness and suicide—haunting the place."

On December 1, 1914, Thomas Mott Osborne assumed office as Warden of Sing Sing Prison. He succeeded Acting-Warden George S. Weed. Weed had been appointed temporarily, following the dismissal of Warden Thomas J. McCormick. The latter had been stripped of office for granting unusual liberties to David A. Sullivan, former Brooklyn banker.

Mr. Osborne, now a man with iron-gray hair, inspected the entire prison plant. As he was visiting the shoe-factory, an elderly convict stepped from the line-up, tipped his gray cap and said: "Good morning, Mr. Osborne."

Warden Osborne's guard-escort got ready to sock the too-familiar convict, but the big warden smiled and pumped the hand of the convict. The guard-escort's eyes bulged. It is believed it cut his life-span by at least ten years.

"Why, hello, Bill," said the Warden. "I didn't expect to see you here." "Oh, yes," said Bill, "I'm here for a six-months' bit."

"I remember you well at Auburn," said the warden. He had an uncanny memory for names and faces.

The new warden tasted the coffee and proclaimed it "rotten." He condemned the medieval bucket-system. He began to make wholesale changes at Sing Sing.

"The State has a right to punish a prisoner," he said. "But it has no right, constitutional or otherwise, to rob him of his health."

Men, diseased or well, washed from the same bucket. There was little running water anywhere in the prison. The fire hazard was great. The cells were antiquated. There were 1,200 cells, each one seven feet long, six feet six inches high and three feet four inches wide. Two men sometimes occupied one cell.

There was a society of prisoners known as The Golden Rule Brother-hood. Osborne interviewed fifty of the so-called delegates of this society.

"There's one grave slip in your organization, boys," he said. "You have no way of disciplining members except by sending them to prison authorities. That's bad. You should be self-governing and self-disciplining. You must have the power to suspend offenders after a trial. Your punishment should consist of taking away the afternoon privileges and recreational hours of an offender."

Osborne had broken up the drug-traffic at Auburn Prison. He now undertook to do likewise at Sing Sing. Certain guards were said to be carrying on a lucrative business, supplying convicts with narcotics. It also was charged that prostitutes were brought into the prison for the entertainment of moneyed inmates. Osborne's drive against these abuses stirred the ire of petty grafters, who presumably were shielded by politicians. The warden began to be praised by some and attacked by others as a "faddist" and a "show-off."

"Out of every ten convicts," Osborne said, "there are nine who want to behave, and one who doesn't. It is up to the nine well-behaved ones to take care of the one dissenter. There must be less 'guarding' and so-called supervision. The men work better if they are not constantly reminded that they are rats in a trap. We will increase their recreational periods."

"But it will make them lazy," said a prison commissioner.

"No. I'd rather have the men work two hours than putter around, cheat and loaf for eight. One of the worst things the State can teach the men is to work badly."

"But these are men of the criminal type."

"There is no criminal type."

"They won't feel they are being punished if you allow so many liberties."

"Nonsense, Commissioner. Prison always will be prison. Punishment consists of curtailing a man's liberty."

Warden Osborne founded the Mutual Welfare League, in which the prisoners virtually governed themselves. Although that system since has been modified and parts of it rejected, it marked the beginning of more intelligent treatment of prisoners all over the country. Osborne shelved the old "silence" rule. Prisoners now might speak to one another under certain conditions. Production in the shops increased when guards were withdrawn. There were abuses, however, and it was said that perverted practices increased among the convicts.

Warden Osborne organized an orchestra in Sing Sing. He allowed baseball games and asked Battling Nelson, the famous lightweight, to promote boxing-bouts inside the prison walls. Superintendent of State Prisons, John B. Riley, refused to sanction these bouts, scheduled for July 4, 1915. Osborne otherwise met with outside interference. But he continued to modernize the prison. He delivered lectures before groups of prominent citizens.

On October 5, 1915, twenty-five ex-convicts tendered a private party to Osborne at the Park Avenue Hotel. They ate a fine dinner and made speeches. All of them had returned to the free world and to good jobs. They raised their glasses to "Tom Brown," who made one of his emotional speeches. He called them "his boys" and would not consent to sitting on a dais. The men sang, talked, and hoisted wine until a late hour. The big, gray-haired warden beamed.

"It's getting late," said one ex-con to another.

"That's O.K.," was the reply. "We got an A-1 alibi while we're here."

Nearly every speech, including "Tom Brown's," began with the preamble: "I'm proud to be an ex-convict . . ."

Warden Osborne permitted the men to ornament their cells with pictures and knickknacks. Most of the pictures either were of a sacred sort or family portraits. He gave each man two suits of underwear, so that one suit could be kept clean. Before Osborne took charge, the correspondence privilege was confined to one out-going letter a week. However, if a convict had a bit of graft-money, he could write oftener. The new warden increased the number of letters allowed.

One convict—in the pre-Osborne régime—received word that his wife was dying. "Would you let me write to her?" the convict asked the "screw."

"You already have wrote one letter this week."

"Please let me write. She's dyin'."

"Well, wait till she dies and I'll give you some paper."

State officials warned Osborne that he was smashing too many rules. He said: "I like to smash rules."

There was a great concert in October, 1915, by the "Tom Brown Band." A lifer played the flute, and a fellow whose sentence had been commuted from death in the electric chair to life imprisonment, banged the drum. The boys rendered "Poet and Peasant" for Osborne. He finally had obtained sanction for the Battling Nelson boxing-program, and it was given with the band concert. Mr. A. J. Drexel Biddle, of the Philadelphia Biddles, a doughty man with the gloves, showed the Sing Sing boys how it should be done. He used the ring-worn chin of Philadelphia Jack O'Brien for his anvil-shots. There were several well-known boxers in the group that performed for the Sing Sing audience, among them Leach Cross (now a dentist), Young Ahearn, Ted Kid Lewis, Eddie Morgan and Freddie Welsh, the pride of Pontypridd, Wales.

Osborne rectified abuses, one by one. There was the laundry situation. Owing to graft in the shirt-tail emporium, it was impossible for a convict to get his handkerchiefs or socks returned unless he paid a fee for "protection." Osborne discovered one case in which a convict's wife sent a weekly cash-dribble from her pitiful earnings to insure her husband's socks.

For good behavior, Osborne distributed presents. He gave away oranges, apples, and bananas, and occasionally tobacco. He was criticised for this by smug gentlemen, who never had breathed the air of incarceration. Several guards, discharged by Osborne, found willing ears for gossip concerning the Warden and his alleged relations with convicts. Word went round that the big, gray-haired man was an epicene.

The Westchester grand jury at White Plains indicted Osborne on December 28, 1915. The accusations charged him with perjury, and neglect of duty. Two indictments, containing seven counts—one of which alleged personal immorality with prisoners—were handed up to Justice Morschauser.

On the question of indicting, the jury stood fourteen for and six against, the affirmative having two more votes than the number needed. The charges may be summarized as follows:

1—That he (Osborne) absented himself from prison, being on duty but four days a week.

2—That he was neglectful in performing his duties, so that there were assaults within the prison.

3—That he neglected to report such assaults.

4—That he permitted at least four persons to visit the deathhouse in violation of the law, when Police Lieutenant Charles Becker (electrocuted for the murder of Gambler Herman Rosenthal by Gyp-the-Blood, Leftie Louie and other gangsters) was there confined.

5—That he allowed certain unfit inmates of Sing Sing to control the discipline of the prison, its management, and its policies.

6—That he failed properly to protect the convicts under his control and permitted lax discipline generally.

7—That he personally was guilty of gross immorality with Paul Vogel, James Connelly, Max Kleinberg, Henry Delara, Sidney Walsh, and others.

The perjury indictment charged that one month after a convict named Harvey had told Osborne that immorality was common in the prison, the warden had sworn before the authorities that there was no immorality.

District Attorney Weeks, in conjunction with his now noteworthy assistant, William J. Fallon, announced he would not ask for a warrant if Osborne would agree to appear the next court-day, December 31.

Mr. Osborne had been expecting adverse action by the grand jury. "It had to come. The politicians are after me. They will leave no vile charge out of their attacks."

The warden simulated serenity. The prison wireless conveyed the news. The "boys" were despondent. The warden assembled the convicts in the mess hall after supper, the day of the indictments. They began filing in from the cell-blocks; not a few were crying.

"They're givin' the old man the business," was the plaint.

Most of the men understood the full weight of the indictments, including the lavender implication. A rousing cheer greeted the warden as he stood before the convicts.

"I have just received one of the greatest honors of my career, boys," he began in a melodious voice. "I have just heard that I've been indicted by the Westchester grand jury. I presume you will all congratulate me."

The sad atmosphere dissolved beneath the warden's dulcet tones. The boys laughed at his sally. He went on:

"But I'm Warden of Sing Sing. I'll be Warden of Sing Sing until they kick me out."

There were cheers and cries of: "The hell with them, Warden!" "We're with you to a man!"

"These indictments," the Warden said, "will make friends for our Mutual Welfare League. I am glad to be attacked for bringing you baseball and movies. I'll fight for you always."

On October 9, 1916, Warden Osborne resigned in a letter to Governor Charles S. Whitman. The letter charged Whitman with having acquiesced in "shameful attacks made upon me in Westchester County." On October 15, 1916, Osborne bid farewell to Sing Sing Prison. He shook hands with the 1,600 convicts. The prisoners almost rioted in an effort to demonstrate their affection. There was a gray line extending from the mess hall into the yard. The line broke suddenly. The men swarmed about the big figure in the light coat and soft hat.

"It's the boss!" they yelled.

The warden's lunch grew cold while he held a long farewell in the prison yard. He called the convicts by name and recounted some personal incident concerning each one. The prisoners God-blessed him. Some of the afternoon newspapers in New York City God-damned him. There were three great cheers for "Tom Brown" as he walked away from his "boys."

The Osborne case added to Fallon's stature, despite the outcome. It gave him greater self-assurance, and it focused the attention of the bar on the young prosecutor. District Attorney Weeks, never a show-off, permitted his brilliant assistant to take whatever credit there was for entering the lists against some of the foremost legal minds of the day.

Osborne may have posed as a martyr before his Sing Sing "boys"; it is true he joked in some of his talks with them. But he was cut deeply. He was, after all, a sensitive big man. So fearful had he been of the outcome of the grand jury inquiry that he had visited the District Attorney's offices in White Plains and pleaded with Weeks not to call any convicts before that body.

Osborne saw on Weeks' desk, a long letter from Superintendent of Prisons John B. Riley. "I wish you'd ignore that," Osborne said.

"It contains a list of fights and assaults at the prison," replied Weeks. "Some of them have resulted in serious injuries. The grand jury's investigation is based on this letter."

"I beg you not to call the convicts," Osborne said.

"How about these alleged assaults?"

"Pooh! Pooh! Just talk. They are incidents that I, as warden, ought to deal with. Just incidents."

"Well," said Weeks, "what would *you* do with the Riley letter?"

"Ignore it."

"What! Would you have me disregard a letter from your superior, and on your say-so?"

Weeks showed Osborne a list of cases. He read off six or seven, each one an instance of first- or second-degree assault.

"I'm no surgeon," said the District Attorney, "but when I see that so-and-so had five stitches taken in his head, I know it was an assault."

Osborne interrupted quickly. "I didn't say to ignore the letter."

"Then I don't understand English," said the D.A.

Osborne's friends engaged George Gordon Battle and a number of other prominent attorneys. His long-time friend, Dean Kirchwey of Columbia, acted in an advisory capacity. Not only was it a crisis in the warden's experiment in prison managements; it was undoubtedly the climacteric of his political life.

Osborne was a Democrat, serving under a Republican administration. He had made enemies among discharged guards. He had put his heel on peculating contractors, insisting on an economic basis of repair and building-bills and on fair prices for good food, instead of enormous prices for bad food. He had four stalwart sons. These factors must be taken into account when considering the thread of lavender that ran the whole length of the mantle of accusation.

Osborne, through his sensational reforms, his undoubted economical practices, his self-evident culture, and his power for organization, up to now looked the sure Democratic candidate for Governor. Mr. Whitman, the Republican incumbent, had come to high office, Osborne charged, over the body of the executed Lieutenant Becker. Gov. Whitman appeared to be entertaining White House aspirations. If he didn't have them, then his friends surely had such hopes for their leader. If Whitman were to miss out at the coming election, the White House dream would become a Willie's-lost-lollipop. Certain Republican leaders believed it was necessary to "get" Osborne.

[The irony of life, love and plug-hats is a bitter dish of tea, when we consider that Mr. Whitman later was sounded out for the candidacy for Vice-President of the United States. He scorned it. Mr. Coolidge accepted. Warren Harding died. Heigho! Set 'em up in the next alley.]

Osborne's influential friends endeavored to block the removal of convicts from Sing Sing as witnesses. The first act by the District Attorney's office—Mr. Fallon working like a bunch of fire-crackers in a kettle—was the transfer of ex-Congressman William Willett of Queens from Sing Sing to the White Plains jail. Mr. Willett had been convicted of trying to buy a Supreme Court nomination. Now he was "chief justice" of the convict-court at Ossining.

Mr. Willett moved from Sing Sing to White Plains on a Friday night in November, 1915, on a writ of *habeas corpus* granted by Justice Morschauser, there to remain at the District Attorney's instructions and until the grand jury inquiry's end. Nearly all assaults and other cases mentioned in Superintendent Riley's letter had been "tried" before Willett as a Mutual Welfare justice. In fact, Willett was himself one of those assaulted.

Willett was one of two principal witnesses against Osborne. The other (not a convict) was a Rochester physician. The latter was said to be ready to go into the lavender implication with medical authority.

Mr. Fallon announced that he would prosecute the twenty or more assault cases, and added:

"But I don't know just *where* this thing will lead."

Bill had an inferential way of making such statements. His phraseology, "not knowing just where it will lead," aroused publicity and speculation.

"It will be useless for anybody but myself to question these men," Osborne said in reference to the convicts. "I am the only one that knows how to get the truth out of them."

"I'll get the truth," said Fallon. "In fact, I *have* the truth. I'll show how you pinched the cheek of one convict, a young chap, and said: 'Why, you have the face of a girl!'"

The Osborne case was destined to drag for months. Dean Kirchwey was Osborne's companion throughout the uncertain days.

The insinuations against the morals of Osborne flared into the wide-open when Fallon read the affidavit of one, Paul Vogel, a convict, charging that Sing Sing love had laughed at locksmiths. The reading occurred on December 13, 1915, in Justice Morschauser's court, White Plains, and during the sitting of the grand jury.

"I'll offer to make *all* the testimony and numerous affidavits public," said Mr. Fallon. His powers of insinuation already were developed to a high degree. "That is," he added, "if Mr. Osborne will *consent.*"

Mr. Battle and Huntington W. Merchant, of Osborne's counsel, surprised Mr. Fallon. "We consent to that," said Mr. Battle. The shrewd Battle was anxious to get his hands on the grand jury minutes. He sensed that Fallon was bluffing. It was to be a long, hard pull before anyone got those minutes. Fallon, then, as later, made daring moves and created exaggerated effects to gain immediate objectives. Right now he was seeking to prejudice Osborne's case with court and political public.

The Osborne counsel alleged they had been trying—without avail—to induce the District Attorney's office to bring the charges into the open.

In this case, Mr. Merchant nominally was Osborne's counsel, Mr. Battle acting for the National Prison Reform Association. They filed with Justice Morschauser a twenty-four-page brief, charging the District Attorney's office with attempting to prejudice Osborne before the grand jury; of forcing convicts (with promises of immunity and pruning-down of sentences, as well as by threats) to testify against the warden; of refusing to call witnesses that Osborne asked to be called; of allowing ex-Congressman Willett to conduct the inquiry, and seeking to compel Osborne to testify to confessions made to him by prisoners—confessions he had believed confidential.

The witnesses whom Osborne had asked the District Attorney to bring before the grand jury were: Dean Kirchwey, George W. Wickersham, former Attorney General of the United States; Charles F. Rattigan, Warden of Auburn Prison; Richard M. Hurd, president of the Lawyer's Mortgage Company and State Prison Commissioner; Clifford E. Harmon, Dr. E. Stagg Whitin, of the National Prison Labor Commission; Miss Madeline Z. Doty and Miss Emily Seaman, both women investigators of the Prison Commission.

Mr. Fallon told the court: "Osborne has evaded answering questions. Here is the testimony of Paul Vogel, a convict. He swore Osborne told him: 'You are a good-looking boy; if I were a girl, I would fall in love with you.' The warden was asked if he knew a boy named Connolly. He said he did. He was asked if Connolly was truthful. His answer was 'yes.' When we read him Connolly's testimony charging him with a crime, Osborne's answer was: 'He's a damned liar.' " Mr. Fallon's voice rose. "Osborne also called District Attorney Weeks a damned liar."

The court interjected: "There is no need of becoming hysterical. Everybody will get his rights here if it takes until next summer."

"Your Honor," said Mr. Battle, "coercion has been used to compel convicts to give testimony, to compel them to make affidavits against the warden."

Mr. Fallon folded his arms. "We have affidavits; yes, innumerable affidavits, showing that this man is the worst kind of degenerate, and for that reason he should not be in the management of Sing Sing Prison."

The court hemmed. "He may be ever so bad a man, and all that you say may be true, Mr. Fallon, but that is not the question before me at this time. The question now is: shall he divulge privileged statements made to him by convicts?"

"I have here an affidavit of Sidney L. Walsh," declared Mr. Fallon. "It was obtained in another prison. This man has not been here. He charges him with the vilest crimes. Shall I read it?"

"No."

"Has Mr. Osborne the right to refuse to answer the questions before the grand jury?" asked Mr. Fallon.

"I refuse to answer that question," said the court.

The lawyers then went to the grand jury room, where ex-Congressman Willett was telling about the Mutual Welfare League. The warden was jubilant and expressed himself confident of clearing himself of all charges.

The case was fated to limp along, however, with political ramifications that at times cloaked the real issue. The trial itself finally was set, but was delayed because of Mr. Weeks' application for a writ of prohibition to prevent Osborne's counsel from moving to strike from the indictment the count charging immorality. M. J. Tierney and others had joined the defendant's counsel.

Justice Arthur S. Tomkins threw the perjury indictment out of court. Mr. Battle kept thundering for a trial and Justice Martin J. Keogh set it for March 20. Fallon reported the People as not ready. He explained that some of the convicts had recanted their grand jury testimony. Other defections were reported. One of the convict-witnesses proved to be a man disciplined by Osborne. After a baseball game at the prison yard, this man had put on the wrong coat. Another convict-player put on the first convict's coat. In the pocket was a memorandum showing the owner's plan to escape. The finder of the coat turned this memorandum over to the warden. The owner of the coat was called to the warden's office and disciplined.

Osborne appeared before Justice Morschauser early in 1916 with a demand for permission to plead to the indictment charging mismanagement and immorality. He also made a new demand for the grand jury minutes. Mr. Fallon refused to surrender the minutes. Osborne's attorneys then went before Justice Tomkins, who ordered all evidence that had been transcribed to be delivered forthwith. When this order was shown to Fallon, he refused to comply. Contempt proceedings were talked of, the first of such proceedings that often threatened Bill later in his career. Even as a prosecutor he was beginning to "get on the nerves of the courts."

Lawyer Huntington W. Merchant visited the District Attorney's office with the Tomkins order at noon, January 21, 1916. "I want the minutes," he told Fallon.

"What minutes?" asked Fallon.

"Come now, Fallon. You know what minutes."

"I certainly don't know, unless you tell me."

Lawyer Merchant was fuming. "I want the minutes of the Osborne case."

"Oh!" said Fallon. *"Those* minutes."

"Yes, *those* minutes."

Fallon could be most annoying. "We have but one copy. But if you really *want* the minutes, you'll have to bring a stenographer to copy our set."

"Oh, no," said Merchant. "Not at all. The court order is that all the testimony, except that of Stenographer Young, be delivered to us at once; the rest in a few days. Now we want 'em, Bill."

"Wanting them is not getting them," Bill said. "Anyway, how *could* we give you the originals? Our typist is away, sick, and you'll have to wait until she gets well. It may be a year."

"Sick or no sick, Bill. Here's the order."

Bill looked at the order. "That won't do. I don't recognize some of the writing. I'll have to see Judge Tomkins to verify it."

Mr. Merchant was beside himself.

A messenger arrived with a notice of intent to ask for an order compelling the District Attorney to permit Osborne to plead to the indictment. The notice was presented to Mr. Fallon in the presence of the inflamed Mr. Merchant.

Fallon pursed his lips and made clucking sounds. "No-o-o," he drawled, "I can't sign this notice 'copy received.' "

"Oh, for God's sake, Fallon, go ahead and sign it," said Merchant. "It will save me the necessity of making an affidavit that the notice has been served."

"No," said Fallon, "we'll have to have five days' notice."

"Come on, Bill."

"No," Fallon said. "You'll have to make out the affidavit."

Mr. Merchant, very hungry by now, retired to an anteroom where he made out the affidavit and wrote a formal demand for the grand jury minutes. Fallon went to lunch. When Mr. Merchant appeared an hour later, he couldn't find Fallon. He had to wait three hours. Bill said he was exceptionally hungry that day.

"I had the finest steak you ever saw," Bill told Merchant. "You don't mean to say you have been *waiting* all this time? Oh, *what* a steak it was! Mushrooms and butter-gravy. French fried potatoes and——"

"Oh, for God's sake!" pleaded the starved counselor.

Among the convict-witnesses held at White Plains jail were Kid Dropper, Joe Rotala, James Connelly, "Mayor" of Sing Sing Prison, and

Bill Trefry, pitcher on the Mutual Welfare Team and operator of the telephone switchboard in the prison office. They told Fallon many tales of alleged mismanagement and sexual aberration. Kid Dropper came to the District Attorney's office by a rear entrance to avoid an appearance of violating the gangster's anti-squealing code. Later he asked for a transfer to Great Meadows Prison, fearing reprisal.

Inasmuch as the new courthouse was being built, the District Attorney's offices were located temporarily in the Realty Building across the street. And here occurred one of the two important behind-the-scenes events that outmaneuvered Bill Fallon for the first and perhaps the last time in his career.

"I'm desperate," Osborne told Mr. Battle. "I'm being jobbed. What would you suggest?"

Mr. Battle said: "I want you to tell your whole story, omitting nothing, to Val O'Farrell."

"A detective, isn't he?"

"One of the best."

Mr. Battle put in a call for Val O'Farrell, former lieutenant of detectives of the New York Police Department, and the nimblest Sherlock in private practice.

"I'll be down as soon as the palm is crossed with silver," said Mr. O'Farrell, who is a good business man.

"Come ahead," said Battle.

O'Farrell brought with him his able assistant, Archie Owen. They listened to Osborne's story. O'Farrell said he believed that a conspiracy was evident. Not only were convicts being forced to testify, he was told, but a certain physician in Rochester—a man of fine professional standing —was being groomed to take the stand against Osborne. The doctor and ex-Congressman Willett were to be the "star" witnesses for the State.

"I'll get my operative, Valentine, to handle the Rochester angle," said O'Farrell. "I'll tend to this end."

In despatching Valentine to Rochester, Mr. O'Farrell purchased twelve of the new and much-discussed violet-ray lamps. "What in the devil?" asked Battle.

"Never mind," said O'Farrell. "We want violet-rays."

As O'Farrell said good-by to Valentine, he called out: "Don't get sunburned."

It was an inclement spring and very cold. Mr. O'Farrell appeared incognito in White Plains as "Col. Trout," late of the British Infantry. He engaged offices in the Realty Building through a "remove," or intermediary, so as not to be discovered. These offices were four floors below the District Attorney's temporary offices, which were on the seventh floor.

Archie Owen, an expert electrician and linesman, set-up a detectaphone apparatus in "Col. Trout's" office. "You might have chosen a warmer night," Owen said to O'Farrell as they "shinnied up" the face of the building with scaling ladders. It was necessary for them to get a night watchman drunk and to put a wire over the top of the building, bringing it down the other side.

On the flat roof of the building, Archie selected a hammer and some staples to make the wire fast. A gale was blowing and it was zero weather. He had been pounding for half a minute, thinking he was driving the staple into mortar. It was very dark. O'Farrell finally risked a flash-lamp to see what was delaying Archie.

"Good God!" O'Farrell said, "don't you know that you're pounding your *finger?*"

"The hell!" said Archie. He had hammered the first joint of his left forefinger to a frozen jelly. A week later it was necessary to amputate it. But the detectaphone was installed.

For some weeks, the O'Farrell stenographers took down everything that was said, not only in the Fallon offices, but in the grand jury room. From that time on, the District Attorney began to be worried by check-matings and counter-moves.

"I think we've got enough to prove a conspiracy," said O'Farrell in March.

"I guess so," Battle said. "But what about that physician in Rochester?"

"We'll hear from Valentine soon."

O'Farrell took from his office the entire detectaphone force and all records. Through his "removes" he hired a complete new staff. Then he deliberately tipped-off Fallon that a detectaphone had been employed wherewith to find out what had been going on. Meanwhile O'Farrell dictated a *new* set of records. He set down tremendous exaggerations, in what purported to be the detectaphone notes. Val became so imaginative that for a time he believed himself related to the late Jules Verne. Val scattered the trumped-up records all over the place.

Fallon's men descended on the office, tracing it through the wire that had cost Archie Owen his pie-finger. They gloated. They seized the "records" and pinched the office force. The members of the new outfit had no more idea of what they had been doing for "Col. Trout" than had Mrs. O'Leary's cow that time in Chicago. The more Fallon questioned the "staff," the more he was at sea. He got the funniest sort of answers.

Sheriff Wiesendanger and a deputy found two young men and a young woman in the "Col. Trout" office. They said they had been employed by Colonel Trout and knew nothing whatsoever about a detectaphone. These bewildered persons were subpoenaed and told to be in court the following Monday, when Mr. Osborne was scheduled to go on trial.

When the anti-Osborne forces read O'Farrell's imaginative records, they were frantic. Mr. O'Farrell chuckled and regarded himself as a modern Charles Dickens. It all sounded true—and very damning. Fallon raised a shout that O'Farrell would be prosecuted for eavesdropping.

"Go ahead and prosecute me," O'Farrell told Fallon. "Eavesdropping has something to do with an ear to the keyhole. We didn't bother about keyholes."

The boys at Albany rushed a bill through, making the installation of a detectaphone a serious offense.

Valentine took his violet-ray machines to Rochester. Inasmuch as he was selling these expensive contraptions at one-third the market-price, he found ready buyers. When he had disposed of several, with appropriate lectures on "Let the sun's own rays cure you of that lost manhood," he visited the offices of the physician who was to be the anti-Osborne star witness.

"It's a marvelous machine," Valentine said. "I've sold them to so-and-so and to so-and-so. They gave me your name. Now, you can help me sell more of them. If you want to come in with me, there's a fortune in it."

"I think they really are good things," said the physician.

"Well, as a starter," said Valentine, "I'll give you one *free,* if you'll write me a testimonial."

The physician was delighted. He went to his desk and wrote the testimonial.

Mr. Fallon had sporadic attacks of sinus trouble during the winter of the Osborne case. At times it was so painful as to threaten his turning over the work to a second assistant. A surgeon removed a small bone from the nasal cavity. Mr. Fallon, in this, his first real illness, refused to quit work.

"Can't you rest a few days?" the surgeon asked.

"I've got to be on the job," said Fallon.

"But you will be in pain for a while."

"I don't need a doctor to tell me that. I'm in pain now."

The doctor poured a drink of rye. "Here. This may brace you up."

"No, thanks," Fallon said, "I don't drink."

"This won't hurt you; but of course, if you have scruples about drinking. . . ."

"Well, give it to me. I guess it won't do any harm."

Mr. Fallon took his first drink. He was twenty-nine years old, almost thirty. He downed other bracers in the busy months that followed. He became what is known as a moderate drinker.

"There is no question in my mind," said District Attorney Weeks, "that efforts are being made to intimidate the State's witnesses. "Not only has a detectaphone been used to anticipate the State's case, but I hear that wives of convicts are being told that if their husbands testify for the State, they will never get a parole, and will be rearrested when their terms expire."

Convicts watching the newspapers noticed that ex-Congressman Willett didn't get his parole for ninety days after he was eligible.

The big trial finally came off before judge and jury. Many political personages were in the doldrums, largely because of the detectaphone records. No one among them knew exactly *what* had been recorded or *to whom* it had been said. The State now depended, it was believed, on the Rochester physician to weave the lavender thread in the rope that was allegedly fashioned to hang Osborne politically. Mr. Battle, supplied with a second round of Val O'Farrell's ammunition, awaited the enemy's charge.

The physician took the stand and qualified as an expert witness. Mr. Battle led him on, calmly. He inquired into all manner of medical matters that at first appeared immaterial. Then finally:

Q: Do you have any faith in the new appliances? the electrical ones, such as the fluroscope? A: Yes, indeed.

Q: And what is your opinion of the violet-ray lamp? A: Why, I think it beneficial in certain cases.

Q: What kind of cases? A: In the treatment of rickets and other maladies that are alleviated by the sun's rays.

Q: Then this machine duplicates the sun's rays?

Mr. Fallon: Your Honor, I object. What has the sun's rays to do with this witness or this case?

Mr. Battle: The sun is an enlightening medium.

The Court: What is the purpose of this line of inquiry, Mr. Battle?

Mr. Battle: Your Honor, I intend to impeach this witness.

Mr. Fallon: With the sun's rays? Your Honor, Mr. Battle thinks he is a Joshua and will make the sun stand still.

The Court: I shall permit the questioning until it is shown what counsel is aiming at. Be more explicit, Mr. Battle. This case already has lagged.

Mr. Battle now asked the witness: "Did you ever write a testimonial in behalf of a violet-ray lamp?"

The witness seemed to be fearing some sort of trap.

"Come," Mr. Battle said. "Answer yes or no."

"Yes. I recommended such a lamp."

Mr. Battle produced the testimonial written for Valentine, the day the free lamp was promised. "Is this the letter?"

The witness read it. "Yes."

Mr. Battle entered the letter in the record, and over the objection of Mr. Fallon, who shouted: "What do we care about a man's correspondence concerning violet-rays? Mr. Osborne is not charged with being a bad electrician. His conduct at the electric chair is not being impugned."

The court allowed the letter. Mr. Battle read it into the record. The document testified to benefits obtained by use of the violet-ray. The letter said, in substance, that the doctor had used this apparatus for several years and had arrived at pleasing results. No one could go far wrong in owning one, especially at such low cost.

"And now," said Mr. Battle, roaring, "this man appears here, swearing to tell the truth. He admits this is his letter. Your Honor, and gentlemen of the jury——"

"Are you summing up?" asked Mr. Fallon.

The Court: Sit down, Mr. Fallon. If you have an objection, make it in the prescribed form.

Mr. Fallon: I make such an objection now.

The Court: Overruled.

Mr. Battle: He writes this letter as a testimonial. This witness says he has—mark the words—*used it for several years*. Your Honor, we shall show that this lamp has not only *not* been on the market for several years; it has been before the public for only *six months!*

Mr. Fallon whispered to Eugene McGee, who had come to hear his Fordham friend in action: "There goes the old ball game!"

It was the theoretical end of the witness and the virtual close of the famous case. The Court granted Mr. Battle's motion to dismiss the charges for lack of evidence. The case did not go to the jury. The gray-haired penologist was absolved of illegal acts as charged in the indictment alleging mismanagement and immorality.

"This defeat," Fallon said, "did me more good than anything that ever happened to me. I learned much. I had the most brilliant opposition. If I had won, perhaps I should have grown too sure of myself."

"The mistake I made," he said at another time, "was being too aggressive at the wrong time. I turned a prosecution into a persecution. And that is always bad."

He was destined to escape a serious charge himself one future day, largely because a prosecution became a persecution.

Thomas Mott Osborne's gubernatorial chances had dimmed, no matter what his legal victory had done to clear his record or his name. He plunged, as usual, into prison work. He returned to Sing Sing as warden in July, 1916. He was promised he would meet with no further interference.

There were gay ceremonies marking "Tom Brown's" return to his "boys." Only one thing marred the reunion. Mr. Osborne's former convict-secretary, Dick Richards, had been paroled during the Osborne absence and had forged a check in Osborne's name for $2,000. His parole was revoked. On the day Osborne returned as warden, members of the Mutual Welfare League stood guard over Richards.

Mr. Osborne's reappearance at Sing Sing was brief. He resigned soon, bitterly attacking Whitman and others, charging that every sort of masked interference had been set against him. When he left, he was commanded by a high prison official "never to set foot again in any State institution."

In June, 1920, Lieutenant-Commander Thomas Mott Osborne of the United States Navy, not only set foot inside Sing Sing's walls, but aroused an enthusiasm said to have surpassed ovations accorded John L. Sullivan, the Hon. William Jennings Bryan, and the Reverend Evangelist William Ashley Sunday on their respective visits to the Big House. Osborne now was commanding the Naval prison at Portsmouth.

The Lieutenant-Commander received the "freedom of Sing Sing." Warden Lewis E. Lawes permitted him to go alone among the inmates. Osborne met "O.K." Bill Myers, the bank burglar, one of the former warden's right-hand men in the old days.

"We miss you a lot, boss," said Myers, "but Major Lawes is a fine man, too."

"I'm sure he is," said the Lieutenant-Commander. "And you can all do me a favor by playing square with him."

The former warden then called on a gangster in the prison hospital. The man was convalescing from an operation for stomach trouble.

"How's your stomach now?" asked Osborne.

"I et too much lead when I was a gun," said the gangster.

"You'll have to go on a diet," said Osborne.

The Fire Island Baker ferried me across Great South Bay in his good white dory. It was late winter and the sheet ice still floated in thin islands on the dark waters. I never knew such a neighborly fellow. He said he would help me write the book. In return, I helped grease his cake-pans. We spent the early mornings together beside the hot oven, and the smell of warm dough was satisfying. The city seemed so far away.

It is sure that certain prosecuting officers believed Osborne guilty of the lavender charge. Fallon maintained as much until the last. After a diligent inquiry into the man's life and into the case itself, I cannot share this belief. I am told that a biographer should not inject editorial opinions into a story, but the Baker on Fire Island wanted to know about this phase, and I think more of him and his cinnamon buns than I do of ten thousand technicians, smug-mugs and literary architects. . . . Only yesterday we rode through a gale to Lonleyville and the Baker said:

"I wish'd to God Admiral Dot was here to tell us about them elephants."

If, however, Mr. Osborne were given to secret practices of the sort alleged, I fall back immediately on the position taken by Captain Jeremiah Dorcas, skipper of *The Four Brothers* out of Halifax.

"And what happened?" the Baker asked.

"Wait until I get this fire-place going," I said, pouring kerosene on the damp wood. It took a long time. There were pale yellow flames. That was the sea-salt. There was a clear, jade flame licking through the yellow. That's where corroded brass was being heated. Rust-caked iron gives off a purple flame, and that's what brought about the whole discussion.

"For the love of God," the Baker said, "hurry up with the Captain's story."

"It was in a gale like this very one," I said, "when *The Four Brothers* finally stopped walking on her heels and the Old Man turned in for some well-earned rest. As was his custom, fair weather or foul, he did a bit of

reading from his favorite story—the account of the death of King Solomon. He was smoking a dingy briar pipe and was at the favorite part
of his favorite story, the portion that tells *how* the people of Solomon's
court tried to revive His Majesty."

"How did they?" the Baker asked.

"We'll get the book and read it after we've had our gin. . . . The captain looked up from his book as the second mate came in and stood with
his back against a bulkhead. The captain kept his place with the stub of
his left thumb. It had been bitten off in 1892 in a fight over a Lascar
woman.

" 'And if you please, sir,' the second mate says, says he, 'if you please,
Cap'n Dorcas.'

" 'Out with it, man,' the Cap'n says, keeping his thumb-stub glued to
the place in his book. 'Out with it.'

"The second mate was gasping and had a horrified look. 'It's the Chink
we shipped the last v'yage outa Rio.'

" 'Quit luffin', man,' the Cap'n says. 'Out with it —— —— ——
and say your piece, and —— —— —— afore I —— —— your
—— ——.'

" 'Well, Cap'n Dorcas,' the mate says, says he, 'you remember the pet
duck the Chink brung aboard?'

" 'Ay, —— —— —— and I do,' says Cap'n Dorcas.

" 'Well, Cap'n Dorcas,' the mate says, says he, turning as red as a fast
lady's hat, 'I just come from the fo-castle and —— —— —— ——
because I thought you ought to know.'

"The Old Man put down his briar and rubbed his nose with his thumb-
stub, losing the place in the book. 'Mr. Spencer,' the Cap'n says, says he,
calling the mate by name, 'Mr. Spencer, —— —— —— ——
—— in the Barbadoes in 1897, and —— —— —— his wife's
mother; but I —— —— —— —— began to fire on me with a pistol until
—— —— ——.'

"The mate didn't know what to say to this, and Cap'n Dorcas continued: 'And ever since that time, Mr. Spencer, I never have interfered in
a man's love affairs.'

" 'Ay, ay, sir,' says Mr. Spencer, saluting."

On October 20, 1926, the body of a huge man with iron-gray hair was
found. A difference of opinion arose as to where it was discovered. Some
said in a box-car. Others held that it had lain beside the railroad right-of-
way. Still others insisted that the body was picked up from a deserted
street in Auburn. The clothes were shabby and the face unshaven—indicating that the man had been wandering for a time, perhaps going incognito among the less prosperous citizens of the open road.

"Why!" the Coroner said, returning from his vacation and after the
body had remained unidentified for some time, "I'm damned if it ain't
Tom Osborne! He was the picture of health a month ago."

Osborne had died of a heart attack.

On October 23, 1926, services for Thomas Mott Osborne were held in the Unitarian Church in Auburn. There were many messages of condolence from prominent persons. The body was taken to Auburn Prison. There were 1,200 inmates in the line filing past the bier. One convict wrote a song, but it was not sung. It began:

"Tom Brown's body lies a-moldering in the grave,
But the Welfare League goes marching on."

Decision Lifting the Ban on *Ulysses*

Hon. John M. Woolsey

UNITED STATES DISTRICT COURT
SOUTHERN DISTRICT OF NEW YORK

United States of America, *Libelant* v. One Book called "Ulysses" Random House, Inc., *Claimant*	OPINION A.110-59

On cross motions for a decree in a libel of confiscation, supplemented by a stipulation—hereinafter described—brought by the United States against the book "Ulysses" by James Joyce, under Section 305 of the Tariff Act of 1930, Title 19 United States Code, Section 1305, on the ground that the book is obscene within the meaning of that Section, and, hence, is not importable into the United States, but is subject to seizure, forfeiture and confiscation and destruction.

United States Attorney—by Samuel C. Coleman, Esq., and Nicholas Atlas, Esq., of counsel—for the United States, in support of motion for a decree of forfeiture, and in opposition to motion for a decree dismissing the libel.

Messrs. Greenbaum, Wolff & Ernst,—by Morris L. Ernst, Esq., and Alexander Lindey, Esq., of counsel—attorneys for claimant Random House, Inc., in support of motion for a decree dismissing the libel, and in opposition to motion for a decree of forfeiture.

WOOLSEY, J:

The motion for a decree dismissing the libel herein is granted, and, consequently, of course, the Government's motion for a decree of forfeiture and destruction is denied.

Accordingly a decree dismissing the libel without costs may be entered herein.

I. The practice followed in this case is in accordance with the suggestion made by me in the case of *United States v. One Book Entitled "Contraception,"* 51 F. (2d) 525, and is as follows:

After issue was joined by the filing of the claimant's answer to the libel for forfeiture against "Ulysses", a stipulation was made between the United States Attorney's office and the attorneys for the claimant providing:

1. That the book "Ulysses" should be deemed to have been annexed to and to have become part of the libel just as if it had been incorporated in its entirety therein.

2. That the parties waived their right to a trial by jury.

3. That each party agreed to move for decree in its favor.

4. That on such cross motions the Court might decide all the questions of law and fact involved and render a general finding thereon.

5. That on the decision of such motions the decree of the Court might be entered as if it were a decree after trial.

It seems to me that a procedure of this kind is highly appropriate in libels for the confiscation of books such as this. It is an especially advantageous procedure in the instant case because on account of the length of "Ulysses" and the difficulty of reading it, a jury trial would have been an extremely unsatisfactory, if not an almost impossible, method of deal-with it.

II. I have read "Ulysses" once in its entirety and I have read those passages of which the Government particularly complains several times. In fact, for many weeks, my spare time has been devoted to the consideration of the decision which my duty would require me to make in this matter.

"Ulysses" is not an easy book to read or to understand. But there has been much written about it, and in order properly to approach the consideration of it it is advisable to read a number of other books which have now become its satellites. The study of "Ulysses" is, therefore, a heavy task.

III. The reputation of "Ulysses" in the literary world, however, warranted my taking such time as was necessary to enable me to satisfy myself as to the intent with which the book was written, for, of course, in any case where a book is claimed to be obscene it must first be determined, whether the intent with which is was written was what is called, according to the usual phrase, pornographic—that is, written for the purpose of exploiting obscenity.

If the conclusion is that the book is pornographic that is the end of the inquiry and forfeiture must follow.

But in "Ulysses", in spite of its unusual frankness, I do not detect anywhere the leer of the sensualist. I hold, therefore, that it is not pornographic.

IV. In writing "Ulysses", Joyce sought to make a serious experiment in a new, if not wholly novel, literary genre. He takes persons of the lower middle class living in Dublin in 1904 and seeks not only to describe what they did on a certain day early in June of that year as they went about the City bent on their usual occupations, but also to tell what many of them thought about the while.

Joyce has attempted—it seems to me, with astonishing success—to show how the screen of consciousness with its ever-shifting kaleidoscopic impressions carries, as it were on a plastic palimpsest, not only what is in the focus of each man's observation of the actual things about him, but also in a penumbral zone residua of past impressions, some recent and some drawn up by association from the domain of the subconscious. He shows how each of these impressions affects the life and behavior of the character which he is describing.

What he seeks to get is not unlike the result of a double or, if that is possible, a multiple exposure on a cinema film which would give a clear foreground with a background visible but somewhat blurred and out of focus in varying degrees.

To convey by words an effect which obviously lends itself more appropriately to a graphic technique, accounts, it seems to me, for much of the obscurity which meets a reader of "Ulysses". And it also explains another aspect of the book, which I have further to consider, namely, Joyce's sincerity and his honest effort to show exactly how the minds of his characters operate.

If Joyce did not attempt to be honest in developing the technique which he has adopted in "Ulysses" the result would be psychologically misleading and thus unfaithful to his chosen technique. Such an attitude would be artistically inexcusable.

It is because Joyce has been loyal to his technique and has not funked its necessary implications, but has honestly attempted to tell fully what his characters think about, that he has been the subject of so many attacks and that his purpose has been so often misunderstood and misrepresented. For his attempt sincerely and honestly to realize his objective has required him incidentally to use certain words which are generally considered dirty words and has led at times to what many think is a too poignant preoccupation with sex in the thoughts of his characters.

The words which are criticized as dirty are old Saxon words known to almost all men and, I venture, to many women, and are such words as would be naturally and habitually used, I believe, by the types of folk whose life, physical and mental, Joyce is seeking to describe. In respect of the recurrent emergence of the theme of sex in the minds of his characters, it must always be remembered that his locale was Celtic and his season Spring.

Whether or not one enjoys such a technique as Joyce uses is a matter of taste on which disagreement or argument is futile, but to subject that technique to the standards of some other technique seems to me to be little short of absurd.

Accordingly, I hold that "Ulysses" is a sincere and honest book and I think that the criticisms of it are entirely disposed of by its rationale.

V. Furthermore, "Ulysses" is an amazing *tour de force* when one considers the success which has been in the main achieved with such a difficult objective as Joyce set for himself. As I have stated, "Ulysses" is not an easy book to read. It is brilliant and dull, intelligible and obscure by turns. In many places it seems to me to be disgusting, but although it contains, as I have mentioned above, many words usually considered dirty, I have not found anything that I consider to be dirt for dirt's sake. Each word of the book contributes like a bit of mosaic to the detail of the picture which Joyce is seeking to construct for his readers.

If one does not wish to associate with such folk as Joyce describes, that is one's own choice. In order to avoid indirect contact with them one may not wish to read "Ulysses"; that is quite understandable. But when such a real artist in words, as Joyce undoubtedly is, seeks to draw a true picture of the lower middle class in a European city, ought it to be impossible for the American public legally to see that picture?

To answer this question it is not sufficient merely to find, as I have found above, that Joyce did not write "Ulysses" with what is commonly called pornographic intent, I must endeavor to apply a more objective standard to his book in order to determine its effect in the result, irrespective of the intent with which it was written.

VI. The statute under which the libel is filed only denounces, in so far as we are here concerned, the importation into the United States from any foreign country of "any obscene book." Section 305 of the Tariff Act of 1930, Title 19 United States Code, Section 1305. It does not marshal against books the spectrum of condemnatory adjectives found, commonly, in laws dealing with matters of this kind. I am, therefore, only required to determine whether "Ulysses" is obscene within the legal definition of that word.

The meaning of the word "obscene" as legally defined by the Courts is: tending to stir the sex impulses or to lead to sexually impure and lustful thoughts. *Dunlop* v. *United States,* 165 U. S. 486, 501; *United States* v.

One Book Entitled "Married Love," 48 F. (2d) 821, 824; *United States* v. *One Book Entitled "Contraception,"* 51 F. (2d) 525, 528; and compare *Dysart* v. *United States,* 272 U. S. 655, 657; *Swearingen* v. *United States,* 161 U. S. 446, 450; *United States* v. *Dennett,* 39 F. (2d) 564, 568 (C. C. A. 2); *People* v. *Wendling,* 258 N. Y. 451, 453.

Whether a particular book would tend to excite such impulses and thoughts must be tested by the court's opinion as to its effect on a person with average sex instincts—what the French would call *l'homme moyen sensuel*—who plays, in this branch of legal inquiry, the same role of hypothetical reagent as does the "reasonable man" in the law of torts and "the man learned in the art" on questions of invention in patent law.

The risk involved in the use of such a reagent arises from the inherent tendency of the trier of facts, however fair he may intend to be, to make his reagent too much subservient to his own idiosyncrasies. Here, I have attempted to avoid this, if possible, and to make my reagent herein more objective than he might otherwise be, by adopting the following course:

After I had made my decision in regard to the aspect of "Ulysses", now under consideration, I checked my impressions with two friends of mine who in my opinion answered to the above stated requirement for my reagent.

These literary assessors—as I might properly describe them—were called on separately, and neither knew that I was consulting the other. They are men whose opinion on literature and on life I value most highly. They had both read "Ulysses", and, of course, were wholly unconnected with this cause.

Without letting either of my assessors know what my decision was, I gave to each of them the legal definition of obscene and asked each whether in his opinion "Ulysses" was obscene within that definition.

I was interested to find that they both agreed with my opinion: that reading "Ulysses" in its entirety, as a book must be read on such a test as this, did not tend to excite sexual impulses or lustful thoughts but that its net effect on them was only that of a somewhat tragic and very powerful commentary on the inner lives of men and women.

It is only with the normal person that the law is concerned. Such a test as I have described, therefore, is the only proper test of obscenity in the case of a book like "Ulysses" which is a sincere and serious attempt to devise a new literary method for the observation and description of mankind.

I am quite aware that owing to some of its scenes "Ulysses" is a rather strong draught to ask some sensitive, though normal, persons to take. But my considered opinion, after long reflection, is that whilst in many places the effect of "Ulysses" on the reader undoubtedly is somewhat emetic, nowhere does it tend to be an aphrodisiac.

"Ulysses" may, therefore, be admitted into the United States.

JOHN M. WOOLSEY

UNITED STATES DISTRICT JUDGE

PART THREE

JUSTICE

Now the men we live with are not perfect and ideally wise, but men who do very well if there be found in them but the semblance of virtue.

CICERO, DE OFFICIIS, *i, 15 (c. 44 B.C.)*.

The Laws of Solon

Plutarch

SOON, HOWEVER, becoming sensible of the good that was done, they laid by their grudges, made a public sacrifice, calling it Seisacthea, and chose Solon to new-model and make laws for the commonwealth, giving him the entire power over everything, their magistrates, their assemblies, courts, and councils; that he should appoint the number, times of meeting, and what estate they must have that could be capable of these, and dissolve or continue any of the present constitution, according to his pleasure.

First, then, he repealed all Draco's laws, except those concerning homicide, because they were too severe, and the punishment too great; for death was appointed for almost all offences, insomuch that those that were convicted of idleness were to die, and those that stole a cabbage or an apple to suffer even as villains that committed sacrilege or murder. So that Demades, in after time, was thought to have said very happily, that Draco's laws were written not with ink but blood; and he himself, being once asked why he made death the punishment of most offences, replied, "Small ones deserve that, and I have no higher for the greater crimes."

Next, Solon, being willing to continue the magistracies in the hands of the rich men, and yet receive the people into the other part of the government, took an account of the citizen's estates, and those that were worth five hundred measures of fruit, dry and liquid, he placed in the first rank, calling them Pentacosiomedimni; those that could keep an horse, or were worth three hundred measures, were named Hippada Teluntes, and made the second class; the Zeugitae, that had two hundred measures, were in the third; and all the others were called Thetes, who were not admitted to any office, but could come to the assembly, and act as jurors; which at first seemed nothing, but afterwards was found an enormous privilege, as almost every matter of dispute came before them in this latter capacity. Even in the cases which he assigned to the archon's cognisance, he allowed an appeal to the courts. Besides, it is said that he was obscure and ambiguous in the wording of his laws, on purpose to increase the

From *Parallel Lives*.

honour of his courts; for since their differences could not be adjusted
by the letter, they would have to bring all their causes to the judges, who
thus were in a manner masters of the laws. Of this equalisation he himself
makes mention in this manner:—

> "Such power I gave the people as might do,
> Abridged not what they had, now lavished new,
> Those that were great in wealth and high in place
> My counsel likewise kept from all disgrace.
> Before them both I held my shield of might,
> And let not either touch the other's right."

And for the greater security of the weak commons, he gave general liberty
of indicting for an act of injury; if any one was beaten, maimed, or
suffered any violence, any man that would and was able might prosecute
the wrong-doer; intending by this to accustom the citizens, like members
of the same body, to resent and be sensible of one another's injuries. And
there is a saying of his agreeable to his law, for, being asked what city was
best modelled, "That," said he, "where those that are not injured try and
punish the unjust as much as those that are."

When he had constituted the Areopagus of those who had been yearly
archons, of which he himself was a member therefore, observing that the
people, now free from their debts, were unsettled and imperious, he
formed another council of four hundred, a hundred out of each of the
four tribes, which was to inspect all matters before they were pro-
pounded to the people, and to take care that nothing but what had
been first examined should be brought before the general assembly. The
upper council, or Areopagus, he made inspectors and keepers of the laws,
conceiving that the commonwealth, held by these two councils, like an-
chors, would be less liable to be tossed by tumults, and the people be more
quiet. Such is the general statement, that Solon instituted the Aeropagus;
which seems to be confirmed, because Draco makes no mention of the
Areopagites, but in all causes of blood refers to the Ephetae; yet Solon's
thirteenth table contains the eighth law set down in these very words:
"Whoever before Solon's archonship were disfranchised, let them be restored, except those that, being condemned by the Areopagus, Ephetae, or
in the Prytaneum by the kings, for homicide, murder, or designs against
the government, were in banishment when this law was made;" and
these words seem to show that the Areopagus existed before Solon's laws,
for who could be condemned by that council before his time, if he was
the first that instituted the court? unless, which is probable, there is some
ellipsis, or want of precision in the language, and it should run thus:—
"Those that are convicted of such offences as belong to the cognisance of
the Areopagites, Ephetae, or the Prytanes, when this law was made,"
shall remain still in disgrace, whilst others are restored; of this the
reader must judge.

Amongst his other laws, one is very peculiar and surprising, which disfranchises all who stand neuter in a sedition; for it seems he would not have any one remain insensible and regardless of the public good, and securing his private affairs, glory that he has no feeling of the distempers of his country; but at once join with the good party and those that have the right upon their side, assist and venture with them, rather than keep out of harm's way and watch who would get the better. It seems an absurd and foolish law which permits an heiress, if her lawful husband fail her, to take his nearest kinsman; yet some say this law was well contrived against those who, conscious of their own unfitness, yet, for the sake of the portion, would match with heiresses, and make use of law to put a violence upon nature; for now, since she can quit him for whom she pleases, they would either abstain from such marriages, or continue them with disgrace, and suffer for their covetousness and designed affront; it is well done, moreover, to confine her to her husband's nearest kinsman, that the children may be of the same family. Agreeable to this is the law that the bride and bridegroom shall be shut into a chamber, and eat a quince together; and that the husband of an heiress shall consort with her thrice a month; for though there be no children, yet it is an honour and due affection which an husband ought to pay to a virtuous, chaste wife; it takes off all petty differences, and will not permit their little quarrels to proceed to a rupture.

In all other marriages he forbade dowries to be given; the wife was to have three suits of clothes, a little inconsiderable household stuff, and that was all; for he would not have marriages contracted for gain or an estate, but for pure love, kind affection, and birth of children. When the mother of Dionysius desired him to marry her to one of his citizens, "Indeed," said he, "by my tyranny I have broken my country's laws, but cannot put a violence upon those of nature by an unseasonable marriage." Such disorder is never to be suffered in a commonwealth, nor such unseasonable and unloving and unperforming marriages, which attain no due end or fruit; any provident governor or lawgiver might say to an old man that takes a young wife what is said to Philoctetes in the tragedy—

"Truly, in a fit state thou to marry!"

and if he find a young man, with a rich and elderly wife, growing fat in his place, like the partridges, remove him to a young woman of proper age. And of this enough.

Another commendable law of Solon's is that which forbids men to speak evil of the dead; for it is pious to think the deceased sacred, and just, not to meddle with those that are gone, and politic, to prevent the perpetuity of discord. He likewise forbade them to speak evil of the living in the temples, the courts of justice, the public offices, or at the games, or else to pay three drachmas to the person, and two to the public. For never to be able to control passion shows a weak nature and ill-breeding; and always to moderate it is very hard, and to some impossible. And laws must look to possibilities, if the maker designs to punish few in order to their amendment, and not many to no purpose.

He is likewise much commended for his law concerning wills; for before him none could be made, but all the wealth and estate of the deceased belonged to his family; but he by permitting them, if they had no children, to bestow it on whom they pleased, showed that he esteemed friendship a stronger tie than kindred, and affection than necessity; and made every man's estate truly his own. Yet he allowed not all sorts of legacies, but those only which were not extorted by the frenzy of a disease, charms, imprisonment, force, or the persuasions of a wife; with good reason thinking that being seduced into wrong was as bad as being forced, and that between deceit and necessity, flattery and compulsion, there was little difference, since both may equally suspend the exercise of reason.

He regulated the walks, feasts, and mourning of the women, and took away everything that was either unbecoming or immodest; when they walked abroad, no more than three articles of dress were allowed them; an obol's worth of meat and drink; and no basket above a cubit high; and at night they were not to go about unless in a chariot with a torch before them. Mourners tearing themselves to raise pity, and set wailings, and at one man's funeral to lament for another, he forbade. To offer an ox at the grave was not permitted, nor to bury above three pieces of dress with the body, or visit the tombs of any besides their own family, unless at the very funeral; most of which are likewise forbidden by our laws, but this is further added in ours, that those that are convicted of extravagance in their mournings are to be punished as soft and effeminate by the censors of women.

Observing the city to be filled with persons that flocked from all parts into Attica for security of living, and that most of the country was barren and unfruitful, and that traders at sea import nothing to those that could give them nothing in exchange, he turned his citizens to trade, and made a law that no son be obliged to relieve a father who had not bred him up to any calling. It is true, Lycurgus, having a city free from all strangers, and land, according to Euripides—

"Large for large hosts, for twice their number much,"

and, above all, an abundance of labourers about Sparta, who should not be left idle, but he kept down with continual toil and work, did well to take off his citizens from laborious and mechanical occupations, and keep them to their arms, and teach them only the art of war. But Solon, fitting his laws to the state of things, and not making things to suit his laws, and finding the ground scarce rich enough to maintain the husbandmen, and altogether incapable of feeding an unoccupied and leisured multitude, brought trades into credit, and ordered the Areopagites to examine how every man got his living, and chastise the idle. But that law was yet more rigid which, as Heraclides Ponticus delivers, declared the sons of unmarried mothers not obliged to relieve their fathers; for he that avoids the honourable form of union shows that he does not take a woman for children, but for pleasure, and thus gets his just reward, and has taken away from himself every title to upbraid his children, to whom he has made their very birth a scandal and reproach.

Solon's laws in general about women are his strangest; for he permitted any one to kill an adulterer that found him in the act; but if any one forced a free woman, a hundred drachmas was the fine; if he enticed her, twenty; except those that sell themselves openly, that is, harlots, who go openly to those that hire them. He made it unlawful to sell a daughter or a sister, unless, being yet unmarried, she was found wanton. Now it is irrational to punish the same crime sometimes very severely and without remorse, and sometimes very lightly, and as it were in sport, with a trivial fine; unless there being little money then in Athens, scarcity made those mulcts the more grievous punishment. In the valuation for sacrifices, a sheep and a bushel were both estimated at a drachma; the victor in the Isthmian games was to have for reward an hundred drachmas; the conqueror in the Olympian, five hundred; he that brought a wolf, five drachmas; for a whelp, one; the former sum, as Demetrius the Phalerian asserts, was the value of an ox, the latter, of a sheep. The prices which Solon, in his sixteenth table, sets on choice victims, were naturally far greater; yet they, too, are very low in comparison of the present. The Athenians were, from the beginning, great enemies to wolves, their fields being better for pasture than corn. Some affirm their tribes did not take their names from the sons of Ion, but from the different sorts of occupation that they followed; the soldiers were called Hoplitæ, the craftsmen Ergades, and, of the remaining two, the farmers Gedeontes, and the shepherds and graziers Ægicores.

Since the country has but few rivers, lakes, or large springs, and many used wells which they had dug, there was a law made, that, where there was a public well within a *hippicon,* that is, four furlongs, all should draw at that; but when it was farther off, they should try and procure a well of their own; and if they had dug ten fathoms deep and could find no water, they had liberty to fetch a pitcherful of four gallons and a half in a day from their neighbours'; for he thought it prudent to make provision against want, but not to supply laziness. He showed skill in his orders about planting, for any one that would plant another tree was not to set it within five feet of his neighbour's field; but if a fig or an olive not within nine; for their roots spread farther, nor can they be planted near all sorts of trees without damage, for they draw away the nourishment, and in some cases are noxious by their effluvia. He that would dig a pit or a ditch was to dig it at the distance of its own depth from his neighbour's ground; and he that would raise stocks of bees was not to place them within three hundred feet of those which another had already raised.

He permitted only oil to be exported, and those that exported any other fruit, the archon was solemnly to curse, or else pay an hundred drachmas himself; and this law was written in his first table, and, therefore, let none think it incredible, as some affirm, that the exportation of figs was once unlawful, and the informer against the delinquents called a sycophant. He made a law, also, concerning hurts and injuries from beasts, in which he commands the master of any dog that bit a man to deliver him up with a log about his neck, four and a half feet long; a happy device for men's security. The law concerning naturalising strangers is of doubtful character; he permitted only those to be made free of Athens who were in perpetual exile from their own country, or came with their whole family to trade there; this he did, not to discourage strangers, but rather to invite them to a permanent participation in the privileges of the government; and, besides, he thought those would prove the more faithful citizens who had been forced from their own country, or voluntarily forsook it. The law of public entertainment (*parasitein* is his name for it) is also peculiarly Solon's; for if any man came often, or if he that was invited refused, they were punished, for he concluded that one was greedy, the other a contemner of the state.

All his laws he established for an hundred years, and wrote them on wooden tables or rollers, named axones, which might be turned round in oblong cases; some of their relics were in my time still to be seen in the Prytaneum, or common hall at Athens. These, as Aristotle states, were called cyrbes, and there is a passage of Cratinus the comedian—

"By Solon, and by Draco, if you please,
Whose Cyrbes make the fires that parch our peas."

But some say those are properly cyrbes, which contain laws concerning sacrifices and the rites of religion, and all the others axones. The council all jointly swore to confirm the laws, and every one of the Thesmothetæ vowed for himself at the stone on the market-place, that if he broke any of the statutes, he would dedicate a golden statue, as big as himself, at Delphi.

Observing the irregularity of the months, and that the moon does not always rise and set with the sun, but often in the same day overtakes and gets before him, he ordered the day should be named the Old and New, attributing that part of it which was before the conjunction to the old moon, and the rest of the new, he being the first, it seems, that understood that verse of Homer—

"The end and the beginning of the month,"—

and the following day he called the new moon. After the twentieth he did not count by addition, but, like the moon itself in its wane, by subtraction; thus up to the thirtieth.

Now when these laws were enacted, and some came to Solon every day, to commend or dispraise them, and to advise, if possible, to leave out or put in something, and many criticised and desired him to explain, and tell the meaning of such and such a passage, he, knowing that to do it was useless, and not to do it would get him ill-will, and desirous to bring himself out of all straits, and to escape all displeasure and exceptions, it being a hard thing, as he himself says—

> "In great affairs to satisfy all sides,"

as an excuse for travelling, bought a trading vessel, and, having leave for ten years' absence, departed, hoping that by that time his laws would have become familiar.

Emperor Claudius as Magistrate

Robert Graves

I soon found myself popular. Among the edicts of Caligula that I annulled were those concerned with his own religious cult, and his treason edicts, and those removing certain privileges of the Senate and the People. I decreed that the word "treason" was henceforth meaningless. Not only would written treason not be held as a criminal offence, but neither would overt acts; in this I was more liberal even than Augustus. My decree opened the prison gates for hundreds of citizens of all degrees. But on Messalina's advice I kept everybody under open arrest until I had satisfied myself that the charge of treason did not include other crimes of a more felonious nature. For the charge of treason was often only a formality of arrest: the crime might be murder, forgery or any other offence. These cases were not ones that I could leave for settlement to the ordinary magistrates. I felt bound to investigate them myself. I went every day to the Market Place and there, in front of the temple of Hercules, tried cases all morning long with a bench of senator colleagues. No Emperor had admitted colleagues to his tribunal for a number of years—not since Tiberius went to Capri. I also paid surprise visits to other courts and always took my place there on the bench of advisers to the presiding judge. My knowledge of legal precedents was very faulty. I had never taken the ordinary course of honours which every Roman noble-man went through, gradually rising in rank from third-class magistrate to Consul, with intervals of military service abroad; and except for the last three years I had lived out of Rome a great deal and very rarely visited the law courts. So I had to rely on my native wit rather than on legal pre-cedent and to struggle hard the whole time against the tricks of lawyers who, trading on my ignorance, tried to entangle me in their legal webs.

Every day as I came into the Market Place from the Palace I used to pass a stuccoed building across the face of which was tarred in enormous letters:

FORENSIC AND LEGAL INSTITUTE Founded and Directed by the most Learned and Eloquent Orator and Jurist Telegonius Macarius of This City and of the City of Athens.

Underneath this on a huge square tablet appeared the following adver-tisement:

Telegonius gives instruction and advice to all who have become involved in financial or personal difficulties ne-cessitating their appearance in Civil or Criminal courts; and has a positively encyclopædic knowledge of all Ro-man edicts, statutes, decrees, proclamations, judicial de-cisions, etcetera, past and present, operative, dormant, or inoperative. At half an hour's notice the most learned and eloquent Telegonius can supply his clients with precise and legally incontrovertible opinions on any judicial matter under the sun that they care to present to him and his staff of highly trained clerks. Not only Roman Law, but Greek Law, Egyptian Law, Jewish Law, Arme-nian, Moroccan or Parthian Law—Telegonius has it all at his fingers' ends. The imcomparable Telegonius, not con-tent with dispensing the raw material of Law, dispenses also the finished product: namely, beautifully contrived forensic presentations of the same complete with appro-priate tones and gestures. Personal appeals to the jury a specialty. Handbook of brilliant rhetorical figures and tropes, suitable for any case, to be had on request. No client of Telegonius has ever been known to suffer an adverse verdict in any court—unless his opponent has by chance also drunk from the same fountain of oratorical wisdom and eloquence. A few vacancies for pupils.

"The tongue is mightier than the blade."

EURIPIDES.

I gradually came to memorize this tablet by seeing it so often, and now when the counsel for the defence or prosecution used to appeal to me with expressions like, "Surely, Cæsar, you are aware of the fifteenth sub-section of the fourth article of Marcus Porcius Cato's Sumptuary Law published in the year that So-and-So and So-and-So were Consuls?" or, "You will agree with me, Cæsar, that in the island of Andros, of which my client is a native, great latitude is shown to forgers if it can be proved that they were influenced by regard for the well-being of their aged parents rather than by hope of personal gain," or similar foolish talk, I would just smile back and reply: "You are mistaken, Sir: I am quite unaware of this. I am not the most learned and eloquent Telegonius, who can supply precise and legally incontrovertible opinions on any judicial matter under the sun. I am merely the Judge of this Court. Proceed, and don't waste my time." If they tried to badger me further I would say: "It's no use. In the first place, if I don't want to answer, I won't answer. You can't make me. I'm a free man, aren't I—in fact one of the freest in Rome? In the second place, if I do answer now, by Heaven you'll wish that I hadn't."

Telegonius, by the way, seemed to be doing quite a thriving business and I came to resent his activities greatly. I detest forensic oratory. If a man cannot state his case in a brief and lucid way, bringing the necessary witnesses and abstaining from irrelevant talk about the nobility of his ancestry, the number of impoverished relatives dependent on him, the clemency and wisdom of the judge, the harsh tricks that Fate plays, the mutability of human fortune and all that stale silly bag of tricks, he deserves the extreme penalty of the law for his dishonesty, pretension and his waste of public time. I sent Polybius to buy Telegonius's hand-book as advertised; and studied it. A few days later I was visiting a lower court when a defendant launched out on one of the brilliant rhetorical figures recommended by Telegonius. I asked the judge to allow me to intervene. He granted me this, and I said to the orator: "Stop, Sir, this will never do. You have made a mistake in your recitation-lesson. Telegonius's figure was as follows—let me see—*'If accused of theft'*—yes, here we are." I produced the handbook:

"Hearing of my neighbour's loss, and filled with pity for him, through what woods and vales, over what windy and inhospitable mountains, in what damp and gloomy caverns did I not search for that lost sheep (or lost cow—lost horse—lost mule) until at last, extraordinary to relate, returning home, weary, footsore and disappointed, I found it (*here shade eyes with hand and look startled*): and where but in my own sheepcote (or cowshed—stable—barn) where it had perversely strayed during my absence!"

"Sir," I said, "you put groves where the vales should have been and you left out 'footsore' and the telling adverb 'perversely.' You didn't look startled, either, at the word 'found,' only stupid. The judgment goes against you. Blame yourself, not Telegonius."

Because I devoted myself to my judicial duties for so many hours every day, religious holidays not excepted; and even ran the summer and winter law-terms together, so that the dispensation of justice should be continuous and no accused person be forced to spend longer than a few days in prison—because of all this, I expected more considerate treatment from lawyers, court-officials and witnesses than I got. I made it quite plain that the non-appearance or late appearance in court of one of the principal parties in any suit could prejudice me in favour of his opponent. I tried to get through cases as quickly as possible and won (most unfairly) a reputation for sentencing prisoners without giving them a proper opportunity for defence. If a man was accused of a crime and I asked him straight out, "Is this accusation substantially true?" and he shuffled and said: "Let me explain, Cæsar. I am not exactly guilty, but . . . ," I would cut him short. I would pronounce, "Fined a thousand gold pieces" or "Banished to the Island of Sardinia" or just "Death," and then turn to the beadle: "Next case, please." The man and his lawyer were naturally vexed that they had not been able to charm me with their extenuating-circumstance pleas. There was one case in which the defendant claimed to be a Roman citizen and so appeared in a gown, but the plaintiff's lawyer objected and said that he was really a foreigner and should be wearing a cloak. It made no difference to this particular case whether or not he was a Roman citizen, so I silenced the lawyers by ordering the man to wear a cloak during all speeches for the prosecution and a gown during all speeches for the defence. The lawyers did not like me for that and told each other that I was ridiculing justice. Perhaps I was. On the whole they treated me very badly. Some mornings if I had been unable to settle as many cases as I had hoped and it was long past the time for my dinner they would make quite a disturbance when I adjourned proceedings until the next day. They would call to me quite rudely to come back and not keep honest citizens waiting for justice, and would even catch me by the gown or foot as if forcibly to prevent me from leaving the court.

I did not discourage familiarity, provided that it was not offensive, and found that an easy atmosphere in court encouraged witnesses to give proper evidence. If anyone answered me back with spirit when I had expressed an ill-advised opinion I never took it ill. On one occasion the counsel for the defence explained that his client, a man of sixty-five, had recently married. His wife was a witness in the case, and was quite a young woman. I remarked that the marriage was illegal. According to the Poppæan-Papian Law (with which I happened to be familiar) a man over sixty was not allowed to marry a woman under fifty: the legal assumption was that a man over sixty is unfit for parentage. I quoted the Greek epigram:

> "The old man weds, for Nature's rule he scorns—
> 'Father a weakly stock, or else wear horns.' "

The lawyer considered for a few moments and then extemporized:

> "And that old man, yourself, is a plain fool
> To foist on Nature this unnatural rule.
> A sturdy old man fathers sturdy sons;
> A weakly young man fathers weakly ones."

This was so just a point and so neatly made that I forgave the poet-lawyer for calling me a plain fool, and at the next meeting of the Senate amended the Poppæan-Papian Law accordingly. The severest anger to which I ever remember having given way in court was roused by a court official whose duty it was to summon witnesses and see that they arrived punctually. I had given a fraud case a hearing but had been forced to adjourn it for lack of evidence, the principal witness having fled to Africa to avoid being charged with complicity in the fraud. When the case came on again I called for this witness; but he was not in court. I asked the court-official whether this man had been duly subpoenaed to attend.

"Oh yes, indeed, Cæsar."

"Then why is he not here?"

"He is unfortunately prevented from attending."

"There is *no* excuse for non-attendance, except illness so serious that he cannot be carried into court without danger to his life."

"I quite agree, Cæsar. No, the witness is not ill now. He has been very ill, I understand. But that is all over."

"What was wrong with him?"

"He was mauled by a lion, I am informed, and afterwards gangrene set in."

"It's a wonder he recovered," I said.

"He didn't," sniggered the fellow. "He's dead. I think that death can stand as an excuse for non-attendance." Everyone laughed.

I was so furious that I flung my writing-tablet at him, took away his citizenship and banished him to Africa. "Go and hunt lions," I shouted, "and I hope they maul you properly, and I hope gangrene sets in." However, six months later I pardoned him and reinstated him in his position. He made no more jokes at my expense.

It is only fair at this point to mention the severest anger that was ever directed in court against myself. A young nobleman was charged with unnatural acts against women. The real complainants were the Guild of Prostitutes, an unofficial but well-managed organization which protected its members pretty effectively from abuse by cheats or ruffians. The prostitutes could not very well bring a charge against the nobleman themselves, so they went to a man who had been done a bad turn by him and wanted revenge—prostitutes know everything—and offered to give evidence if he brought the charge: a prostitute was a capable witness in a lawcourt. Before the case came on, I sent a message to my friend Calpurnia, the pretty young prostitute who had lived with me before I married Messalina and had been so tender and faithful to me in my misfortunes: I asked her to interview the women who were to give evidence and privately find out whether the nobleman had really abused them in the manner alleged, or whether they had been bribed by the person who was bringing the charge. Calpurnia sent me word a day or two later that the nobleman had really behaved in a very brutal and disgusting way, and that the women who had complained to the Guild were decent girls, one of whom was a personal friend of hers.

I tried the case, took sworn evidence (overruling the objection of the defending lawyer that prostitutes' oaths were both proverbially and actually worth nothing) and had this put in writing by the court-recorder. When one girl repeated some very filthy and vulgar remark that the accused had made to her, the recorder asked, "Shall I put that down, Cæsar?" and I answered, "Why not?" The young nobleman was so angry that he did just what I had done to the court-official who teased me— he threw his writing-tablet at my head. But whereas I had missed my aim, his aim was true. The sharp edge of the tablet gashed my cheek and drew blood. But all I said was, "I am glad to see, my Lord, that you still have some shame left." I found him guilty and put a black mark against his name in the roll, which disqualified him from becoming a candidate for public office. But he was a relative by marriage of Asiaticus, who asked me some months later to scratch out the black mark, because his young relative had lately reformed his ways: "I'll scratch it out, to please you," I answered, "but it will still show." Asiaticus later repeated this remark of mine to his friends as a proof of my stupidity. He could not understand, I suppose, that a reputation was, as my mother used to say, like an earthenware plate. "The plate is cracked; the reputation is damaged by a criminal sentence. The plate is then mended with rivets and becomes 'as good as new'; the reputation is mended by an official pardon. A mended plate or a mended reputation is better than a cracked plate or a damaged reputation. But a plate that has never been cracked and a reputation that has never been damaged are better still."

A schoolmaster always appears a very queer fellow to his pupils. He has certain stock-phrases which they come to notice and giggle at whenever he uses them. Everyone in the world has stock-phrases or tricks of speech, but unless he is in a position of authority—as a schoolmaster, or an army captain or a judge—nobody notices them particularly. Nobody noticed them in my case until I became Emperor, but then of course they became world-famous. I had only to remark in court, "No malice or favour whatsoever" or (turning to my legal secretary after summing-up a case), "That's right, isn't it?" or "When once my mind is made up, the thing is fixed with a nail," or quote the old tag:

> "As the rascal did he must
> Himself be done by. And that's just."

or utter the family oath, "Ten thousand furies and serpents!"—and a great roar of laughter would go up about me as though I had let fall either the most absurd solecism imaginable or the most exquisitely witty epigram.

In the course of my first year in the courts I must have made hundreds of ridiculous mistakes, but I did get the cases settled and sometimes surprised myself by my brilliance. There was one case, I remember, where one of the witnesses for the defence, a woman, denied any relationship with the accused man, who was alleged by the prosecution to be really her son. When I told her that I would take her word for it and that in my quality as High Pontiff I would immediately join her and him in marriage she was so frightened by the prospect of having incest forced upon her that she pleaded guilty of perjury. She said she had concealed her relationship in order to seem an impartial witness. That gave me a great reputation, which I lost almost at once in a case where the treason charge covered one of forgery. The prisoner was a freedman of one of Caligula's freedmen, and there were no extenuating circumstances to his crime. He had forged his master's will just before his death—whether he was responsible for the death could not be proved—and had left his mistress and her children completely destitute. I grew very angry with this man as I heard his story unfolded and determined to inflict the maximum penalty. The defence was very weak—no denial of the charge, only a stream of Telegonian irrelevancies. It was long past my dinner-time and I had been sitting in judgment solidly for six hours. A delicious whiff of cooking came floating into my nostrils from the dining-chamber of the Priests of Mars near by. They eat better than any other priestly fraternity: Mars never lacks for sacrificial victims. I felt faint with hunger. I said to the senior of the magistrates who were sitting with me, "Please take over this case from me and impose the maximum penalty, unless the defence has any better evidence to offer than has yet been produced."

"Do you really mean the maximum penalty?" he asked.

"Yes, indeed, whatever it may be. The man deserves no mercy."

"Your orders shall be obeyed, Cæsar," he replied.

So my chair was brought and I joined the priests at their dinner. When I returned that afternoon I found that the accused man's hands had been chopped off and hung around his neck. That was a punishment ordained for forgery by Caligula and had not yet been removed from the penal code. Everyone considered that I had acted most cruelly, for the judge had told the Court that it was my sentence, not his own. It was hardly my fault, though. . . .

I limited barristers' fees to a hundred gold pieces a case. This limitation was directed against men like Suilius, Asiaticus's prosecutor, who could sway a jury to convict or acquit as surely as a farmer drives his pigs to market. Suilius would accept any brief, however desperate, so long as he got his whole fee: which was four thousand a case. And it was the impressiveness of the fee as much as the assurance and eloquence with which he addressed the court that influenced the jury. Occasionally, of course, even Suilius could not hope to pull a case off, because his client's guilt was too clear to be concealed; but so as not to lose his credit with the court, which he would need in future cases where there was at least a fighting chance, he as good as directed the jury to decide against his client. There was a scandal about this; a rich knight accused of robbing the widow of one of his freedmen had paid Suilius his usual fee and had then been betrayed by him in this way. He went to Suilius and asked for a return of his four thousand gold pieces. Suilius said that he he had done his best and regretted he could not pay back the money—that would be a dangerous precedent. The knight committed suicide on Suilius's doorstep.

By thus reducing the barristers' fees, which in Republican Rome had been pronounced illegal, I damaged their prestige with the juries, who were thereafter more inclined to give verdicts corresponding with the facts of the case. I waged a sort of war with the barristers. Often when I was about to judge a case I used to warn the court with a smile: "I am an old man, and my patience is easily tried. My verdict will probably go to the side that presents its evidence in the briefest, frankest and most lucid manner, even if it is somewhat incriminating, rather than to the side that spoils a good case by putting up an inappropriately brilliant dramatic performance." And I would quote Homer:

"Yea, when men speak, that man I most detest
Who locks the verity within his breast."

I encouraged the appearance of a new sort of advocate, men without either eloquence or great legal expertness, but with common sense, clear voices and a talent for reducing cases to their simplest elements. The best of these was called Agatho. I always gave him the benefit of the doubt when he pleaded a case before me in his pleasant, quick, precise way, in order to encourage others to emulate him.

The Forensic and Legal Institute of Telegonius, "that most learned and eloquent orator and jurist," was closed down about three years ago. It happened as folows. Telegonius, fat, bustling and crop-haired, appeared one day in the Court of Appeal where I was presiding, and conducted a case of his own. He had been ordered by a magistrate to pay a heavy fine, on the ground that he had incited one of his slaves to kill a valuable slave of Vitellius's, in a dispute. It appears that Telegonius's slave, in a barber's shop, had put on insufferable airs as a lawyer and orator. A dispute started between this fellow and Vitellius's slave, who was waiting his turn to be shaved and was known as the best cook (except mine) in all Rome, and worth at the very least ten thousand gold pieces. Telegonius's slave, with offensive eloquence, contrasted the artistic importance of oratory and cookery. Vitellius's cook was not quarrelsome but made a few dispassionate statements of fact, such as that no proper comparison could be drawn between domestic practitioners of splendid arts and splendid practitioners of domestic arts; that he expected, if not deference, at least politeness from slaves of less importance than himself; and that he was worth at least a hundred times more than his opponent. The orator, enraged by the sympathy the cook got from the other customers, snatched the razor from the barber's hand and cut the cook's throat with it, crying: "I'll teach you to argue with one of Telegonius's men." Telegonius had therefore been fined the full value of the murdered cook, on the ground that his slave's violence was due to an obsession of argumental infallibility, inculcated by the Institute in all its employees. Telegonius now appealed on the ground that the slave had not been incited to murder by violence, for the very motto of the Institute was: *"The tongue is mightier than the blade,"* which constituted a direct injunction to keep to that weapon in any dispute. He also pleaded that it had been a very hot day, that the slave had been subjected to a gross insult by the suggestion that he was not worth more than a miserable hundred gold pieces—the lowest value that could be put upon his services as a trained clerk would be fifty gold pieces annually—and that therefore the only fair view could be that the cook had invited death by provocative behaviour.

Vitellius appeared as a witness. "Cæsar," he said, "I see it this way. This Telegonius's slave has killed my head-cook, a gentle, dignified person, and a perfect artist in his way, as you will yourself agree, having often highly praised his sauces and cakes. It will cost me at least ten thousand gold pieces to replace him and even then, you may be sure, I'll never get anyone half so good. His murderer used phrases, in praise of oratory and in dispraise of cookery, that have been proved to occur, word for word, in Telegonius's own handbooks; and it has been further proved that in the same handbooks, in the sections devoted to 'Liberty,' many violent passages occur which seek to justify a person in resorting to armed force when arguments and reason fail."

Telegonius cross-examined Vitellius, and I must admit that he was scoring heavily when a chance visitor to the court sprang a surprise. It was Alexander the Alabarch, who happened to be in Rome and had strolled into court for amusement. He passed me up a note:

"The person who calls himself Telegonius of Athens and Rome is a runaway slave of mine named Joannes, born at Alexandria in my own household, of a Syrian mother. I lost him twenty-five years ago. You will find the letter A, within a circle, pricked on his left hip, which is my household brand.

"Signed: ALEXANDER, ALABARCH."

I stopped the case while Telegonius was taken outside by my yeomen and identified as indeed the Alabarch's property. Imagine, he had been masquerading as a Roman citizen for nearly twenty years! His entire property should have gone to the State, except for the ten thousand gold pieces which had been awarded to Vitellius, but I let the Alabarch keep half of it. In return the Alabarch made me a present of Telegonius, whom I handed over to Narcissus for disposal: Narcissus set him to work at the useful, if humble, task of keeping court-records.

This, then, was the sort of way I governed. And I widely extended the Roman citizenship, intending that no province whose inhabitants were loyal, orderly and prosperous should long remain inferior in civic status to Rome and the rest of Italy.

A Labor Dispute

Milton Steinberg

T HE INCIDENT at Tiberias began innocuously enough with Elisha's receipt of a communication from Gamliel.

Rabbi Tarfon, the messenger informed him, was ill and could not fulfill his engagement to attend the forthcoming district assizes. Since the court was to be under lay auspices, the bench consisting of two unordained scholars and one presiding rabbi, the presence of some sage was imperative. Would Rabbi Elisha be so kind as to give his services in his colleague's place?

Without the least hesitation Elisha accepted the call. The year since his ordination had been an unbroken round of assignments, judicial and academic. This special request was so much of a piece with a familiar routine that it never occurred to him to inquire the identity of the lay judges nor the nature of the business with which they were to deal.

Only when he rode into Tiberias the next morning did Elisha receive the first intimation that inadvertently he had involved himself in a tangled situation. The streets seethed with people. Roman soldiers patrolled the marketplace and a restless assembly stood before the courthouse.

As he entered the building. Elisha came upon one of his disciples loitering in the doorway.

"Why all the excitement?" he asked curiously.

"Master," the young man replied, amazed, "haven't you heard? Two days ago the laborers of Benjamin, the linen-weaver, asked for higher wages and, when he refused, quit their work. Now he wants the court to compel them to return. What's more, he is suing them for damages. It seems that they left flax in the vats. He is inside waiting for the judges. And he has been swearing great oaths that if he cannot get justice here, he will go to the Roman courts for it."

"But why are the soldiers on the streets?"

"That's his work too. He claims that he has been threatened with violence, that his workshop may be attacked. A lie, Master, I'm sure. You know those men. Do you believe . . ."

"Hush," Elisha shut him off. "The case is still to be tried."

At the dais Elisha found one of his colleagues, Jonah the merchant, a venerable old man greatly respected by the townspeople for his piety and learning. They were exchanging greetings when he sensed that a third person had joined them. Turning about, he discovered Shraga the Levite. Both men were taken aback. For a moment they stared at each other.

"I thought when I accepted the assignment," Shraga began tentatively, "that Rabbi Tarfon was to preside. . . ."

As he spoke, he drew from his wallet a parchment sheet splotched with a great official seal.

But Elisha, who had recovered his composure, waved the credential aside.

"Welcome," he said politely.

After an awkward interval in which no one said anything, the three men took their places.

The preliminary rituals were performed, the first unimportant cases on the docket heard and decided with every appearance of deliberateness. But the judges like the spectators were eager for the airing of the dispute that had disturbed the entire community. And if there was no untoward haste, the court proceeded with dispatch. Meantime, Elisha and Shraga addressed each other only when necessary and then with meticulous courtesy. Of the latent tension between them neither gave overt sign.

It was shortly before noon that the marshal announced the case of Benjamin the linen-weaver against his laborers. A stir of suppressed excitement passed through the spectators. The plaintiff, a portly, ruddy-faced man, came forward, exuding an air of prosperity and self-importance. The half-dozen defendants, shabbily dressed, pale from their habitual confinement indoors but determined in manner, collected themselves at the other end of the dais.

Without waiting for an invitation, Benjamin stated his complaint, relating with blustering impatience the story which Elisha had already heard.

"But we had to quit, Masters," one of the defendants said resolutely when the weaver was done. "You know what corn prices have been of late. That man must work to live was God's ordinance to Adam. But where is it enjoined that one must labor to go hungry?"

"Am I responsible for the fact that the grain crop failed last year?" Benjamin retorted angrily. "Is it my fault that bread has become so expensive? Or do I control the linen market? The pagan weavers use slave labor. If I am to pay the wages these fools demand, I shall have no work for them at all. And then they will starve altogether."

The laborers looked at him contemptuously.

"That's not so, Masters," one of them denied. "He makes a great profit. He could well afford . . ."

"That," Elisha interrupted, "is totally irrelevant. What is more, if you were determined to quit work, why did you wait until your stoppage was certain to ruin an expensive consignment of flax?"

"But, Master," the workers protested in chorus, "that was our only course."

"Whenever we broached the question he refused to talk to us."

"We thought we could compel him to deal with us."

"Is my workshop an academy," Benjamin roared, "that I should engage in conferences? I hire men to work. If they do not like the wages I pay, let them go elsewhere."

"Exactly," one of the laborers crowed. "Then why have you hailed us to court?"

A tumult broke out at the dais and spread through the courtroom. Only after administering a sharp reproof to litigants and spectators alike did Elisha restore order.

By then it was well past noon and, since the case for both sides had been set forth, Elisha declared a recess.

Over a simple luncheon, served by the marshal in a chamber back of the courtroom, the judges considered the case.

On one point they agreed instantly: Benjamin's weavers had acted within their rights. "Unto Me are the children of Israel servants," Scripture said. From this statement, the Tradition had drawn the deductions: "No Israelite may be coerced into working for another" and, as a further inference, "The laborer shall be free to quit even at high noon."

With authoritative, unequivocal principles to guide them, the three men voted unanimously and unhesitatingly to deny Benjamin's petition that his men be ordered back to his factory. But when they had finished polling one another on the second issue, whether the weaver was entitled to compensation, Elisha smiled quizzically. For he, the patrician employer, had balloted for the laborers, as had Jonah, the prosperous merchant, while Shraga, the penniless plebeian, notoriously resentful of men of wealth, had sided with Benjamin.

"The influence of your teachers on you, gentlemen," Jonah chuckled, alluding to Joshua's liberalism and Eliezer's conservatism.

Perplexed by the paradoxical turn of events, Elisha turned to Shraga for an explanation.

"Perhaps," he suggested affably, "you will interpret your position. Here we are all agreed that the right of a laborer to quit work is unrestricted. Now every stoppage involves some injury to the employer. If then, employees can be held liable for restitution, their liberty of action is limited in effect. In fact, under certain circumstances it is annulled altogether."

For a long time Shraga did not reply. He sat arranging the earthenware dishes on the table into a symmetrical design. But his hands were unsteady and his lowered face very pale.

"And the public welfare?" he muttered at last, without raising his head.

"Public welfare?" Elisha echoed wonderingly. "What Jonah and I are doing is in the best interests of our people. Is it not the central motif of all our law—yes, and its unique virtue in contrast with that of the heathen— that we put the rights of persons above that of property."

"Words, high-sounding, empty words," Shraga rasped, shoving the dishes into disarray with an impatient gesture. "Do you know that a war is coming—a war with Rome? . . ."

The old obsession, Elisha thought wearily. Aloud he said, "I know nothing of the kind. But even if you are right, what conceivable relevance can that have to this case?"

Shraga looked up and fixed his eyes on Elisha. The scar on his face was livid.

"I am no rabbi," he said in a soft trembling voice. "I am not regarded as worthy to be a rabbi. And I hold no brief for rich Jewish employers. But we shall need their wealth when the next clash with Rome comes. They are having enough difficulty competing with Gentiles and their slaves. If our law penalizes them further and gives our laborers too much latitude, do you know what will happen? We will force them out of business, impoverish them and through them our whole country. I tell you," he rose slowly, his voice mounting meantime, "this land is being bled white. It is our duty to husband our resources, or we shall have none to conserve. And then where shall we derive our power? To perdition then with sophistries over human and property rights, and with logical deductions. Only one policy is right, that which trains our hands for battle and strengthens our sinews for war.

"What is more, we have no right to force upon Jews defiance of our authority, to foment breaches in our national unity. Do you imagine that Benjamin will abide by our decision? Have you not heard what he has been saying? He will walk out of this building straight into the basilica where pagan judges can be relied on to be sensible."

"He will not dare," Elisha countered confidently. "And if he should, since when are questions of Jewish law determined by threats?"

"Go ahead," Shraga threw at him furiously. "Hasten the debilitation that is spreading through our land like a creeping paralysis. Undermine our discipline by driving Jews into the Roman courts. What can one expect from the son of . . ."

"Silence," Jonah thundered, his open hand slapping the table resoundingly.

Shraga stopped short. For a moment he was discomfited by the old man's angry face and Elisha's cold stare. Then he shrugged to demonstrate his unconcern. Elisha breathed deeply once, while he regained his self-control, then spoke with a steady voice.

"No purpose will be served by further discussion. I had hoped to obtain a unanimous verdict as would be desirable. But failing it we shall perforce be content with a decision by majority vote. Shall the laborers be ordered to return to work?"

Three nays sounded together.

"Shall they be held liable for the damages?"

Two nays and one aye, that of Shraga, were spoken simultaneously.

The persons standing in the aisles or before the benches scurried to their seats as soon as the judges appeared in the courtroom. The plaintiff and the defendants resumed their places at the dais. The hall was altogether quiet even before the marshal tapped the floor with his wand and proclaimed, "The suit of Benjamin the weaver against his laborers."

"The court rejects," Elisha announced through the tense silence, "the petition of Benjamin that his employees be ordered to return to work."

"The court holds further that the laborers are free of responsibility for any damages . . ."

Whatever his last words were, they were lost in the uproar that rose in the room. Men climbed onto benches and called excitedly to one another and to the defendants who were embracing one another enthusiastically.

Benjamin the weaver had paled with anger on hearing the verdict. He stood struggling to control himself.

"No," he bellowed above the din, "I will not comply."

A gasp of incredulity swept the chamber. The clamor of voices died away.

"I beg your pardon?" Elisha inquired softly.

"I said," Benjamin shouted defiantly, "that I refuse to accept the verdict."

"I still do not understand," Elisha persisted, a forbidding frown knitting his brow. "Exactly what do you propose to do?"

Men held their breath for fear of missing the least word.

Benjamin's lips opened for speech. But he looked into the narrowed blue eyes of Rabbi Elisha and his courage failed him. His mouth closed slowly. A flush mounted his cheeks, deepening in hue until his face was aflame with embarrassment.

"I shall appeal to the Sanhedrin," he mumbled lamely.

"That," Elisha commented coldly, "is your privilege."

Then, as Benjamin and his opponents joined the spectators streaming toward the door, Shraga's voice, thin and tense with passion, sounded in Elisha's ears.

"You have despised my counsel. I shall remember that fact. You have handed down a dangerous verdict, one that may do harm to our people. I shall hold you responsible for it."

The arrogance of the remark was so egregious that Elisha was first stunned, then amused. Deliberately he smiled into the blazing eyes before him, and turned away.

Thanks to Benjamin, who complained bitterly of the trial to every merchant he met, and to Shraga, who hastened to spread a report of it among his acquaintances, the proceedings at Tiberias became a matter of comment and debate throughout the land.

When then, as good as his word, the weaver appeared at the next session of the Sanhedrin to ask for a reversal of judgment, the sages, with few exceptions, were thoroughly familiar with the issues involved. They listened to the plaintiff and to the defendants, interrogated the three judges, and after a brief discussion, voted by a substantial majority to sustain Elisha's verdict.

To Elisha, the action of his colleagues was a source of relief. His judgment was vindicated and he was rid at last of a distasteful controversy. But he was not yet done with the quarrel between the weaver and his employees. For Benjamin, although he uttered no protest to the Sanhedrin at the time of its verdict, proceeded promptly to appeal from Jewish justice to Roman. He entered his suit in the civil court at Tiberias and out of malice named the scholars who had presided over the first hearing of the case as material witnesses. In consequence, Elisha had scarcely returned from Jamnia to his own home when he was summoned to appear in the basilica at Tiberias.

Once again, Elisha met with Shraga and Jonah at the airing of a dispute of which they were by now thoroughly weary. But this time they sat abjectly among the spectators, waiting to be heard. In accordance with Roman legal practice, both the plaintiff and the defendants were represented by professional counsel. And when at long last the Jewish judges were called to testify, Benjamin, hiding behind his Gentile attorney, exacted a safe, subtle revenge through the humiliating examination to which they were subjected.

After three days of proceedings the ordeal came to its end. The Roman judge, a wizened, nearsighted man, read his findings in a thin dry voice from a papyrus roll. It was a learned document, replete with references. It alluded to a stoppage by free workers in Egypt under Ptolemy Euergetes II, to a strike in a factory at Pergamum during the reign of Attalus Philadelphus, to a rebellion of slaves at the Athenian mines at Laurium, and to other precedents in Greek, Hellenistic and Roman law. But through the confusion of citations the purport of the decision was clear after its first words. The entire verdict of the Jewish courts was being reversed. Approaching the end of the document the judge paused, looked up from the scroll and peered at the spectators. His manner suggested clearly that he was about to make a statement of grave import. The silence in the room was suddenly tense with expectation.

"The plaintiff," he resumed, "has appealed to this court for protection against an edict of excommunication with which he is threatened by the authorities of his people. To penalize recourse to the justice of the Empire is to deny a free man his rights. Wherefore, I enjoin the rabbis and the Sanhedrin against attempting to punish Benjamin of Tiberias by any ban or restriction whatsoever."

Instantly Elisha was on his feet protesting furiously against the decision as an infringement of Jewish autonomy. But the judge was adamant.

"The case is closed," he snapped decisively and, refusing to listen further, withdrew from the chamber.

Stunned by shock and dismay, Elisha was scarcely aware of the angry talk which shook the chamber. But he did hear with painful clarity two gibes hurled at him.

"I congratulate you, Rabbi," Shraga cried wildly in his ears. "You have made a great contribution to the welfare of our people."

"Master," Benjamin chimed in sneeringly, "may I give you your own advice. You may appeal for a reversal—to Caesarea."

But as they turned to leave, the smirk of satisfaction faded quickly from the weaver's face. For, confronting him with clenched fists, stood his fellow Jews, glaring with a hatred so palpable that in panic Benjamin looked about for aid. The sight of the Roman soldiers stationed in the hall reassured him somewhat. Yet he was pale and trembling as he made his way through the crowd that parted sullenly before him.

That night a group of stalwart young Jews slipped through the cordon of guards stationed to protect Benjamin's home. What they told the weaver in the privacy of his own bedchamber, the townspeople of Tiberias never learned. But when, the next day, his employees failed to appear at his workshop he made no complaint to the Roman authorities. Nor did he ever attempt to collect the damages which had been awarded him. In subsequent months he was given additional occasion to rue his wiliness and insubordination. For though he had succeeded in heading off an edict of excommunication, he was benefited but little. Spontaneously, the Jews of Tiberias, indeed of all Palestine, leagued themselves against him as in obedience to a formal ban. No one conversed or traded with him. Eventually, his business ruined, his will broken by universal hostility, he traveled to Jamnia to apologize to the Sanhedrin for his disobedience. On the eve of the next Day of Atonement, he did public penance in the great synagogue of Tiberias. Only then was his ostracism mitigated. Thus, quietly, unobtrusively but effectively the verdict of the Roman court was nullified.

Yet, it had its damaging consequences. For the Sanhedrin could not accept passively even in principle any restraint on its right to impose penalties. It appealed first to Caesarea, then to the proconsul at Antioch. In the first instance its request was evaded, in the second denied. Finally, a legation sailed for Rome. When it, too, returned empty-handed, a wave of exasperation swept Palestine. Many who had hitherto remained aloof from the illegal army now joined it as recruits. Everywhere throughout the land people talked with increased gravity of the inevitability of conflict with Rome.

Nor was Elisha left altogether unscathed by the general indignation. Among sober responsible persons, it was understood that he had acted in the light of reason and conscience. But the popular mind tended to regard him as responsible in some vague fashion for the trial and all its unfortunate consequences. Blinded by animosity and fanaticism, Shraga in particular made much of the incident, charging that like his father the young rabbi had been motivated by sympathy for the heathen world and

gross disloyalty to the interests of his own nation. Few people took Shraga's grotesque accusation seriously. But into the members of his group
with whom his influence was considerable, he succeeded for the first time
in inculcating something of his resentment of Elisha.

Pantagruel Attends the Trial of Bridlegoose
Who Decided Cases by the Fall of Dice

François Rabelais
Translated and Annotated by Samuel Putnam

THE DAY following at the appointed hour, Pantagruel reached Myre-
lingues. The presiding judge, senators, and counsel begged that
he would sit with them and hear the case and assist them in reaching a decision as to the causes and reasons set forth by Bridlegoose
as to why he had pronounced a certain sentence against an official by the
name of Toucheronde, a sentence that did not appear in the least equitable to the centumviral court.

Pantagruel readily agreed and, upon entering the courtroom, found
Bridlegoose seated in the center of the room. The latter, upon being duly
interrogated, would give no reasons or excuses and make no answer, except that he had grown old and had not, upon the occasion in question,
been able to see quite so well as usual. He proceeded to cite the divers
miseries and calamities that old age brings with it, the which are noted
per Archid., d. lxxxvi, c. Tanta; and for this reason, he had not been able
to recognize the points on the dice so distinctly as in the past. And so, just
as Isaac, an old man with failing sight, had taken Jacob for Esau, it was
possible that he had taken a *four* for a *five,* especially since, it was to be
noted, he had made use of his small dice, and the law expressly provides
that imperfections of nature are not to be imputed as a crime; as clearly
ff. De re milit., l. Qui cum uno; ff. De reg. jur., l. Fere; ff. De edil. ed

---

From *Pantagruel.*

(*per totum*); *ff. De termo., l. Divus Adrianus, resolu. per Lud. Ro. in l.: Si vero, ff. Solv. matri.;* and that whoever did otherwise would be accusing not man but Nature, as is evident in *l.: Maximum vitium, c. De lib. praeter.*

"What dice, my friend, do you mean?" inquired Bluster, the presiding judge.

"The dice of judgment," responded Bridlegoose, "the *alea judiciorum*, the dice of judgment, those specified in *Decr., c. 26, q. ii, c. Sors; l., Nec emptio, ff. De contrah. empt.; l. Quod debetur, ff. De pecul., et ibi Barthol.*, and of which you gentlemen commonly make use in this your sovereign court, as do all other judges in the decision of cases, in accordance with the notation of D. Henr. Ferrandat, *et no. Gl. in c. fin. De sortil., et l. Sed cum ambo, ff. De judi., ubt Doct.* who observe that games of chance are decent, respectable, useful, and necessary in the voidance of suits and dissensions at law. *Bal., Bart.* and *Alex., c. Communia, de l. Si duo,* have spoken still more clearly on this subject."

"And just how," queried Bluster, "do you work it, my friend?"

"I will reply briefly," said Bridlegoose, "according to the prescriptions of *l. Ampliorem,* ∫ *in refutatoriis, c. De appela.,* and the statement of *Gl. l. i, ff. Quod met, caus. gaudent brevitate moderni.* I do the same as you gentlemen; I act in accordance with judicial custom, to which our laws advise us always to defer, *ut no. Extra., De consuet., c. ex. literis, et ibi, Innoc.*

"What I do is this. Having well viewed, reviewed, read, reread, rummaged, and leafed through all the complaints, summonses, appearances, warrants, interrogatories, preliminary hearings, exhibits, citations, bills, cross-bills, petitions, inquiries, answers, rejoinders, trijoinders, documents, exceptions, pleas, rebuttals, briefs, collations, hearings, libels, appeals, letters-royal, examinations, demurrers, injunctions, changes of venue, mittimuses, remands, decisions, nolle-prosses, stipulations, mandamuses, statements, processes, and other such tidbits on the one hand or the other, as a good judge ought to do, according to the notations *Spec., De ordinario,* ⎱ *iii, et tit. De offi. om: ju.,* ∫ *fi., et De rescriptis praesenta,* ⎱ *i*—having done this, I place at one end of the table, in my chambers, all the defendant's bags, and then give him the first throw, just the same as you other gentlemen, *et est not., l. Favorabiliores, ff. De reg. jur., et in c. Cum sunt, eod. tit., lib. vi,* which says: *Cum sunt partium jura obscura reo favendum est potius actori.*

"Having done this, I place the plaintiff's bags, just as you other gentlemen do, at the other end of the table, *visum visu, car opposita, juxta se posita, magis elucescunt, ut not. in l. i.* ∫ *Videamus, ff. De his qui sunt sui vel alieni jur., et in l. i, Munerum mixta, ff. De muner et honor.:* and then, I proceed to give him a due and equal chance."

"But, my friend," inquired Bluster, "how do you become familiar with the obscure points of law brought up by the two parties to the proceedings?"

"The same way you other gentlemen do," answered Bridlegoose, "that is, by the number of bags at one end and at the other. And then, I proceed to make use of my small dice, just the same as you other gentlemen, according to the law: *Semper in stipulationibus, ff. De reg. jur.,* and the versal law in verse, *p. edo. tit. Semper in obscuris quod minimum est sequimur, canonized in c. In obscuris, edo. tit., lib. vi.*

"I have other big dice, very pretty and melodious, of which I make use, just like you other gentlemen, when the matter is more fluid, that is to say, when there are fewer bags."

"And when you have done that," said Bluster, "how do you set about handing down a decision?"

"Just like you other gentlemen," replied Bridlegoose. "I give the decision to the one who wins the throw, in accordance with the judicial, tribunary, praetorian, first-come-first-served dice. For we are thus instructed in our laws *ff. Qui po. in pig. l. Potior, leg. Creditor., c. De consul., l. i., and De reg. jur., in vi.: Qui prior est tempore potior est jure.*"

Professor Lefranc believes that Bridlegoose (Bridoye) had his counterpart in real life and that this passage in Rabelais may be based upon an incident that actually happened; he even thinks the documents may some time be found among the archives of the Parliament of Paris. The French scholar is inclined to identify Bluster (Trinquamelle), presiding magistrate at Bridlegoose's trial, as André Tiraqueau. He rejects the etymology of the name that is usually given—fanfaron, fendeur de naseaux, a swaggerer or boaster, or "nose-splitter" (compare our "bruiser")—and sees, rather, an anagrammatic allusion to the author of the De Legibus Connubialibus.

"*This chapter and the following one are filled with citations from the* Corpus Juris Justiniani *and the* Decretals. *It would be pointless to reproduce them all* in extenso *and to undertake to explain them here. It will be sufficient to remark that, in general, they are correct but facetiously applied by way of showing the unreflecting use which Bridlegoose made of them*" (Marty-Laveaux).

"*By the name of Toucheronde*": *Toucheronde (meaning round wood or copse) is not an invented name but that of a hamlet in Poitou, near Ligugé.*——"*The centumviral court*": *a court composed of a hundred men; one of Rabelais' Latin neologisms.*——"*Just as Isaac had taken Jacob for Esau*": Genesis, *xxvii.*——"*The dice of judgment*": *play on the expression: "the hazard of judgments."*——"*Et ibi Barthol.*": *and there is your Bartolus for you; Bartolus was professor of law at Bologna and Pisa, in the fourteenth century.*——"*With the notation of D. Henri Ferrandat*": *Ferrandat was a commentator of the* Decretals.——"*Gaudent brevitate moderni*": *the moderns like brevity.*——"*Cum sunt partium jurum obscurum*": *when the law in the case is obscure, one should lean to the defendant rather than to the plaintiff.*——"*Visum viso*": *directly opposite; vis-a-vis.*——"*Car opposita, juxta si posita*": "*for opposed things, being juxtaposed, become more clear.."*——*"The versal law in verse* . . . Semper in obscuris": *this law, as a matter of fact, forms a Latin penta-meter; the somewat doubtful sense of the adjective* versale *would appear to be that of "capital"* (majuscule), *but our "versal" is a fairly adequate rendering; the meaning of the law is*: *in case of doubt, we always take the course that entails the least consequences.*——"Qui prior est tempore": *the first in date has the preference at law.*

Bridlegoose Sets Forth the Reasons Why He Employed Dice in the Cases That He Was Called Upon to Decide

"WELL, my friend," persisted Bluster, "but since you give your decisions by throwing dice, why do you not have the throwing done the very day and hour that the parties to the controversy appear before you, without any further postponement? Of what use to you are the documents and records contained in the bags?"

"The same use that they are to you other gentlemen," was Bridle-goose's answer. "They serve me for three exquisite, requisite, and authentic purposes.

"*First,* as a Formality, without which whatever is done is of no value, as is very well proved, *Spec., tit. De instr. edi., et tit. De rescrip. praesent.;* moreover, you know only too well that very often, in judicial procedure, the formalities destroy the materialities and substance, for *Forma mutata, mutata Substantia, ff. ad exhib., l. Julianus; ff. ad leg. Falcid., l. Si is qui quadrigenta, et Extra., De Deci., c. Ad audientiam, et De celebra. Miss., c. In quadam.*

"*Secondly,* as with you other gentlemen, they serve me as a dignified and salutary form of exercise. The late M. Othoman Vadare, a great physician as you might say, *C. De comit, et archi., lib. xii,* has very often remarked to me that a lack of bodily exercitation is the sole cause of the unhealthiness and shortness of life of you other gentlemen and of all the officers of justice. Which had been very well observed before him by Bart. *in l. i. C. De senten.* 'quae' *pro* 'eo quod.' Gentlemen, to us, respectively, *quia accessorium naturam sequitur principalis, De reg. jur. lib. vi. et l.: Cum principalis, et l. Nihil dolo., ff. eod. titu.: ff. De fidejusso., l. Fide-jussor, et Extra. De offi., deleg., c.i.,* are conceded certain forms of respectable and recreative diversion, *ff. De al. lus. et aleat., l. Solent, et Autent. Ut omnes obediant, in princ., coll. vii, et ff. De praescript. verb., I. Si gratuitam., et l. i, C.: De spect., lib. xi,* and such is the opinion *D. Thomae, in Secunda Secundae, quaest, clxviii,* very patly cited by D. Alber. de Ros., who was *magnus practicus* and a solemn doctor, as Barbatias attests, *in prin. Consil.* The reason is set forth *per Gl. in Praemio ff.,* ⌡ *Ne autem tertii*:

> *Interpone tuis interdum gaudia curis.*

"That is to say, mingle occasional joys with your cares. And the truth is,

one day, in the year 1489, having a little fiscal business to look after
before the Gentlemen of the Excise Court, and entering the said court
by pecuniary permission of the bailiff, like you other gentlemen, for you
know that *pecuniae obediunt omnia,* as has been observed by *Bald. in l.
Singularia, ff. Si certum pet., et Salic., in l. Receptitia, C. De constit.
pecun., et Card., in Cle. i, De baptis.,* I found them all playing fly, which
is a most salubrious exercise, either before or after meals, it is all one to
me, provided that *hic no.* that the said game of fly is respectable, salubrious,
ancient and legal, *a Musco iventore, de quo C., De petit, haered., l. Si
post motam, et Muscarii, i.,* those who play at housefly are excusable in
law, *l. i., C., De excus. artif. lib. x.*

"For the moment, M. Tielman Picquet was the fly, as I remember, and
he was laughing because all the gentlemen of the said court were ruining
their bonnets from drubbing his shoulders so hard; but he added that,
notwithstanding, they would not be excusable for this spoiling of their
bonnets upon their return from the Palace to their wives, by *c. i, Extra.
De praesump., et ibi Gl.*

"And now, *resolutorie loquendo* I should say, like you other gentlemen,
that there is no other such exercise, and none more aromaticizing, in this
palatial world, than voiding bags, leafing through papers, indexing port-
folios, filling baskets, and examining pleas, *ex Bart. et Jo. de Pra., in l.
Falsa de condit. et de mon. ff.*

"*Thirdly,* like you other gentlemen, I am mindful of the fact that time
ripens all things, and in time all things come to light; time is the father
of truth, *Gl in l. i, C. De Servit. Autent., De restit. et ea quae pa., et Spec.
cit., De requis. cons.* That is why, like you other gentlemen, I suspend,
delay, and defer judgment until the case, having been well aired, sifted,
and argued, comes in the course of time to its maturity; and the outcome
which comes after will then be more gracefully borne by the condemned
parties, as *no. Gl., ff. De excu. tut., l. Tria onera: Portatur leviter, quod
portat quisque libenter.*

"In judging it roughly, greenly, and in the beginning there would be
danger of that inconvenience that the physicians say is incurred when an
abscess is opened before it is ripe or when the human body is purged of
some noxious humor before the reaction is complete. For, as we read *in
Autent., haec Constit. Inno. const., in prin., and this is repeated by Gl. in
c. Caeterum, Extra., De jura. calum.: Quod medicamenta morbis exhibent,
hoc jura negotiis.* Nature, moreover, instructs us to pluck and eat fruits
when they are ripe, *Instit., de re di., ⎱ Is ad quem, et ff. De acti. empt., l.
Julianus,* and to marry off the girls when they are ripe, *ff. de donat, int,
vir. et uxo., l. Cum hic status, ⎱ Si quia sponsa, et xxvii. Q., i. c., sicut Gl.*
says: *Jam matura thoris plenis adoleverat annis Virginitas.*

"Do nothing except in all maturity, *xxiii. Q., c. ii, ⎱ ult., clxxxiii. d.,
c. ult.*"

"*Forma mutatur . . .*": "*when the form is changed, the substance is changed."*—"*M. Othoman Vadare*": *unidentified personage, possibly a German.*—"Quia accessorium . . .": "*because the accessory follows the nature of the principal.*"—"*D. Alber. de Ros.*": *Alberico de Rosata, four-teenth-century canonist of Bergamo.*—"*Who was* magnus practicus": "*who was a great practitioner.*"—"Pecuniae obediunt omnia": "*all things are obedient to money.*" "*All playing fly*": *a schoolboys' game in which one plays the part of the fly* (la mouche) *and all the others fall upon and chase him; this was one of the infant Gargantua's pastimes.* —"Hic no.": "*note here.*" —"A Musco inventore": *this is a play on the Latin* musca, *Italian* mosca, *a fly, and certain expressions that occur in the legal texts.* —"*M. Tielman Picquet*": *the Picquet family was a prominent one in Montpellier, furnishing a number of professors of medicine for the university.* —"Resolutorio loquendo": "*speaking judicially.*" —"*In this pa-latial world*": *that of the Palace of Justice.* —"Quod portat quisque liben-ter": "*that which one bears willingly is borne lightly.*" —"Quod medica-menta morbis exhibent": "*what medicines do for diseases, judgments do for business.*" —"Jam matura thoris . . .": "*long ripe for the nuptial couch, virginity has been maturing for many years.*"

Sancho Panza Decides Three Disputes

Cervantes

O THOU ceaseless discoverer of the antipodes, torch of the world, eye of heaven, and sweet cause of earthen wine-coolers;* here Thymbrius, there Phoebus; here archer, there physician, father of poesy, inventor of music; thou who always risest and, though thou seemest to do so, never settest: to thee I speak, O sun! thee I invoke to favor and enlighten the obscurity of the great Sancho Panza: without thee I find myself indolent, dispirited, and confused!

From *Don Quixote*.
* In Spain they call cantimploras small glass decanters or very small earthen pitchers, which, to cool the water in the summer, are hung in a current of air. Hence the odd epithet Cervantes applies to the sun.

Sancho, then, with all his attendants, arrived at a town containing about a thousand inhabitants, which was one of the largest and best the duke had. They gave him to understand that it was called the island of Barataria, either because Barataria was really the name of the place, or because he obtained the government of it at so cheap a rate. On his arrival near the gates of the town, which was walled about, the municipal officers came out to receive him. The bells rung, and, with all the demonstrations of a general joy, and a great deal of pomp, the people conducted him to the great church to give thanks to God. Presently after, with certain ridiculous ceremonies, they presented him the keys of the town, and constituted him perpetual governor of the island of Barataria. The garb, the beard, the thickness and shortness of the new governor, surprised all who were not in the secret, and, indeed, those who were, who were not a few. In fine, as soon as they had brought him out of the church, they carried him to the tribunal of justice, and placed him in the chair. The duke's steward then said to him, "It is an ancient custom here, my lord governor, that he who comes to take possession of this famous island is obliged to answer a question put to him, which is to be somewhat intricate and difficult. By his answer the people are enabled to feel the pulse of their new governor's understanding, and, accordingly, are either glad or sorry for his coming."

While the steward was saying this, Sancho was staring at some capital letters written on the wall opposite to his chair, and, being unable to read, he asked what that writing was on the wall. He was answered, "Sir, it is there written on what day your honor took possession of this island. The inscription runs thus: 'This day, such a day of the month and year, Signor Don Sancho Panza took possession of this island. Long may he enjoy it.'" "Pray who is it they call Don Sancho Panza?" demanded Sancho. "Your lordship," answered the steward; "for no other Panza, besides him now in the chair, ever came into this island." "Take notice, then, brother," returned Sancho, "that the *Don* does not belong to me, nor ever did to any of my family. I am called plain Sancho Panza; my father was a Sancho, and my grandfather was a Sancho, and they were all Panzas, without any addition of *Dons,* or any other title whatever. I fancy there are more *Dons* than stones on this island. But enough. God knows my meaning; and, perhaps, if my government lasts four days, I may weed out these *Dons* that overrun the country, and, by their numbers, are as troublesome as mosquitoes and cousins.* On with your question, Master Steward, and I will answer the best I can, let the people be sorry or rejoice."

About this time two men came into the court, the one clad like a country fellow, and the other like a tailor, with a pair of shears in his hand; and the tailor said, "My lord governor, I and this countryman

---

* Many plebeians in Cervantes' time already arrogated to themselves the title of Don which was, until then, reserved exclusively for the nobility.

come before your worship by reason this honest man came yesterday to my shop (saving your presence, I am a tailor, and have passed my examination, God be thanked), and putting a piece of cloth into my hands, asked me, 'Sir, is there enough of this to make me a cap?' I, measuring the piece, answered Yes. Now he, thinking that doubtless I had a mind to cabbage some of the cloth, grounding his conceit upon his own knavery, and upon the common ill opinion of tailors, bade me view it again, and see if there was not enough for two. I guessed his drift, and told him there was. Persisting in his knavish intentions, my customer went on increasing the number of caps, and I still saying Yes, till we came to five caps. A little time ago he came to claim them. I offered them to him, but he refuses to pay me for the making, and insists I shall either return him his cloth or pay him for it." "Is all this so, brother?" demanded Sancho. "Yes," answered the man; "but pray, my lord, make him produce the five caps he has made me." "With all my heart," answered the tailor; and pulling his hand from under his cloak, he showed the five caps on the ends of his fingers and thumb, saying, "Here are the five caps this honest man would have me make, and on my soul and conscience, not a shred of cloth is left, and I submit the work to be viewed by any inspectors of the trade." All present laughed at the number of the caps and the novelty of the suit. Sancho reflected a moment, and then said, "I am of opinion there needs no great delay in this suit, and it may be decided very equitably off hand. Therefore I pronounce that the tailor lose the making and the countryman the stuff, and that the caps be confiscated to the use of the poor; and there is an end of that."

If the sentence Sancho afterwards passed on the purse of the herdsman caused the admiration of all the bystanders, this excited their laughter. However, what the governor commanded was executed, and two old men next presented themselves before him. One of them carried a cane in his hand for a staff; and the other, who had no staff, said to Sancho, "My lord, some time ago I lent this man ten crowns of gold to oblige and serve him, upon condition that he should return them on demand. I let some time pass without asking for them, being loth to put him to a greater strait to pay me than he was in when I lent them. But at length, thinking it full time to be repaid, I asked him for my money more than once, but to no purpose: he not only refuses payment, but denies the debt, and says I never lent him any such sum, or, if I did, that he had already paid me. I have no witnesses to the loan, nor has he of the payment which he pretends to have made, but which I deny; yet if he will swear before your worship that he has returned the money, I from this minute acquit him before God and the world." "What say you to this, old gentleman?" quoth Sancho. "I confess, my lord," replied the old fellow, "that he did lend me the money; and if your worship pleases to hold down your wand of justice, since he leaves it to my oath, I will swear I have really and truly returned it to him." The governor accordingly held down his wand, and the old fellow, seeming encumbered with his staff, gave it to his creditor to hold while he was swearing; and then taking hold of the cross of the wand, he said it was true indeed the other had lent him ten crowns, but that he had restored them to him into his own hand; but having, he supposed, forgotten it, he was continually dunning him for them. Upon which his lordship the governor demanded of the creditor what he had to say in reply to the solemn declaration he had heard. He said that he submitted, and could not doubt that his debtor had sworn to the truth: for he believed him to be an honest man and a good Christian; and that, as the fault must have been in his own memory, he would thenceforward ask him no more for his money. The debtor now took his staff again, and, bowing to the governor, went out of court.

Sancho having observed the defendant take his staff and walk away, and noticing also the resignation of the plaintiff, he began to meditate, and laying the forefinger of his right hand upon his forehead, he continued a short time apparently full of thought; and then, raising his head, he ordered the old man with the staff to be called back; and when he had returned, "Honest friend," said the governor, "give me that staff, for I have occasion for it." "With all my heart," answered the old fellow, and delivered it into his hand. Sancho took it, and immediately giving it to the other old man, he said, "There, take that, and go about your business, in God's name, for you are now paid." "I paid, my lord!" answered the old man; "what! is this cane worth ten golden crowns?" "Yes," quoth the governor, "or I am the greatest dunce in the world; and it shall now appear whether or not I have a head to govern a whole kingdom." He then ordered the cane to be broken in court; which being done, ten crowns of gold were found within it. All the spectators were struck with admiration, and began to look upon their new governor as a second Solomon. They asked him how he had discovered that the ten crowns were in the cane. He told them that, having observed the defendant give it to the plaintiff to hold, while he took his oath that he had truly restored the money into his own hands, and that being done, he took his staff again, it came into his head that the money in dispute must be inclosed within it. From this, he added, they might see that it sometimes pleased God to direct the judgments of those who govern, though otherwise little better than blockheads. Besides, he had heard the curate of his parish tell of such another business, which was still in his mind; indeed, he had so special a memory, that were it not that he was so unlucky as to forget all that he chiefly wanted to remember, there would not have been a better in the whole island. The cause being ended, the two old men went away, the one abashed, and the other satisfied; and the secretary, who minuted down the words, actions, and behavior of Sancho Panza, could not yet determine in his own mind whether he should set him down for wise or simple.

This cause was no sooner ended than there came into court a woman, keeping fast hold of a man clad like a rich herdsman. She came, crying aloud, "Justice, my lord governor, justice! If I cannot find it on earth, I will seek it in heaven! Lord governor of my soul, this wicked man surprised me in the middle of a field, and used me as if I had been a dishclout! Woe is me! he has robbed me of what I have kept above these three and twenty years. Have I been as hard as a cork tree, and preserved myself as entire as a salamander in the fire, or as wool among briers, that this honest man should came with his clean hands to harm me!" "That remains to be inquired into," said Sancho, "let us now proceed to see whether this gallant's hands are clean or not:" and, turning to the man, he asked him what he had to say in answer to this woman's complaint. The man, all in confusion, replied: "Sir, I am a poor herdsman, and deal in swine: and this morning I went out of this town, after having sold, under correction be it spoken, four hogs, and what between dues and exactions, the officers took from me little less than they were worth. As I was returning home, by the way I lighted upon this good dame, and the author of all mischief, brought us together. I gave her money, but she, not contented, laid hold of me, and has never let me go till she has dragged me to this place. She says I wronged her; but, by the oath I have taken, or am to take, she lies. This is the whole truth."

Then the governor asked him if he had any silver money about him. The man answered that he had about twenty ducats in a leathern purse in his bosom. Sancho ordered him to produce it, and deliver it just as it was to the plaintiff. The woman took the purse, and making a thousand curtseys, and praying to God for the life and health of the lord governor, who took such care of poor orphans and maidens, out of the court she went, holding the purse with both hands, taking care first to see that the money that was in it was silver.

She had no sooner left the room than Sancho said to the herdsman, who was in tears, and whose eyes and heart were gone after his purse: "Honest man, follow that woman, and take away the purse from her, whether she will or not, and come back hither with it." This was not said to one deaf or stupid, for the man instantly flew after her like lightning, and went about doing what he was bidden.

All present were in great suspense, expecting the issue of this suit. In a few minutes came in the man and the woman, clinging together closer than the first time, she with her petticoat tucked up, the purse lapped up in it, and the man struggling to take it from her, but in vain, she defended it so stoutly. "Justice from God and the world!" cried she, at the top of her lungs: "see, my lord governor, the impudence and want of fear of this varlet, who, in the midst of the town and of the street, would take from me the purse your worship commanded to be given to me." "And has he got it?" demanded the governor. "Got it!" answered the woman: "I would sooner let him take away my life than my purse. A pretty baby I should be, indeed! Other guise cats must claw my beard, and not such pitiful sneaking fools as this. Pincers and hammers, crows and chisels, shall not get it out of my clutches, not even the paws of a lion. My soul and body shall sooner part." "She is in the right," added the man: "I yield myself worsted and spent, and confess I have not strength enough to take it from her." That said, he left her.

Then said the governor to the woman, "Give me that purse, chaste and valiant heroine." She presently delivered it, and the governor returned it to the man, and said to the violent damsel, "Sister of mine, had you shown the same, or but half as much, courage and resolution in defending yourself as you have done in defending your purse, the strength of Hercules could not have harmed you. Begone, in God's name, and in an ill hour, and be not found in all this island, nor in six leagues round about it, upon pain of two hundred stripes. Begone instantly I say, thou prating, shameless, cheating hussey!" The woman was confounded, and went away hanging down her head and not pleased. "Now, friend," said the governor to the man, "in Heaven's name get you home with your money, and henceforward, if you would avoid worse luck, yoke not with such cattle." The countryman thanked him in the best manner he could, and went his way, leaving all the court in admiration at the acuteness and wisdom of their new governor: all of whose sentences and decrees, being noted down by the appointed historiographer, were immediately transmitted to the duke, who waited for these accounts with the utmost impatience.

A Magistrate of Bordeaux

Michel de Montaigne

As Translated and Edited by Marvin Lowenthal

A S A YOUNG MAN I was plunged over the ears in law—magistrate of the king in the Cour du Parlement of Bordeaux and, before that, magistrate in the Cour des Aides of Perigueux.

There is nothing more subject to mutation than the laws. Since I was born I have seen those of our neighbors, the English, changed three or four times, not only in civil matters but, what is worse, in religious. I am more concerned and mortified at this, because they are a nation with whom our part of the country formerly had a long and familiar acquaintance.

Here, among us, I have known a capital offence to become lawful; and we who hold a different opinion of it run the chance, if the fortunes of war go against us, of being strung up for high treason.

Men amuse me when they try to give certainty to our laws by saying that some of them are perpetual and unchangeable—which they call 'natural laws.' Some men reckon them at three or four, others at more or less —a sign that the number is as doubtful as the rest of the matter. But we are indeed unfortunate that there is not one of these picked natural laws which is not denounced and disowned by not one nation, but several. The Spartans esteemed cleverness in thievery. One people or another have sanctioned the murder of infants or fathers, community of wives, traffic in robbery, and all manner of licentious pleasures.

It is credible that natural laws exist for us as for other creatures. But they are lost to us, thanks to our fine human reason which has insinuated itself into governing, shuffling, and confounding the fact of things into the image of its own futility and fickleness.

It is a pity that there is not a closer relation between the laws we do have and our capacity to obey them. To set a mark we can seldom hit is not an honest game.

There is no man so good who, if he were to submit all his thoughts and

From *The Autobiography of Montaigne*, translated and edited by Marvin Lowenthal. By permission of Houghton Mifflin Company.

actions to the law, would not deserve hanging ten times in his life. And he would be the very man it were unjust to punish and a shame to kill. On the other hand, many a man who has broken no law is so far from being virtuous that our philosophy would look with composure on his being soundly whipped.

Is a man wrong for not doing what he cannot do? To whom do we prescribe the laws which we expect no one will obey? We take good care not to be righteous according to the laws of God, and we make it impossible for us to be righteous according to our own.

I often notice that we propose rules of conduct which neither the lawmakers nor the public ever hope or, what is worse, ever wish to observe. From the same sheet of paper on which a judge writes his sentence against an adulterer, he tears off a piece to scribble a love-note to his colleague's wife. There are judges who will condemn men to death for a crime which they do not themselves think is so much as a misdemeanor.

At best this two-facedness, this doing one thing and saying another, may pass with authors who treat of things outside of us, but not with me who must write about myself. I must move my pen as I do my feet. The life of a public servant, I admit, must have some relation to other men's lives. In a man dedicated to public office, who takes part in the government of men, the virtue of a Cato is, if not unvirtuous, at least useless and out of place. Maybe I am wrong in being disgusted with the world I frequent. Certainly I would be wrong if I complained at its being disgusted with me, since I am utterly so with it.

How does it happen that our ordinary language, which works nicely in other matters, becomes involved and unintelligible in wills and contracts? Unless it is that the princes of this art, by applying themselves with peculiar attention to raking up solemn words and devising artful phrases, and weighing every syllable and plucking over every seam, have so confounded and obfuscated themselves in an endless number of clauses and points that the result baffles rule, order, and understanding. By sowing and retailing questionable details they create for themselves a splendid harvest of suits and disputes. And, as far as I can make out, experience shows that a multitude of interpretations dissipates and destroys the truth.

The Barone of Caupene and I hold in common the right of appointment to a benefice of large extent, called Lahontan, at the foot of our mountains. The inhabitants of this nook lived a life apart, with clothes, manners, and fashions of their own, and governed themselves solely by the force of custom. They managed so happily that from time out of mind no neighboring judge was ever put to the trouble of looking into their affairs.

Then, so I am told, one of these people became fired with a noble ambition. For the honor of the family he resolved to have 'Counsellor-at-Law' tacked to the name of his son. So Pierre or Jean was sent to some nearby town to learn how to write, and in due course he became a village lawyer. Now that he was a 'Monsieur,' the fellow began to sneer at the old ways. Presently, when someone cut off the horn of a goat belonging to one of his cronies, he advised him to bring suit before a royal magistrate in the vicinity. One thing led to another, and in the end he had corrupted the whole place.

I am little pleased with the opinion that a multiplicity of laws curbs the authority of the judges. The man responsible for it cannot be aware that there is as much latitude and liberty in the interpretation of laws as in the making of them. We have more laws in France than in all the rest of the world put together; yet so much is left to the opinion and decision of our judges that never was their liberty more unshackled.

What have our legislators gained by culling out one hundred thousand individual actions and pasting a law to each of them? Add one hundred thousand more, and still human behavior will never fit any one of them exactly, and there will always remain circumstances at the mercy of interpretation and opinion.

The most desirable laws are the simplest, the most general, and the least likely to be invoked. I am of the further opinion that none at all would be better than our present prodigious number. What danger would there be if the wisest heads decided each controversy as it arose and on its own merits? King Ferdinand wisely provided that no lawyers could join in the new colonies sent to America, lest law-suits should get a footing in the new world: he agreed with Plato that 'lawyers and doctors are the pest of a country.'

What can be more outrageous than to see a nation like ours where, by lawful custom, the office of judge is bought and sold, where judgments are paid for cash down, and where justice may legally be denied a man who cannot pay! A country, moreover, where justice becomes such a profitable article of merchandise, as it is with us, that at the side of church, nobility, and commons has arisen a fourth estate of lawyers, who manage the laws and hold sovereign power over men's lives and fortunes. The result is, we have two codes of law: one of honor and one of the law-courts. And they frequently collide.

In some of our courts the magistrates, upon being admitted to office, are examined only as to their learning. Other courts, however, add to this a test of their understanding, by asking their judgment on some cases in law. I think the latter proceed with better method; for, though both are necessary, judgment can indeed make a shift without knowledge, but knowledge is helpless without judgment. Would to God that, for the sake of justice, our gentlemen of the robe were as well furnished with understanding and conscience as they are stuffed with knowledge!

I have heard tell of a judge who, when he read a sharp conflict of opinion between Bartolus and Aldus or other points bristling with contradictions, used to write in the margin of his book: 'Question for a friend.' That is to say, in such a disputed case the truth was so obscured, he might well favor whichever party he pleased. He needed only a little more wit and discernment to write in the margin of all cases, "Question for a friend.' The lawyers and judges in our time find enough things aslant in every case to justify their taking any side that suits them.

In a field of learning so illimitable as law, which depends for its authority on multitudinous opinions, and the subject of which is itself so obscure, an endless confusion of decisions must result. One court decides differently from another, and on occasion differs from itself. And then there is that remarkable blemish in our justice which, as we frequently see, allows a case to be dragged from judge to judge, and court to court. I am reminded of Chrysippus who said, 'A philosopher will turn a dozen somersaults, yes, and without his breeches, for the sake of a dozen olives.'

A chief magistrate once bragged in my presence that he had packed two hundred and some passages from out-of-the-way sources into one of his decisions. In tooting this abroad, he robbed himself of whatever glory he might have won by it. A fatuous and absurd boast, as I see it, for such an exploit and such a person!

I have often been angered to see our judges shamelessly make use of fraud and false hopes of pardon in order to trick a criminal into confessing his crime. This is a malicious justice; and it violates itself, I think, as much as any wrong-doer.

The use of torture is a dangerous device, and seems to me more a trial of endurance than of truth. The man who can withstand the pain conceals the truth, but so does the man who cannot. For why should pain force me to confess the truth rather than a falsehood? And, on the contrary, if an innocent man has the courage to withstand these torments, why shouldn't a guilty one have the same courage—with life and liberty as his reward? The ground for this device lies, I think, in the power of conscience. It is considered that conscience will aid the rack in making the guilty confess, and strengthen the innocent to bear its torments.

But, when all is said, it is, in plain truth, a dubious and dangerous method. What will a man not say to escape such horrible pain? The result is, a man whom the judge has racked in order not to put him to death if he is innocent, dies both innocent and racked. How can torture help out our ignorance? Are you not unjust who, in order to avoid killing a man without cause, do worse than kill him? Thousands upon thousands have lost their lives through false confessions. 'But it is,' we are told, 'the least evil that human frailty can contrive!' Nevertheless, it is altogether inhuman and, in my opinion, altogether useless.

Our law cannot expect that a man who will not be deterred from crime by the fear of being hanged or beheaded, will be any more awed at the thought of being punished by burning pincers, slow fire, or the wheel. I do not so much pity the dead—and should rather envy them; but I deeply pity the dying. I cannot look with a steady eye on even the reasonable executions of justice.

Even in justice itself, anything that exceeds simple death seems to me sheer cruelty. This holds especially true for us who are Christians and who ought to have regard for the souls of men, and dismiss them in a calm and composed frame, which cannot be when we have rent them with unbearable torments.

If we intend that our severity shall impress the public, I advise that we exercise it on the bodies of the criminals after they are dead. To see them deprived of burial, or quartered and hung, works almost as much upon the imagination of the crowd as pain inflicted upon the living.

In Rome, I happened to be passing by when they were executing Catena, a notorious robber. He was strangled to death without the slightest emotion on the part of the spectators. But when they came to cut his body in quarters, every blow of the hangman was followed by a doleful cry from the people, as though everyone present had lent his feelings to the miserable carcass. These inhuman excesses should be inflicted on the bark, and not the living core.

I live in a time when we abound in incredible examples of this vice of cruelty—as a result of our civil wars. Nothing in history is more extreme than we bear proof to every day. Before I saw it with my own eyes, I could hardly believe that men can be so savage as, for the sole pleasure of killing, to hack and lop off the limbs of their fellows, and sharpen their wits to invent strange torments and new forms of death—all this without hatred or profit, but simply to enjoy the pleasant spectacle of anguished gestures and lamentable groans and cries. For this is the utmost limit to which cruelty can attain: 'that a man should kill a man, without anger or fright, but merely for the spectacle' [Seneca].

How often I have done myself a manifest injustice to avoid the risk of having our judges do me a worse one; and that, after interminable vexations and vile and foul practices more hateful to me than fire and rack! If we are wise, we will boast and rejoice like the boy I once heard telling, with innocence and in high glee, that his mother had lost her law-suit— as if it were a cough, a fever, or something equally annoying to keep.

Even the favors which fortune might have given me through my kinship or friendliness with those in high office I have scrupulously avoided using, either to the disadvantage of others or the unmerited advancement of myself. In fine, I have made such a good day's work of it (thanks to luck, I may say) that I am still a virgin at law-suits. And this, despite the fact that I have often been tempted by having very just and promising grounds.

I am virgin of quarrels too. Soon I shall have passed a long life without having given or received an offense of any moment, and without ever hearing myself called a worse name than my own—a rare grace of heaven!

I am so slow to offend that I cannot do it even in behalf of reason itself. When occasion has demanded that I sentence criminals, I have rather chosen to fail in justice. 'I would prefer men not to sin, but I have not the heart to condemn them for it' [Livy].

Most men exasperate themselves to punishment out of horror at the crime; but it is precisely this which cools me off. The horror of one man killing another makes me fear the horror of killing him: the hideousness of his cruelty makes me abhor any imitation of it.

It may be said of me, who am but a two-spot in the deck, what was said of Charillus, King of Sparta: 'He cannot be a good man, for he is not bad to the wicked.' Just as in lawful actions I am loathe to proceed against a man if it will be to his hurt, so, too, I am not so conscientious to refrain from an unlawful action if it is in behalf of someone who consents to it.

Since the laws of ethics which govern the duty of the individual within himself are so hard to teach and observe, it is no wonder that our public laws are even more so. Do but consider this justice which rules over us: it is the true testimony to human frailty, filled as it is with error and contradiction.

Some peasants have just come to me in great haste, to tell me they left in one of my woods a man stricken with a hundred blows. He was still breathing, and begged a drop of water for pity's sake, and help to raise him from the ground. But they told me they dared not go near him, but ran off, lest the officers of justice should catch them there, and, as it happens to those found near a murdered body, they should be called into question—to their utter ruin, having neither friends nor money to defend their innocence. What could I say to them? It is certain that this act of humanity could have plunged them into trouble.

How many innocent persons have we known to be punished—and without fault of the judge! And how many more that we do not know of? This happened in my time: certain men were condemned to die; the sentence was concluded upon, but not pronounced. At the last moment the judges learned that other men had unquestionably committed the crime. Whereat they proceeded to ponder the novelty of the situation: the fact that once the death sentence was passed, the judges had no power to revoke it; and what effect the reversal of judgment might have on precedent. So the poor devils were sacrificed to the formalities of justice. And how many sentences have I seen more criminal than the crimes they punished!

There is no remedy. I am at one with Alcibiades: I will never, if I can help it, put myself into the hands of a man who shall determine my head, and where my honor and life shall depend more on the skill and diligence of my lawyer than on my own innocence.

No judge, thank God! has ever yet spoken a word to me in his office as judge, on any account whatever—my own or that of another, civil or criminal. No prison has ever yet received me, even as a visitor. Imagination renders the very outside of a jail odious to me.

I so love freedom that if someone forbade me access to the remotest corner of the Indies I should feel myself a little hemmed in. While I can find earth or air in any part of the globe, I shall never live where I must keep in hiding. If the authorities under whom I live should so much as wag a finger at me, I would immediately go in search of others, no matter where. All my little prudence in these civil wars of ours is employed in keeping me free to come and go as I will.

Now our laws maintain their credit not because they are just, but because they are laws. This is the mystic foundation of their authority—which is their good luck. For they are often made by fools, and more often by men who because they hate equality deny equity, and always by men—that is to say, futile and irresolute creatures. Whoever obeys them because he thinks they are just does not obey them as he ought. And our French laws, by their disorder and botchery, lend a generous hand to the corruption manifest in their execution.

True justice, natural and universal, is quite another thing from this national justice which is tied to the necessities of our government, whose laws not only permit but often instigate wickedness. 'There are crimes authorized by the decrees of the Senate and the votes of the people,' says Seneca. I use the ordinary language which makes a distinction between useful things and righteous things; and in my way of speaking, there are not only useful but necessary actions which are knavish and filthy.

The Judicial Acumen of Wouter Van Twiller

Washington Irving

THE RENOWNED Wouter (or Walter) Van Twiller was descended from a long line of Dutch burgomasters, who had successively dozed away their lives and grown fat upon the bench of magistracy in Rotterdam; and who had comported themselves with such singular wisdom and propriety that they were never either heard or talked of—which, next to being universally applauded, should be the object of ambition of all sage magistrates and rulers.

From *A History of New York by Diedrich Knickerbocker.*

The surname of Twiller is said to be a corruption of the original *Twijfler,* which in English means *doubter;* a name admirably descriptive of his deliberative habits. For, though he was a man shut up within himself like an oyster, and of such a profoundly reflective turn that he scarcely ever spoke except in monosyllables, yet did he never make up his mind on any doubtful point. This was clearly accounted for by his adherents, who affirmed that he always conceived every object on so comprehensive a scale that he had not room in his head to turn it over and examine both sides of it, so that he always remained in doubt, merely in consequence of the astonishing magnitude of his ideas!

There are two opposites ways by which some men get into notice—one by talking a vast deal and thinking a little, and the other by holding their tongues and not thinking at all. By the first, many a vaporing, superficial pretender acquires the reputation of a man of quick parts; by the other, many a vacant dunderpate, like the owl, the stupidest of birds, comes to be complimented by a discerning world with all the attributes of wisdom. This, by the way, is a mere casual remark, which I would not for the universe have it thought I apply to Governor Van Twiller. On the contrary, he was a very wise Dutchman, for he never said a foolish thing—and of such invincible gravity that he was never known to laugh, or even to smile, through the course of a long and prosperous life. Certain, however, it is, there never was a matter proposed, however simple, and on which your common narrow-minded mortals would rashly determine at the first glance, but what the renowned Wouter put on a mighty, mysterious, vacant kind of look, shook his capacious head, and, having smoked for five minutes with redoubled earnestness, sagely observed that "he had his doubts about the matter"—which in process of time gained him the character of a man slow in belief, and not easily imposed on.

The person of this illustrious old gentleman was as regularly formed, and nobly proportioned, as though it had been molded by the hands of some cunning Dutch statuary, as a model of majesty and lordly grandeur. He was exactly five feet six inches in height and six feet five inches in circumference. His head was a perfect sphere, and of such stupendous dimensions that Dame Nature, with all her sex's ingenuity, would have been puzzled to construct a neck capable of supporting it; wherefore she wisely declined the attempt and settled it firmly on the top of his backbone, just between the shoulders. His body was of an oblong form, particularly capacious at bottom; which was wisely ordered by Providence, seeing that he was a man of sedentary habits, and very averse to the idle labor of walking. His legs, though exceeding short, were sturdy in proportion to the weight they had to sustain; so that when erect he had not a little the appearance of a robustious beer-barrel, standing on skids. His face, that infallible index of the mind, presented a vast expanse, perfectly unfurrowed or deformed by any of those lines and angles which disfigure the human countenance with what is termed expression. Two small gray eyes twinkled feebly in the midst like two stars of lesser magnitude in the hazy firmament; and his full-fed cheeks, which seemed to have taken toll of everything that went into his mouth, were curiously mottled and streaked with dusty red, like a Spitzenberg apple.

His habits were as regular as his person. He daily took his four stated meals, appropriating exactly an hour to each; he smoked and doubted eight hours, and he slept the remainder twelve of the four-and-twenty. Such was the renowned Wouter Van Twiller—a true philosopher, for his mind was either elevated above, or tranquilly settled below, the cares and perplexities of this world. He had lived in it for years without feeling the least curiosity to know whether the sun revolved round it, or it round the sun; and he had watched, for at least half a century, the smoke curling from his pipe to the ceiling, without once troubling his head with any of those numerous theories, by which a philosopher would have perplexed his brain, in accounting for its rising above the surrounding atmosphere.

In his council he presided with great state and solemnity. He sat in a huge chair of solid oak, hewn in the celebrated forest of the Hague, fabricated by an experienced timmerman of Amsterdam, and curiously carved about the arms and feet into exact imitations of gigantic eagle's claws. Instead of a scepter, he swayed a long Turkish pipe, wrought with jasmin and amber, which had been presented to a Stadtholder of Holland at the conclusion of a treaty with one of the petty Barbary powers. In this stately chair would he sit, and this magnificent pipe would he smoke, shaking his right knee with a constant motion, and fixing his eye for hours together upon a little print of Amsterdam which hung in a black frame against the opposite wall of the council chamber. Nay, it has even been said that when any deliberation of extraordinary length and intricacy was on the carpet, the renowned Wouter would absolutely shut his eyes for full two hours at a time, that he might not be disturbed by external objects—and at such times the internal commotion of his mind was evinced by certain regular guttural sounds, which his admirers declared were merely the noise of conflict made by his contending doubts and opinions.

It is with infinite difficulty I have been enabled to collect these biographical anecdotes of the great man under consideration. The facts respecting him were so scattered and vague, and divers of them so questionable in point of authenticity, that I have had to give up the search after many, and decline the admission of still more, which would have tended to heighten the coloring of his portrait.

I have been the more anxious to delineate fully the person and habits of the renowned Van Twiller, from the consideration that he was not only the first but also the best governor that ever presided over this ancient and respectable province; and so tranquil and benevolent was his reign that I do not find throughout the whole of it a single instance of any offenders being brought to punishment—a most indubitable sign of a merciful governor, and a case unparalleled, excepting in the reign of the illustrious King Log, from whom it is hinted, the renowned Van Twiller was a lineal descendant.

The very outset of the career of this excellent magistrate was distinguished by an example of legal acumen that gave flattering presage of a wise and equitable administration. The morning after he had been solemnly installed in office, and at the moment that he was making his breakfast, from a prodigious earthen dish, filled with milk and Indian pudding, he was suddenly interrupted by the appearance of one Wandle Schoonhoven, a very important old burgher of New Amsterdam, who complained bitterly of one Barent Bleecker, inasmuch as he fraudulently refused to come to a settlement of accounts, seeing that there was a heavy balance in favor of the said Wandle. Governor Van Twiller, as I have already observed, was a man of few words; he was likewise a mortal enemy to multiplying writings—or being disturbed at his breakfast. Having listened attentively to the statement of Wandle Schoonhoven, giving an occasional grunt, as he shoveled a spoonful of Indian pudding into his mouth—either as a sign that he relished the dish or comprehended the story—he called unto him his constable, and pulling out of his breeches pocket a huge jack-knife, dispatched it after the defendant as a summons, accompanied by his tobacco-box as a warrant.

This summary process was as effectual in those simple days as was the seal-ring of the great Haroun Alraschid among the true believers. The two parties being confronted before him, each produced a book of accounts written in a language and character that would have puzzled any but a High Dutch commentator, or a learned decipherer of Egyptian obelisks, to understand. The sage Wouter took them one after the other, and having poised them in his hands, and attentively counted over the number of leaves, fell straightway into a very great doubt, and smoked for half an hour without saying a word; at length, laying his finger beside his nose, and shutting his eyes for a moment, with the air of a man who has just caught a subtle idea by the tail, he slowly took his pipe from his mouth, puffed forth a column of tobacco-smoke, and with marvelous gravity and solemnity pronounced—that having carefully counted over the leaves and weighed the books, it was found that one was just as thick and as heavy as the other—therefore it was the final opinion of the court that the accounts were equally balanced—therefore Wandle should give Barent a receipt, and Barent should give Wandle a receipt—and the constable should pay the costs.

This decision being straightway made known diffused general joy throughout New Amsterdam, for the people immediately perceived that they had a very wise and equitable magistrate to rule over them. But its happiest effect was that not another lawsuit took place throughout the whole of his administration—and the office of constable fell into such decay that there was not one of those losel scouts known in the province for many years. I am the more particular in dwelling on this transaction, not only because I deem it one of the most sage and righteous judgments on record, and well worthy the attention of modern magistrates, but because it was a miraculous event in the history of the renowned Wouter— being the only time he was ever known to come to a decision in the whole course of his life.

The Laws of the Lilliputians

Jonathan Swift

A LTHOUGH I intend to leave the description of this empire to a particular treatise, yet, in the meantime, I am content to gratify the curious reader with some general ideas. As the common size of the natives is somewhat under six inches high, so there is an exact proportion in all other animals, as well as plants and trees; for instance, the tallest horses and oxen are between four and five inches in height, the sheep an inch and half, more or less; their geese about the bigness of a sparrow, and so the several gradations, downward, till you come to the smallest, which, to my sight, were almost invisible; but nature hath adapted the eyes of the Lilliputians to all objects proper for their view; they see with great exactness, but at no great distance. And to show the sharpness of their sight toward objects that are near, I have been much pleased observing a cook pulling a lark, which was not so large as a common fly; and a young girl threading an invisible needle with invisible silk. Their tallest trees are about seven foot high; I mean some of those in the great royal park, the tops whereof I could but just reach with my fist clenched. The other vegetables are in the same proportion; but this I leave to the reader's imagination.

I shall say but little at present of their learning, which for many ages hath flourished in all its branches among them; but their manner of writing is very peculiar, being neither from the left to the right, like the Europeans; nor from the right to the left, like the Arabians; nor from

From *Gulliver's Travels.*

up to down like the Chinese; but aslant from one corner of the paper to the other, like ladies in England.

They bury their dead with their heads directly downward, because they hold an opinion, that in eleven thousand moons they are all to rise again; in which period the earth (which they conceive to be flat) will turn upside down, and by this means they shall at their resurrection be found ready standing on their feet. The learned among them confess the absurdity of this doctrine; but the practice still continues, in compliance to the vulgar.

There are some laws and customs in this empire very peculiar; and if they were not so directly contrary to those of my own dear country, I should be tempted to say a little in their justification. It is only to be wished that they were as well executed. The first I shall mention relates to informers. All crimes against the state are punished here with the utmost severity; but if the person accused maketh his innocence plainly to appear upon his trial, the accuser is immediately put to an ignominious death; and out of his goods or lands the innocent person is quadruply recompensed for the loss of his time, for the danger he underwent, for the hardship of his imprisonment, and for all the charges he hath been at in making his defense. Or, if that fund be deficient, it is largely supplied by the crown. The emperor does also confer on him some public mark of his favor, and proclamation is made of his innocence through the whole city.

They look upon fraud as a greater crime than theft, and therefore seldom fail to punish it with death; for they allege that care and vigilance, with a very common understanding, may preserve a man's goods from thieves, but honesty has no fence against superior cunning; and, since it is necessary that there should be a perpetual intercourse of buying and selling, and dealing upon credit, where fraud is permitted or connived at, or hath no law to punish it, the honest dealer is always undone, and the knave gets the advantage. I remember when I was once interceding with the king for a criminal who had wronged his master of a great sum of money, which he had received by order and ran away with; and happening to tell his majesty, by way of extenuation, that it was only a breach of trust, the emperor thought it monstrous in me to offer as a defense the greatest aggravation of the crime; and truly I had little to say in return, further than the common answer, that different nations had different customs; for I confess I was heartily ashamed.

Although we usually call reward and punishment the two hinges upon which all government turns, yet I could never observe this maxim to be put in practice by any nation, except that of Lilliput. Whoever can there bring sufficient proof that he hath strictly observed the laws of his country for seventy-three moons hath a claim to certain privileges, according to his quality and condition of life, with a proportionable sum of money, out of a fund appropriated for that use; he likewise acquires the title of *snilpall,* or legal, which is added to his name, but does not descend to his posterity. And these people thought it a prodigious defect of policy among us when I told them that our laws were enforced only by penalties, without any mention of reward. It is upon this account that the image of Justice, in their courts of judicature, is formed with six eyes, two before, as many behind, and on each side one, to signify circumspection; with a bag of gold open in her right hand, and a sword sheathed in her left, to show she is more disposed to reward than to punish.

In choosing persons for all employments they have more regard to good morals than to great abilities; for, since government is necessary to mankind, they believe that the common size of human understandings is fitted to some station or other; and that Providence never intended to make the management of public affairs a mystery to be comprehended only by a few persons of sublime genius, of which there seldom are three born in an age; but they suppose truth, justice, temperance, and the like, to be in every man's power; the practice of which virtues, assisted by experience and a good intention, would qualify any man for the service of his country, except where a course of study is required. But they thought the want of moral virtues was so far from being supplied by superior endowments of the mind that employments could never be put into such dangerous hands as those of persons so qualified; and at least, that the mistakes committed by ignorance, in a virtuous disposition, would never be of such fatal consequence to the public weal, as the practices of a man whose inclinations led him to be corrupt, and had great abilities to manage, and multiply, and defend, his corruptions.

In like manner the disbelief of a Divine Providence renders a man incapable of holding any public station; for, since kings avow themselves to be the deputies of Providence, the Lilliputians think nothing can be more absurd than for a prince to employ such men as disown the authority under which he acts.

In relating these and the following laws, I would only be understood to mean the original institutions, and not the most scandalous corruptions, into which these people are fallen by the degenerate nature of man. For, as to that infamous practice of acquiring great employments by dancing on the ropes, or badges of favor and distinction by leaping over sticks and creeping under them, the reader is to observe, that they were first introduced by the grandfather of the emperor now reigning, and grew to the present height by the gradual increase of party and faction.

Ingratitude is among them a capital crime, as we read it to have been in some other countries; for they reason thus, that whoever makes ill returns to his benefactor must needs be a common enemy to the rest of mankind, from whom he hath received no obligation, and therefore such a man is not fit to live.

Two Hearings Before Isaac Bickerstaffe

Joseph Addison

I

TRIAL OF THE WINE-BREWERS.

THERE is in this city a certain fraternity of chymical operators, who work under ground in holes, caverns, and dark retirements, to conceal their mysteries from the eyes and observation of mankind. These subterraneous philosophers are daily employed in the transmigration of liquors, and, by the power of medical drugs and incantations, raising under the streets of London the choicest products of the hills and valleys of France. They can squeeze Bordeaux out of a sloe, and draw Champagne from an apple. Virgil, in that remarkable prophecy,

> Incultisque rubens pendebit sentibus Uva,
> "The ripening grape shall hang on every thorn,"

seems to have hinted at this art, which can turn a plantation of northern hedges into a vineyard. These adepts are known among one another by the name of wine-brewers, and I am afraid do great injury, not only to her Majesty's customs, but to the bodies of many of her good subjects.

Having received sundry complaints against these invisible workmen, I ordered the proper officer of my court to ferret them out of their respective caves, and bring them before me, which was yesterday executed accordingly.

The person who appeared against them was a merchant, who had by him a great magazine of wines that he had laid in before the war: but these gentlemen (as he said) had so vitiated the nation's palate, that no man could believe his to be French, because it did not taste like what they sold for such. As a man never pleads better than where his own

From *The Tatler's Court* and *The Court of Honor*.

personal interest is concerned, he exhibited to the court with great eloquence, That this new corporation of druggists had inflamed the bills of
mortality, and puzzled the college of physicians with diseases, for which
they neither knew a name or cure. He accused some of giving all their
customers cholics and megrims; and mentioned one who had boasted, he
had a tun of claret by him, that in a fortnight's time should give the
gout to a dozen of the healthfullest men in the city, provided that their
constitutions were prepared for it by wealth and idleness. He then en-
larged, with a great show of reason, upon the prejudice which these
mixtures and compositions had done to the brains of the English nation;
as is too visible (said he) from many late pamphlets, speeches, and sermons, as well as from the ordinary conversations of the youth of this
age. He then quoted an ingenious person, who would undertake to
know by a man's writings, the wine he most delighted in; and on that
occasion named a certain satirist, whom he had discovered to be the
author of a lampoon, by a manifest taste of the sloe, which showed itself
in it by much roughness and little spirit.

In the last place, he ascribed to the unnatural tumults and fermenta-
tions, which these mixtures raise in our blood, the divisions, heats, and
animosities that reign among us; and in particular, asserted most of the
modern enthusiasms and agitations to be nothing else but the effects of
adulterated port.

The counsel for the brewers had a face so extremely inflamed and il-
luminated with carbuncles that I did not wonder to see him an advocate
for these sophistications. His rhetoric was likewise such as I should have
expected from the common draught which I found he often drank to a
great excess. Indeed I was so surprised at his figure and parts that I ordered him to give me a taste of his usual liquor; which I had no sooner
drank, but I found a pimple rising in my forehead; and felt such a sensible decay in my understanding, that I would not proceed in the trial till
the fume of it was entirely dissipated.

This notable advocate had little to say in the defense of his clients,
but that they were under a necessity of making claret if they would keep
open their doors, it being the nature of mankind to love everything that
is prohibited. He further pretended to reason, that it might be as profitable to the nation to make French wine as French hats, and concluded
with the great advantage that this had already brought to part of the
kingdom. Upon which he informed the court, "That the lands in Here-
fordshire were raised two years' purchase since the beginning of the
war."

When I had sent out my summons to these people, I gave at the same
time orders to each of them to bring the several ingredients he made use
of in distinct phials, which they had done accordingly, and ranged them
into two rows on each side of the court. The workmen were drawn up
in ranks behind them. The merchant informed me, that in one row of
phials were the several colors they dealt in, and in the other the tastes.

He then showed me on the right hand one who went by the name of Tom Tintoret, who (as he told me) was the greatest master in his coloring of any vintner in London. To give me a proof of his art, he took a glass of fair water; and by the infusion of three drops out of one of his phials, converted it into a most beautiful pale Burgundy. Two more of the same kind heightened it into a perfect Languedoc; from thence it passed into a florid Hermitage: and after having gone through two or three other changes, by the addition of a single drop, ended in a very deep Pontac. This ingenious virtuoso, seeing me very much surprised at his art, told me, that he had not an opportunity of showing it in perfection, having only made use of water for the ground-work of his coloring; but that if I were to see an operation upon liquors of stronger bodies, the art would appear to much greater advantage. He added, "That he doubted not but it would please my curiosity to see the cider of one apple take only a vermilion, when another, with a less quantity of the same infusion, would rise into a dark purple, according to the different texture of parts in the liquor." He informed me also, "That he could hit the different shades and degrees of red, as they appear in the pink and the rose, the clove and the carnation, as he had Rhenish or Moselle, Perry or White Port, to work in."

I was so satisfied with the ingenuity of this virtuoso, that, after having advised him to quit so dishonest a profession, I promised him, in consideration of his great genius, to recommend him as a partner to a friend of mine, who has heaped up great riches, and is a scarlet dyer.

The artists on my other hand were ordered in the second place to make some experiments of their skill before me: upon which the famous Harry Sippet stept out, and asked me, "What I would be pleased to drink?" At the same time he filled out three or four white liquors in a glass, and told me, "That it should be what I pleased to call for;" adding very learnedly, "That the liquor before him was as the naked substance or first matter of his compound, to which he and his friend, who stood over against him, could give what accidents or form they pleased." Finding him so great a philosopher, I desired he would convey into it the qualities and essence of right Bourdeaux. "Coming, coming, sir," (said he,) with the air of a drawer; and after having cast his eye on the several tastes and flavors that stood before him, he took up a little cruet that was filled with a kind of inky juice, and pouring some of it out into the glass of white wine, presented it to me, and told me, "This was the wine over which most of the business of the last term had been despatched." I must confess, I looked upon the sooty drug which he held up in his cruet, as the quintessence of English Bourdeaux, and therefore desired him to give me a glass of it by itself, which he did with great unwillingness. My cat at that time sat by me, upon the elbow of my chair; and as I did not care for making the experiment upon myself, I reached it to her to sip of it, which had like to have cost her life; for notwithstanding it flung her at first into freakish tricks, quite contrary to her usual gravity, in less than a quarter of an hour she fell into convulsions; and had it not been a creature more tenacious of life than any other, would certainly have died under the operation.

I was so incensed by the tortures of my innocent domestic, and the unworthy dealings of these men, that I told them, if each of them had as many lives as the injured creature before them, they deserved to forfeit them for the pernicious arts which they used for their profit. I therefore bid them look upon themselves as no better than a kind of assassins and murderers within the law. However, since they had dealt so clearly with me, and laid before me their whole practise, I dismissed them for that time; with a particular request, That they would not poison any of my friends and acquaintance, and take to some honest livelihood without loss of time.

For my own part, I have resolved hereafter to be very careful in my liquors, and have agreed with a friend of mine in the army, upon their next march, to secure me two hogsheads of the best stomach-wine in the cellars of Versailles, for the good of my lucubrations, and the comfort of my old age.

II

CASES OF FALSE DELICACY

A Continuation of the Journal of the Court of Honor, held in Sheer Lane, on Monday, the 27th of November, before Isaac Bickerstaffe, Esq., Censor of Great Britain.

ELIZABETH MAKEBATE, of the parish of St. Catherine's, spinster, was indicted for surreptitiously taking away the hassoc from under the Lady Grave-Airs, between the hours of four and five, on Sunday the 26th of November. The prosecutor deposed, that as she stood up to make a curtsey to a person of quality in a neighboring pew, the criminal conveyed away the hassoc by stealth, insomuch that the prosecutor was obliged to sit all the whole while she was at church, or to say her prayers in a posture that did not become a woman of her quality. The prisoner pleaded inadvertency; and the jury were going to bring it in chance-medley, had not several witnesses been produced against the said Elizabeth Makebate, that she was an old offender, and a woman of a bad reputation. It appeared in particular, that on the Sunday before she had detracted from a new petticoat of Mrs. Mary Doelittle, having said in the hearing of several credible witnesses, that the said petticoat was scowered, to the great grief and detriment of the said Mary Doelittle. There were likewise many evidences produced against the criminal, that though she never failed to come to church on Sunday, she was a most notorious sabbath-breaker, and that she spent her whole time, during divine service, in disparaging other people's clothes, and whispering to those who sat next her. Upon the whole, she was found guilty of the indictment, and received sentence to ask pardon of the prosecutor upon her bare knees, without either cushion or hassoc under her, in the face of the court.

N. B. As soon as the sentence was executed on the criminal, which was done in open court with the utmost severity, the first lady of the bench on Mr. Bickerstaffe's right hand stood up, and made a motion to the court, that whereas it was impossible for women of fashion to dress themselves before the church was half done, and whereas many confusions and inconveniences did arise thereupon, it might be lawful for them to send a footman, in order to keep their places, as was usual in other polite and well-regulated assemblies. The motion was ordered to be entered in the books, and considered at a more convenient time.

Charles Cambrick, Linen-draper, in the city of Westminster, was indicted for speaking obscenely to the Lady Penelope Touchwood. It appeared, that the prosecutor and her woman going in a stage-coach from London to Brentwood, where they were to be met by the lady's own chariot, the criminal and another of his acquaintance traveled with them in the same coach, at which time the prisoner talked bawdy for the space of three miles and a half. The prosecutor alleged, "That over against the Old Fox at Knightsbridge, he mentioned the word linen; that at the further end of Kensington he made use of the term smock; and that before he came to Hammersmith, he talked almost a quarter of an hour upon wedding-shifts." The prosecutor's woman confirmed what her lady had said, and added further, "that she had never seen her lady in so great confusion, and in such a taking, as she was during the whole discourse of the criminal." The prisoner had little to say for himself, but that he talked only in his own trade, and meant no hurt by what he said. The jury, however, found him guilty, and represented by their forewoman, that such discourses were apt to sully the imagination, and that by a concatenation of ideas, the word linen implied many things that were not proper to be stirred up in the mind of a woman who was of the prosecutor's quality, and therefore gave it as their verdict, that the linendraper should lose his tongue. Mr. Bickerstaffe said, "He thought the prosecutor's ears were as much to blame as the prisoner's tongue, and therefore gave sentence as follows: That they should both be placed over against one another in the midst of the court, there to remain for the space of one quarter of an hour, during which time, the linen-draper was to be gagged, and the lady to hold her hands close upon both her ears;" which was executed accordingly.

Edward Callicoat was indicted as an accomplice to Charles Cambrick, for that he the said Edward Callicoat did, by his silence and his smiles, seem to approve and abet the said Charles Cambrick in everything he said. It appeared, that the prisoner was foreman of the shop to the aforesaid Charles Cambrick, and by his post obliged to smile at everything that the other should be pleased to say: upon which he was acquitted.

Josias Shallow was indicted in the name of Dame Winifred, sole relict of Richard Dainty, Esq., for having said several times in company, and in the hearing of several persons there present, that he was extremely obliged to the widow Dainty, and that he should never be able sufficiently to express his gratitude. The prosecutor urged, that this might blast her reputation, and that it was in effect a boasting of favors which he had never received. The prisoner seemed to be much astonished at the construction which was put upon his words, and said, "That he meant nothing by them, but that the widow had befriended him in a lease, and was very kind to his younger sister." The jury finding him a little weak in his understanding, without going out of the court, brought in their verdict, *ignoramus.*

Ursula Goodenough was accused by the Lady Betty Wou'dbe, for having said, that she the Lady Betty Wou'dbe was painted. The prisoner brought several persons of good credit to witness to her reputation, and proved by undeniable evidences, that she was never at the place where the words were said to have been uttered. The Censor observing the behavior of the prosecutor, found reason to believe that she had indicted the prisoner for no other reason but to make her complexion be taken notice of, which indeed was very fresh and beautiful; he therefore asked the offender with a very stern voice, how she could presume to spread so groundless a report? And whether she saw any colors in the Lady Wou'dbe's face that could procure credit to such a falsehood? "Do you see (says he) any lilies or roses in her cheeks, any bloom, any probability?"—The prosecutor, not able to bear such language any longer, told him, that he talked like a blind old fool, and that she was ashamed to have entertained any opinion of his wisdom: but she was put to silence, and sentenced to wear her mask for five months, and not presume to show her face till the town should be empty.

Benjamin Buzzard, Esq., was indicted for having told the Lady Everbloom at a public ball, that she looked very well for a woman of her years. The prisoner not denying the fact, and persisting before the court that he looked upon it as a compliment, the jury brought him in *non compos mentis.*

Jonathan Thrasher, Esq., Justice of the Peace, Deals with Sundry Offenders

Henry Fielding

O N THE FIRST of April, in the year——, the watchmen of a certain parish (I know not particularly which) within the liberty of Westminster brought several persons whom they had apprehended the preceding night before Jonathan Thrasher, Esq., one of the justices of the peace for that liberty.

But here, reader, before we proceed to the trials of these offenders, we shall, after our usual manner, premise some things which it may be necessary for thee to know.

It hath been observed, I think, by many, as well as the celebrated writer of three letters, that no human institution is capable of consummate perfection. An observation which, perhaps, that writer at least gathered from discovering some defects in the polity even of this well-regulated nation. And, indeed, if there should be any such defect in a constitution which my Lord Coke long ago told us "the wisdom of all the wise men in the world, if they had all met together at one time, could not have equalled," which some of our wisest men who were met together long before said was too good to be altered in any particular, and which, nevertheless, hath been mending ever since, by a very great number of the said wise men: if, I say, this constitution should be imperfect, we may be allowed, I think, to doubt whether any such faultless model can be found among the institutions of men.

It will probably be objected, that the small imperfections which I am about to produce do not lie in the laws themselves, but in the ill execution of them; but, with submission, this appears to me to be no less an absurdity than to say of any machine that it is excellently made, though incapable of performing its functions. Good laws should execute themselves in a well-regulated state; at least, if the same legislature which provides the laws doth not provide for the execution of them, they act as Graham would do, if he should form all the parts of a clock in the most

From *Amelia*.

exquisite manner, yet put them so together that the clock could not go. In this case, surely, we might say that there was a small defect in the constitution of the clock.

To say the truth, Graham would soon see the fault, and would easily remedy it. The fault, indeed, could be no other than the parts were improperly disposed.

Perhaps, reader, I have another illustration which will set my intention in still a clearer light before you. Figure to yourself then a family the master of which should dispose of the several oeconomical offices in the following manner; viz. should put his butler in the coach-box, his steward behind his coach, his coachman in the butlery, and his footman in the stewardship, and in the same ridiculous manner should misemploy the talents of every other servant; it is easy to see what a figure such a family must make in the world.

As ridiculous as this may seem, I have often considered some of the lower officers in our civil government to be disposed in this very manner. To begin, I think, as low as I well can, with the watchmen in our metropolis, who, being to guard our streets by night from thieves and robbers, an office which at least requires strength of body, are chosen out of those poor old decrepit people who are, from their want of bodily strength, rendered incapable of getting a livelihood by work. These men, armed only with a pole, which some of them are scarce able to lift, are to secure the persons and houses of his majesty's subjects from the attacks of gangs of young, bold, stout, desperate, and well-armed villains.

> Quae non viribus istis
> Munera conveniunt.

If the poor old fellows should run away from such enemies, no one I think can wonder, unless it be that they were able to make their escape.

The higher we proceed among our public officers and magistrates, the less defects of this kind will, perhaps be observable. Mr. Thrasher, however, the justice before whom the prisoners above mentioned were now brought, had some few imperfections in his magistratical capacity. I own, I have been sometimes inclined to think that this office of a justice of peace requires some knowledge of the law: for this simple reason; because, in every case which comes before him, he is to judge and act according to law. Again, as these laws are contained in a great variety of books, the statutes which relate to the office of a justice of peace making of themselves at least two large volumes in folio; and that part of his jurisdiction which is founded on the common law being dispersed in above a hundred volume, I cannot conceive how his knowledge should be acquired without reading; and yet certain it is, Mr. Thrasher never read one syllable of the matter.

This, perhaps, was a defect; but this was not all: for where mere ignorance is to decide a point between two litigants, it will always be an even chance whether it decides right or wrong: but sorry am I to say, right was often in a much worse situation than this, and wrong hath often had five hundred to one on his side before that magistrate; who, if he was ignorant of the law of England, was yet well versed in the laws of nature. He perfectly well understood that fundamental principle so strongly laid down in the institutes of the learned Rochefoucault, by which the duty of self-love is so strongly enforced, and every man is taught to consider himself as the centre of gravity, and to attract all things thither. To speak the truth plainly, the justice was never indifferent in a cause but when he could get nothing on either side.

Such was the justice to whose tremendous bar Mr. Gotobed the constable, on the day above mentioned, brought several delinquents, who, as we have said, had been apprehended by the watch for diverse outrages.

The first who came upon his trial was as bloody a spectre as ever the imagination of a murderer or a tragic poet conceived. This poor wretch was charged with a battery by a much stouter man than himself; indeed the accused person bore about him some evidence that he had been in an affray, his cloaths being very bloody, but certain open sluices on his own head sufficiently shewed whence all the scarlet stream had issued; whereas the accuser had not the least mark or appearance of any wound. The justice asked the defendant, What he meant by breaking the king's peace?— To which he answered—"Upon my shoul I do love the king very well, and I have not been after breaking anything of his that I do know; but upon my shoul this man hath brake my head, and my head did brake his stick; that is all, gra." He then offered to produce several witnesses against this improbable accusation; but the justice presently interrupted him, saying, "Sirrah, your tongue betrays your guilt. You are an Irishman, and that is always sufficient evidence with me."

The second criminal was a poor woman, who was taken up by the watch as a street-walker. It was alleged against her that she was found walking the streets after twelve o'clock, and the watchman declared he believed her to be a common strumpet. She pleaded in her defence (as was really the truth) that she was a servant, and was sent by her mistress, who was a little shopkeeper and upon the point of delivery, to fetch a midwife; which she offered to prove by several of the neighbours, if she was allowed to send for them. The justice asked her why she had not done it before? to which she answered, she had no money, and could get no messenger. The justice than called her several scurrilous names, and, declaring she was guilty within the statute of street-walking, ordered her to Bridewell for a month.

A genteel young man and woman were then set forward, and a very grave looking person swore he caught them in a situation which we cannot as particularly describe here as he did before the magistrate; who, having received a wink from his clerk, declared with much warmth that the fact was incredible and impossible. He presently discharged the accused parties, and was going, without any evidence, to commit the accuser for perjury; but this the clerk dissuaded him from, saying he doubted whether a justice of peace had any such power. The justice at first differed in opinion, and said, "He had seen a man stand in the pillory about perjury; nay, he had known a man in gaol for it too; and how came he there if he was not committed thither?" "Why that is true, sir," answered the clerk; "and yet I have been told by a very great lawyer that a man cannot be committed for perjury before he is indicted; and the reason is, I believe, because it is not against the peace before the indictment makes it so." "Why, that may be," cries the justice, "and indeed perjury is but scandalous words, and I know a man cannot have no warrant for those, unless you put for rioting* them into the warrant."

The witness was now about to be discharged, when the lady whom he had accused declared she would swear the peace against him, for that he had called her a whore several times. "Oho! you will swear the peace, madame, will you?" cries the justice: "Give her the peace, presently; and pray, Mr. Constable, secure the prisoner, now we have him, while a warrant is made to take him up." All which was immediately performed, and the poor witness, for want of securities, was sent to prison.

A young fellow, whose name was Booth, was now charged with beating the watchman in the execution of his office and breaking his lanthorn. This was deposed by two witnesses; and the shattered remains of a broken lanthorn, which had been long preserved for the sake of its testimony, were produced to corroborate the evidence. The justice, perceiving the criminal to be but shabbily drest, was going to commit him without asking any further questions. At length, however, at the earnest request of the accused, the worthy magistrate submitted to hear his defence. The young man then alleged, as was in reality the case, "That as he was walking home to his lodging he saw two men in the street cruelly beating a third, upon which he had stopt and endeavoured to assist the person who was so unequally attacked; that the watch came up during the affray, and took them all four into custody; that they were immediately carried to the round-house, where the two original assailants, who appeared to be men of fortune, found means to make up the matter, and were discharged by the constable, a favour which he himself having no money in his pocket, was unable to obtain. He utterly denied having assaulted any of the watchmen, and solemnly declared that he was offered his liberty at the price of half a crown."

Though the bare word of an offender can never be taken against the oath of his accuser, yet the matter of this defence was so pertinent, and delivered with such an air of truth and sincerity, that, had the magistrate

---

* *Opus est interprete.* By the laws of England abusive words are not punishable by the magistrate; some commissioners of the peace, therefore, when one scold hath applied to them for a warrant against another, from a too eager desire of doing justice, have construed a little harmless scolding into a riot, which is in law an outrageous breach of the peace committed by several persons, by three at the least, nor can a less number be convicted of it. Under this word rioting, or riotting (for I have seen it spelt both ways), many thousands of old women have been arrested and put to expense, sometimes in prison, for a little intemperate use of their tongues. This practice began to decrease in the year 1749.

been endued with much sagacity, or had he been very moderately gifted with another quality very necessary to all who are to administer justice, he would have employed some labour in cross-examining the watchmen; at least he would have given the defendant the time he desired to send for the other persons who were present at the affray; neither of which he did. In short, the magistrate had too great an honour for truth to suspect that she ever appeared in sordid apparel; nor did he ever sully his sublime notions of that virtue by uniting them with the mean ideas of poverty and distress.

There remained now only one prisoner, and that was the poor man himself in whose defence the last-mentioned culprit was engaged. His trial took but a very short time. A cause of battery and broken lanthorn was instituted against him, and proved in the same manner; nor would the justice hear one word in defence; but, though his patience was exhausted, his breath was not; for against this last wretch he poured forth a great many volleys of menaces and abuse.

The delinquents were then all dispatched to prison under a guard of watchmen, and the justice and the constable adjourned to a neighbouring alehouse to take their morning repast.

The Citizen of the World
in Westminster Hall

Oliver Goldsmith

I HAD some intentions lately of going to visit Bedlam, the place where those who go mad are confined. I went to wait upon the man in black to be my conductor, but I found him preparing to go to Westminster Hall, where the English hold their courts of justice. It gave me some surprise to find my friend engaged in a law-suit, but more so when he informed me that it had been pending for several years. "How is it possible," cried I, "for a man who knows the world to go to law? I am well acquainted with the courts of justice in China: they resemble rat-traps every one of them; nothing more easy than to get in, but to get out again is attended with some difficulty, and more cunning than rats are generally found to possess!"

"Faith," replied my friend, "I should not have gone to law but that I was assured of success before I began; things were presented to me in so alluring a light, that I thought by barely declaring myself a candidate for the prize, I had nothing more to do but to enjoy the fruits of the victory. Thus have I been upon the eve of an imaginary triumph every term these ten years; have travelled forward with victory ever in my view, but ever out of reach; however, at present, I fancy we have hampered our antagonist in such a manner that, without some unforeseen demur, we shall this day lay him fairly on his back."

"If things be so situated," said I, "I do not care if I attend you to the courts, and partake in the pleasure of your success. But prithee," continued I, as we set forward, "what reasons have you to think an affair at last concluded, which has given you so many former disappointments?" "My lawyer tells me," returned he, "that I have Salkeld and Ventris strong in my favour and that there are no less than fifteen cases in point."—"I understand," said I, "those are two of your judges who have already declared their opinions."—"Pardon me," replied my friend, "Salkeld and Ventris are lawyers who some hundred years ago gave their

From *A Citizen of the World*.

opinions on cases similar to mine; these opinions, which make for me, my lawyer is to cite; and those opinions which look another way are cited by the lawyer employed by my antagonist: as I have observed, I have Salkeld and Ventris for me; he has Coke and Hale for him; and he that has most opinions is most likely to carry his cause."—"But where is the necessity," cried I, "of prolonging a suit by citing the opinions and reports of others, since the same good sense which determined lawyers in former ages, may serve to guide your judges at this day? They at that time gave their opinions only from the light of reason; your judges have the same light at present to direct them; let me even add, a greater, as in former ages there were many prejudices from which the present is happily free. If arguing from authorities be exploded from every other branch of learning, why should it be particularly adhered to in this? I plainly foresee how such a method of investigation must embarrass every suit, and even perplex the student; ceremonies will be multiplied, formalities must increase, and more time will thus be spent in learning the arts of litigation, than in the discovery of right."

"I see," cries my friend, "that you are for a speedy administration of justice; but all the world will grant, that the more time that is taken up in considering any subject, the better it will be understood. Besides, it is the boast of an Englishman, that his property is secure, and all the world will grant, that a deliberate administration of justice is the best way to secure his property. Why have we so many lawyers, but to secure our property? why so many formalities, but to secure our property? Not less than one hundred thousand families live in opulence, elegance, and ease, merely by securing our property."

"To embarrass justice," returned I, "by a multiplicity of laws, or to hazard it by a confidence in our judges, are, I grant, the opposite rocks on which legislative wisdom has ever split; in one case, the client resembles that emperor, who is said to have been suffocated with the bed-clothes which were only designed to keep him warm; in the other, to that town which let the enemy take possession of its walls, in order to show the world how little they depended upon aught but courage for safety.—But, bless me! what numbers do I see here—all in black!—how is it possible that half this multitude can find employment?"—"Nothing so easily conceived," returned my companion; "they live by watching each other. For instance, the catchpole watches the man in debt, the attorney watches the catchpole, the counsellor watches the attorney, the solicitor the counsellor, and all find sufficient employment."—"I conceive you," interrupted I, "they watch each other, but it is the client that pays them all for watching; it puts me in mind of a Chinese fable, which is entitled, 'Five Animals at a Meal.'—"

"A grasshopper, filled with dew, was merrily singing under a shade; a whangam, that eats grasshoppers, had marked it for its prey, and was just stretching forth to devour it; a serpent, that had for a long time fed only on whangams, was coiled up to fasten on the whangam; a yellow bird was just upon the wing to dart upon the serpent; a hawk had just stopped from above to seize the yellow bird; all were intent on their prey, and unmindful of their danger; so the whangam ate the grass-hopper, the serpent ate the whangam, the yellow bird the serpent, and the hawk the yellow bird; when, souding from on high, a vulture gob-bled up the hawk, grasshopper, whangam, and all in a moment."

I had scarce finished my fable, when the lawyer came to inform my friend, that his cause was put off till another term, that money was wanted to retain, and that all the world was of opinion, that the very next hearing would bring him off victorious. "If so, then," cries my friend, "I believe it will be my wisest way to continue the cause for an-other term; and, in the meantime, my friend here and I will go and see Bedlam." Adieu.

Prairie Lawyer

Carl Sandburg

W HEN Lincoln and his wife started housekeeping at the corner house on Eighth and Jackson Streets, they could look from their kitchen windows away from the town and out onto cornfields. Since then the prairie had been filling up with houses between them and the tracks of the Great Western Railroad, later known as the Wabash. As Lincoln went to drive up his cow for milking, he could rest his gaze on cottages standing where he once had seen patches of cabbages and onions. He was living in town instead of on the edge of town. Hundreds of other towns in the northwestern states were edging farther out into the cornfields. A pavement of wooden planks had been laid around the public square in Springfield. The new gas company was laying pipes and had hired Lincoln to certify title to the gas-works city lot.

From *Abraham Lincoln: The Prairie Years*, by Carl Sandburg. Copyright, 1926, by Harcourt, Brace and Company, Inc.

The Alton Railroad and the Rock Island had spanned the spaces between Chicago and the Mississippi River so that barbecue orators, discussing progress, sang it as a proud fact that now the iron horse that sipped his morning draught from the crystal waters of Lake Michigan slaked his evening thirst on the banks of the majestic "Father of Waters." On passenger trains it happened occasionally in zero weather that the hose from the water tank to the engine boiler froze, and in an hour or two, or an afternoon, would be lost while the fireman and engineer thawed out the hose; also the railroads had not learned to be particular about fences along the right of way, and cows often got caught under the locomotive wheels and spoiled the time tables for a day.

These delays in transportation were familiar to Lincoln, along with many other phases of the transportation revolution. Lawyer friends of his, such as O. H. Browning of Quincy, were addressing gatherings of farmers in schoolhouses and courtrooms, collecting subscriptions to stock payments for the building of railroads to come. Farmers and storekeepers, as well as speculators and big landowners, saw romance, civilization, and big winnings in iron trails that would be carriers of a commerce for constantly increasing populations. Railroads, new settlers, new farm machinery, were sending farm lands higher in price every year. Corn shellers, revolving horse-rakes, a cob and corn crusher, threshing machines, revolving churns, windmills, wheat drills, refrigerators, were advertised in the *Bloomington Pantograph* in the fall of 1856.

Leading lawyers took cases for and against railroads. Norman B. Judd, the Republican leader in Chicago, was an attorney for the Rock Island Railroad; Joe Gillespie was with the Alton; Browning took cases for the Burlington; Stephen A. Douglas was the particular friend of the Illinois Central. And Abraham Lincoln's reputation as a lawyer went up several notches because of a famous decision he had won for the Illinois Central.

When the Illinois Central got its charter, the legislature provided that it should be free from payment of all taxes, and instead should pay seven per cent of its gross earnings into the state treasury. By this act all counties were stopped from assessing and taxing the railroad. But it happened in 1853 that McLean County decided to assess and tax the Illinois Central Railroad property as it did any other property. Lincoln wrote a letter to T. R. Webber, a McLean County official, saying if they wanted to be sure to have him on their side there was no time to lose. "The company are offering to engage me for them. You have the first right to my services, if you choose to secure me a fee something near such as I can get from the other side." It was understood that if McLean County could win the case, then all other counties through which the railroad line ran would also have the power to assess and tax the corporation's property.

Lincoln described the issue as involving "the largest law question that can now be got up in the state," adding, "and therefore in justice to myself, I cannot afford, if I can help it, to miss a fee altogether." This letter was dated September 12, 1853. Having given his McLean County friends first chance at retaining his services, he wrote three weeks later to Mason Brayman, counsel for the Illinois Central Railroad: "Neither the county of McLean nor any one on its behalf has yet made any engagement with me in relation to its suit with the Illinois Central Railroad on the subject of taxation. I am now free to make an engagement for the road, and if you think of it you may 'count me in.' Please write me on receipt of this."

As the case came to trial in the McLean circuit court, Lincoln represented the railroad corporation and had against him his old law partners, John T. Stuart and Stephen A. Logan. His case was beaten in the circuit court; the decision was that the railroad must pay a tax in every county through which it passed. The cost in taxes would mount into millions and bankrupt the corporation. Lincoln appealed to the supreme court, argued the case twice, and in December, 1855, won a decision reversing the lower court.

He presented his bill to the Illinois Central Railroad corporation at their Chicago office. The bill was for $2,000.00. The official handling the bill looked at it and said, "Why, this is as much as a first-class lawyer would have charged!" adding that it was "as much as Daniel Webster himself would have charged." And Lincoln was paid a fee of $200.00.

When he got back on the circuit and told the other lawyers, they didn't know whether to laugh or cry at this treatment of a lawyer by a corporation that had been saved millions of dollars through Lincoln's victory in court. Lincoln started a suit against the Illinois Central for a fee of $5,000.00. The case was called; the lawyer for the railroad didn't show up; Lincoln was awarded his $5,000.00 one morning, in the afternoon the railroad lawyer arrived and begged Lincoln for a retrial. Lincoln said he was willing, the case was called, and Lincoln read a statement signed by six of the highest-priced lawyers in Illinois that the sum of $5,000.00 for the services rendered in the case "is not unreasonable." Before the jury went out he told them he had been paid $200.00 by the railroad and they should make the verdict for $4,800.00. Which they did.

Thirty-eight days went by and the railroad company failed to pay the $4,800.00 fee. An execution was issued directing the sheriff to seize property of the railroad. Then the fee was paid. And high officers of the railroad stated, "The payment of so large a fee to a western lawyer would embarrass the general counsel with the board of directors in New York."

Lincoln deposited the $4,800.00 in the Springfield Marine Bank, and later, in handing Herndon half of the fee, he pushed it toward his partner, then held it back an instant, and said with a smile, "Billy, it seems to me it will be bad taste on your part to keep saying severe things I have heard from you about railroads and other corporations. Instead of criticizing them, you and I ought to thank God for letting this one fall into our hands." And Herndon wrote, "We both thanked the Lord for letting the Illinois Central fall into our hands."

No bad feeling developed, however, between Lincoln and the Illinois Central Railroad. Five months after he had forced them by court action to pay him the fee he asked for, he met John M. Douglas, the Illinois Central lawyer, and gave him a letter to carry to Jesse K. Dubois, a neighbor of Lincoln in Springfield, a Republican, holding the office of state auditor. The letter:

BLOOMINGTON, DEC. 21, 1857.

DEAR DUBOIS:

J. M. Douglas of the I. C. R. R. Co. is here and will carry this letter. He says they have a large sum (near $90,000) which they will pay into the treasury now, if they have an assurance that they shall not be sued before Jany. 1860— otherwise not. I really wish you would consent to this. Douglas says they *cannot* pay more and I believe him. I do not write this as a lawyer seeking an advantage for a client; but only as a friend, only urging you to do what I think I would do if I were in your situation. I mean this as private and confidential only, but I feel a good deal of anxiety about it.

Yours, as ever,

A. LINCOLN.

He was called on to decide disputes between railroad companies. J. F. Joy, the Illinois Central Railroad official, telegraphed to him from Chicago once: "Can you come here immediately and act as arbitrator in the crossing case between the Illinois Central and Northern Indiana R. R. Companies if you should be appointed? Answer and say yes if possible."

In one case Lincoln argued that the railroad corporation he was defending in a damage suit had more of a soul than a lying witness who brought the damage suit. The opposing lawyer had said his client had a soul and the railroad hadn't. Lincoln replied:

"But our client is but a conventional name for thousands of widows and orphans whose husbands' and parents' hard earnings are represented by this defendant, and who possess souls which they would not swear away as the plaintiff has done for ten million times as much as is at stake here."

Lincoln tried to remind the jury of the farmers who in that time had mortgaged their farms, and the farmers' wives who often had subscribed their butter-and-egg money to get a railroad connecting them with better markets.

When his annual pass on the Alton Railroad was used up, he wrote the superintendent, Richard P. Morgan: "Says John to Tom, 'Here's your old rotten wheelbarrow. I've broke it usin' on it. I wish you would mend it, 'case I shall want to borrow it this afternoon.' Acting on this as a precedent, I say, 'Here's your old "chalked hat." I wish you would take it and send me a new one, 'case I shall want to use it by the 1st of March.' "

He had become a responsible lawyer, trusted with important affairs of property. The McLean County Bank retained him to bring suit against the City of Bloomington. In Springfield, the Gas Works asked him to make certain their title to the two city lots on which they were located, which Lincoln did, later sending the Gas Works a bill for $500.00.

He had influence among judges and lawyers; not only was he a power in politics so that he counted in putting judges on the bench and taking them off; he was also an attorney who had personal qualities and social attractions that gave him influence. He was asked by a caller in his office one day to use his influence in a certain legal quarter; he was offered $500.00 if he would use his influence.

Herndon heard the offer made, and said later: "I heard him refuse the $500.00 over and over again. I went out and left them together. I suppose Lincoln got tired of refusing, for he finally took the money; but he never offered any of it to me; and it was noticeable that whenever he took money in this way, he never seemed to consider it his own or mine. In this case, he gave the money to the Germans in the town, who wanted to buy themselves a press. A few days later, he said to me in the coolest way, 'Herndon, I gave the Germans $250.00 of yours the other day.' 'I am glad you did, Mr. Lincoln,' I answered. Of course I could not say I was glad he took it."

When he traveled from Springfield to Chicago he sometimes took a long way around, he didn't have a pass on the direct route. Henry C. Whitney took a midnight train at Champaign once, and found Lincoln on board. "He explained to me that he was going to Chicago," said Whitney, "and he had passes on the Illinois Central and the Great Western, both; he could get to Chicago by the circuitous route free, while he had no pass by the direct route."

In the famous Rock Island Bridge case Lincoln figured as the apostle of the march of civilization. Against threats of lawsuits and injunctions, the Rock Island Railroad had built a bridge 1,582 feet long, across the Mississippi River, from Rock Island on the Illinois side across to Davenport on the Iowa side. The engineers paid out toil and sweat to make sure that the first railroad spans across the world's greatest river should be strong and safe for passenger and freight trains to rumble over with their cargoes from Council Bluffs to Chicago.

But—the bridge had enemies. There were men who hated the bridge. They swore vengeance against the bridge. They had a contempt for railroads, and especially any railroad that ran over a river where their boats ran. The cargoes of the world should be carried by steamboats, they believed; yet somehow the bridge arose and crossed the river without being shattered by the steamboatmen riding on their proud, white side-wheelers, with their pork and grain and roustabouts on the lower decks, their saloons, dining-rooms and passengers, banjoists, gamblers, and gay women on the upper decks. The bridge got built.

The bridge was built, even though the Chamber of Commerce of St. Louis voted, at the time the cornerstone of the bridge pier was laid, that a bridge across the Mississippi River was "unconstitutional, an obstruction to navigation, dangerous, and that it was the duty of every western state, river city, and town to take immediate action to prevent the erection of such a structure." Threats to force removal of the bridge were heard in

congressional committee rooms in Washington. The effort persisted at
Washington "to abolish the Rock Island bridge nuisance."

Then, on May 6, 1856, came the steamboat *Effie Afton*. She rammed
into a pier of the Rock Island Railroad bridge, took fire, and burned to
a total loss, while part of the bridge burned and tumbled into the river.
And steamboatmen up and down the Mississippi had a jubilee, shouted
the news; there was ringing of bells and blowing of whistles on all boats
in view of the burning, sagging truss of the bridge.

Then the owners of the *Effie Afton* sued the bridge company for
damages. And Norman B. Judd, general counsel of the Rock Island Railroad, and one of the Bloomington convention organizers of the Republican party, called on Abraham Lincoln to represent the company in the
hearing before the District Court of the United States for the Northern
District of Illinois, holding sessions in what was known as the "Saloon
Building" at the southeast corner of Clark and Lake streets in Chicago,
with Judge McLean presiding.

Engineers, pilots, boat owners, river men, bridge builders, were called
as witnesses. Lincoln had made himself so familiar with the figures,
measurements, distances, facts in the case, that sometimes there was laughter as he rambled around the room looking abstracted, but occasionally
turning suddenly to correct a witness on a matter of feet or inches or the
span of a truss. Once he sat down by a big box stove, surrounded with
cuspidors and whittled, seemingly lost to the world. An instant came
when he straightened up, walked toward a witness and demanded that
the original notes as to certain measurements be produced. The witness
was shown to be mistaken; it had its effect on the jury. Lincoln went back
to whittling by the big box stove, seemingly lost to the world.

In his argument Lincoln plainly felt the call of all the old romance of
the Mississippi River and its boat life. He began with pointing out that
St. Louis might wish that the Rock Island bridge should not stand, that
with the bridge gone a larger volume of Iowa products would have
to be shipped by way of St. Louis. Meetings held in St. Louis so indicated.
He pointed to the great channel of the Mississippi flowing "from where it
never freezes to where it never thaws"; it would not be pleasing to block
up such a channel.

Yet there was a growing travel from east to west that had to be considered; it was as important as the Mississippi traffic. It was growing larger
and larger, this east-to-west traffic, building up new country with a
rapidity never before seen in the history of the world. In his own memory
he had seen Illinois grow from almost empty spaces to a population of a
million and a half; there were Iowa and other rising communities in the
Northwest. "This current of travel has its rights as well as that of north
and south." Across the burned bridge the railroad had hauled 12,586
freight cars and 74,179 passengers in eleven months. During four months
of the year the river could not be navigated. But the bridge and the railroad could be used. "This bridge must be treated with respect in this

court and is not to be kicked about with contempt."

The opposing counsel, Judge Wead, had alluded even to a dissolution of the Union of states. "The proper mode for all parties in this affair is 'to live and let live,' and then we will find a cessation of this trouble about the bridge."

The suggestion had been made that a suspension bridge, having no piers, for steamboats to ram, might solve the difficulty. How so? "A suspension bridge cannot be built so high but that the chimneys of the boats will grow up till they cannot pass. The steamboat men will take pains to make them grow."

He analyzed the angles of the piers, the curve of the river, the depth of the channel, the velocity of the current, and showed the final smash of the boat was "in the splash door aft the wheel." And he proved to general satisfaction that the pilot ran his boat as though the river had no bridge with piers standing in it, and the starboard wheel were not working. But the main drive of his argument was that one man had as good a right to cross a river as another had to sail up or down it.

He asked if the products of the boundless, fertile country lying west of the Mississippi must for all time be forced to stop on its western bank, be unloaded from the cars and loaded on a boat, and after passage across the river be reloaded into cars on the other side. Civilization in the region to be west was at issue.

With a whimsical sarcasm, he touched on the testimony that the boat had "smelled a bar," remarking, "For several days we were entertained with depositions about boats 'smelling a bar.' Why, then, did the *Afton,* after she had come up smelling so close to the long pier, sheer off so strangely? When she had got to the centre of the very nose she was smelling, she seemed suddenly to have lost her sense of smell and to have flanked over to the short pier."

The jury listened two days. The speaker came to a pause. He knew that in handling a jury there is a certain moment when it is an advantage to quit talking. He said: "Gentlemen, I have not exhausted my stock of information, and there are more things I could suggest regarding this case, but as I have doubtless used up my time I presume I had better close."

The jury were locked up; when they came out they had agreed to disagree; their action was generally taken as a victory for railroads, bridges, and Chicago, as against steamboats, rivers, and St. Louis.

As he practiced law and earned from two to three thousand dollars a year, he saw other lawyers adding farm after farm to their possessions. Land was the favorite and general form for the material riches of rich men. Among the men with whom he mixed and joked and worked in his daily life were those who owned more land than they could walk across in a week. Stephen T. Logan, the little frowzy-headed lawyer with whom he had once been in partnership, was adding farm to farm. Judge David Davis had ten thousand acres in Iowa, besides his Illinois farms; he was worth a million dollars, people said. The judge had entered tracts of land in Champaign County and sold sections of them. When notes on these lands were not paid and were overdue, he gave them to Henry C. Whitney, who brought suits for payment.

And Whitney told what happened, in this manner: "At a convenient season, when it came time to adjourn court, he did not adjourn, but remained on the bench till everybody filed out, except the clerk and the sheriff, he busying himself reading some court papers. Then I arose and called up the case of 'Davis vs. Smith.' 'Well,' said the Judge nonchalantly, 'what is wanted?' 'Default on a note.' 'Has the defendant been served in time and no appearance?' asked he. 'Yes, your Honor, all is regular.' 'Mr. Sheriff, call John Smith.' 'Jaw Smy—Jaw Smy—Jaw Smy,' said the sheriff perfunctorily. No answer. 'Judgment by default: clerk assess damages,' said the Judge, and went on with his reading a decent length of time, and then formally adjourned court."

"There was no prearrangement at all about this. I instinctively knew what the judge wanted and how he wanted it done; and he instinctively knew how to play his part, and how I would play mine; and no one in all Champaign County knew that the judge had really rendered judgment in his own case, but himself, the clerk, sheriff, and myself. Could he not have accomplished it thus—he must necessarily have brought another judge there to enter these formal judgments or sent them to another circuit by change of venue. As there was no inherent wrong in this, the judge didn't care for its appearance—provided it could be done in the sly way it was."

One day a check for $500.00 came into Lincoln's hands, the largest retaining fee that he had ever handled for himself as a lawyer. He was hired for a law case that interested him from start to finish. It sent his imagination back to the day when he went to the fields and harvested grain with scythe and cradle, when he had formed calluses on the insides of his hands from holding the scythe handle. Since that time the reaper had come; the farmer sat and drove a team of horses while revolving scythes behind cut swaths of grain; one farmer was as good as a gang. Two factories in Illinois were making these reaping machines. It was part of the agricultural revolution, the urge to make the prairies pay out with bigger crops.

In Chicago was Cyrus M. McCormick, with his big shops for making a reaping machine; in Rockford was John M. Manny with his shops, also for making a reaping machine. And McCormick was bringing court action against Manny, claiming that Manny's patents were not lawful and valid, and that they infringed on the McCormick rights. If McCormick could win his case he would stop the Manny factory at Rockford and get $400,000.00 as damages. His lawyers were E. N. Dickerson and Reverdy Johnson, while Manny had George Harding, Edwin M. Stanton, and Abraham Lincoln.

Testimony had been taken in Cincinnati and sent on to Lincoln at

Springfield for him to read. He was expected to go on to Cincinnatti later and make a famous argument before Judge McLean, the same Federal judge before whom the Rock Island bridge case had been tried, with victory for Lincoln's client. His colleague, Stanton, had also figured in a bridge case, the finest steamer on the Ohio River having smashed into the Wheeling suspension bridge in order to show that the bridge stood in the way of free navigation.

A serious man was this Stanton; at his father's knee he had sworn an oath to fight slavery till death; he had toiled through Kenyon College in Ohio and practiced law before he was of legal age; he had swallowed poison while defending a client in a murder trial so as to describe its effects and save his client from hanging, which he did; at his bedside he kept the ashes of hs firstborn child in an urn. He was a man strict in language, dress, duty. When his eyes lighted on Lincoln at the Burnett House in Cincinnati, wearing heavy boots, loose clothes, farmer-looking, he used language which sounded like a question, "Where did that long-armed baboon come from?" And he described Lincoln as wearing a linen duster with splotches like "a map of the continent," and was quoted as saying he wouldn't associate with "such a damned, gawky, long-armed ape as that."

Up and down the courtroom walked Lincoln as the testimony was being taken, stopping to listen now and then, resuming his walk, thinking it all over as though he were in his own law office at home. In his coat pocket he had a manuscript of his argument; it was packed with the cunning and attraction he felt about man and machinery, farming and civilization.

The moment came when Stanton told the court that only two arguments would be made for the defense whether he, Stanton, spoke or not. He suggested to Lincoln that he should speak. Lincoln answered, "No, you speak." Stanton replied, "I will," and picking up his hat said he would go and prepare his speech.

Thus Lincoln was frozen out, and his carefully planned speech was not delivered. He sent the manuscript to Harding, with the request that Harding should not show it to Stanton. And Harding, it was said in Cincinnati, threw it into a waste basket without reading it.

A young representative of the Manny company, Ralph Emerson, had come on from Rockford, Illinois, and struck up an acquaintance with Lincoln. They took long walks of evenings. Emerson told Lincoln that the study of law interested him; he had read a little and believed he might choose it for a life work. He wanted to ask a question. "Mr. Lincoln, is is possible for a man to practice law and always do by others as he would be done by?"

Lincoln's chin dropped lower into his bosom as they walked the grade of a long Cincinnati hill in the quiet of evening haze and the peace of hours after sundown. When Lincoln spoke at last he had no answer to the young man's question. And the young man decided that the lack of an answer was in itself one; he decided not to be a lawyer, and said afterward, "That walk turned the course of my life."

Lincoln visited the courts in Cincinnati and enjoyed watching Bellamy Storer, a judge in Room No. 1 of the Superior Court. Storer had careless manners and direct methods; it was said he could "mingle in the same hour the gravity of the judge and the jest of the clown." Lincoln took it all in, and remarked: "I wish we had that judge in Illinois. I think he would share with me the fatherhood of the legal jokes of the Illinois bar."

On leaving Cincinnati he told young Emerson that he was going back to Illinois to study law; eastern lawyers seemed to be coming West for practice. "They have got as far as Cincinnati now; they will soon be in Illinois. I will be ready for them."

Back in Springfield he divided the $2,000.00 fee, half and half, with Herndon, said he had been "roughly handled by that man Stanton," and discussed Judge McLean, classifying the judge as "an old granny." Getting specific, he said of the judge, "If you were to point your finger at him and a darning needle at the same time, he never would know which was the sharper."

Often Lincoln used his inborn sense of the comic to strip the opposition of dignity. In one case his client was a rich man who had beaten an editor with a stick; the editor sued for $10,000.00 damages. The opposition lawyer roused the jury and people who crowded the courtroom to high excitement; many faces were wet with tears. It was Lincoln's turn to speak. And Abram Bergen, who was young and was thinking of studying law, was wondering what Lincoln would do. His impression was: "Lincoln dragged his feet off the table, on the top of which they had been resting, set them on the floor, gradually lifted up and straightened out his length of legs and body, and took off his coat. While removing his coat it was noticed by all present that his eyes were intently fixed on something on the table before him. He picked up the object, a paper, scrutinized it closely, and, without uttering a word, indulged in a long, loud laugh, accompanied by his wonderfully grotesque facial expression. It was magnetic; the whole audience grinned.

"Then he laid the paper down slowly, took off his cravat, again picked up the paper, re-examined it, and repeated the laugh. It was contagious. He then deliberately removed his vest, showing his one yarn suspender, took up the paper, again looked at it curiously, and again indulged in his peculiar laugh. Its effect was absolutely irresistible; the judge, jury, and whole audience joined in the merriment, and this before Lincoln had spoken a single word.

"When the laughter had subsided, he apologized to the court for his seemingly rude behavior and explained that the amount of damages claimed was at first written $1,000.00 He supposed the plaintiff afterward had taken a second look and concluded that the wounds to his honor were worth an additional $9,000.00. He immediately and fully admitted that the plaintiff was entitled to some amount, told a funny story, and specially urged the jury to agree on some amount. The verdict was for a few hundred dollars and was entirely satisfactory to Lincoln's client."

A witness said his name was J. Parker Green. Lincoln cross-examined: Why J. Parker Green?—What did the J. stand for?—John?—Well, why didn't the witness call himself John P. Green?—That was his name, wasn't it?—Well, what was the reason he didn't wish to be known by his right name. Did J. Parker Green have anything to conceal; and, if not, why did J. Parker Green part his name in that way? As he rang the changes on the name and shifted the tones of his voice in pronouncing the name, he took all dignity away from the witness; it was so ridiculous that boys in the street that day were calling at each other, "J. Parker Green." A Bloomington lawyer, Adlai Stevenson, said: "There was something in Lincoln's way of intoning his questions which made me suspicious of the witness, and I was never able to rid my mind of the absurd impression that there was something not quite right about J. Parker Green. He was discredited and the defendant went free."

In three big cases, involving railroad taxes, a railroad bridge over a great river, and a farmer's reaping-machine patent, he had dug deep in the philosophy of changing civilizations, and the technical engineering as well as the economic structure of the society in which he was living.

He had carried a textbook on astronomy, and he had shared hours with the essayist Francis Bacon, who on the topic, "Of Vicissitude of Things," wrote: "There is an abstruse astrologer that saith, If it were not for two things that are constant (the one is, that the fixed stars ever stand at a like distance one from another, and never came nearer together, nor go further asunder; the other, that the diurnal motion perpetual keepeth time), no individual would last one moment. Certain it is, that the matter is in a perpetual flux, and never at a stay."

The county seat of Logan County had been given his name. Three settlers there had received early information that a railroad was to cross their county and had bought a big tract of land where they guessed the county seat might be located. Lincoln drew up the papers for incorporating the town.

And when he asked them what the name of the new town was to be he was told to call it Lincoln. He warned them, "You better not do that, for I never knew anything named Lincoln that amounted to much." Then he wrote in the name of Lincoln, and it was so spelled out on the maps and the railroad time tables.

The Quincy lawyer, O. H. Browning, kept a diary. Often he made the note that, when stopping in Springfield, he had "spent the evening at the Lincolns." He told the Lincolns how, in driving on rain-soaked prairie roads, the buggy got stuck in the mud, and he waded knee-deep in mud and took fence rails to lift the wheels out and help the horses start—or how, "before we reached Mill Creek bridge, and about two miles west of Burton, we lost a tire from one of the wheels of the carriage, and before we discovered it had broken the felloes and spokes of the wheel to pieces.

We walked on to Burton—took dinner—hired a common two-horse lumber wagon of a Mr. Childers, and drove on."

Browning heard Ralph Waldo Emerson lecture in the state-house in Springfield, on "The Anglo-Saxon," and noted, "He limned a good picture of an Englishman, and gave us some hard raps for our apishness of English fashions and manners." And concerning Emerson the next night, on "Power," he noted: "He is chaste and fascinating, and whilst I cannot approve of all his philosophy, I still listen and delight in his discourses. They contain much that is good, and are worth hearing. After the lecture I attended a supper in the senate chamber given by the ladies of the First Presbyterian Church, and spent a pleasant evening."

When Browning was defending two young men charged with cattle stealing, the judge made remarks indicating that he, the judge, believed the young men very likely were cattle thieves. Browning wrote, "I am not one who thinks the world is retrograding, and human nature is sinking deeper in depravity, but there certainly has been a lamentable deterioration in the judiciary of Illinois within the last few years both mentally and morally, and I cannot witness such things as occurred today without well-grounded alarm."

Three July days he once noted in his diary as having cool weather. On Monday he wrote: "Attending court. Commenced trial of Williamson, formerly postmaster at Lacon, who is indicted for robbing the mail. I am assisting Lincoln at his request. Rain in afternoon." On Tuesday: "Argued case against Williamson. The evidence was very strong, almost conclusive. I was so discouraged that I wished to decline a speech, but at the persuasion of Lincoln I addressed the jury for something over two hours. The case was then given to them at 4 P.M. and they are yet out at 9. The defendant is a young man, who lost a leg in the Mexican War, and does not look to be very bright, a total stranger to me, and I believe him to be guilty, but wish him acquitted. My sympathies are awakened. I am sorry for the poor devil." And on Wednesday: "Jury found Williamson guilty. Will yet try to arrest the judgment but have not much hope. Weather much cooler."

Browning knew, and so did other lawyers in Illinois, that hidden under his brick-dust coloring Lincoln had queer soft spots and his feelings ran out into understanding of blunderers and stumblers; he spoke their languages and stories.

Lincoln defended an old farmer who had taken a bunch of sheep "on shares," fattened them with his year's crop through the winter, and in the spring, when they all died, couldn't pay the sheep owner for them. The sheep owner sued for the money. The first trial was a mistrial; the second trial was lost, and the cost and damages stripped the old man of nearly all his property. At seventy he was starting west to hunt cheap land and make a new home. As he shook hands with the old man and spoke good-by, Lincoln's eyes were wet and he had to hold back tears.

Lincoln had brought suit one year against Frink & Walker, whose stagecoach between Rushville and Frederick had tipped over on one side, cutting and bruising passengers. And two years later he had brought suit against the Great Western Railway Company in behalf of a brakeman, Jasper Harris, who had, as Lincoln's brief recited, "his right foot, ankle, leg and thigh, while in the services of said company, so greatly torn, crushed and broken that amputation of his said right limb above the knee was necessary."

A woman client of Lincoln's had him survey and lay off into lots a piece of land she owned near the Springfield city limits. He found that by some mistake the woman had become owner of three more acres of land than she was entitled to, and Charles Matheny, the former owner, was the loser of the three acres. Lincoln notified her she ought to pay the heirs of Matheny the money owed them at the price per acre first agreed on. The woman couldn't see it; Lincoln wrote her again; the Matheny heirs were poor and needed the money, he told her. And again he wrote explaining to the woman what seemed to him plain justice. One day the woman sent him payment in full and he hunted up the heirs and shared them out their money.

One lawyer who often talked, walked, and slept in the same bed with Lincoln was Henry C. Whitney of Urbana. To Whitney it seemed that Lincoln, when he had taken a case, wanted to win, like most lawyers— only there were tricks and twists he wouldn't use.

"In a clear case of dishonesty, he would hedge in some way so as not himself to partake of the dishonesty; in a doubtful case of dishonesty, he would give his client the benefit of the doubt," was Whitney's impression. And he told of a murder case in which Lincoln "hedged" after getting into it. Leonard Swett and Whitney had spoken for the defence, and believed they would get a verdict of acquittal. Then Lincoln spoke to the jury, took up the facts and the evidence, and was all of a sudden making arguments and admissions that spoiled the case for the prisoner at the bar. The jury came in with a verdict that sent the client to the penitentiary for three years.

And the case got to working in Lincoln's mind. Somehow he hadn't done just right. Having helped get the man in the penitentiary, he worked to get him out, and in a year handed him a pardon from the governor of the state.

He could weep over the old man out of luck, losing a year's fodder crop and, what with dying sheep, losing a farm and moving farther west for a fresh start in life. He was of the frontier, had grown up with it, and seen its line shift west. He understood the frontier scorn and hate for a horse thief. In the case in Edgar County of George W. A. Albin versus Thomas Badine, in slander, he briefed the slanderous remarks: "1st. Albin stole Brady's horse out of my pasture last night. He is a horse thief and that is what he came here for. 2nd. Albin stole that horse last night out of my pasture; and he is a horse thief, and I know that was his business here. 3d. He is a horse thief and I always believed his business was horse stealing, and that is what brought him here. 4th. Albin stole Brady's horse out of my pasture last night, and it is not the first horse he has stolen. He is a horse thief and follows that business. 5th. You stole that horse out of my pasture, and it is not the first one you have stole. 6th. You know you stole that horse, and it is not the first horse you have stole, and I believe you follow the business. 7th. You are a horse thief and you came here for that business—and I believe you came here for nothing else. You are a horse thief. 8th. He is a damn'd little thief, his business is horse stealing and I can prove it."

The home of Lincoln's friend and colleague, Whitney, was in Urbana, and Lincoln came one summer day in 1856 to Urbana to speak at a public meeting in a church. Calling Whitney to one side, he whispered: "There is a boy in your jail I want to see, but I don't want any one beside yourself to know it. I wish you would speak to the jailer."

The boy was a cripple, had stolen a watch from an old man named Green in Urbana, and was under a charge of stealing a gun in Charleston; also the boy was the son of Lincoln's step-brother, John D. Johnston, and so a grandson of Sally Bush Lincoln. "I'm going to help him out of these two cases," said Lincoln, "but that's the last; after that, if he wants to continue his thieving, I shall do nothing for him."

The jail was a rough log cabin, with a one-foot-square hole through which prisoners talked with callers. And Whitney told later what happened: "The prisoner heard us and set up a hypocritical wailing and thrust out toward us a very dirty Bible which Lincoln took and turned over the leaves mechanically. He then said, 'Where were you going, Tom?' The latter attempted to reply, but his wailing made it incoherent, so Lincoln cut it short by saying: 'Now, Tom, do what they tell you—behave yourself—don't talk to any one, and when court closes I will be here and see what I can do for you. Now stop crying and behave yourself.' And with a few more words we left. Lincoln was very sad; I never saw him more so.

"At the fall term of the court, Amzi McWilliams, the prosecuting attorney, agreed with us that if the Greens would come into court and state that they did not desire to press the case further he would file a *nolle pros*. That same evening Lincoln and others were to speak in a church, and at my suggestion Lincoln and I left the meeting and made our way to the house where the Greens lived. They were a venerable old couple, and we found them seated in their humble kitchen greatly astonished at our visit. I introduced Lincoln, who explained his position and wishes in the matter in a homely, plain way, and the good old couple assented. The next day they came into court, willing that the boy should be released, which was promptly done."

Once it happened that Lincoln classified himself as a sort of detective. There came to Springfield an Englishman who had been in St. Louis, passing himself off as a nobleman and buying land and cattle without settling his debts. Claims against him had been put in the hands of the

Springfield banker, Jacob Bunn, whose brother, John, sat up with Lincoln nearly all of one summer night in front of the hotel where the confidence man was staying. Noticing that he was closely watched, the Englishman took Lincoln to one side and said he could pay a thousand dollars if that would wipe out the claims against him. Lincoln took the offer to Bunn, who agreed to the settlement, the money was paid, and the Englishman went his way with no one at his heels.

Bunn asked Lincoln what the fee would be. Lincoln answered he had been more of a detective than a lawyer in the case; if some time in the future he felt he had a fee coming he would ask Bunn for it.

And Bunn had nearly forgotten all about the fee, when one morning, as he was eating breakfast, Lincoln came in and asked for a hundred-dollar fee in the case. Bunn said he would be glad to pay the fee but wished to know why Lincoln had let the matter go so long, and why the fee should be collected in the middle of a morning breakfast.

And as Bunn told it later, "Lincoln's answer was that he needed the money, not for himself, but for another who was in trouble and needed his help. Three of his friends had spent the night in a spree, had broken in almost the entire front of a grocery or saloon; they were in the sheriff's office and would be placed in jail unless some one should settle for the damage done. In a few moments I secured the money and turned it over to him. He seemed more or less relieved, and hurriedly left to interview the sheriff and release his friends. I did not press him for names, but learned that two of his friends were the sons of wealthy parents and the third was his law partner. Lincoln was poorer than any of them, and yet he seemed to regard it his duty to crawl out of his bed before daybreak to their rescue. I doubt if another man in Springfield would have done it. No wonder Lincoln sometimes thanked God he was not born a woman!"

In the town of Danville, Lincoln's law partner there, Ward Hill Lamon, brought the case of a girl named Scott, who was, as they said, "not in her right mind." She had $10,000 in property, mostly cash, and a schemer had struck up an acquaintance with her and asked her to marry him. Her brother wanted a conservator appointed by the court to take care of her and her property, and had agreed with Lamon to pay a fee of $250.00 when the case was won. On trial it took Lincoln and Lamon only twenty minutes to win their case, and Lamon was paid $250.00. Lincoln was sore and hurt, forced Lamon to give back to Miss Scott one-half of the $250.00.

Judge Davis said, in the wheezing whisper of a man weighing 300 pounds, "Lincoln, you are impoverishing this bar by your picayune charges of fees, and the lawyers have reason to complain of you." Other lawyers murmured approval. Lincoln stuck to the point: "That money comes out of the pocket of a poor, demented girl, and I would rather starve than swindle her in this manner." In the evening at the hotel, the lawyers held a mock court and fined him; he paid the fine, rehearsed a new line of funny stories, and stuck to his original point that he wouldn't belong to a law firm that could be styled "Catch 'em and Cheat 'em."

The spitework of human tongues, the lashing and snarling of hate that hunts for stinging names to fasten on other people, this came before him in his work, for review and analysis. A dark-complexioned Portuguese named Dungey married a woman named Spencer, whose brother called Dungey a "negro." As it was a crime under Illinois laws then for a white man to marry a negro, the words were slanderous, and Dungey had Lincoln bring a slander suit. Lincoln's brief recited that Spencer, referring to Dungey as "Black Bill," "in the presence of divers good citizens falsely and maliciously spoke and uttered of and concerning the plaintiff, these false, scandalous, malicious, and defamatory words: 'Black Bill (meaning the plaintiff) is a negro and it will be easily proved if called for.' "

In addressing the jury, he mentioned Spencer as having called Dungey a "nigger," and argued: "Gentlemen of the jury, my client is not a negro, though it is no crime to be a negro—no crime to be born with a black skin. But my client is not a negro. His skin may not be as white as ours, but I say he is not a negro, though he may be a Moor." Not only had Spencer called Dungey a "nigger" but he had followed it up with adding "a nigger married to a white woman."

"And," said Lincoln, "if the malice of the defendant had rested satisfied with speaking the words once or twice, or even thrice, my client would have borne it in silence; but when he went from house to house, *gabbling,* yes, *gabbling* about it, then it was that my client determined to bring this suit." The jury gave a verdict of $600.00 for the Portuguese, who on the advice of Lincoln cut the amount $400.00.

The verdict also required Spencer to pay Lincoln's fee and the court cost; Lincoln asked two other lawyers what he should charge; they told him he would have to fix the fee; he asked, "Well, gentlemen, don't you think I have honestly earned twenty-five dollars?" They could hardly believe their ears; for Lincoln had handled the case through two terms of court, had fought hard in court two days of trial, and the opposition had to pay the bill. They expected a sum more like a hundred dollars; the charge was twenty-five.

Lincoln and Leonard Swett took the defense of Father Chiniquiy, a French Catholic priest in Kankakee County, who was accused by one of his parishioners, Peter Spink, of falsely accusing Spink of perjury. Father Chiniquiy said he could prove his case; he would contest to the last. So a change of venue was taken to Champaign County, where there came to the courthouse in Urbana hundreds of principals, lawyers, witnesses, onlookers, with camp outfits, musicians, parrots, dogs, and changes of clothing. The hotels of Urbana were filled and the overflow slept in tents. The trial dragged on for weeks, and finally the jury went out, and came back unable to agree on a verdict.

Again, at the next term of court, the case was to be called. Hundreds of people had again arrived with camp outfits, musicians, parrots, dogs, and changes of clothing, to hear the testimony and gossip. Lincoln had between-times been at work on a peaceable settlement, and as the gossips and onlookers were getting ready to hear again all the ins and outs of the scandal, he brought into court a paper that wiped the case off the books. It read: "Peter Spink *vs.* Charles Chiniquiy. This day came the parties and the defendant denies that he has ever charged, or believed the plaintiff to be guilty of perjury; that whatever he has said from which such a charge could be inferred, he said on the information of others, protesting his own disbelief in the charge; and that he now disclaims any belief in the truth of said charge against said plaintiff." And they split the court costs and paid their lawyers and everybody went home.

There came a day when Lincoln dropped all his big law cases, dropped all big political affairs then stirring, and threw himself with all he had into the defense of a young man charged with murder, a young man who had grown up since the days at Clary's Grove when he was a baby and Lincoln rocked him in a cradle. As the years passed by, Jack and Hannah Armstrong had moved from Clary's Grove over into Mason County, where they had located on a bluff of the Sangamon River near the mouth of Salt Creek. And Jack Armstrong had died and they had buried him back in Menard County, in Old Concord graveyard where Ann Rutledge had been buried, and where Abe Lincoln had sat alone through long hours. The death of Jack Armstrong had come sooner because a little before he died one of his twin sons, William, nicknamed "Duff" Armstrong, had got into a terrible scrape that many people were talking about; many were saying there had been too much reckless fighting and too many killings, and it might be a good time for a hanging.

At a place called Virgin Grove, not far from the Armstrong home, a camp meeting religious revival had been held; and because it was against the law to sell whisky inside of one mile of a camp meeting, a saloon keeper from Chandlerville had prepared a shack just a little over a mile from the camp-meeting grounds. The bar was made of rough lumber, and poles and brush formed the sides and roof.

And to this place came the wild boy, Duff Armstrong, buying whisky of the bartender, Thomas Steel. For two or three days he was a steady customer, and one evening he was stretched out on a dry-goods box sleeping off the whisky he had taken, when a man named Metzker came in, grabbed Duff Armstrong by the feet and dragged him off the box. Armstrong got up and swore at Metzker, who answered, "Don't be a damn fool; come on and have a drink."

They stood up to the bar and each poured out a glass of whisky. As Armstrong lifted his glass to his lips and started to drink, Metzker threw the whisky from his glass into Armstrong's face and eyes. Armstrong wiped the whisky off his face with his shirt-sleeves, and as soon as his eyes could see and he could make out Metzker, he drove a blow into

Metzker's face, knocked him down, and was going to stamp his boots on Metzker when the bartender, Thomas Steel, stepped in and kept Armstrong off.

As feelings cooled down, Armstrong lay down again on the dry-goods box, and went to sleep. Then in came Jim Norris, a friend of Armstrong, took a few drinks, and a fight started between him and Metzker. The bartender stepped between them, gave Metzker a present of a pint of whisky to go home. And they loaded Metzker onto his horse, started him for home, but he fell off the horse and had to be helped on again.

At the house of Ed Ormie, three miles away, where Metzker was staying, they noticed he acted queer the next morning, but he had looked a good deal the same, the other times before, when sobering up. This time he was sick five days and then died. A coroner's jury and the doctors decided he had died from a blow over the eye caused by a blunt instrument. A house painter named Charles Allen from Petersburg swore that he saw the fight between Armstrong and Metzker, that it was between ten and eleven o'clock at night, and, by the light of a moon shining nearly straight over them, he saw Armstrong hit Metzker with a sling shot and throw the sling shot away and he, Allen, picked it up. Jim Norris and Duff Armstrong were arrested. And Jack Armstrong, with whom Abe Lincoln had wrestled on the level green next to Offut's store twenty-six years before, told Hannah, "Sell everything you have and clear Duff."

Then Jim Norris, who had killed a man, gone to trial and won acquittal a year or two previous, was put on trial, convicted, and sent to the penitentiary for eight years. And the two lawyers defending Duff took a change of venue to Beardstown, and it was there Lincoln told Hannah Armstrong he remembered all her old-time kindness to him and his services were free to her as long as he should live. The two defending lawyers were glad to have the help of Lincoln. And the trial began.

First was the picking of a jury; Lincoln aimed to have young men on the jury; young, hot blood would understand other young, hot blood better, perhaps; the average age of the jurymen, as finally picked, was twenty-three years. Then came the witnesses. With each one Lincoln tried to find some ground of old acquaintance. "Your name?" he asked one. "William Killian. " "Bill Killian. . . . Tell me, are you a son of old Jake Killian?" "Yes, sir." "Well, you are a smart boy if you take after your dad."

Of the witnesses, the one that seemed to make out that Duff Armstrong was a murderer was Allen, the house painter, who said he saw Armstrong by the light of a moon nearly overhead, on a clear night, hit Metzker with a sling shot. Against him was a witness, Nelson Watkins of Menard County, who testified that he had been to camp meeting the day after the fight, that he had with him a sling shot, and that he had thrown it away because it was too heavy and bothersome to carry. He had made the sling shot himself, he testified; he had put an eggshell into the ground, filled it with lead, poured melted zinc over the lead, but the two metals wouldn't stick; then he had cut a cover from a calfskin bootleg, sewed it together with a squirrel-skin string, using a crooked awl to make the holes; and he had then cut a strip from a groundhog skin that he had tanned, and fixed it so it would fasten to his wrist.

Lincoln took out his knife, cut the string with which the cover was sewed, showed it to be squirrel-skin, and then took out the inside metals and showed they were of two different sorts that did not stick together. He had shown that the sling shot which Allen testified he had picked up was identical with one that Watkins testified he had made and thrown away. Meantime, he had sent out for an almanac, and when the moment came he set the courtroom into a buzz of excitement, laughter, whispering, by showing that, instead of the moon being in the sky at "about where the sun is at ten o'clock in the morning," as the leading witness testified, a popular, well-known family almanac for 1857 showed that on the night of August 29, 1857, the moon had set and gone down out of sight at three minutes before midnight, or exactly 11:57 P.M. The almanac raised the question whether there was enough light by which a murder could be competently and materially witnessed.

In his speech to the jury, Lincoln told them he knew the Armstrongs; he knew whether the Armstrongs were good people or bad people; the wild boy, Duff Armstrong, he had held in his arms when Duff was a baby; he had rocked the baby in the cradle at the pioneer home at Clary's Grove; he was sure in his mind and heart about whether Duff Armstrong ought to be hanged or locked in a prison; he could tell good citizens from bad citizens and if there was anything he was certain of, it was that the Armstrong people were good people; they were plain people; they worked for a living; they made their mistakes; but they were kindly, lovely people and belonged with the salt of the earth. He had told the mother of Duff, "Aunt Hannah, your son will be free before sundown." And it so happened. As the jury had filed out to vote a verdict, one of the jurymen winked an eye at Duff, so he afterwards told it.

Stories started later that Lincoln had played a trick, rubbed out numbers and put in other numbers in the almanac, or he had used an almanac for the wrong year, or he had pasted a bogus page into a good almanac, so as to prove his own case. But when men went and hunted up almanacs for the night of August 29, 1857, they found that all the almanacs had the moon setting at three minutes before midnight, so that a murder at eleven o'clock couldn't have had much light from the sky for a witness to see by.

Lincoln was careless and easy-going sometimes about collecting money owed to him by clients. Occasionally when money to be paid him was mentioned to him, he didn't seem to be listening. But when he was short of cash he would try to collect by mail, through writing a letter such as one to David A. Smith. He had touched on other matters between him and Smith, and then finished the letter: "One other little matter. I am short of funds and intended to ask Col. Dunlap for my fee in the case in the United States court, but he left sooner than I expected. He is in no default with me, for he once mentioned the subject to me, and I passed it by. But I now need the money and I will take it as a favor if you will show him this note and get him to send it to me.We never agreed on the amount; but I claim $50—which I suppose neither he or you will think unreasonable."

Among the lawyers and among the people along the circuit of court-houses that Lincoln traveled, he was known as odd in his ways; they joined in the feeling of Dennis Hanks, "There's suthin' peculiarsome about him." John W. Bunn, the Springfield banker, was asked by a Chicago firm to have a local attorney help them in an attachment suit involving several thousand dollars; Lincoln won the suit and charged $25.00; the Chicago firm wrote Bunn, "We asked you to get the best lawyer in Springfield, and it certainly looks as if you had secured one of the cheapest."

He wrote Abraham Bale that a "difficulty" about a wheat sale ought to be settled out of court. "I sincerely hope you will settle it. I think you can if you *will*." The other party, wrote Lincoln, "I have always found a fair man in his dealings." He made his client the offer: "If you settle, I will charge nothing for what I have done, and thank you to boot. By settling, you will more likely get your money sooner, and with much less trouble and expense."

A lease on a valuable hotel property in Quincy was handled by Lincoln for George P. Floyd, who mailed a check for $25.00, to which Lincoln replied: "You must think I am a high-priced man. You are too liberal with your money. Fifteen dollars is enough for the job. I send you a receipt for fifteen dollars and return to you a ten-dollar bill." In coopera-tion with a Chicago lawyer he saved a farm in Brown County for Isaac Hawley, a Springfield man, and Hawley had $50.00 ready to pay a fee; Lincoln smiled into Hawley's face and drawled, "Well, Isaac, I think I will charge you about ten dollars." To another client he said, "I will charge you $25.00, and if you think that is too much I will make it less."

He wrote free advice to a farmer in Woodford County. "If fraud can be proved, the sale will be set aside. This is all that can be done. Any lawyer will know how to do it."

A woman gave him a check to push a real-estate claim in court; he found the claim no good and told the woman on her next visit to his office that there was no action; she thanked him, took her papers and was going, when Lincoln said, "Wait—here is the check you gave me." A district school-library committee, along with the state superintendent of public instruction, met him on the courthouse steps with a green bag in his hand; he drew up a contract for them with a New York publisher's representative, and on their mentioning a fee he said he couldn't take pay for legal services on a question of public interest.

In notes for a law lecture, he wrote: "The matter of fees is important, far beyond the mere question of bread and butter involved. Properly attended to, fuller justice is done both to lawyer and client. An exorbitant fee should never be claimed. As a general rule never take your whole fee in advance. Then you will feel that you are working for something and you are sure to do your work faithfully and well."

In the case of clients far off, he would take the fee as early as possible, however, for he once wrote James S. Irwin: "Whatever fees we earn at a distance, if not paid before, we have noticed, we never hear of after the work is done. We, therefore, are growing a little sensitive on that point."

When he believed it necessary, and for reasons of his own, wished to hurry up the collection of a claim, he could act as in a letter to Henry Dummer, saying, "While I was at Beardstown, I forgot to tell you that William Butler says if you will give him charge, and full discretion, of a claim in your hands, against George G. Grubb, late of Springfield, now of Chicago, he knows how, and can and will make something out of it for you."

Sitting as a judge in Tazewell County, he heard two farmers testify against each other. Trowbridge had let a corner of his farm lands to Hartsfeller, who had raised a small crop of corn and cribbed it on the same land he raised it on. And Trowbridge had fenced his farm, turned his cattle in, and they had got to Hartsfeller's corn. Their stories told, Lincoln turned a keen eye on each of them, and said to the defendant, Trowbridge, "And you say you went over and fenced the corn after you asked him not to crib it on your land?" "Yes, sir." "Trowbridge, you have won your case."

He had been known to call himself a "jack-leg lawyer," just pegging along, or a "mast-fed" lawyer, referring to hogs fed on "mast" or acorns and other wild foods picked up by hogs let loose to get up their own living in field and timberland. In the Dungey case, when opposing lawyers had the case thrown out of court because Lincoln had not drawn up his papers in a technically correct way, he leaned across the trial table, shook a long bony finger at them, and grinned, "Now, by jing, I'll beat you boys!" Which he did.

In the case of Samuel Short, living near Taylorville, Lincoln cleared him of charges of maliciously and feloniously firing a shotgun at boys stealing watermelons on Short's farm; Short didn't pay his fee and Lincoln collected it through a suit in the court of a justice of the peace. Ending a letter that notified a client his case was won, he wrote, "As the Dutch justice said when he married folks, 'Now vere ish my hundred dollars?' " There was a personal tang or smack in slight things he did. A man asked him for advice on a point of law and he told the man he'd have to look it up; meeting the man again, he gave him the advice wanted on that particular point of law; but when the man wished to know what the fee would be Lincoln answered that there would be no fee because it was a point he ought to have known without looking it up.

On Herndon asking him why he was so prompt in always paying Herndon half of the fees, the answer was: "Well, Billy, there are three reasons: first, unless I did so I might forget I had collected the money; secondly, I explain to you how and from whom I received the money, so that you will not be required to dun the man who paid it; thirdly, if I were to die you would have no evidence that I had your money."

Three or four cases were talked about among other lawyers, in which Lincoln had gone in as counsel for the defense, and as the evidence developed, he said to a colleague: "The man is guilty. You defend him; I can't. If I try to speak the jury will see that I think he is guilty, and convict him." Asked to help a litigant named Harris in a suit, his reply was, "Tell Harris it's no use to waste money on me in that case; he'll get beat." When a rapscallion claimed money was owing him and hired Lincoln to prove it, the opposition lawyer brought in a receipt showing the money had been paid. Lincoln left the courtroom and was sitting in the hotel office with his feet on the stove when word came that he was wanted at court. "Tell the judge," he said, "that I can't come; I have to wash my hands." Joe Gillespie said, "I often listened to Lincoln when I thought he would certainly state his case out of court."

A client complained to Whitney about the way he and Lincoln had managed a case; Whitney tried to get Lincoln to smooth it over with the client, Lincoln's answer being, "Let him howl." Usually he was calm, bland, easy-going with other lawyers; but sometimes he wasn't; Amzi McWilliams, handling a witness on Lincoln's side of a case, called out, "Oh! No! No! No!!" which brought Lincoln undoubling out of a chair with a slow yelling of, "Oh! Yes! Yes! Yes!!" putting a stop to the bulldozing of the witness. To a young lawyer he whispered, as the jury was filing out to vote on the case of a slippery client, "Better try and get your money now; if the jury comes in with a verdict for him, you won't get anything."

Another time he undoubled out of a chair when an opposition lawyer had told a jury, "You have been listening for the last hour to an actor, who knows well how to play the role of seeming, for effect," Lincoln was solemn, cool, wrathy, and eying the other lawyer, said, "You have known me for years, and *you know* that not a word of that language can be truthfully applied to me." And part of what the other lawyer said was, "I take it all back, Mr. Lincoln."

A letter from Pekin asked about a land-title case, putting the question, "What is lacking to perfect a title on the part of the defendants?" Lincoln's reply stated: "The trouble with this deed was, that the plaintiff proved it to be a forgery; and I see no way in which the defendants can ever succeed unless they can somehow prove that the deed is not a forgery. This is the whole story. The case cannot be gained by much talking."

A Spoon River client was notified though he had justice and the law on his side he might not win the case. "This position of theirs seems absurd to me; and I found several authorities against it; but they find one *for it,* and, worse than all, the Judge intimates that he is with them."

The widow of a Revolutionary War soldier told Lincoln that a pension agent named Wright had got her a payment from the Federal Government amounting to $400.00—and had kept half of it for himself as a commission. Lincoln told Herndon, "I am going to skin Wright and get that money back." He brought suit and put the tottering widow on the witness stand, where she told her story through her tears.

He told the jury, as Herndon recalled the speech: "She was not always thus. She was once a beautiful young woman. Her step was as elastic, her face as fair, and her voice as sweet as any that rang in the mountains of old Virginia. But now she is poor and defenseless. Out here on the prairies of Illinois, many hundreds of miles from the scenes of her childhood, she appeals to us, who enjoy the privileges achieved for us by the patriots of the Revolution, for our sympathetic aid and manly protection. All I ask is, shall we befriend her?" He pictured the sufferings of the soldiers of the Revolutionary War, and scored the defendant with fierce adjectives.

Some of the jurymen wept. The verdict gave the widow the full amount of money Wright had taken from her. Lincoln paid her hotel bill, bought her a railroad ticket back home, and later sent her the full amount of pension money—with no charge for lawyer's fee. Herndon had picked up Lincoln's notes for his speech to the jury. They read: "No contract.—No professional services.—Unreasonable charge.—Money retained by Def't not given to Pl'ff.—Revolutionary War.—Describe Valley Forge Privations.— Ice.—Soldier's bleeding feet.—Pl'ff's husband.—Soldier leaving home for army.—Skin Def't.—Close."

E. J. Rice, a judge, made several rulings against Lincoln one morning in a murder trial, and he told Herndon at dinner, "I have determined to crowd the court to the wall." And as the trial went on that afternoon he gradually got the judge puzzled and lost. He read authorities to show that the great jurists and the lessons of the past were against the judge. He hurled facts and questions fast from point to point, insulting the judge and making the court look ridiculous, while keeping clear of remarks that would lay him open to fine or reprimand for contempt of court. He was contemptuous of the court in manner, voice, insinuation, and allegation, without being technically guilty of contempt of court. It was a superb performance, as Bill Herndon saw it. "Figuratively speaking, he peeled the court from head to foot," said Herndon. "The judge reversed his decision in Lincoln's favor. His client was acquitted of murder, and he swept the field. I shall never forget the scene."

Fifteen women came into court in Clinton; they had knocked in the heads of the whisky-barrels of a saloon in a near-by town, and were indicted for trespass. One woman called on Lincoln to help their lawyer, and he argued, "In this case I would change the order of indictment and have it read The State *vs.* Mr. Whisky instead of the State *vs.* The Ladies." He mentioned the Boston Tea Party, said the saloon keeper had neither feared God nor regarded man, gave some of his own observations on the ruinous effects of whisky on men and families. And the court dismissed the women, saying if they were to be fined he would let them know.

An odd case was put into his hands by Abraham Brokaw of Bloomington, who had sued a neighbor and had a debt collected by the sheriff, who went bankrupt; and Brokaw couldn't get his money. And so Brokaw put his case into the hands of Stephen A. Douglas, who sued the sheriff's bondsmen and collected the debt; but Brokaw couldn't get his money from Douglas.

Then he hired Lincoln to collect from Douglas. And Lincoln sent the claim to "Long John" Wentworth, the Chicago congressman and editor, who pushed the claim in Washington; and Douglas sniffed and almost snorted; but he paid Brokaw, who remarked to friends: "What do you suppose Lincoln charged me? Exactly three dollars and fifty cents for collecting nearly six hundred dollars." And Lincoln, asked about this low fee, replied: "I had no trouble with it. I sent it to my friend in Washington, and was only out the postage."

Though he made fifty speeches and traveled far, paying his own expenses in one campaign, he was surprised when a committee of Republicans in Champaign County called on him at his hotel and handed him $35.00. As he held the money, he asked, "What will I do with it?" looking puzzled and sheepish. "Put it in your pocket and keep it there," he was told. Which he did—but with a laughing demurrer, "Don't you fellows do that again."

A rich newcomer to Springfield wanted Lincoln to bring suit against an unlucky, crack-brained lawyer who owed him two dollars and a half; Lincoln advised him to hold off; he said he would go to some other lawyer who was more willing. So Lincoln took the case, collected a ten-dollar fee in advance, entered suit, hunted up the defendant and handed him half of the ten dollars and told him to show up in court and pay the debt. Which was done. And all litigants and the lawyer were satisfied.

A horse thief in the Champaign County jail told his local lawyer, William D. Somers, that he wanted Lincoln to help in the defense. When Lincoln and Somers arrived at the jail they found their client talking with his wife, who was in a delicate condition of health, as Lincoln noticed. When the client handed Lincoln ten dollars and said that was all the money he had, Lincoln looked at the woman again, and asked: "How about your wife? Won't she need this?" The answer was, "She'll get along somehow," which didn't satisfy Lincoln. He handed the woman five dollars, and divided the other five with Somers.

He lighted a candle one night and toiled on arguments to show that election bets don't have to be paid. Isaac Smith, the plaintiff in error, made a bet of $110.00 against a buggy owned by a man named Moffett, that the vote of Millard Fillmore for President of the United States was not behind the vote of the other candidates in the state of New York. The winner of the bet didn't call for his buggy, and the loser had traded it off so that it was gone from the stakeholder's barn when the winner came for his buggy. And Lincoln wrote: "Is this gambling debt contrary to the laws of this state, or public policy, or morality? And this being the case, as we think it is, the seller of the buggy has a right to repent of the law's violation and to revoke the bet."

He made the point that betters can call off their bets. He cited the statutes against gambling, and wrote: "We think that betting on Presidential elections over the Union, or in particular states thereof, comes within the spirit of the laws; and if not such betting is contrary to public policy and morality and therefore void; i.e., that bets may be revoked while the decision is pending."

It appeared that Moffett had sold the buggy before he bet it, and Lincoln's brief stated, "This bet was revoked by sale to the plaintiff, long before the decision of the question by the stakeholder, and this repenting and revoking the law allows—yea, favors."

As Lincoln and Whitney stood near the courthouse in Decatur and he pointed to the exact place where he had driven into the town twenty-six years before with an all-wood ox-wagon and four yoke of steers, Whitney asked him if he expected then to be a lawyer. "No, I didn't know I had sense enough to be a lawyer."

Reading authorities in court once he suddenly read one against himself, and, drawing up his shoulders and half laughing, finished reading it, first saying: "There, may it please the court, I reckon I've scratched up a snake; but as I'm in for it, guess I'll read it through." On Whitney's asking him about a mixed point in law, he threw his head back, looked at the ceiling, and chuckled, "Damfino." Helping Whitney in a railroad case, when Whitney was worried about points the opposition was making, Lincoln told him, "All that is very easily answered." And when his time came, Whitney said, "He blew away what seemed to me almost an unanswerable argument as easily as a beer drinker blows off the froth from his foaming tankard."

Yet he had to take his losses at law practice; once he traveled all around the circuit, all his cases were for defendants, and he was beaten every time; so he told Bunn, the banker, in Springfield. And he told himself that people had said, without disturbing his self-respect, "Well, he isn't lawyer enough to hurt him."

In the parlor or barroom of a hotel, there was no telling of an evening whether he would spin yarns or conduct philosophic inquiries. "I have heard Lincoln," said Joe Gillespie, "descant upon the problem whether a ball discharged from a gun in a horizontal position would be longer in reaching the ground than one dropped at the instant of discharge from the muzzle."

As he spoke to juries, men felt that he believed what he had once said to the Washingtonian Temperance Society in Springfield: "There are few things wholly evil or wholly good; almost everything is an inseparable compound of the two." Once in Springfield he was one of five lawyers defending a woman and a man accused of murdering the woman's husband by poison. A handsome young man sat next to the woman, showed an interest in her, frisked around the courtroom, got law books and pointed out pages to Lincoln and other lawyers for the defense. And Usher F. Linder, an assistant prosecutor, began his speech to the jury after Lincoln and three other lawyers had spoken for the defense. Pointing his finger at the handsome young man who had sat next to the accused woman, Linder said, "Gentlemen of the jury, if you wanted any additional evidence of this man's guilt, it would only be necessary for you to recur to his boldness and impudence on this trial." He directed his index finger straight at the face of the young man and cried, "You can see guilt written all over his countenance." And the handsome young man arose and said with warm feeling: "General Linder, you are mistaken; I am not the criminal. My name is Rosette; I am a lawyer, and one of the counsel for the defendants."

Lincoln came to know in whispered consultation and public cross-examination the minds and hearts of a quarreling, chaffering, suspicious, murderous, loving, lavish, paradoxical humanity.

Lincoln defended a man who had thirty-five indictments against him for obstruction of the public highway. He took to the supreme court of the state a case involving a dispute over the payment of three dollars in a hog sale. He became versed in the questions whether a saloon license can be transferred, whether damages can be collected from a farmer who starts a prairie fire that spreads to other farms, whether the divorced wife of a man can compel him to give her custody of her children, and to supply her the means for support of the children; these were causes in which Lincoln argued before the state supreme court. He also argued before that tribunal in cases involving wills, mortgages, notes, land titles, railroad condemnation proceedings, breaches of contract, validity of patents, ejectments, personal injury. A merchant set fire to his stock of goods, collected the insurance, bought a new stock, and was sued by the insurance company for the possession of the new stock. A man and his wife were put off a railroad train because they refused to pay excess cash fare, claiming that the station agent had no tickets to their point of destination; they sued the railroad company. A man named Banet sued the Alton & Sangamon Railroad Company because after he had subscribed for stock in their road they changed its route and ran the line of it twelve miles distant from his real-estate holdings in New Berlin.

Such were a few of the human causes, disputes, and actions in which Lincoln versed himself thoroughly, carrying his arguments up to the highest court in the state, and winning more than half of his cases there.

His memory was indexed and cross-indexed with tangled human causes.

Crainquebille

Anatole France

I

IN EVERY SENTENCE pronounced by a judge in the name of the sovereign people, dwells the whole majesty of justice. The august character of that justice was brought home to Jérôme Crainquebille, costermonger, when, accused of having insulted a policeman, he appeared in the police court. Having taken his place in the dock, he beheld in the imposing sombre hall magistrates, clerks, lawyers in their robes, the usher wearing his chains, *gendarmes,* and, behind a rail, the bare heads of the silent spectators. He, himself, occupied a raised seat, as if some sinister honour were conferred on the accused by his appearance before the magistrate. At the end of the hall, between two assessors, sat the Président Bourriche. The palm-leaves of an officer of the Academy decorated his breast. Over the tribune were a bust representing the Republic and a crucifix, as if to indicate that all laws divine and human were suspended over Crainquebille's head. Such symbols naturally inspired him with terror. Not being gifted with a philosophic mind, he did not inquire the meaning of the bust and the crucifix; he did not ask how far Jesus and the symbolical bust harmonized in the Law Courts. Nevertheless, here was matter for reflection; for, after all, pontifical teaching and canon law are in many points opposed to the constitution of the Republic and to the civil code. So far as we know the Decretals have not been abolished. To-day, as formerly, the Church of Christ teaches that only those powers are lawful to which it has given its sanction. Now the French Republic claims to be independent of pontifical power. Crainquebille might reasonably say:

"Gentlemen and magistrates, in so much as President Loubet has not been anointed, the Christ, whose image is suspended over your heads, repudiates you through the voice of councils and of Popes. Either he is here to remind you of the rights of the Church, which invalidate yours, or His presence has no rational signification."

Whereupon President Bourriche might reply:

From *Crainquebille*, by Anatole France. Reprinted by permission of Dodd, Mead & Co., Inc. and John Lane The Bodley Head Ltd.

"Prisoner Crainquebille, the kings of France have always quarrelled with the Pope. Guillaume de Nogaret was excommunicated, but for so trifling a reason he did not resign his office. The Christ of the tribune is not the Christ of Gregory VII or of Boniface VIII. He is, if you will, the Christ of the Gospels, who knew not one word of canon law, and had never heard of the holy Decretals."

Then Crainquebille might not without reason have answered:

"The Christ of the Gospels was an agitator. Moreover, he was the victim of a sentence, which for nineteen hundred years all Christian peoples have regarded as a grave judicial error. I defy you Monsieur le Président, to condemn me in His name to so much as forty-eight hours' imprisonment."

But Crainquebille did not indulge in any considerations either historical, political or social. He was wrapped in amazement. All the ceremonial, with which he was surrounded, impressed him with a very lofty idea of justice. Filled with reverence, overcome with terror, he was ready to submit to his judges in the matter of his guilt. In his own conscience he was convinced of his innocence; but he felt how insignificant is the conscience of a costermonger in the face of the panoply of the law, and the ministers of public prosecution. Already his lawyer had half persuaded him that he was not innocent.

A summary and hasty examination had brought out the charges under which he laboured.

II

Up and down the town went Jérôme Crainquebille, costermonger, pushing his barrow before him and crying: "Cabbages! Turnips! Carrots!" When he had leeks he cried: "Asparagus!" For leeks are the asparagus of the poor. Now it happened that on October 20, at noon, as he was going down the Rue Montmartre, there came out of her shop the shoemaker's wife, Madame Bayard. She went up to Crainquebille's barrow and scornfully taking up a bundle of leeks, she said:

"I don't think much of your leeks. What do you want a bundle?"

"Sevenpence halfpenny, mum, and the best in the market!"

"Sevenpence halfpenny for three wretched leeks?"

And disdainfully she cast the leeks back into the barrow.

Then it was that Constable 64 came and said to Crainquebille:

"Move on."

Moving on was what Crainquebille had been doing from morning till evening for fifty years. Such an order seemed right to him, and perfectly in accordance with the nature of things. Quite prepared to obey, he urged his customer to take what she wanted.

"You must give me time to choose," she retorted sharply.

Then she felt all the bundles of leeks over again. Finally, she selected the one she thought the best, and held it clasped to her bosom as saints in church pictures hold the palm of victory.

"I will give you sevenpence. That's quite enough; and I'll have to fetch it from the shop, for I haven't anything on me."

Still embracing the leeks, she went back into the shop, whither she had been preceded by a customer, carrying a child.

Just at this moment Constable 64 said to Crainquebille for the second time:

"Move on."

"I'm waiting for my money," replied Crainquebille.

"And I'm not telling you to wait for your money; I'm telling you to move on," retorted the constable grimly.

Meanwhile, the shoemaker's wife in her shop was fitting blue slippers on to a child of eighteen months, whose mother was in a hurry. And the green heads of the leeks were lying on the counter.

For the half century that he had been pushing his barrow through the streets, Crainquebille had been learning respect for authority. But now his position was a peculiar one: he was torn asunder between what was his due and what was his duty. His was not a judicial mind. He failed to understand that the possession of an individual's right in no way exonerated him from the performance of a social duty. He attached too great importance to his claim to receive sevenpence, and too little to the duty of pushing his barrow and moving on, for ever moving on. He stood still.

For the third time Constable 64 quietly and calmly ordered him to move on. Unlike Inspector Montauciel, whose habit it is to threaten constantly but never to take proceedings, Constable 64 is slow to threaten and quick to act. Such is his character. Though somewhat sly he is an excellent servant and a loyal soldier. He is as brave as a lion and as gentle as a child. He knows naught save his official instructions.

"Don't you understand when I tell you to move on?"

To Crainquebille's mind his reason for standing still was too weighty for him not to consider it sufficient. Wherefore, artlessly and simply he explained it:

"Good Lord! Don't I tell you that I am waiting for my money."

Constable 64 merely replied:

"Do you want me to summons you? If you do you have only to say so."

At these words Crainquebille slowly shrugged his shoulders, looked sadly at the constable, and then raised his eyes to heaven, as if he would say:

"I call God to witness! Am I a law-breaker? Am I one to make light of the by-laws and ordinances which regulate my ambulatory calling? At five o'clock in the morning I was at the market. Since seven, pushing my barrow and wearing my hands to the bone, I have been crying: 'Cabbages! Turnips! Carrots!' I am turned sixty. I am worn out. And you ask me whether I have raised the black flag of rebellion. You are mocking me and your joking is cruel."

Either because he failed to notice the expression on Crainquebille's face, or because he considered it no excuse for disobedience, the constable inquired curtly and roughly whether he had been understood.

Now, just at that moment the block of traffic in the Rue Montmartre was at its worst. Carriages, drays, carts, omnibuses, trucks, jammed one against the other, seemed indissolubly welded together. From their quivering immobility proceeded shouts and oaths. Cabmen and butchers' boys grandiloquent and drawling insulted one another from a distance, and omnibus conductors, regarding Crainquebille as the cause of the block, called him "a dirty leek."

Meanwhile, on the pavement the curious were crowding round to listen to the dispute. Then the constable, finding himself the centre of attention, began to think it time to display his authority:

"Very well," he said, taking a stumpy pencil and a greasy notebook from his pocket.

Crainquebille persisted in his idea, obedient to a force within. Besides, it was now impossible for him either to move on or to draw back. The wheel of his barrow was unfortunately caught in that of a milkman's cart.

Tearing his hair beneath his cap he cried:

"But don't I tell you I'm waiting for my money! Here's a fix! *Misère de misère! Bon sang de bon sang!*"

By these words, expressive rather of despair than of rebellion, Constable 64 considered he had been insulted. And, because to his mind all insults must necessarily take the consecrated, regular, traditional, liturgical, ritual form so to speak of *Mort aux vaches,** thus the offender's words were heard and understood by the constable.

"Ah! You said: *Mort aux vaches.* Very good. Come along."

Stupefied with amazement and distress, Crainquebille opened his great rheumy eyes and gazed at Constable 64. With a broken voice proceeding now from the top of his head and now from the heels of his boots, he cried, with his arms folded over his blue blouse:

"I said '*Mort aux vaches?*' I? . . . Oh!"

The tradesmen and errand boys hailed the arrest with laughter. It gratified the taste of all crowds for violent and ignoble spectacles. But there was one serious person who was pushing his way through the throng; he was a sad-looking old man, dressed in black, wearing a high hat; he went up to the constable and said to him in a low voice very gently and firmly:

"You are mistaken. This man did not insult you."

"Mind your own business," replied the policeman, but without

---

* It is impossible to translate this expression. As explained later, it means "down with spies," the word spies being used to indicate the police.

threatening, for he was speaking to a man who was well dressed.

The old man insisted calmly and tenaciously. And the policeman ordered him to make his declaration to the Police Commissioner.

Meanwhile Crainquebille was explaining:

"Then I did say *'Mort aux vaches!'* Oh! . . ."

As he was thus giving vent to his astonishment, Madame Bayard, the shoemaker's wife, came to him with sevenpence in her hand. But Constable 64 already had him by the collar; so Madame Bayard, thinking that no debt could be due to a man who was being taken to the police-station, put her sevenpence into her apron pocket.

Then, suddenly beholding his barrow confiscated, his liberty lost, a gulf opening beneath him and the sky overcast, Crainquebille murmured:

"It can't be helped!"

Before the Commissioner, the old gentleman declared that he had been hindered on his way by the block in the traffic, and so had witnessed the incident. He maintained that the policeman had not been insulted, and that he was labouring under a delusion. He gave his name and profession: Dr. David Matthieu, chief physician at the Ambroise-Paré Hospital, officer of the Legion of Honour. At another time such evidence would have been sufficient for the Commissioner. But just then men of science were regarded with suspicion in France.

Crainquebille continued under arrest. He passed the night in the lock-up. In the morning he was taken to the Police Court in the prison van.

He did not find prison either sad or humiliating. It seemed to him necessary. What struck him as he entered was the cleanliness of the walls and of the brick floor.

"Well, for a clean place, yes, it is a clean place. You might eat off the floor."

When he was left alone, he wanted to draw out his stool; but he perceived that it was fastened to the wall. He expressed his surprise aloud:

"That's a queer idea! Now there's a thing I should never have thought of, I'm sure."

Having sat down, he twiddled his thumbs and remained wrapped in amazement. The silence and the solitude overwhelmed him. The time seemed long. Anxiously he thought of his barrow, which had been confiscated with its load of cabbages, carrots, celery, dandelion and corn-salad. And he wondered, asking himself with alarm: "What have they done with my barrow?"

On the third day he received a visit from his lawyer, Maitre Lemerle, one of the youngest members of the Paris Bar, President of a section of La Ligue de la Patrie Française.

Crainquebille endeavoured to tell him his story; but it was not easy, for he was not accustomed to conversation. With a little help he might perhaps have succeeded. But his lawyer shook his head doubtfully at everything he said; and, turning over his papers, muttered:

"Hm! Hm! I don't find anything about all this in my brief."

Then, in a bored tone, twirling his fair moustache he said:

"In your own interest it would be advisable, perhaps, for you to confess. Your persistence in absolute denial seems to me extremely unwise."

And from that moment Crainquebille would have made confession if he had known what to confess.

III

President Bourriche devoted six whole minutes to the examination of Crainquebille. This examination would have been more enlightening if the accused had replied to the questions asked him. But Crainquebille was unaccustomed to discussion; and in such a company his lips were sealed by reverence and fear. So he was silent: and the President answered his own question; his replies were staggering. He concluded: "Finally, you admit having said, *'Mort aux vaches.'* "

He meant that, being overwhelmed by the most unexpected of accusations, he had in his amazement merely repeated the curious words falsely attributed to him, and which he had certainly never pronounced. He had said, *"Mort aux vaches!"* as he might have said, "I capable of insulting anyone! how could you believe it?"

President Bourriche put a different interpretation on the incident.

"Do you maintain," he said, "that the policeman was, himself, the first to utter the exclamation?"

Crainquebille gave up trying to explain. It was too difficult.

"You do not persist in your statement. You are quite right," said the President.

And he had the witness called.

Constable 64, by name Bastien Matra, swore he spoke the truth and nothing but the truth. Then he gave evidence in the following terms:

"I was on my beat on October 20, at noon, when I noticed in the Rue Montmartre a person who appeared to be a hawker, unduly blocking the traffic with his barrow opposite No. 328. Three times I intimated to him the order to move on, but he refused to comply. And when I gave him warning that I was about to charge him, he retorted by crying: *'Mort aux vaches!'* Which I took as an insult."

This evidence, delivered in a firm and moderate manner, the magistrates received with obvious approbation. The witnesses for the defence were Madame Bayard, shoemaker's wife, and Dr. David Matthieu, chief physician to the Hospital Ambroise Paré, officer of the Legion of Honour. Madame Bayard had seen nothing and heard nothing. Dr. Matthieu was in the crowd which had gathered round the policeman, who was ordering the costermonger to move on. His evidence led to a new episode in the trial.

"I witnessed the incident," he said, "I observed that the constable had made a mistake; he had not been insulted. I went up to him and called his attention to the fact. The officer insisted on arresting the costermonger, and told me to follow him to the Commissioner of Police. This I did. Before the Commissioner, I repeated my declaration."

"You may sit down," said the President. "Usher, recall witness Matra."

"Matra, when you proceeded to arrest the accused, did not Dr. Matthieu point out to you that you were mistaken?"

"That is to say, Monsieur le Président, that he insulted me."

"What did he say?"

"He said, '*Mort aux vaches!*'"

Uproarious laughter arose from the audience.

"You may withdraw," said the President hurriedly.

And he warned the public that if such unseemly demonstrations occurred again he would clear the court. Meanwhile, Counsel for the defence was haughtily fluttering the sleeves of his gown, and for the moment it was thought that Crainquebille would be acquitted.

Order having been restored, Maitre Lemerle rose. He opened his pleading with a eulogy of policemen: "those unassuming servants of society who, in return for a trifling salary, endure fatigue and brave incessant danger with daily heroism. They were soldiers once, and soldiers they remain; soldiers, that word expresses everything. . . ."

From this consideration Maitre Lemerle went on to descant eloquently on the military virtues. He was one of those, he said, who would not allow a finger to be laid on the army, on that national army, to which he was so proud to belong.

The President bowed. Maitre Lemerle happened to be lieutenant in the Reserves. He was also nationalist candidate for Les Vieilles Haudriettes. He continued:

"No, indeed, I do not esteem lightly the invaluable services unassumingly rendered, which the valiant people of Paris receive daily from the guardians of the peace. And had I beheld in Crainquebille, gentlemen, one who had insulted an ex-soldier, I should never have consented to represent him before you. My client is accused of having said: '*Mort aux vaches!*' The meaning of such an expression is clear. If you consult *Le Dictionnaire de la Langue Verte* (slang) you will find: '*Vachard* a sluggard, an idler, one who stretches himself out lazily like a cow instead of working. *Vache,* one who sells himself to the police; spy.' *Mort aux vaches* is an expression employed by certain people. But the question resolves itself into this: how did Crainquebille say it? And, further, did he say it at all? Permit me to doubt it, gentlemen.

"I do not suspect Constable Matra of any evil intention. But, as we have said, his calling is arduous. He is sometimes harassed, fatigued, overdone. In such conditions he may have suffered from an aural hallucination. And, when he comes and tells you, gentlemen, that Dr. David Matthieu, officer of the Legion of Honour, chief physician at the Ambroise-

Paré Hospital, a gentleman and a prince of science, cried: '*Mort aux vaches*,' then we are forced to believe that Matra is obsessed, and if the term be not too strong, suffering from the mania of persecution.

"And even if Crainquebille did cry: '*Mort aux vaches*,' it remains to be proved whether such words on his lips can be regarded as an offence. Crainquebille is the natural child of a costermonger, depraved by years of drinking and other evil courses. Crainquebille was born alcoholic. You behold him brutalized by sixty years of poverty. Gentlemen you must conclude that he is irresponsible."

Maitre Lemerle sat down. Then President Bourriche muttered a sentence condemning Jérôme Crainquebille to pay fifty francs fine and to go to prison for a fortnight. The magistrates convicted him on the strength of the evidence given by Constable Matra.

As he was being taken down the long dark passage of the Palais, Crainquebille felt an intense desire for sympathy. He turned to the municipal guard who was his escort and called him three times:

" 'Cipal! . . . 'cipal! . . . Eh! 'cipal!" And he sighed:

"If anyone had told me only a fortnight ago that this would happen!"

Then he reflected:

"They speak too quickly, these gentlemen. They speak well, but they speak too quickly. You can't make them understand you. . . . 'cipal, don't you think they speak too quickly?"

But the soldier marched straight on without replying or turning his head.

Crainquebille asked him:

"Why don't you answer me?"

The soldier was silent. And Crainquebille said bitterly:

"You would speak to a dog. Why not to me? Do you never open your mouth? Is it because your breath is foul?"

IV

After the sentence had been pronounced, several members of the audience and two or three lawyers left the hall. The clerk was already calling another case. Those who went out did not reflect on the Crainquebille affair, which had not greatly interested them; and they thought no more about it. Monsieur Jean Lermite, an etcher, who happened to be at the Palais, was the only one who meditated on what he had just seen and heard. Putting his arm on the shoulder of Maitre Joseph Aubarrée, he said:

"President Bourriche must be congratulated on having kept his mind free from idle curiosity, and from the intellectual pride which is determined to know everything. If he had weighed one against the other the contradictory evidence of Constable Matra and Dr. David Matthieu, the magistrate would have adopted a course leading to nothing but doubt and uncertainty. The method of examining facts in a critical spirit would be fatal to the administration of justice. If the judge were so imprudent as to follow that method, his sentences would depend on his personal sagacity, of which he has generally no very great store, and on human infirmity which is universal. Where can he find a criterion? It cannot be denied that the historical method is absolutely incapable of providing him with the certainty he needs. In this connexion you may recall a story told of Sir Walter Raleigh.

" 'One day, when Raleigh, a prisoner in the Tower of London, was working, as was his wont, at the second part of his "History of the World," there was a scuffle under his window. He went and looked at the brawlers; and when he returned to his work, he thought he had observed them very carefully. But on the morrow, having related the incident to one of his friends who had witnessed the affair and had even taken part in it, he was contradicted by his friend on every point. Reflecting, therefore, that if he were mistaken as to events which passed beneath his very eyes, how much greater must be the difficulty of ascertaining the truth concerning events far distant, he threw the manuscript of his history into the fire.'

"If the judges had the same scruples as Sir Walter Raleigh, they would throw all their notes into the fire. But they have no right to do so. They would thus be flouting justice; they would be committing a crime. We may despair of knowing, we must not despair of judging. Those who demand that sentences pronounced in Law Courts should be founded upon a methodical examination of facts, are dangerous sophists, and perfidious enemies of justice both civil and military. President Bourriche has too judicial a mind to permit his sentences to depend on reason and knowledge, the conclusions of which are eternally open to question. He founds them on dogma and moulds them by tradition, so that the authority of his sentences is equal to that of the Church's commandments. His sentences are indeed canonical. I mean that he derives them from a certain number of sacred canons. See, for example, how he classifies evidence, not according to the uncertain and deceptive qualities of appearances and of human veracity, but according to intrinsic, permanent and manifest qualities. He weighs them in the scale, using weapons of war for weights. Can anything be at once simpler and wiser? Irrefutable for him is the evidence of a guardian of the peace, once his humanity be abstracted, and he conceived as a registered number, and according to the categories of an ideal police. Not that Matra (Bastien), born at Cinto-Monte in Corsica, appears to him incapable of error. He never thought that Bastien Matra was gifted with any great faculty of observation, nor that he applied any secret and vigorous method to the examination of facts. In truth it is not Bastien Matra he is considering, but Constable 64. A man is fallible, he thinks. Peter and Paul may be mistaken. Descartes and Gassendi, Leibnitz and Newton, Bichat and Claude Bernard were capable of error. We may all err and at any moment. The causes of error are innumerable. The perceptions of our senses and the judgment of our minds are sources of illusion and causes of uncertainty. We dare not rely on the evidence of a single man: *Testis unus, testis nullus*. But we may have faith in a number. Bastien Matra, of Cinto-Monte, is fallible. But Constable 64, when abstraction has been made of his humanity, cannot err. He is an entity. An entity has nothing in common with a man, it is free from all that confuses, corrupts and deceives men. It is pure, unchangeable and unalloyed. Wherefore the magistrates did not hesitate to reject the evidence of the mere man, Dr. David Matthieu, and to admit that of Constable 64, who is the pure idea, an emanation from divinity come down to the judgment bar.

"By following such a line of argument, President Bourriche attains to a kind of infallibility, the only kind to which a magistrate may aspire. When the man who bears witness is armed with a sword, it is the sword's evidence that must be listened to, not the man's. The man is contemptible and may be wrong. The sword is not contemptible and is always right. President Bourriche has seen deeply into the spirit of laws. Society rests on force; force must be respected as the august foundation of society. Justice is the administration of force. President Bourriche knows that Constable 64 is an integral part of the government. The Government is immanent in each one of its officers. To slight the authority of Constable 64 is to weaken the State. To eat the leaves of an artichoke is to eat the artichoke, as Bossuet puts it in his sublime language. (*Politique tirée de l'Ecriture sainte, passim*.)

"All the swords of the State are turned in the same direction. To oppose one to the other is to overthrow the Republic. For that reason, Crainquebille, the accused, is justly condemned to a fortnight in prison and a fine of fifty francs, on the evidence of Constable 64. I seem to hear President Bourriche, himself, explaining the high and noble considerations which inspired his sentence. I seem to hear him saying:

" 'I judged this person according to the evidence of Constable 64, because Constable 64 is the emanation of public force. And if you wish to prove my wisdom, imagine the consequences had I adopted the opposite course. You will see at once that it would have been absurd. For if my judgments were in opposition to force, they would never be executed. Notice, gentlemen, that judges are only obeyed when force is on their side. A judge without policemen would be but an idle dreamer. I should be doing myself an injury if I admitted a policeman to be in the wrong. Moreover, the very spirit of laws is in opposition to my doing so. To disarm the strong and to arm the weak would be to subvert that social order which it is my duty to preserve. Justice is the sanction of established injustice. Was justice ever seen to oppose conquerors and usurpers? When an unlawful power arises, justice has only to recognize it and it becomes lawful. Form is everything; and between crime and innocence there is but the thickness of a piece of stamped paper. It was for you, Crainquebille, to be the strongest. If, after having cried: *"Mort aux vaches!"* you had declared yourself emperor, dictator, President of the Republic or even town councillor, I assure you you would not have been sentenced to pass a fortnight in prison, and to pay a fine of fifty francs. I should have acquitted you. You may be sure of that.'

"Such would have doubtless been the words of President Bourriche; for he has a judicial mind, and he knows what a magistrate owes to society. With order and regularity he defends social principles. Justice is social. Only wrong-headed persons would make justice out to be human and reasonable. Justice is administered upon fixed rules, not in obedience to physical emotions and flashes of intelligence. Above all things do not ask justice to be just, it has no need to be just since it is justice, and I might even say that the idea of just justice can have only arisen in the brains of an anarchist. True, President Magnaud pronounces just sentences; but if they are reversed, that is still justice.

"The true judge weighs his evidence with weights that are weapons. So it was in the Crainquebille affair, and in other more famous cases."

Thus said Monsieur Jean Lermite as he paced up and down the Salle des Pas Perdus.

Scratching the tip of his nose, Maitre Joseph Aubarrée, who knows the Palais well, replied:

"If you want to hear what I think, I don't believe that President Bourriche rose to so lofty a metaphysical plane. In my opinion, when he received as true the evidence of Constable 64, he merely acted according to precedent. Imitation lies at the root of most human actions. A respectable person is one who conforms to custom. People are called good when they do as others do."

V

Having been taken back to his prison, Crainquebille sat down on his chained stool, filled with astonishment and admiration. He, himself, was not quite sure whether the magistrates were mistaken. The tribunal had concealed its essential weakness beneath the majesty of form. He could not believe that he was in the right, as against magistrates whose reasons he had not understood: it was impossible for him to conceive that anything could go wrong in so elaborate a ceremony. For, unaccustomed to attending Mass or frequenting the Elysée, he had never in his life witnessed anything so grand as a police court trial. He was perfectly aware that he had never cried *"Mort aux vaches!"* That for having said it he should have been sentenced to a fortnight's imprisonment seemed to him an august mystery, one of those articles of faith to which believers adhere without understanding them, an obscure, striking, adorable and terrible revelation.

This poor old man believed himself guilty of having mystically offended Constable 64, just as the little boy learning his first Catechism believes himself guilty of Eve's sin. His sentence had taught him that he had cried: *"Mort aux vaches!"* He must, therefore have cried *"Mort aux vaches!*" in some mysterious manner, unknown to himself. He was transported into a supernatural world. His trial was his apocalypse.

If he had no very clear idea of the offence, his idea of the penalty was still less clear. His sentence appeared to him a solemn and superior ritual, something dazzling and incomprehensible, which is not to be discussed, and for which one is neither to be praised nor pitied. If at that moment he had seen President Bourriche, with white wings and a halo round his forehead, coming down through a hole in the ceiling, he would not have been surprised at this new manifestation of judicial glory. He would have said: "This is my trial continuing!"

On the next day his lawyer visited him:

"Well, my good fellow, things aren't so bad after all! Don't be discouraged. A fortnight is soon over. We have not much to complain of."

"As for that, I must say the gentlemen were very kind, very polite: not a single rude word. I shouldn't have believed it. And the *cipal* was wearing white gloves. Did you notice?"

"Everything considered, we did well to confess."

"Perhaps."

"Crainquebille, I have a piece of good news for you. A charitable person, whose interest I have elicited on your behalf, gave me fifty francs for you. The sum will be used to pay your fine."

"When will you give me the money?"

"It will be paid into the clerk's office. You need not trouble about it."

"It does not matter. All the same I am very grateful to this person." And Crainquebille murmured meditatively: "It's something out of the common that's happening to me."

"Don't exaggerate, Crainquebille. Your case is by no means rare, far from it."

"You couldn't tell me where they've put my barrow?"

VI

After his discharge from prison, Crainquebille trundled his barrow along the Rue Montmartre, crying: "Cabbages, turnips, carrots!" He was neither ashamed nor proud of his adventure. The memory of it was not painful. He classed it in his mind with dreams, travels and plays. But, above all things, he was glad to be walking in the mud, along the paved streets, and to see overhead the rainy sky as dirty as the gutter, the dear sky of the town. At every corner he stopped to have a drink; then, gay and unconstrained, spitting in his hands in order to moisten his horny palms, he would seize the shafts and push on his barrow. Meanwhile a flight of sparrows, as poor and as early as he, seeking their livelihood in the road, flew off at the sound of his familiar cry: "Cabbages, turnips, carrots!" An old house wife, who had come up, said to him as she felt his celery:

"What's happened to you, Père Crainquebille? We haven't seen you for three weeks. Have you been ill? You look rather pale."

"I'll tell you, M'ame Mailloche, I've been doing the gentleman."

Nothing in his life changed, except that he went oftener to the pub, because he had an idea it was a holiday and that he had made the acquaintance of charitable folk. He returned to his garret rather gay. Stretched on his mattress he drew over him the sacks borrowed from the chestnut-seller at the corner which served him as blankets and he pondered: "Well, prison is not so bad; one has everything one wants there. But all the same one is better at home."

His contentment did not last long. He soon perceived that his customers looked at him askance.

"Fine celery, M'ame Cointreau!"

"I don't want anything."

"What! nothing! do you live on air then?"

And M'ame Cointreau without deigning to reply returned to the large bakery of which she was the mistress. The shopkeepers and caretakers, who had once flocked round his barrow all green and blooming, now turned away from him. Having reached the shoemaker's, at the sign of l'Ange Gardien, the place where his adventures with justice had begun, he called.

"M'ame Bayard, M'ame Bayard, you owe me sevenpence halfpenny from last time."

But M'ame Bayard, who was sitting at her counter, did not deign to turn her head.

The whole of the Rue Montmartre was aware that Père Crainquebille had been in prison, and the whole of the Rue Montmartre gave up his acquaintance. The rumour of his conviction had reached the Faubourg and the noisy corner of the Rue Richer. There, about noon, he perceived Madame Laure, a kind and faithful customer, leaning over the barrow of another costermonger, young Martin. She was feeling a large cabbage. Her hair shone in the sunlight like masses of golden threads loosely twisted. And young Martin, a nobody, a good-for-nothing, was protesting with his hand on his heart that there were no finer vegetables than his. At this sight Crainquebille's heart was rent. He pushed his barrow up to young Martin's, and in a plaintive broken voice said to Madame Laure: "It's not fair of you to forsake me."

As Madame Laure herself admitted, she was no duchess. It was not in society that she had acquired her ideas of the prison van and the police-station. But can one not be honest in every station in life? Every one has his self respect; and one does not like to deal with a man who has just come out of prison. So the only notice she took of Crainquebille was to give him a look of disgust. And the old costermonger resenting the affront shouted:

"Dirty wench, go along with you."

Madame Laure let fall her cabbage and cried:

"Eh! Be off with you, you bad penny. You come out of prison and then insult folk!"

If Crainquebille had had any self-control he would never have reproached Madame Laure with her calling. He knew only too well that one is not master of one's fate, that one cannot always choose one's occupation, and that good people may be found everywhere. He was accustomed discreetly to ignore her customers' business with her; and he despised no one. But he was beside himself. Three times he called Madame Laure drunkard, wench, harridan. A group of idlers gathered round Madame Laure and Crainquebille. They exchanged a few more insults as serious as the first; and they would soon have exhausted their vocabulary, if a policeman had not suddenly appeared, and at once, by his silence and immobility, rendered them as silent and as motionless as himself. They separated. But this scene put the finishing touch to the discrediting of Crainquebille in the eyes of the Faubourg Montmartre and the Rue Richer.

VII

The old man went along mumbling:

"For certain she's a hussy, and none more of a hussy than she."

But at the bottom of his heart that was not the reproach he brought against her. He did not scorn her for being what she was. Rather he esteemed her for it, knowing her to be frugal and orderly. Once they had liked to talk together. She used to tell him of her parents who lived in the country. And they had both resolved to have a little garden and keep poultry. She was a good customer. And then to see her buying cabbages from young Martin, a dirty, good-for-nothing wretch; it cut him to the heart; and when she pretended to despise him, that put his back up, and then . . .!

But she, alas! was not the only one who shunned him as if he had the plague. Every one avoided him. Just like Madame Laure, Madame Cointreau the baker, Madame Bayard of l'Ange Gardien scorned and repulsed him. Why! The whole of society refused to have anything to do with him.

So because one had been put away for a fortnight one was not good enough even to sell leeks! Was it just? Was it reasonable to make a decent chap die of starvation because he had got into difficulties with a copper? If he was not to be allowed to sell vegetables then it was all over with him. Like a badly doctored wine he turned sour. After having had words with Madame Laure, he now had them with every one. For a mere nothing he would tell his customers what he thought of them and in no ambiguous terms, I assure you. If they felt his wares too long he would call them to their faces chatterer, soft head. Likewise at the wine-shop he bawled at his comrades. His friend, the chestnut seller, no longer recognized him; old Père Crainquebille, he said, had turned into a regular porcupine. It cannot be denied: he was becoming rude, disagreeable, evil-mouthed, loquacious. The truth of the matter was that he was discovering the imperfections of society; but he had not the facilities of a Professor of

Moral and Political Science for the expressions of his ideas concerning the vices of the system and the reforms necessary; and his thoughts evolved devoid of order and moderation.

Misfortune was rendering him unjust. He was taking his revenge on those who were weaker than he. One day he boxed Alphonse, the wine-seller's little boy, on the ear, because he had asked him what it was like to be sent away. Crainquebille struck him and said:

"Dirty brat! it's your father who ought to be sent away instead of growing rich by selling poison."

A deed and a speech which did him no honour; for, as the chestnut-seller justly remarked, one ought not to strike a child, neither should one reproach him with a father whom he has not chosen.

Crainquebille began to drink. The less money he earned the more brandy he drank. Formerly frugal and sober he himself marvelled at the change.

"I never used to be a waster," he said. "I suppose one doesn't improve as one grows old."

Sometimes he severely blamed himself for his misconduct and his laziness:

"Crainquebille, old chap, you ain't good for anything but liftin' your glass."

Sometimes he deceived himself and made out that he needed the drink.

"I must have it now and then; I must have a dope to strengthen me and cheer me up. It seems as if I had a fire in my inside; and there's nothing like the drink for quenching it."

It often happened that he missed the auction in the morning and so had to provide himself with damaged fruit and vegetables on credit. One day, feeling tired and discouraged, he left his barrow in its shed, and spent the livelong day hanging round the stall of Madame Rose, the tripe-seller, or lounging in and out of the wine-shops near the market. In the evening, sitting on a basket, he meditated and became conscious of his deterioration. He recalled the strength of his early years: the achievements of former days, the arduous labours and the glad evenings: those days quickly passing, all alike and fully occupied; the pacing in the darkness up and down the Market pavement, waiting for the early auction; the vegetables carried in armfuls and artistically arranged in the barrow; the piping hot black coffee of Mère Théodore swallowed standing, and at one gulp; the shafts grasped vigorously; and then the loud cry, piercing as cock crow, rending the morning air as he passed through the crowded streets. All that innocent, rough life of the human pack-horse came before him. For half a century, on his travelling stall, he had borne to townsfolks worn with care and vigil the fresh harvest of kitchen gardens. Shaking his head he sighed:

"No! I'm not what I was. I'm done for. The pitcher goes so often to the well that at last it comes home broken. And then I've never been the same since my affair with the magistrates. No, I'm not the man I was."

In short he was demoralized. And when a man reaches that condition he might as well be on the ground and unable to rise. All the passers-by tread him under foot.

VIII

Poverty came, black poverty. The old costermonger who used to come back from the Faubourg Montmartre with a bag full of five-franc pieces, had not a single coin now. Winter came. Driven out of his garret, he slept under the carts in a shed. It had been raining for days; the gutters were overflowing, and the shed was flooded.

Crouching in his barrow, over the pestilent water, in the company of spiders, rats and half-starved cats, he was meditating in the gloom. Having eaten nothing all day and no longer having the chestnut-seller's sacks for a covering, he recalled the fortnight when the Government had provided him with food and clothing. He envied the prisoner's fate. They suffer neither cold nor hunger, and an idea occurred to him:

"Since I know the trick why don't I use it?"

He rose and went out into the street. It was a little past eleven. The night was dark and chill. A drizzling mist was falling, colder and more penetrating than rain. The few passers-by crept along under cover of the houses.

Crainquebille went past the Church of Saint-Eustache and turned into the Rue Montmartre. It was deserted. A guardian of the peace stood on the pavement, by the apse of the church. He was under a gas-lamp, and all around fell a fine rain looking reddish in the gaslight. It fell on to the policeman's hood. He looked chilled to the bone; but, either because he preferred to be in the light or because he was tired of walking he stayed under the lamp, and perhaps it seemed to him a friend, a companion. In the loneliness of the night the flickering flame was his only entertainment. In his immobility he appeared hardly human. The reflection of his boots on the wet pavement, which looked like a lake, prolonged him downwards and gave him from a distance the air of some amphibious monster half out of water. Observed more closely he had at once a monkish and a military appearance. The coarse features of his countenance, magnified under the shadow of his hood, were sad and placid. He wore a thick moustache, short and grey. He was an old copper, a man of some two-score years. Crainquebille went up to him softly, and in a weak hesitating voice, said: *"Mort aux vaches!"*

Then he awaited the result of those sacred words. But nothing came of them. The constable remained motionless and silent, with his arms folded under his short cloak. His eyes were wide open; they glistened in the darkness and regarded Crainquebille with sadness, vigilance and scorn.

Crainquebille, astonished, but still resolute, muttered:

"Mort aux vaches! I tell you."

There was a long silence in the chill darkness and the falling of the fine penetrating rain. At last the constable spoke:

"Such things are not said. . . . For sure and for certain they are not said. At your age you ought to know better. Pass on."

"Why don't you arrest me?" asked Crainquebille.

The constable shook his head beneath his dripping hood:

"If we were to take up all the addle-pates who say what they oughtn't to, we should have our work cut out! . . . And what would be the use of it?"

Overcome by such magnanimous disdain, Crainquebille remained for some time stolid and silent, with his feet in the gutter. Before going, he tried to explain:

"I didn't mean to say: *Mort aux vaches!* to you. It was not for you more than for another. It was only an idea."

The constable replied sternly but kindly:

"Whether an idea or anything else it ought not to be said, because when a man does his duty and endures much, he ought not to be insulted with idle words. . . . I tell you again to pass on."

Crainquebille, with head bent and arms hanging limp, plunged into the rain and the darkness.

The Big Fine

Finley Peter Dunne

"THAT WAS a splendid fine they soaked Jawn D. with," said Mr. Dooley.

"What did they give him?" asked Mr. Hennessy.

"Twinty-nine millyon dollars," said Mr. Dooley.

"Oh, great!" said Mr. Hennessy. "That's a grand fine. It's a gorjous fine. I can't hardly believe it."

"It's thrue, though," said Mr. Dooley. "Twinty-nine millyon dollars. Divvle th' cent less. I can't exactly make out what th' charge was that they arrested him on, but th' gin'ral idee is that Jawn D. was goin' around loaded up to th' guards with Standard Ile, exceedin' th' speed limit in acquirin' money, an' singin' 'A charge to keep I have' till th' neighbors cud stand it no longer. The judge says: 'Ye're an old offender an' I'll have to make an example iv ye. Twinty-nine millyon dollars or fifty-eight millyon days. Call th' next case, Misther Clerk.'

"Did he pay th' fine? He did not. Iv coorse he cud if he wanted to. He wuddent have to pawn annything to get th' money, ye can bet on that. All he'd have to do would be to put his hand down in his pocket, skin twinty-nine millyon dollar bills off iv his roll an' hurl thim at th' clerk. But he refused to pay as a matter iv principle. 'Twas not that he needed th' money. He don't care f'r money in th' passionate way that you an' me do, Hinnissy. Th' likes iv us are as crazy about a dollar as a man is about his child whim he has on'y wan. Th' chances are we'll spoil it. But Jawn D., havin' a large an' growin' fam'ly iv dollars, takes on'y a kind iv gin'ral inthrest in thim. He's issued a statement sayin' that he's a custojeen iv money appinted be himsilf. He looks afther his own money an' th' money iv other people. He takes it an' puts it where it won't hurt thim an' they won't spoil it. He's a kind iv a society f'r th' previntion of croolty to money. If he finds a man misusing his money

From *Mr. Dooley Says,* by Finley Peter Dunne.

This piece was occasioned by the $29,000,000 fine imposed by Federal Judge Kenesaw Mountain Landis on the Standard Oil Company in 1907 for violating the federal law against rebating. The judgment was reversed, however, on appeal.

he takes it away fr'm him an' adopts it. Ivry Saturdah night he let's th' man see it f'r a few hours. An' he says he's surprised to find that whin, with th' purest intintions in th' wurruld, he is found thryin' to coax our little money to his home where it'll find conjanial surroundings an' have other money to play with, th' people thry to lynch him an' th' polis arrest him f'r abduction.

"So as a matther iv principle he appealed th' case. An appeal, Hinnissy, is where ye ask wan coort to show it's contempt f'r another coort. 'Tis sthrange that all th' pathrites that have wanted to hang Willum Jennings Bryan an' mesilf f'r not showin' proper respect f'r th' joodicyary, are now showin' their respect f'r th' joodicyary be appealin' fr'm their decisions. Ye'd think Jawn D. wud bow his head reverentially in th' awful presence iv Kenesaw Mt. Landis an' sob out: 'Thank ye'er honor. This here noble fine fills me with joy. But d'ye think ye give me enough? If agreeable I'd like to make it an even thirty millyons.' But he doesn't. He's like mesilf. Him an' me bows to th' decisions iv th' coorts on'y if they bow first.

"I have gr-reat respect f'r th' joodicyary, as fine a lot iv cross an' indignant men as ye'll find annywhere. I have th' same respect f'r thim as they have f'r each other. But I niver bow to a decision iv a judge onless, first, it's pleasant to me, an', second, other judges bow to it. Ye can't be too careful about what decisions ye bow to. A decision that seems agreeable may turn out like an acquaintance ye scrape up at a picnic. Ye may be ashamed iv it to-morrah. Manny's th' time I've bowed to a decree iv a coort on'y to see it go up gayly to th' supreem coort, knock at th dure an' be kicked down stairs be an angry old gintleman in a black silk petticoat. A decree iv th' coort has got to be pretty vinrable befure I do more thin greet it with a pleasant smile.

"Me idee was whin I read about Jawn D.'s fine that he'd settle at wanst, payin' twenty-eight millyon dollars in millyon dollar bills an' th' other millyon in chicken-feed like ten thousand dollar bills just to annoy th' clerk. But I ought to've known betther. Manny's th' time I've bent me proud neck to a decision iv a coort that lasted no longer thin it took th' lawyer f'r th' definse to call up another judge on th' tillyphone. A judge listens to a case f'r days an' hears, while he's figurin' a possible goluf score on his blotting pad, th' argymints iv two or three lawyers that no wan wud dare to offer a judgeship to. Gin'rally speakin', judges are lawyers. They get to be judges because they have what Hogan calls th' joodicyal timp'ramint, which is why annybody gets a job. Th' other kind people won't take a job. They'd rather take a chance. Th' judge listens to a case f'r days an' decides it th' way he intinded to. D'ye find th' larned counsel that's just been beat climbin' up on th' bench an' throwin' his arms around th' judge? Ye bet ye don't. He gathers his law books into his arms, gives th' magistrate a look that means, 'There's an eliction next year,' an' runs down th' hall to another judge. Th' other judge hears his kick an' says he: 'I don't know annything about this here case except what ye've whispered to me, but I know me larned collague an' I wuddent thrust him to referee a roller-skatin' contest. Don't pay th' fine till ye hear fr'm me.' Th' on'y wan that bows to th' decision is th' fellow that won, an' pretty soon he sees he's made a mistake, f'r wan day th' other coort comes out an' declares that th' decision of th' lower coort is another argymint in favor iv abolishing night law schools.

"That's th' way Jawn D. felt about it an' he didn't settle. I wondher will they put him away if he don't pay ivinchooly? 'Twill be a long sentence. A frind iv min wanst got full iv kerosene an' attempted to juggle a polisman. They thried him whin he come out iv th' emergency hospital an' fined him a hundhred dollars. He didn't happen to have that amount with him at th' moment or at anny moment since th' day he was born. But the judge was very lenient with him. He said he needn't pay it if he cudden't. Th' coort wud give him a letther of inthroduction to th' bridewell an' he cud stay there f'r two hundhred days. At that rate it'll be a long time befure Jawn D. an' me meet again on the goluf-links. Hogan has it figured out that if Jawn D. refuses to go back on his Puritan principles an' separate himsilf fr'm his money he'll be wan hundhred an' fifty-eight thousand years in cold storage. A man ought to be pretty good at th' lock step in a hundhred an' fifty-eight thousand years.

"Well, sir, glory be but times has changed whin they land me gr-reat an' good frind with a fine that's about akel to three millyon dhrunk an' disorderly cases. 'Twud've been cheaper if he'd took to dhrink arly in life. I've made a vow, Hinnissy, niver to be very rich. I'd like to be a little rich, but not rich enough f'r anny wan to notice that me pockets bulged. Time was whin I dhreamed iv havin' money an' lots iv it. 'Tis thrue I begun me dhreams at th' wrong end, spent th' money befure I got it. I was always clear about th' way to spend but oncertain about th' way to get it. If th' Lord had intinded me to be a rich man He'd've turned me dhreams around an' made me clear about makin' th' money but very awkward an' shy about gettin' rid iv it. There are two halves to ivry dollar. Wan is knowin' how to make it an' th' other is not knowin' how to spend it comfortably. Whin I hear iv a man with gr-reat business capacity I know he's got an akel amount iv spending incapacity. No matter how much he knew about business he wuddent be rich if he wasn't totally ignorant iv a science that we have developed as far as our means will allow. But now, I tell ye, I don't dhream iv bein' rich. I'm afraid iv it. In th' good old days th' polis coorts were crowded with th' poor. They weren't charged with poverty, iv coorse, but with the results iv poverty, d'ye mind. Now, be Hivens, th' rich have invaded even th' coorts an' the bridewell. Manny a face wearin' side whiskers an' gold rimmed specs peers fr'm th' windows iv th' black Maria. 'What's this man charged with?' says th' coort. 'He was found in possession iv tin millyon dollars,' says th' polisman. An' th' judge puts on th' black cap."

"Well," said Mr. Hennessy, " 'tis well they got what was comin' to thim."

"I'll not say ye're wrong," said Mr. Dooley. "I see th' way me frind Jawn D. feels about it. He thinks he's doin' a great sarvice to th' worruld collectin' all th' money in sight. It might remain in incompetint hands if he didn't get it. 'Twuld be a shame to lave it where it'd be misthreated. But th' on'y throuble with Jawn is that he don't see how th' other fellow feels about it. As a father iv about thirty dollars I want to bring thim up mesilf in me own foolish way. I may not do what's right be thim. I may be too indulgent with thim. Their home life may not be happy. Perhaps 'tis clear that if they wint to th' Rockyfeller institution f'r th' care iv money they'd be in betther surroundings, but whin Jawn thries to carry thim off I raise a cry iv 'Polis,' a mob iv people that niver had a dollar iv their own an' niver will have wan, pounce on th' misguided man, th' polis pinch him, and th' government condemns th' institution an' lets out th' inmates an' a good manny iv thim go to th' bad."

"D'ye think he'll iver sarve out his fine?" asked Mr. Hennessy.

"I don't know," said Mr. Dooley. "But if he does, whin he comes out at the end iv a hundhred and fifty-eight thousand years he'll find a great manny changes in men's hats an' th' means iv transportation but not much in annything else. He may find flyin' machines, though it'll be arly f'r thim, but he'll see a good manny people still walkin' to their wurruk."

The Most Outrageous Consequences

James Reid Parker

MR. DEVORE almost never lost a client except through the regrettable but inescapable eventuality—in his own restful phrase—of death. It was unthinkable that he should lose the Wolverine Commercial Car Corporation, which presumably wasn't susceptible to death and whose affairs at the New York end were as profitable to the law firm of Forbes, Hathaway, Bryan & Devore as those of any business they looked after. And yet this very catastrophe, Mr. Devore told himself, might occur if he continued to suffer reversals in court, as he had been doing lately. Suppose this latest difficulty, *Drucker v. Wolverine Comm. Cor Corp.,* a rather minor case in its own way, proved to be the breaking point? Mr. Devore, who was about to go over and have a scheduled talk with Mr. Hibben, Wolverine's vice-president in charge of the New York office, was thoroughly downcast. There could be no doubt that Drucker, a taxi-driver who had been driving a Wolverine-built cab for the Sun-Lite system at the time of his accident, had a legal precedent for action. In the State of New York, at least. It was really a horrible precedent, handed down by a judge for whom Mr. Devore entertained bitter loathing, but in Mr. Hibben's eyes this would not excuse defeat, as Mr. Devore knew very well.

Perhaps what grieved the old lawyer most was that his sympathies were with Wolverine, for basically there was something about a Comm. Car Corp. that appealed to him. He loved Wolverine. Nor was his devotion altogether that of a pensioner; he felt toward Wolverine much as a dog might feel toward a life-long, if at times unreasonable, master. Mr. Devore put on his derby, selected Ames and Smith's "Law of Torts" from his bookcase, and gloomily started for the Wolverine offices. His first job, clearly, was to mollify Mr. Hibben, if such a thing could be accomplished.

Mr. Hibben greeted him with the barest civility and at once asked the question that Mr. Devore least wanted to hear.

"Well, what chance have we got?"

Before replying, Mr. Devore seated himself very solemnly, although the vice-president had not suggested that he do so, placed the tort collection on the desk in an impressively deliberate manner, and tried to look as much as possible like Mr. Chief Justice Stone on a Monday afternoon.

"The first thing we must consider," he said slowly, caressing the torts as if to put himself under the protection of all the great adjudicators of the past, "is the historic attitude of the courts toward liability."

Mr. Hibben failed to assume the attentive expression of one about to enjoy a scholarly excursion into legal history. "That's not answering my question," he said.

Recklessly, Mr. Devore evaded the issue. "When a somewhat similar case was decided in the Court of the Exchequer in 1842, our American courts lost no time in adopting the decision as a precedent for this country. I'm happy to say that it was a complete and triumphant vindication of the defendant."

"And you say America adopted the same law intact?" Mr. Hibben asked eagerly.

"America accepted the precedent," Mr. Devore acknowledged, wondering how on earth to proceed from this point. It had perhaps been bad strategy to appease Mr. Hibben at the very beginning. The vice-president was nodding with satisfaction and saying, "Fine! Good thing Americans knew enough to tell right from wrong in those days. They don't seem to any more." If Mr. Hibben would only refrain from asking whether the precedent had ever been set aside!

"Is this law still O.K.?" Mr. Hibben asked. "You're sure the judges all know about it?"

"Oh, yes, they all know about it," said Mr. Devore soothingly and with perfect truth. "The case that set the precedent was really very much like the Drucker affair. I'd like to tell you about it."

Mr. Hibben now seemed more disposed toward a little excursion into the annals of the Court of the Exchequer. He offered his counsellor a cigar.

"It involved a chattel-maker's liability, or to be more exact, a chattel *vendor's* liability, to a third person," said Mr. Devore, making a heroic effort to be elementary. "The defendant Wright had contracted to supply mailcoaches to the Postmaster General, who had in turn contracted with a man named Atkinson, and his business associates, for a regular supply of horses and coachmen. Atkinson engaged the plaintiff Winterbottom to drive a coach between Hartford and Holyhead. In other words, A contracted with B, who contracted with C, who contracted with D. One day, most unfortunately, Winterbottom's mailcoach broke down because of a latent defect in its manufacture and he became lamed for life. Seeking damages, D sued not C, his employer, nor B, the Postmaster General, but the original A, with whom D had entered into no contract of any sort whatever."

After digesting these complications, Mr. Hibben said, "If D was hired by C, I think C was the one D should have picked to sue."

Mr. Devore agreed that this would have been a more usual procedure, but added that A was probably a wealthier firm and therefore a more tempting victim against whom to secure a judgment. The analogy was at once apparent to Mr. Hibben, who grunted in a shocked manner. Matters were progressing smoothly at the moment, but it meant only temporary relief for Mr. Devore. Nevertheless, he opened his Ames and Smith with convincing equanimity and turned to *Winterbottom v. Wright.*

"I'm sure you'll agree with me that Lord Abinger, the Chief Baron, expressed the whole issue very satisfactorily when he said, 'If the plaintiff can sue, every passenger, or even every person passing along the road, who was injured by the upsetting of the coach, might bring similar action. Unless we confine the operations of such contracts as this to the parties who entered into them, the most absurd and outrageous consequences, to which I can see no limit, would ensue.' "

"Exactly!" said Mr. Hibben. "That's almost word for word what I told our legal adviser in Flint when I talked to him on the phone several days ago. It looks as if you've found a loophole all right, Devore." Mr. Hibben beamed at him. "I've always *said* it wouldn't pay Wolverine to maintain a full-sized legal department when we've got Forbes, Hathaway to take care of us. Frankly, Devore, the fellows out in Flint have been a little disappointed with your work lately, but they'll be tickled to death about *this."*

Mr. Devore tried to smile but wasn't quite able to manage it. Something told him that the fellows in Flint weren't going to do any elaborate rejoicing. And if Wolverine were suddenly to install a full-sized legal department, what would happen to Forbes, Hathaway, Bryan & Devore? What, especially, would happen to Devore?

"I certainly like what he says about confining the operations of such contracts," said Mr. Hibben. "Let's hear that part again."

"Unless we confine the operations of such contracts to the parties who entered into them?"

"That's it!" Mr. Hibben said. "That's telling 'em! Why, we never had any dealings at all with Drucker. What we did was sell a cab to the Sun-Lite people, and Drucker was hired by Sun-Lite. Furthermore, it was a defective steering column that broke, and we don't even make steering columns. We buy them from Collins & Kemper!"

His exuberance was a terrible spectacle to Mr. Devore, who didn't quite know how to cut it short.

"Every passer-by," Mr. Hibben said, "every Tom, Dick, and Harry under the sun would start suing. They'd say they were suffering from mental shock or something as a result of being on the scene when the accident happened. Who is this man Abinger, anyway? I'd like to meet him."

"You're forgetting when the case was decided," Mr. Devore reminded him gently. "It was decided back in 1842."

He turned to another section of his Ames and Smith and, marshalling such courage as he had left, prepared to explain why Wolverine, and not Sun-Lite, would be required by law to yield to the plaintiff.

"In recent years," he began, "the most malign forces imaginable have been at work in this country. They have penetrated our government and —much as I dislike confessing the fact—our bar and our bench as well."

A look of surprise crossed Mr. Hibben's face. "You don't have to tell me that!" he snapped.

The unhappy counsellor not only had to tell him but had to tell him without any further postponement.

"You'd be amazed at something that happened once in the Court of Appeals right here in New York," Mr. Devore said lightly. "It was the really unusual case of MacPherson against the Buick Motor Company—I mean the old Buick company, not the General Motors subsidiary. What happened was that the manufacturer sold one of its cars to a retail dealer, who in turn sold it to this man MacPherson. While MacPherson was driving the car, one of the wheels suddenly collapsed. He was thrown out and injured. The wheel had been made of faulty wood. The wheel wasn't made by Buick; it was bought from another manufacturer, just as you buy your steering columns from Collins & Kemper. The Court decided there was evidence, however, that the defects could have been discovered by reasonable inspection, and that inspection was omitted."

"Certainly inspection was omitted," said Mr. Hibben. "They probably bought their wheels from a reputable firm, and they certainly couldn't go around inspecting hundreds of thousands of wheels just on the chance that maybe they'd find one that wasn't exactly uniform. Why, in our case the steering column on Drucker's cab was the first defective column we'd ever heard about."

"I rather imagined that you'd see a similarity between the Drucker case and MacPherson against Buick."

"Of course I see a similarity," said Mr. Hibben.

Mr. Devore took a deep breath and jumped into the flames.

"I think you'll be interested in hearing what one of the judges said about it." The vice-president nodded, evidently retaining great faith in the book from which Mr. Devore had produced the fascinating mailcoach decision. "The judge held that 'if the nature of a thing is such that it is reasonably certain to place life and limb in peril when negligently made, it is then a thing of danger. Its nature gives warning of the consequences to be expected. If to the element of danger there is added knowledge that the thing will be used by persons other than the purchaser, and used without new tests, then, irrespective of contract, the manufacturer of this thing of danger is under a duty to make it carefully.' " He coughed nervously as he neared the most disagreeable part of the whole wretched decision. " 'We are dealing now with the manufacturer of the finished product, who puts it on the market to be used without inspection by his customers. If he is negligent where danger is to be foreseen, a liability will follow.' "

"Wait a minute," said Mr. Hibben. "That line about 'the manufacturer of the finished product' would apply to Collins & Kemper. Drucker could sue *them* if he wanted to. Why don't you write him a letter and tell him about it?"

Mr. Devore shook his head and went on hastily.

" 'We think the defendant was not absolved from a duty of inspection because it bought the wheels from a reputable manufacturer.' " Here Mr. Hibben opened his mouth in horrified astonishment but made no comment. " 'It was not merely a dealer in automobiles. It was a manufacturer of automobiles. It was responsible for the finished product. It was not at liberty to put the finished product on the market without subjecting the component parts to ordinary and simple tests.' "

"You mean to say he's blaming the automobile manufacturers even though it was someone else who made the defective wheel?" asked Mr. Hibben. "You mean they'd be just as likely to blame *us?*"

But Mr. Devore, now that his great step had been taken, was unable to stop reading. " 'The defendant knew the danger. It knew also that the car would be used by persons other than the buyer.' "

"Why, it might be a *child* talking," Mr. Hibben gasped.

" 'Precedents drawn from the days of travel by stagecoach do not fit the conditions of travel today,' " Mr. Devore quoted, reading as quickly as possible. " 'The principle that the danger must be imminent does not change, but the things subject to the principle do change. They are whatever the needs of life in a developing civilization require them to be.' " He closed the book with an abrupt gesture. His own patience had worn quite as thin as the vice-president's.

There was a long silence before Mr. Hibben said wearily, "Where did you say this terrible thing happened? Here in New York?"

"Yes. In 1916."

"Couldn't we take it to the Supreme Court? They may have *some* sense of honor and decency left."

Mr. Devore lighted one of his own cigars and closed his eyes. "That opinion was written by Benjamin Cardozo. No court in the United States would reverse a Cardozo ruling, even if it wanted to. Not in times like these."

"I see what you mean," murmured the vice-president. "Good God!" There was infinite worry in the way he spoke the words.

"Well, there you are, Hibben," said Mr. Devore presently. He waited for the storm to break. And then, even as he waited, the realization came to him that everything was going to be all right. It had been Cardozo, and not he, who had jumped into the flames. If Mr. Hibben entertained any feeling toward him, it was the sympathetic feeling that the same malign forces were in league against them both. Wolverine still loved him, and if he played his cards carefully, it would continue to do so. He leaned back and for the first time really tasted the flavor of his cigar.

PART FOUR

CRIME

The safety of the people is the highest law, and the safety of the people is contained in the repressing offences by punishment.

BACON, MAXIMS OF THE LAW, *no. 12 (1596).*

Billy Budd

Herman Melville

LSEWHERE IT has been said that owing to the lack of frigates (of course better sailors than line-of-battle ships) in the English squadron up the Straits at that period, the *Indomitable* was occasionally employed not only as an available substitute for a scout, but at times on detached service of more important kind. This was not alone because of her sailing qualities, not common in a ship of her rate, but quite as much, probably, that the character of her commander—it was thought—specially adapted him for any duty where, under unforeseen difficulties, a prompt initiative might have to be taken in some matter demanding knowledge and ability in addition to those qualities employed in good seamanship. It was on an expedition of the latter sort, a somewhat distant one, and when the *Indomitable* was almost at her furthest remove from the fleet, that in the latter part of an afternoon-watch she unexpectedly came in sight of a ship of the enemy. It proved to be a frigate. The latter—perceiving through the glass that the weight of men and metal would be heavily against her—invoking her light heels, crowded on sail to get away. After a chase urged almost against hope—and lasting until about the middle of the first dog-watch she signally succeeded in effecting her escape.

Not long after the pursuit had been given up, and ere the excitement incident thereto had altogether waned away, the Master-at-arms, ascending from his cavernous sphere, made his appearance (cap in hand) by the mainmast: respectfully awaiting the notice of Captain Vere—then solitary walking the weather-side of the quarter-deck—doubtless somewhat chafed at the failure of the pursuit. The spot where Claggart stood was the place allotted to the men of lesser grades when seeking some more particular interview either with the officer-of-the-deck or the Captain himself. But from the latter it was not often that a sailor or petty-officer of those days would seek a hearing; only some exceptional cause, would, according to established custom, have warranted that.

Presently, just as the Commander, absorbed in his reflections, was on the point of turning aft in his promenade, he became sensible of Claggart's

From *Billy Budd, Foretopman: What Befell Him in the Year of the Great Mutiny.*

presence, and saw the doffed cap held in deferential expectancy. Here be it said that Captain Vere's personal knowledge of this petty-officer had only begun at the time of the ship's last sailing from home, Claggart then for the first, in transfer from a ship detained for repairs, supplying on board the *Indomitable* the place of a previous master-at-arms disabled and ashore.

No sooner did the Commander observe who it was that now so deferentially stood awaiting his notice, than a peculiar expression came over him. It was not unlike that which uncontrollably will flit across the countenance of one at unawares encountering a person, who, though known to him, indeed, has hardly been long enough known for thorough knowledge, but something in whose aspect nevertheless now, for the first time, provokes a vaguely repellent distaste. Coming to a stand and resuming much of his wonted official manner, save that a sort of impatience lurked in the intonation of the opening word, he said, "Well? what is it, Master-at-arms?"

With the air of a subordinate grieved at the necessity of being a messenger of ill tidings, and while conscientiously determined to be frank, yet equally resolved upon shunning overstatement, Claggart at this invitation, or rather summons to disburthen, spoke up. What he said, conveyed in the language of no uneducated man, was to the effect following if not altogether in these words, namely, that during the chase and preparations for the possible encounter he had seen enough to convince him that at least one sailor aboard was a dangerous character in a ship mustering some who not only had taken a guilty part in the late serious trouble, but others also who, like the man in question, had entered His Majesty's service under another form than enlistment.

At this point Captain Vere, with some impatience, interrupted him: "Be direct, man; say impressed men."

Claggart made a gesture of subservience and proceeded. Quite lately he (Claggart) had begun to suspect that some sort of movement prompted by the sailor in question was covertly going on, but he had not thought himself warranted in reporting the suspicion so long as it remained indistinct. But from what he had that afternoon observed in the man referred to, the suspicion of something clandestine going on had advanced to a point less removed from certainty. He deeply felt—he added—the serious responsibility assumed in making a report involving such possible consequences to the individual mainly concerned, besides tending to augment those natural anxieties which every naval commander must feel in view of the extraordinary outbreak so recent as those which, he sorrowfully said it, it needed not to name.

Now at the first broaching of the matter Captain Vere, taken by surprise, could not wholly dissemble his disquietude, but as Claggart went on, the former's aspect changed into restiveness under something in the testifier's manner in giving his testimony. However, he refrained from interrupting him. And Claggart, continuing, concluded with this:

"God forbid, your honour, that the *Indomitable's* should be the experience of the—"

"Never mind that!" here peremptorily broke in the superior, his face altering with anger instantly, divining the ship that the other was about to name, one in which the Nore Mutiny assumed a singularly tragical character that for a time jeopardized the life of its commander. Under the circumstances he was indignant at the purposed allusion. When the commissioned officers themselves were on all occasions very heedful how they referred to the recent events—for a petty-officer unnecessarily to allude to them in the presence of his captain, this struck him as a most immodest presumption. Besides, to his quick sense of self-respect, it even looked under the circumstances something like an attempt to alarm him. Nor at that was he without some surprise that one who, so far as he had hitherto come under his notice, had shown considerable tact in his function, should in this particular evince such lack of it.

But these thoughts and kindred dubious ones flitting across his mind were suddenly replaced by an intuitional surmise, which though as yet obscure in form, served practically to affect his reception of the ill tidings. Certain it is that, long versed in everything pertaining to the complicated gun-deck life (which like every other form of life has its secret mines and dubious side; the side popularly disclaimed), Captain Vere did not permit himself to be unduly disturbed by the general tenor of his subordinate's report. Furthermore, if in view of recent events prompt action should be taken at the first palpable sign of recurring insubordination—for all that, not judicious would it be, he thought, to keep the idea of lingering disaffection alive by undue forwardness in crediting an informer, even if his own subordinate, and charged with police surveillance of the crew. This feeling would not perhaps have so prevailed with him were it not that upon a prior occasion the patriotic zeal officially evinced by Claggart had somewhat irritated him as appearing rather supersensible and strained. Furthermore, something even in the official's self-possessed and somewhat ostentatious manner in making his specifications strangely reminded him of a bandsman, a perjured witness in a capital case before a court-martial ashore of which when a lieutenant he, Captain Vere, had been a member.

Now the peremptory check given to Claggart in the matter of the arrested allusion was quickly followed up by this: "You say that there is at least one dangerous man aboard. Name him."

"William Budd, a foretopman, your honour—"

"William Budd," repeated Captain Vere with unfeigned astonishment, "and mean you the man our Lieutenant Ratcliffe took from the merchantman not very long ago—the young fellow who seems to be so popular with the men—Billy, the Handsome Sailor, as they call him?"

"The same, your honour, but for all his youth and good looks, a deep one. Not for nothing does he insinuate himself into the good will of his shipmates, since at the least they will at a pinch say a good word for him at all hazards. Did Lieutenant Ratcliffe happen to tell your honour of that adroit fling of Budd's jumping up in the cutter's bow under the merchant-man's stern when he was being taken off? It is even masqued by that sort of good-humoured air that at heart he resents his impressment. You have but noted his fair cheek. A man-trap may be under his fine ruddy-tipped daisies."

Now the *Handsome Sailor,* as a signal figure among the crew, had nat-urally enough attracted the Captain's attention from the first. Though in general not very demonstrative to his officers, he had congratulated Lieu-tenant Ratcliffe upon his good fortune in lighting on such a fine specimen of the *genus homo* who, in the nude, might have posed for a statue of young Adam before the fall.

As to Billy's adieu to the ship *Rights-of-Man,* which the boarding lieu-tenant had indeed reported to him, Captain Vere,—but in a deferential way—more as a good story than aught else,—though mistakenly under-standing it as a satiric sally, had but thought so much the better of the impressed man for it; as a military sailor, admiring the spirit that could take an arbitrary enlistment so merrily and sensibly. The foretopman's conduct, too, so far as it had fallen under the Captain's notice had con-firmed the first happy augury, while the new recruit's qualities as a *sailor-man* seemed to be such that he had thought of recommending him to the executive officer for promotion to a place that would more frequently bring him under his own observation, namely, the captaincy of the mizzen-top replacing there in the starboard-watch a man not so young whom partly for that reason he deemed less fitted for the post. Be it parenthesized here that since the mizzentopmen have not to handle such breadths of heavy canvas as the lower sailors on the mainmast and foremast, a young man if of the right stuff not only seems best adapted to duty there, but, in fact, is generally selected for the captaincy of that top, and the company under him are light hands, and often but striplings. In sum, Captain Vere had from the beginning deemed Billy Budd to be what in the naval par-lance of the times was called a *"King's bargain,"* that is to say, for His Britannic Majesty's navy a capital investment at small outlay or none at all.

After a brief pause—during which the reminiscences above mentioned passed vividly through his mind—he weighed the import of Claggart's last suggestion, conveyed in the phrase, "pitfall under the clover," and the more he weighed it the less reliance he felt in the informer's good faith. Suddenly he turned upon him: "Do you come to me, Master-at-arms, with so foggy a tale? As to Budd, cite me an act or spoken word of his con-firmatory of what you here in general charge against him. Stay," drawing nearer to him, "heed what you speak. Just now and in a case like this, there is a yard-arm-end for the false-witness."

"Ah, your honour!" sighed Claggart mildly shaking his shapely head as in sad deprecation of such unmerited severity of tone. Then bridling—erecting himself as in virtuous self-assertion, he circumstantially alleged certain words and acts, which collectively if credited, led to presumptions mortally inculpating Budd, and for some of these averments, he added, substantiating proof was not far.

With grey eyes now impatient and distrustful, essaying to fathom to the bottom Claggart's calm violet ones, Captain Vere again heard him out; then for the moment stood ruminating. The mood he evinced, Claggart—himself for the time liberated from the other's scrutiny—steadily regarded with a look difficult to render:—a look curious of the operation of his tactics, a look such as might have been that of the spokesman of the envious children of Jacob deceptively imposing upon the troubled patriarch the blood-dyed coat of young Joseph.

Though something exceptional in the moral quality of Captain Vere made him, in earnest encounter with a fellowman, a veritable touchstone of that man's essential nature, yet, now as to Claggart and what was really going on in him his feeling partook less of intuitional conviction than of strong suspicion clogged by strange dubieties. The perplexity he evinced proceeded less from aught touching the man informed against— as Claggart doubtless opined—than from consideration how best to act in regard to the informer. At first, indeed, he was naturally for summoning that substantiation of his allegations which Claggart said was at hand. But such a proceeding would result in the matter at once getting abroad— which—in the present stage of it, he thought, might undesirably affect the ship's company. If Claggart was a false witness,—that closed the affair. And therefore, before trying the accusation, he would first practically test the accuser; and he thought this could be done in a quiet undemonstrative way.

The measure he determined upon involved a shifting of the scene—a transfer to a place less exposed to observation than the broad quarter-deck. For although the few gun-room officers there at the time had, in due observance of naval etiquette, withdrawn to leeward the moment Captain Vere had begun his promenade on the deck's weather-side; and though during the colloquy with Claggart they of course ventured not to diminish the distance; and though throughout the interview Captain Vere's voice was far from high, and Claggart's silvery and low; and the wind in the cordage and the wash of the sea helped the more to put them beyond earshot; nevertheless, the interview's continuance already had attracted observation from some topmen aloft, and other sailors in the waist or further forward.

Having now determined upon his measures, Captain Vere forthwith took action. Abruptly turning to Claggart he asked, "Master-at-arms, is it now Budd's watch aloft?"

"No, your honour." Whereupon—"Mr. Wilkes," summoning the nearest midshipman, "tell Albert to come to me." Albert was the Captain's hammock-boy, a sort of sea-valet in whose discretion and fidelity his master had much confidence. The lad appeared. "You know Budd the foretopman?"

"I do, Sir."

"Go find him. It is his watch off. Manage to tell him out of ear-shot that he is wanted aft. Contrive it that he speaks to nobody. Keep him in talk yourself. And not till you get well aft here, not till then, let him know that the place where he is wanted is my cabin. You understand. Go. —Master-at-arms, show yourself on the decks below, and when you think it time for Albert to be coming with his man, stand by quietly to follow the sailor in."

Now when the foretopman found himself closeted, as it were, in the cabin with the Captain and Claggart, he was surprised enough. But it was a surprise unaccompanied by apprehension or distrust. To an immature nature, essentially honest and humane, forewarning intimations of subtler danger from one's kind come tardily, if at all. The only thing that took shape in the young sailor's mind was this: "Yes, the Captain, I have always thought, looks kindly upon me. I wonder if he's going to make me his coxswain. I should like that. And maybe now he is going to ask the Master-at-arms about me."

"Shut the door, there, sentry," said the Commander. "Stand without and let nobody come in.—Now, Master-at-arms, tell this man to his face what you told of him to me;" and stood prepared to scrutinize the mutually confronting visages.

With the measured step and calm collected air of an asylum physician approaching in the public hall some patient beginning to show indications of a coming paroxysm, Claggart deliberately advanced within short range of Billy, and mesmerically looking him in the eye, briefly recapitulated the accusation.

Not at first did Billy take it in. When he did the rose-tan of his cheek looked struck as by white leprosy. He stood like one impaled and gagged. Meanwhile the accuser's eyes, removing not as yet from the blue, dilated ones, underwent a phenomenal change, their wonted rich violet colour blurring into a muddy purple. Those lights of human intelligence losing human expression, gelidly protruding like the alien eyes of certain uncatalogued creatures of the deep.

The first mesmeric glance was one of surprised fascination; the last was the hungry lurch of the torpedo-fish.

"Speak, man!" said Captain Vere to the transfixed one, struck by his aspect even more than by Claggart's, "Speak! defend yourself." Which appeal caused but a strange, dumb gesturing and gurgling in Billy; amazement at such an accusation so suddenly sprung on inexperienced nonage; this, and it may be horror at the accuser, serving to bring out his lurking defect, and in this instance for the time intensifying it into a convulsive tongue-tie; while the intent head and entire form straining forward in an agony of ineffectual eagerness to obey the injunction to speak and defend himself, gave an expression to the face like that of a condemned vestal priestess in the moment of her being buried alive, and in the first struggle against suffocation.

Though at the time Captain Vere was quite ignorant of Billy's liability to vocal impediment, he now immediately divined it, since vividly Billy's aspect recalled to him that of a bright young schoolmate of his whom he had seen struck by much the same startling impotence in the act of eagerly rising in the class to be foremost in response to a testing question put to it by the master. Going close up to the young sailor, and laying a soothing hand on his shoulder, he said, "There is no hurry, my boy. Take your time, take your time." Contrary to the effect intended, these words, so fatherly in tone, doubtless touching Billy's heart to the quick, prompted yet more violent efforts at utterance—efforts soon ending for the time in confirming the paralysis, and bringing to the face an expression which was as a crucifixion to behold. The next instant, quick as the flame from a discharged cannon at night—his right arm shot out and Claggart dropped to the deck. Whether intentionally, or but owing to the young athlete's superior height, the blow had taken effect full upon the forehead, so shapely and intellectual-looking a feature in the Master-at-arms; so that the body fell over lengthwise, like a heavy plank tilted from erectness. A gasp or two and he lay motionless.

"Fated boy," breathed Captain Vere in a tone so low as to be almost a whisper, "what have you done! But here, help me."

The twain raised the felled one from the loins up into a sitting position. The spare form flexibly acquiesced, but inertly. It was like handling a dead snake. They lowered it back. Regaining erectness, Captain Vere with one hand covering his face stood to all appearance as impassive as the object at his feet. Was he absorbed in taking in all the bearings of the event, and what was best not only now at once to be done, but also in the sequel? Slowly he uncovered his face; forthwith the effect was as if the moon, emerging from eclipse, should reappear with quite another aspect than that which had gone into hiding. The father in him, manifested towards Billy thus far in the scene, was replaced by the military disciplinarian. In his official tone he bade the foretopman retire to a stateroom aft, (pointing it out), and there remain till thence summoned. This order Billy in silence mechanically obeyed. Then, going to the cabin door where it opened on the quarter-deck, Captain Vere said to the sentry without, "Tell somebody to send Albert here." When the lad appeared his master so contrived it that he should not catch sight of the prone one. "Albert," he said to him, "tell the surgeon I wish to see him. You need not come back till called."

When the surgeon entered—a self-poised character of that grave sense and experience that hardly anything could take him aback—Captain Vere advanced to meet him, thus unconsciously interrupting his view of Claggart and interrupting the other's wonted ceremonious salutation, said, "Nay, tell me how it is with yonder man," directing his attention to the prostrate one.

The surgeon looked, and for all his self-command, somewhat started at the abrupt revelation. On Claggart's always pallid complexion, thick black blood was now oozing from mouth and ear. To the gazer's professional eyes it was unmistakably no living man that he saw.

"Is it so, then?" said Captain Vere intently watching him. "I thought it. But verify it." Whereupon the customary tests confirmed the surgeon's first glance, who now looking up in unfeigned concern, cast a look of intense inquisitiveness upon his superior. But Captain Vere, with one hand to his brow, was standing motionless. Suddenly, catching the surgeon's arm convulsively, he exclaimed pointing down to the body,—"It is the divine judgment of Ananias! Look!"

Disturbed by the excited manner he had never before observed in the *Indomitable's* Captain, and as yet wholly ignorant of the affair, the prudent surgeon nevertheless held his peace, only again looking an earnest interrogation as to what it was that had resulted in such a tragedy.

But Captain Vere was now again motionless, standing absorbed in thought. Once again starting, he vehemently exclaimed—"Struck dead by an angel of God. Yet the angel must hang!"

At these interjections, incoherences to the listener as yet unapprised of the antecedent events, the surgeon was profoundly discomfited. But now, as recollecting himself, Captain Vere in less harsh tone briefly related the circumstances leading up to the event.

"But come; we must despatch," he added, "help me to remove him (meaning the body) to yonder compartment"—designating one opposite where the foretopman remained immured. Anew disturbed by a request that, as implying a desire for secrecy, seemed unaccountably strange to him, there was nothing for the subordinate to do but comply.

"Go now," said Captain Vere, with something of his wonted manner, "Go now. I shall presently call a drum-head court. Tell the lieutenants what has happened, and tell Mr. Morton"—meaning the captain of marines. "And charge them to keep the matter to themselves."

Full of disquietude and misgivings, the surgeon left the cabin. Was Captain Vere suddenly affected in his mind, or was it but a transient excitement brought about by so strange and extraordinary a happening? As to the drum-head court, it struck the surgeon as impolitic, if nothing more. The thing to do, he thought, was to place Billy Budd in confinement, and in a way dictated by usage, and postpone further action in so extraordinary a case to such time as they should again join the squadron, and then transfer it to the Admiral. He recalled the unwonted agitation of Captain Vere and his exciting exclamations so at variance with his normal manner. Was he unhinged? But assuming that he was, it were not so susceptible of proof. What then could he do? No worse trying situation is conceivable than that of an officer subordinated under a captain whom he suspects to be, not mad indeed, but yet not quite unaffected in his intellect. To argue his order to him would be insolence. To resist him would be mutiny. In obedience to Captain Vere he communicated to the lieutenants and captain of marines what had happened; saying nothing as to the Captain's state. They stared at him in surprise and concern. Like him they seemed to think that such a matter should be reported to the Admiral.

Who in the rainbow can draw the line where the violent tint ends and the orange tint begins? Distinctly we see the difference of the colour, but where exactly does the first one visibly enter into the other? So with sanity and insanity. In pronounced cases there is no question about them. But in some cases, in various degrees supposedly less pronounced, to draw the line of demarcation few will undertake, though for a fee some professional experts will. There is nothing namable but that some men will undertake to do for pay. In other words, there are instances where it is next to impossible to determine whether a man is sane or beginning to be otherwise.

Whether Captain Vere, as the surgeon professionally surmised, was really the sudden victim of any degree of aberration, one must determine for himself by such light as this narrative may afford.

The unhappy event which has been narrated could not have happened at a worse juncture. For it was close on the heel of the suppressed insurrections, an after-time very critical to naval authority, demanding from every English sea-commander two qualities not readily interfusable—prudence and rigour. Moreover, there was something crucial in the case.

In the jugglery of circumstances preceding and attending the event on board the *Indomitable* and in the light of that martial code whereby it was formally to be judged, innocence and guilt, personified in Claggart and Budd, in effect changed places.

In the legal view the apparent victim of the tragedy was he who had sought to victimize a man blameless; and the indisputable deed of the latter, navally regarded, constituted the most heinous of military crimes. Yet more. The essential right and wrong involved in the matter, the clearer that might be, so much the worse for the responsibility of a loyal sea-commander, inasmuch as he was authorized to determine the matter on that primitive legal basis.

Small wonder then that the *Indomitable's* Captain, though in general a man of rigid decision, felt that circumspectness not less than promptitude was necessary. Until he could decide upon his course, and in each detail; and not only so, but until the concluding measure was upon the point of being enacted he deemed it advisable, in view of all the circumstances, to guard as much as possible against publicity. Here he may or may not have erred. Certain it is, however, that subsequently in the confidential talk of more than one or two gun-rooms and cabins he was not a little criticized by some officers, a fact imputed by his friends, and vehemently by his cousin Jack Denton, to professional jealousy of Starry Vere. Some imaginative ground for invidious comment there was. The maintenance of secrecy in the matter, the confining all knowledge of it

for a time to the place where the homicide occurred—the quarter-deck
cabin; in these particulars lurked some resemblance to the policy adopted
in those tragedies of the palace which have occurred more than once in
the capital founded by Peter the Barbarian, great chiefly by his crimes.

The case was such that fain would the *Indomitable's* Captain have deferred taking any action whatever respecting it further than to keep the
foretopman a close prisoner till the ship rejoined the squadron, and then
submitting the matter to the judgment of his Admiral.

But a true military officer is, in one particular, like a true monk. Not
with more of self-abnegation will the latter keep his vows of monastic
obedience than the former his vows of allegiance to martial duty.

Feeling that unless quick action were taken on it, the deed of the foretopman, as soon as it should be known on the gun-decks, would tend to
awaken any slumbering embers of the Nore among the crews—a sense
of the urgency of the case overruled in Captain Vere all other considerations. But though a conscientious disciplinarian, he was no lover of authority for mere authority's sake. Very far was he from embracing opportunities for monopolizing to himself the perils of moral responsibility,
none at least that could properly be referred to an official superior, or
shared with him by his official equals or even subordinates. So thinking,
he was glad it would not be at variance with usage to turn the matter
over to a summary court of his own officers, reserving to himself, as the
one on whom the ultimate accountability would rest, the right of maintaining a supervision of it, or formally or informally interposing at need.
Accordingly a drum-head court was summarily convened, he electing the
individuals composing it, the First Lieutenant, the Captain of Marines,
and the Sailing Master.

In associating an officer of marines with the sea-lieutenants in a case
having to do with a sailor, the Commander perhaps deviated from general
custom. He was prompted thereto by the circumstances that he took that
soldier to be a judicious person, thoughtful and not altogether incapable
of gripping with a difficult case unprecedented in his prior experience. Yet
even as to him he was not without some latent misgiving, for withal he
was an extremely good-natured man, an enjoyer of his dinner, a sound
sleeper, and inclined to obesity. The sort of man who, though he would
always maintain his manhood in battle, might not prove altogether reliable in a moral dilemma involving aught of the tragic. As to the First
Lieutenant and the Sailing Master, Captain Vere could not but be aware
that though honest natures, of approved gallantry upon occasion, their
intelligence was mostly confined to the matter of active seamanship, and
the fighting demands of their profession. The court was held in the same
cabin where the unfortunate affair had taken place. This cabin, the Commander's, embraced the entire area under the poop-deck. Aft, and on
either side, was a small state-room—the one room temporarily a jail, and
the other a dead-house—and a yet smaller compartment leaving a space
between, expanding forward into a goodly oblong of length coinciding

with the ship's beam. A skylight of moderate dimension was overhead, and at each end of the oblong space were two sashed port-hole windows, easily convertible back into embrasures for short cannonades.

All being quickly in readiness, Billy Budd was arraigned, Captain Vere necessarily appearing as the sole witness in the case, and as such temporarily sinking his rank, though singularly maintaining it in a matter apparently trivial, namely, that he testified from the ship's weather-side, with that object having caused the court to sit on the lee-side. Concisely he narrated all that had led up to the catastrophe, omitting nothing in Claggart's accusation and deposing as to the manner in which the prisoner had received it. At this testimony the three officers glanced with no little surprise at Billy Budd, the last man they would have suspected, either of mutinous design alleged by Claggart, or of the undeniable deed he himself had done. The First Lieutenant, taking judicial primacy and turning towards the prisoner, said, "Captain Vere has spoken. Is it or is it not as Captain Vere says?" In response came syllables not so much impeded in the utterance as might have been anticipated. They were these:

"Captain Vere tells the truth. It is just as Captain Vere says, but it is not as the Master-at-arms said. I have eaten the King's bread and I am true to the King."

"I believe you, my man," said the witness, his voice indicating a suppressed emotion not otherwise betrayed.

"God will bless you for that, your honour!" not without stammering said Billy, and all but broke down. But immediately was recalled to self-control by another question, with which the same emotional difficulty of utterance came: "No, there was no malice between us. I never bore malice against the Master-at-arms. I am sorry that he is dead. I did not mean to kill him. Could I have used my tongue I would not have struck him. But he foully lied to my face, and in the presence of my Captain, and I had to say something, and I could only say it with a blow. God help me!"

In the impulsive above-board manner of the frank one the court saw confirmed all that was implied in words which just previously had perplexed them, coming as they did from the testifier to the tragedy, and promptly following Billy's impassioned disclaimer of mutinous intent—Captain Vere's words, "I believe you, my man."

Next it was asked of him whether he knew of or suspected aught savouring of incipient trouble (meaning a mutiny, though the explicit term was avoided) going on in any section of the ship's company.

The reply lingered. This was naturally imputed by the court to the same vocal embarrassment which had retarded or obstructed previous answers. But in main it was otherwise here; the question immediately recalling to Billy's mind the interview with the afterguardsman in the fore-chains. But an innate repugnance to playing a part at all approaching that of an informer against one's own shipmates—the same erring sense of uninstructed honour which had stood in the way of his reporting the matter at the time; though as a loyal man-of-war's man it was incumbent on him and failure so to do charged against him and, proven, would have subjected him to the heaviest of penalties. This, with the blind feeling now his, that nothing really was being hatched, prevailing with him. When the answer came it was a negative.

"One question more," said the officer of marines now first speaking and with a troubled earnestness. "You tell us that what the Master-at-arms said against you was a lie. Now why should he have so lied, so maliciously lied, since you declare there was no malice between you?"

At that question unintentionally touching on a spiritual sphere wholly obscure to Billy's thoughts, he was nonplussed, evincing a confusion indeed that some observers, such as can be imagined, would have construed into involuntary evidence of hidden guilt. Nevertheless he strove some way to answer, but all at once relinquished the vain endeavour, at the same time turning an appealing glance towards Captain Vere as deeming him his best helper and friend. Captain Vere, who had been seated for a time, rose to his feet, addressing the interrogator. "The question you put to him comes naturally enough. But can he rightly answer it?—or anybody else? unless indeed it be he who lies within there," designating the compartment where lay the corpse. "But the prone one there will not rise to our summons. In effect though, as it seems to me, the point you make is hardly material. Quite aside from any conceivable motive actuating the Master-at-arms, and irrespective of the provocation of the blow, a martial court must needs in the present case confine its attention to the blow's consequence, which consequence is to be deemed not otherwise than as the striker's deed!"

This utterance, the full significance of which it was not at all likely that Billy took in, nevertheless caused him to turn a wistful, interrogative look towards the speaker, a look in its dumb expressiveness not unlike that which a dog of generous breed might turn upon his master, seeking in his face some elucidation of a previous gesture ambiguous to the canine intelligence. Nor was the same utterance without marked effect upon the three officers, more especially the soldier. Couched in it seemed to them a meaning unanticipated, involving a prejudgment on the speaker's part. It served to augment a mental disturbance previously evident enough.

The soldier once more spoke, in a tone of suggestive dubiety addressing at once his associates and Captain Vere: "Nobody is present—none of the ship's company, I mean, who might shed lateral light, if any is to be had, upon what remains mysterious in this matter."

"That is thoughtfully put," said Captain Vere; "I see your drift. Ay, there is a mystery; but to use a Scriptural phrase, it is 'a mystery of inquiry,' a matter for only psychologic theologians to discuss. But what has a military court to do with it? Not to add that for us any possible investigation of it is cut off by the lasting tongue-tie of him in yonder," again designating the mortuary state-room. "The prisoner's deed. With that alone we have to do."

To this, and particularly the closing reiteration, the marine soldier, knowing not how aptly to reply, sadly abstained from saying aught. The First Lieutenant, who at the outset had not unnaturally assumed primacy in the court, now overrulingly instructed by a glance from Captain Vere (a glance more effective than words), resumed that primacy. Turning to the prisoner: "Budd," he said, and scarce in equable tones, "Budd, if you have aught further to say for yourself, say it now."

Upon this the young sailor turned another quick glance towards Captain Vere; then, as taking a hint from that aspect, a hint confirming his own instinct that silence was now best, replied to the Lieutenant, "I have said all, Sir."

The marine—the same who had been the sentinel without the cabin-door at the time that the foretopman, followed by the Master-at-arms, entered it—he, standing by the sailor throughout their judicial proceedings, was now directed to take him back to the after compartment originally assigned to the prisoner and his custodian. As the twain disappeared from view, the three officers, as partially liberated from some inward constraint associated with Billy's mere presence—simultaneously stirred in their seats. They exchanged looks of troubled indecision, yet feeling that decide they must, and without long delay; for Captain Vere was for the time sitting unconsciously with his back towards them, apparently in one of his absent fits, gazing out from a sashed port-hole to windward upon the monotonous blank of the twilight sea. But the court's silence continuing, broken only at moments by brief consultations in low earnest tones, this seemed to assure him and encourage him. Turning, he to-and-fro paced the cabin athwart; in the returning ascent to windward, climbing the slant deck in the ship's lee roll; without knowing it symbolizing thus in his action a mind resolute to surmount difficulties even if against primitive instincts strong as the wind and the sea. Presently he came to a stand before the three. After scanning their faces he stood less as mustering his thoughts for expression, than as one in deliberating how best to put them to well-meaning men not intellectually mature—men with whom it was necessary to demonstrate certain principles that were axioms to himself. Similar impatience as to talking is perhaps one reason that deters some minds from addressing any popular assemblies; under which head is to be classed most legislatures in a Democracy.

When speak he did, something both in the substance of what he said and his manner of saying it showed the influence of unshared studies, modifying and tempering the practical training of an active career. This, along with his phraseology now and then, was suggestive of the grounds whereon rested that imputation of a certain pedantry socially alleged against him by certain naval men of wholly practical cast, captains who nevertheless would frankly concede that His Majesty's navy mustered no more efficient officers of their grade than "Starry Vere."

What he said was to this effect: "Hitherto I have been but the witness, little more; and I should hardly think now to take another tone, that of your coadjutor, for the time, did I not perceive in you—at the crisis too—a troubled hesitancy, proceeding, I doubt not, from the clashing of military duty with moral scruple—scruple vitalized by compassion. For the compassion, how can I otherwise but share it. But, mindful of paramount obligation, I strive against scruples that may tend to enervate decision. Not, gentlemen, that I hide from myself that the case is an exceptional one. Speculatively regarded, it well might be referred to a jury of casuists. But for us here, acting not as casuists or moralists, it is a case practical and under martial law practically to be dealt with.

"But your scruples! Do they move as in a dusk? Challenge them. Make them advance and declare themselves. Come now—do they import something like this: If, mindless of palliating circumstances, we are bound to regard the death of the Master-at-arms as the prisoner's deed, then does that deed constitute a capital crime whereof the penalty is a mortal one? But in natural justice is nothing but the prisoner's overt act to be considered? Now can we adjudge to summary and shameful death a fellow-creature innocent before God, and whom we feel to be so?—Does that state it aright? You sign sad assent. Well, I, too, feel that, the full force of that. It is Nature. But do these buttons that we wear attest that our allegiance is to Nature? No, to the King. Though the ocean, which is inviolate Nature primeval, though this be the element where we move and have our being as sailors, yet as the King's officers lies our duty in a sphere correspondingly natural? So little is that true, that in receiving our commissions we in the most important regards ceased to be natural free-agents. When war is declared, are we the commissioned fighters previously consulted? We fight at command. If our judgments approve the war, that is but coincidence. So in other particulars. So now, would it be so much we ourselves that would condemn as it would be martial law operating through us? For that law and the rigour of it, we are not responsible. Our vowed responsibility is in this: That however pitilessly that law may operate, we nevertheless adhere to it and administer it.

"But the exceptional in the matter moves the heart within you. Even so, too, is mine moved. But let not warm hearts betray heads that should be cool. Ashore in a criminal case will an upright judge allow himself when off the bench to be waylaid by some tender kinswoman of the accused seeking to touch him with her tearful plea? Well, the heart here is as that piteous woman. The heart is the feminine in man, and hard though it be, she must here be ruled out."

He paused, earnestly studying them for a moment; then resumed.

"But something in your aspect seems to urge that it is not solely that heart that moves in you, but also the conscience, the private conscience. Then, tell me whether or not, occupying the position we do, private conscience should not yield to that imperial one formulated in the code under which alone we officially proceed?"

Here the three men moved in their seats, less convinced than agitated by the course of an argument troubling but the more the spontaneous conflict within. Perceiving which, the speaker paused for a moment; then abruptly changing his tone, went on:

"To steady us a bit, let us recur to the facts.—In war-time at sea a man-of-war's man strikes his superior in grade, and the blow kills. Apart from its effect, the blow itself is, according to the Articles of War, a capital crime. Furthermore—"

"Ay, Sir," emotionally broke in the officer of marines, "in one sense it was. But surely Budd purposed neither mutiny nor homicide."

"Surely not, my good man. And before a court less arbitrary and more merciful than a martial one that plea would largely extenuate. At the Last Assizes it shall acquit. But how here? We proceed under the law of the Mutiny Act. In feature no child can resemble his father more than that Act resembles in spirit the thing from which it derives—War. In His Majesty's service—in this ship indeed—there are Englishmen forced to fight for the King against their will. Against their conscience, for aught we know. Though as their fellow-creatures some of us may appreciate their position, yet as navy officers, what reck we of it? Still less recks the enemy. Our impressed men he would fain cut down in the same swath with our volunteers. As regards the enemy's naval conscripts, some of whom may even share our own abhorrence of the regicidal French Directory, it is the same on our side. War looks but to the frontage, the appearance. And the Mutiny Act, War's child, takes after the father. Budd's intent or non-intent is nothing to the purpose.

"But while, put to it by those anxieties in you which I cannot but respect, I only repeat myself—while thus strangely we prolong proceedings that should be summary, the enemy may be sighted and an engagement result. We must do; and one of two things must we do—condemn or let go."

"Can we not convict and yet mitigate the penalty?" asked the Junior Lieutenant here speaking, and falteringly, for the first time.

"Lieutenant, were that clearly lawful for us under the circumstances, consider the consequences of such clemency. The people" (meaning the ship's company) "have native sense; most of them are familiar with our naval usage and tradition; and how would they take it? Even could you explain to them—which our official position forbids—they, long moulded by arbitrary discipline, have not that kind of intelligent responsiveness that might qualify them to comprehend and discriminate. No, to the people the foretopman's deed, however it be worded in the announcement, will be plain homicide committed in a flagrant act of mutiny. What penalty for that should follow, they know. But it does not follow. *Why?* they will ruminate. You know what sailors are. Will they not revert to the recent outbreak at the Nore? Ay, they know the well-founded alarm—the panic it struck throughout England. Your clement sentence they would account pusillanimous. They would think that we flinch, that we are afraid of them—afraid of practising a lawful rigour singularly demanded at this juncture lest it should provoke new troubles. What shame to us such a conjecture on their part, and how deadly to discipline. You see then whither, prompted by duty and the law, I steadfastly drive. But I beseech you, my friends, do not take me amiss. I feel as you do for this unfortunate boy. But did he know our hearts, I take him to be of that generous nature that he would feel even for us on whom in this military necessity so heavy a compulsion is laid."

With that, crossing the deck, he resumed his place by the sashed port-hole, tacitly leaving the three to come to a decision. On the cabin's opposite side the troubled court sat silent. Loyal lieges, plain and practical, though at bottom they dissented from some points Captain Vere had put to them, they were without the faculty, hardly had the inclination to gainsay one whom they felt to be an earnest man—one, too, not less their superior in mind than in naval rank. But it is not improbable that even such of his words as were not without influence over them, less came home to them than his closing appeal to their instinct as sea-officers, in the forethought he threw out as to the practical consequences to discipline (considering the unconfirmed tone of the fleet at the time)—should a man-of-war's man's violent killing at sea of a superior in grade be allowed to pass for aught else than a capital crime, demanding prompt infliction of the penalty?

Not unlikely they were brought to something more or less akin to that harassed frame of mind which in the year 1842 actuated the commander of the U.S. brig-of-war *Somers* to resolve (under the so-called Articles of War—Articles modelled upon the English Mutiny Act) to resolve upon the execution at sea of a midshipman and two petty-officers as mutineers designing the seizure of the brig. Which resolution was carried out, though in a time of peace and within not many days' sail of home. An act vindicated by a naval court of inquiry subsequently convened ashore—history, and here cited without comment. True, the circumstances on board the *Somers* were different from those on board the *Indomitable*. But the urgency felt, well-warranted or otherwise, was much the same.

Says a writer whom few know, "Forty years after a battle it is easy for a non-combatant to reason about how it ought to have been fought. It is another thing personally and under fire to direct the fighting while involved in the obscuring smoke of it. Much so with respect to other emergencies involving considerations both practical and moral, and when it is imperative promptly to act. The greater the fog, the more it imperils the steamer, and speed is put on though at the hazard of running somebody down. Little ween the snug cardplayers in the cabin of the responsibilities of the sleepless man on the bridge."

In brief, Billy Budd was formally convicted and sentenced to be hung at the yard-arm in the early morning-watch, it being now night. Otherwise, as is customary in such cases, the sentence would forthwith have been carried out. In war-time on the field or in the fleet, a mortal punishment decreed by a drum-head court—on the field sometimes decreed by but a nod from the general—follows without a delay on the heel of conviction without appeal.

It was Captain Vere himself who, of his own motion, communicated the finding of the court to the prisoner; for that purpose going to the compartment where he was in custody, and bidding the marine there to withdraw for the time.

Beyond the communication of the sentence, what took place at this interview was never known. But, in view of the character of the twain briefly closeted in that state-room, each radically sharing in the rarer qualities of one nature—so rare, indeed, as to be all but incredible to average minds however much cultivated—some conjectures may be ventured.

It would have been in consonance with the spirit of our Captain Vere should he on this occasion have concealed nothing from the condemned one—should he indeed have frankly disclosed to him the part he himself had played in bringing about the decision, at the same time revealing his actuating motives. On Billy's side it is not improbable that such a confession would have been received in much the same spirit that prompted it. Not without a sort of joy indeed he might have appreciated the brave opinion of him implied in his Captain making such a confidant of him. Nor as to the sentence itself could he have been insensible that it was imparted to him as to one not afraid to die. Even more may have been. Captain Vere in the end may have developed the passion sometimes latent under an exterior stoical or indifferent. He was old enough to have been Billy's father. The austere devotee of military duty, letting himself melt back into what remains primeval in our formalized humanity, may in the end have caught Billy to heart, even as Abraham may have caught young Isaac on the brink of resolutely offering him up in obedience to the exacting behest. But there is no telling the sacrament—seldom if in any case revealed to the gadding world wherever under circumstances at all akin to those here attempted to be set forth—two of great Nature's nobler order embrace. There is privacy at the time, inviolable to the survivor, and holy oblivion (the sequel to each diviner magnanimity) providentially covers all at last.

The first to encounter Captain Vere in the act of leaving the compartment was the Senior Lieutenant. The face he beheld, for the moment one expressive of the agony of the strong, was to that officer, though a man of fifty, a startling revelation. That the condemned one suffered less than he who mainly had effected the condemnation was apparently indicated by the former's exclamation in the scene soon perforce to be touched upon.

Of a series of incidents within a brief term rapidly following each other, the adequate narration may take up a term less brief, especially if explanation or comment here and there seem requisite to the better understanding of such incidents. Between the entrance into the cabin of him who never left it alive, and him who when he did leave it left it as one condemned to die; between this and the closeted interview just given, less

than an hour and a half had elapsed. It was an interval long enough, however, to awaken speculations among no few of the ship's company as to
what it was that could be detaining in the cabin the Master-at-arms and
the sailor, for it was rumoured that both of them had been seen to enter
it and neither of them had been seen to emerge. This rumour had got
abroad upon the gun-decks and in the tops; the people of a great war-ship
being in one respect like villagers, taking microscopic note of every untoward movement or non-movement going on. When therefore in
weather not at all tempestuous all hands were called in the second dog-
watch, a summons under such circumstances not usual in those hours,
the crew were not wholly unprepared for some announcement extraordinary, one having connection, too, with the continued absence of the two
men from their wonted haunts.

There was a moderate sea at the time; and the moon, newly risen and
near to being at its full, silvered the white spar-deck wherever not blotted
by the clear-cut shadows horizontally thrown of fixtures and moving men.
On either side of the quarter-deck the marine guard under arms was
drawn up; and Captain Vere, standing up in his place surrounded by all
the ward-room officers, addressed his men. In so doing his manner showed
neither more nor less than that properly pertaining to his supreme position aboard his own ship. In clear terms and concise he told them what
had taken place in the cabin; that the Master-at-arms was dead; that he
who had killed him had been already tried by a summary court and condemned to death; and that the execution would take place in the early
morning-watch. The word *mutiny* was not named in what he said. He refrained, too, from making the occasion an opportunity for any preach-
ment as to the maintenance of discipline, thinking, perhaps, that under
existing circumstances in the navy the consequences of violating discipline
should be made to speak for itself.

Their Captain's announcement was listened to by the throng of standing sailors in a dumbness like that of a seated congregation of believers in
Hell listening to the clergyman's announcement of his Calvinistic text.

At the close, however, a confused murmur went up. It began to wax
all but instantly, then, as a sign, was pierced and suppressed by shrill
whistles of the boatswain and his mates piping "Down one watch."

To be prepared for burial Claggart's body was delivered to certain
petty-officers of his mess. And here, not to clog the sequel with lateral
matters, it may be added that at a suitable hour, the Master-at-arms was
committed to the sea with every funeral honour properly belonging to his
naval grade.

In this proceeding, as in every public one growing out of the tragedy,
strict adherence to usage was observed. Nor in any point could it have
been at all deviated from, either with respect to Claggart or Billy Budd,
without begetting undesirable speculations in the ship's company, the
sailors, and more particularly the men-of-war's men, being of all men the
greatest sticklers for usage.

For similar cause all communication between Captain Vere and the condemned one ended with the closeted interview already given, the latter being now surrendered to the ordinary routine preliminary to the end. This transfer under guard from the Captain's quarters was effected without unusual precautions—at least no visible ones.

If possible, not to let the men so much as surmise that their officers anticipate aught amiss from them is the tacit rule in a military ship. And the more that some sort of trouble should really be apprehended, the more do the officers keep that apprehension to themselves; though not the less unostentatious vigilance may be augmented.

In the present instance the sentry placed over the prisoner had strict orders to let no one have communication with him but the Chaplain. And certain unobstrusive measures were taken absolutely to insure this point.

In a seventy-four of the old order the deck known as the upper gun-deck was the one covered by the spar-deck, which last, though not without its armament, was for the most part exposed to the weather. In general it was at all hours free from hammocks; those of the crew swinging on the lower gun-deck, and berth-deck, the latter being not only a dormitory but also the place for the stowing of the sailors' bags, and on both sides lined with the large chests or movable pantries of the many messes of the men.

On the starboard side of the *Indomitable's* upper gun-deck, behold Billy Budd under sentry lying prone in irons in one of the bays formed by the regular spacing of the guns comprising the batteries on either side. All these pieces were of the heavier calibre of that period. Mounted on lumbering wooden carriages, they were hampered with cumbersome harness of breeching and strong side-tackles for running them out. Guns and carriages, together with the long rammers and shorter lintstocks lodged in loops overhead—all these, as customary, were painted black; and the heavy hempen breechings, tarred to the same tint, wore the like livery of the undertakers. In contrast with the funeral tone of these surrounding the prone sailor's exterior apparel, white *jumper* and white duck trousers, each more or less soiled, dimly glimmered in the obscure light of the bay like a patch of discoloured snow in early April lingering at some upland cave's black mouth. In effect he is already in his shroud or the garments that shall serve him in lieu of one. Over him, but scarce illuminating him, two battle-lanterns swing from two massive beams of the deck above. Fed with the oil supplied by the war-contractors (whose gains, honest or otherwise, are in every land an anticipated portion of the harvest of death), with flickering splashes of dirty yellow light they pollute the pale moonshine all but ineffectually struggling in obstructed flecks through the open ports from which the tamponed cannon protrude. Other lanterns at intervals serve but to bring out somewhat the obscurer bays which, like small confessionals or side-chapels in a cathedral, breach from the long, dim-vasted, broad aisle between the two batteries of that covered tire.

Such was the deck where now lay the Handsome Sailor. Through the rose-tan of his complexion, no pallor could have shown. It would have taken days of sequestration from the winds and the sun to have brought about the effacement of that young sea-bloom. But the skeleton in the cheek-bone at the point of its angle was just beginning delicately to be defined under the warm-tinted skin. In fervid hearts self-contained some brief experiences devour our human tissue as secret fire in a ship's hold consumes cotton in the bale.

But now, lying between the two guns, as nipped in the vice of fate, Billy's agony, mainly proceeding from a generous young heart's virgin experience of the diabolical incarnate and effective in some men—the tension of that agony was over now. It survived not the something healing in the closeted interview with Captain Vere. Without movement, he lay as in a trance, that adolescent expression previously noted as his, taking on something akin to the look of a slumbering child in the cradle when the warm hearth-glow of the still chamber of night plays on the dimples that at whiles mysteriously form in the cheek, silently coming and going there. For now and then in the gyved one's trance, a serene happy light born of some wandering reminiscence or dream would diffuse itself over his face, and then wane away only anew to return.

The Chaplain coming to see him and finding him thus, and perceiving no sign that he was conscious of his presence, attentively regarded him for a space, then slipping aside, withdrew for the time, peradventure feeling that even he, the minister of Christ, though receiving his stipend from wars, had no consolation to proffer which could result in a peace transcending that which he beheld. But in the small hours he came again. And the prisoner, now awake to his surroundings, noticed his approach, and civilly, all but cheerfully, welcomed him. But it was to little purpose that in the interview following the good man sought to bring Billy Budd to some godly understanding that he must die, and at dawn. True, Billy himself freely referred to his death as a thing close at hand; but it was something in the way that children will refer to death in general, who yet among their other sports will play a funeral with hearse and mourners. Not that like children Billy was incapable of conceiving what death really is. No, but he was wholly without irrational fear of it, a fear more prevalent in highly civilized communities than those so-called barbarous ones which in all respects stand nearer to unadulterate Nature. And, as elsewhere said, a barbarian Billy radically was; as much so, for all the costume, as his countrymen the British captives, living trophies made to march in the Roman triumph of Germanicus. Quite as much so as those later barbarians, young men probably, and picked specimens among the earlier British converts to Christianity, at least nominally such, and taken to Rome (as to-day converts from lesser isles of the sea may be taken to London), of whom the Pope of that time, admiring the strangeness of their personal beauty—so unlike the Italian stamp, their clear, ruddy complexions and curled flaxen locks, explained, "Angles" (meaning in English the modern derivative)—"Angels do you call them? And is it because they look so like *angels?*" Had it been later in time one would think that the Pope had in mind Fra Angelico's seraphs, some of whom, plucking apples in gardens of Hesperides, have the faint rose-bud complexion of the more beautiful English girls.

If in vain the kind Chaplain sought to impress the young barbarian with ideas of death akin to those conveyed in the skull, dial and crossbones on old tombstones; equally futile to all appearances were his efforts to bring home to him the thought of salvation and a Saviour. Billy listened, but less out of awe or reverence, perhaps, than from a certain natural politeness; doubtless at bottom regarding all that in much the same way which most mariners of his class take any discourse abstract or out of the common tone of the workaday world. And this sailor way of taking clerical discourse is not wholly unlike the way in which the pioneer of Christianity—full of transcendent miracles—was received long ago on tropic isles by any superior *savage* so called: a Tahitian say of Captain Cook's time or shortly after that time. Out of natural courtesy he received but did not appreciate. It was like a gift placed in the palm of an outstretched hand upon which the fingers do not close.

But the *Indomitable's* Chaplain was a discreet man possessing the good sense of a good heart. So he insisted not in his vocation here. At the instance of Captain Vere, a lieutenant had apprised him of pretty much of everything as to Billy; and since he felt that innocence was even a better thing than religion wherewith to go to judgment, he reluctantly withdrew; but in his emotion not without performing an act strange enough in an Englishman, and under the circumstances yet more so in any regular priest. Stooping over he kissed on the fair cheek his fellowman, a felon in martial law, one who, though in the confines of death, he felt he could never convert to a dogma; nor for all that did he fear for his future.

Marvel not that, having been made acquainted with the young sailor's essential innocence, the worthy man lifted not a finger to avert the doom of such a martyr to martial discipline. So to do would not only have been as idle as invoking the desert, but would also have been an audacious transgression of the bounds of his function—one as exactly prescribed to him by military law as that of any other naval officer. Bluntly put, a chaplain is the minister of the Prince of Peace serving in the host of the God of War—Mars. As such, he is as incongruous as a musket would be on the altar at Christmas. Why then is he there? Because he indirectly subserves the purpose attested by the cannon; because, too, he lends the sanction of the religion of the meek to that which practically is the abrogation of everything but force.*

The night so luminous on the spar–deck, but otherwise on the cavern-

---

* Melville notes on this passage: "An irruption of heretic thought hard to suppress."

ous ones below—levels so very like the tiered galleries in a coal-mine—the luminous night passed away. Like the prophet in the chariot disappearing in heaven and dropping his mantle to Elisha, the withdrawing night transferred its pale robe to the peeping day. A meek shy light appeared in the East, where stretched a diaphanous fleece of white furrowed vapour. That light slowly waxed. Suddenly *one bell* was struck aft, responded to by one louder metallic stroke from forward. It was four o'clock in the morning. Instantly the silver whistles were heard summoning all hands to witness punishment. Up through the great hatchway rimmed with racks of heavy shot, the watch below came pouring, overspreading with the watch already on deck the space between the mainmast and foremast, including that occupied by the capacious *launch* and the black booms tiered on either side of it—boat and booms making a summit of observation for the powder boys and younger tars. A different group comprising one watch of topmen leaned over the side of the rail of that sea-balcony, no small one in a seventy-four, looking down on the crowd below. Man or boy, none spake but in whisper, and few spake at all. Captain Vere—as before, the central figure among the assembled commissioned officers—stood nigh the break of the poop-deck, facing forward. Just below him on the quarter-deck the marines in full equipment were drawn up much as at the scene of the promulgated sentence.

At sea in the old time, the execution by halter of a military sailor was generally from the fore-yard. In the present instance—for special reasons—the main-yard was assigned. Under an arm of that yard the prisoner was presently brought up, the Chaplain attending him. It was noted at the time, and remarked upon afterwards, that in this final scene the good man evinced little or nothing of the perfunctory. Brief speech indeed he had with the condemned one, but the genuine gospel was less on his tongue than in his aspect and manner towards him. The final preparations personal to the latter being speedily brought to an end by two boatswain's-mates, the consummation impended. Billy stood facing aft. At the penultimate moment, his words, his only ones, words wholly unobstructed in the utterance, were these—"God bless Captain Vere!" Syllables so unanticipated coming from one with the ignominious hemp about his neck—a conventional felon's benediction directed aft towards the quarters of honour; syllables, too, delivered in the clear melody of a singing-bird on the point of launching from the twig, had a phenomenal effect, not unenhanced by the rare personal beauty of the young sailor, spiritualized now through late experiences so poignantly profound.

Without volition, as it were, as if indeed the ship's populace were the vehicles of some vocal electric current, with one voice, from alow and aloft, came a resonant echo—"God bless Captain Vere!" And yet, at that instant, Billy alone must have been in their hearts, even as he was in their eyes.

At the pronounced words and the spontaneous echo that voluminously rebounded them, Captain Vere, either through stoic self-control or a sort of momentary paralysis induced by emotional shock, stood erectly rigid as a musket in the ship-armour's rack.

The hull, deliberately recovering from the periodic roll to leeward, was just regaining an even keel—when the last signal, the preconcerted dumb one, was given. At the same moment it chanced that the vapoury fleece hanging low in the east was shot through with a soft glory as of the fleece of the Lamb of God seen in mystical vision; and simultaneously therewith, watched by the wedged mass of upturned faces, Billy ascended; and ascending, took the full rose of the dawn.

In the pinioned figure, arrived at the yard-end, to the wonder of all no motion was apparent save that created by the slow roll of the hull, in moderate weather so majestic in a great ship heavy-cannoned.

Murder at Harvard

Stewart Holbrook

N oт ALL of the sons of Harvard, not even Harvard doctors of philosophy, appear to know that the university on the Charles was the scene of one of the most celebrated crimes in American annals. This is a melancholy state of affairs, for the setting of the murder was indubitably a college building and the criminal, who was John White Webster, A.B. 1811, and M.D. 1815, remains the only Harvard professor to perform lethally while a member of the faculty, and the sole college professor to gain entrance to the *Dictionary of American Biography* on the strength not of his scholarship but of his stout and murderous right arm.

The painful celebrity that came to Harvard has gradually been dissipated in the ninety-five years intervening, yet more than one member of the faculty long felt the blight cast by Professor Webster. Bliss Perry has related how his mother at Williamstown, Massachusetts, refused to entertain a Harvard professor who had come there, circa 1870, as a dele-

Reprinted from *The American Scholar*. Volume 14, No. 4, Autumn, 1945.

gate to a convention of New England college officials. Mrs. Perry vowed most firmly on this occasion that she could not sleep "if one of those Harvard professors was in the house." Incidentally, the professor, who had to find quarters elsewhere than in the Perry home, was James Russell Lowell.

One reason the crime achieved such notoriety was pungently pointed out at the time by the eminent Jared Sparks. "Our professors," said the then president of Harvard College, "do not often commit murder." Another reason for notoriety was the prominence of the victim, Dr. George Parkman. And witnesses at the trial read like the index to one of Mr. Van Wyck Brook's charming studies of New England.

But let us move upon the *corpus delicti*.

At about half-past one on the gray twenty-third of November, in 1849, Dr. George Parkman, one of Boston's best-known citizens, was seen afoot near the corner of Blossom and North Grove streets, moving rapidly toward Harvard Medical College, on the Boston side of the Charles. He was always in a hurry, Dr. Parkman, and his tall, lean figure, together with a prognathous jaw and a set of false teeth so white they fairly glittered, made him a marked man. Yet somewhere near or at the entrance to the Medical College he walked straight into Valhalla. Nor has he been seen since.

A man of Dr. Parkman's standing could not disappear without being missed immediately. It was he, a Harvard man himself, who had given the very land on which the then new Medical College building stood. He had also endowed the Parkman Chair of Anatomy, currently occupied by Dr. Oliver Wendell Holmes. His family was prominent, and his brother, the Rev. Francis Parkman, was a well-known clergyman whose son of the same name was about to achieve fame as a historian. The Parkmans were in-laws of many old Boston families, including that of Robert Gould Shaw.

When Dr. Parkman did not return to his home on Walnut Street that afternoon of the twenty-third, search was begun at once by Charles M. Kingsley, the agent who looked after Parkman's many properties in the city. And next day, Robert Gould Shaw himself, after conferring with the Parkmans, had 28,000 handbills distributed announcing a reward of $3,000 for recovery of the doctor alive, or $1,000 for his body. Mr. Gould told police that he suspected a man who several months previously had robbed Dr. Parkman.

While police were looking for this unnamed thug, an astonishing event occurred. On Sunday, two days after the doctor's disappearance, there appeared at the door of the Rev. Francis Parkman's home, Professor John White Webster, who acted in "an abrupt and peculiar manner." Webster said that he had had an interview (a tremendous understatement, that) with the missing man in the Medical College on Friday afternoon, at which time he had paid Dr. Parkman $483 "and some cents."

The latter had then, said Webster, rushed out of the college. All of which favored the popular theory that Parkman had been waylaid, robbed, and doubtless murdered.

John White Webster was fifty-six years of age. After graduation from Harvard Medical School he had served in Guy's Hospital, London, and married Harriet Hickling, a daughter of the American vice-consul at St. Michael. Since 1824 he had taught chemistry at Harvard, and from 1827 had held the Erving Chair of Chemistry and Mineralogy. The Websters, who had four lovely daughters, lived in Cambridge and were much given to hospitality.

Hospitality of the sort the generous Websters lavished on faculty members and wives, as well as local and visiting celebrities, cost a good deal, even in the Cambridge of a century ago. And Professor Webster's salary of $1,200 a year was not equal to it. True, he had the income from his lectures; but he was far from brilliant on the platform, and the income from this source was meager. Yet, while it was known to Robert Gould Shaw that on November 23 his brother-in-law had gone to collect money owed him by Webster, he did not suspect that Webster was responsible for Parkman's disappearance. Who, indeed, *could* suspect any such indiscretion in a faculty member of the college on the Charles?

It was a fact, though, that the financial affairs of Professor Webster had reached something of a climax. They were so involved that many whole pages of finely printed testimony were required, a bit later, to make them clear—if ever they did become clear—to the jury. Briefly, it would appear that as early as 1842 Webster had first borrowed money from Parkman, in the sum of $400. For this he gave his note secured by personal property. Then, in 1847, at a time when the first loan had not been repaid, Parkman had been one of a group to lend Webster more than $2,000, this time taking a mortgage on all of his personal property, which included a cabinet of minerals. A year later, unknown to Parkman, Webster went to Robert Gould Shaw and by pathetic tales of misfortune prevailed on that kindly man to buy the cabinet of minerals outright for $1,200. He failed to mention that this collection was already in pawn to Parkman.

Well, it was bound to happen soon or late, and one day the matter of Professor Webster's cabinet of minerals—soon to be the most famous collection in history—occurred in a conversation between Gould and Parkman. Now, Doctor Parkman patently enjoyed a low boiling point, and he became furious. From that moment onward poor Professor Webster knew what it was like to have a Yankee bloodhound on his trail. His creditor was a punctilious man who paid his own obligations when due and he expected the same of everybody else, even a Harvard professor.

Nothing came of the search for Doctor Parkman. The Charles was dragged. The Medical College was visited by swarms of police who also entered all of the college buildings in Cambridge. Strangers in Boston were picked up by the score, to be questioned and released. The theory of robbery and murder still held the fancy of both police and public, and apparently nobody suspected Professor Webster until a morose and obscure man named Ephraim Littlefield began to translate his brooding into action. Littlefield was janitor at the Medical College. He must have been of a particularly suspicious nature, for his entrance into the case as an amateur detective was brought about by a generous act of Professor Webster's. On the Tuesday following Parkman's disappearance, Webster had presented Littlefield with a thumping big turkey—an astounding event, since it was the first gift the janitor had received in seven years of work at the college. Littlefield brooded over the turkey, which one is happy to note came from Foster's store, next door to the Howard Atheneum, which a bit later became the place where generations of Harvard undergraduates were to study anatomy. Littlefield not only brooded over the gift of the turkey, but he was troubled because talk on the street had it that "they'll sure find Doctor Parkman's body somewhere in the Medical College." (In those days medical colleges, both abroad and at home, were held to be notorious receivers of the products of professional body-snatchers.)

"I got tired," said Littlefield in explaining his next move, "of hearing all that talk about the Medical College." Accordingly, he procured what appears to have been a sufficient number of demolition tools to have supplied wreckers for all of Harvard University. Into his dismal basement apartment at the Medical College he lugged drills, hammers, chisels, crowbars. He told his wife that he was going to do nothing less than to dig through the brick vault under Professor Webster's room in the College. Mrs. Littlefield was dreadfully frightened. She objected that her husband would be dismissed from his job, should knowledge of his suspicions reach officials of the college. But she apparently felt differently about the matter after her husband related a conversation he had overheard between Webster and Parkman.

A few days before Parkman's disappearance, according to Littlefield, the janitor was helping Webster putter around his laboratory. The two men were busy and didn't hear a footstep. But suddenly, as if from nowhere, Doctor Parkman appeared on cat's feet. Immediately, said Littlefield, Doctor Parkman spoke up quick and loud—and harsh: "Doctor Webster, are you ready for me tonight?" And Webster replied: "No, Doctor, I am not ready tonight." Parkman moved back toward the door, raised one arm and shook one fist. "Doctor Webster," he said savagely, "something must be accomplished tomorrow." Then he went out.

For the next several days Littlefield brooded and wondered whether, on the next call Doctor Parkman made on Professor Webster, the latter *had* been ready for him. So, on what must have been a gloomy and foreboding Thanksgiving Day, and while Mrs. Littlefield stood watch for possible interruptions, the janitor hammered and drilled and crowbarred his way into the solid brick wall of the vault beneath Professor Webster's laboratory. Progress was slow. At noon Littlefield refreshed himself with the astounding turkey, then returned to his labors, which were great. They really laid brick walls to stay, in the era of solid craftsmanship, and night found the janitor only part way through the bricks. He was a determined man, however, and on the folowing day, after performing his regular duties, he resumed his attack on the vault. And that night he broke through. "I held my light forward," he related, "and the first thing I saw was the pelvis of a man and two parts of a leg. I knew," he added darkly, "this was no place for such things."

Nor was it. Littlefield notified the police of his find, and when they had taken one look at the ghastly contents of the vault, they drove madly to Cambridge in a hack and called on Professor Webster. Constable Derastus Clapp, a man of devious Yankee ways, told Webster they should like him to attend them at the Medical College while a new search was being made. Webster replied that although the building already had been searched a number of times, nevertheless he would be glad to accompany the officers. He got into the hack, which soon crossed the bridge into Boston—and continued on past North Grove Street and toward Leverett Street Jail.

"Stop," cried Webster. "We are going in the wrong direction."

But devious Constable Derastus Clapp answered: "Oh, that's all right, Professor. He is a new coachman and somewhat green, but he will doubtless discover and correct his mistake." Boston had constables in those days of Transcendentalism.

In a few moments, however, the professor realized that he was not a free aid in a search, but a prisoner in Boston jail. Reporters came, and next day the press and all the town went delirious. "Horrible Suspicions!!" screamed the usually seemly and genteel *Evening Transcript,* "Arrest of Professor J. W. Webster." And it continued:

Since last evening our whole population has been in a state of the greatest possible excitement in consequence of the astounding rumor that the body of Dr. Parkman has been discovered and that Dr. John W. Webster, professor of chemistry at the Medical School of Harvard College, and a gentleman connected by marriage with some of our most distinguished families, has been arrested and imprisoned, on suspicion of being the murderer. . . . Never in the annals of crime in Massachusetts has such a sensation been produced.

And then, because Epes Sargent was editor of the *Transcript,* and because he probably wrote the story himself, we get the full flavor of the *Evening Transcript's* idea of reporting the crime of the century. The item continues:

In the streets, in the market-place, at every turn, men greet each other with pale, eager looks, and the inquiry, "Can it be true?" And then the terrible reply, "The circumstances begin to gather weight against him," is wrung forth; the agitated listener can only vent his sickening sense of horror, in some such expression as that of Hamlet—

O, horrible! O, horrible! most horrible!

Never again, so far as I am aware, did the *Transcript* feel that a murder called for Shakespeare. Not even the famous Richardson and Pretty
Choir Singer affair of later years rated the Bard.

The trial opened on the nineteenth of March, 1850, when Professor
Webster, "his step light and elastic, crossed and took his seat in the dock,
his countenance betraying a degree of calm and dignified composure."
He was quite short in stature, and seemed of no great strength to the
"expert stenographer," John A. French, who noted and took down
everything for publication in a "splendidly illustrated" pamphlet put out
by the Boston Herald Steam Press. I cherish a worn copy of this horribly
printed pamphlet, and had a distant forebear of mine not been otherwise
so tremendously occupied, family folklore might have added considerably
to my knowledge of the trial. Peter B. Brigham was excused from jury
duty at the Webster trial on the improbable plea that he belonged to the
Boston militia, was "liable to call at any moment," and was "thus exempt
by the statute from serving on a jury."

The State promptly put Janitor Littlefield on the stand, and his accumulated testimony was bad indeed for Professor Webster. Defense attempted to throw suspicion on Littlefield himself, and it also presented a
long and highly distinguished array of character and other witnesses. The
Hon. John Gorham Palfrey, historian, former editor of the *North American Review,* and member of Congress, declared sonorously that Professor
Webster was a man of some temper but of extremely good heart. President Jared Sparks of Harvard thought Webster "kind and humane." Nathaniel Bowditch, probably a son of the great mathematician, said that
Webster was "irritable though kind-hearted." Other witnesses included
members of prominent families—Bigelow, Codman, Dana, Lovering,
Sanger, Wyman. Oliver Wendell Holmes, who gave his occupation as
physician, testified at some length, both for the State and the defense.
For the former he said that whoever had cut up the body alleged to be that
of Doctor Parkman had certainly been handy with surgical knives.

The State, of course, was attempting to prove that the remnants of human mortality which had been discovered in the vault, in a tin box filled
mostly with tanbark in Webster's laboratory, and in the laboratory stove,
were those of Dr. Parkman; and the defense was doing its best to prove
the fragments to be those of almost anybody except Doctor Parkman.

While Dr. Nathan C. Keep was on the stand identifying the mineral
teeth found in the stove to be the very same teeth he had made for Doctor
Parkman, suddenly "here the City bells were rung for fire, and it being
announced that the Tremont House was on fire, the Court granted an intermission, to allow the Attorney General, who boarded at the Tremont,
to save his papers."

Upon resumption of the trial the spectators were given a grisly enough
treat when Dr. Woodbridge Strong took the stand to discuss the matter
of burning bodies. "I have dissected a good many bodies in my day," said

Doctor Strong with evident relish. "I recollect a pirate I had given me one time, and as I only wanted the bones, I dissected him rapidly, and . . ." so on and on, until some of the less avid spectators left the courtroom.

Little by little, over what must have been ten terrible days for Professor Webster, the coils of circumstantial evidence could be seen closing around him, and late on the eleventh day the jury was charged by Chief Justice Lemuel Shaw, another Harvard man (1800), in an address which is still considered by lawyers to be one of the greatest expositions of the law of circumstantial evidence ever delivered, and is referred to, in the quaint way of lawyers, as *Cushing* 295. Three hours later the jury returned with a verdict of guilty. There was no demonstration, for "an awful and unbroken silence ensued, in which the Court, the jury, the clerk, and spectators seemed to be absorbed in their own reflections."

Professor Webster wasn't quite ready to greet the hangman, but his writ of error was denied, and he then addressed the Governor and Council, protesting his innocence and piously calling on the Great Searcher of human hearts as his witness. To no avail. And long before Professor Webster's neck was broken, quickly and efficiently, on August 30, 1850, he made a long confession. Janitor Littlefield had been right. Professor Webster *was* ready for Doctor Parkman, when he called on that fatal Friday. What had happened, according to Webster's confession, was this:

Doctor Parkman had come that day with the idea of getting some money. When denied it, he had called Webster both liar and scoundrel, and had shaken his fist in the professor's face. Then, said Webster, "I felt nothing but the sting of his words . . . and in my fury I seized whatever thing was handiest—it was a stick of wood—and dealt him an instantaneous blow with all the force that passion could give it." The one blow was enough. Parkman fell, bleeding at the mouth. Webster hurriedly bolted all the doors, stripped the dead man, hoisted him into the sink, and there dismembered him with the deft professional strokes that had been apparent to Dr. Oliver Wendell Holmes.

The Webster-Parkman affair unquestionably has had mention in more autobiographies and memoirs than any other murder case in America. The case probably comes nearer to filling the definition "classic" than any other crime in the nineteenth-century United States. Boston never quite forgave Charles Dickens for his interest in it. For, on his visit in 1869, when asked what he should most like to see of the city's great landmarks, he promptly replied, "the room where Doctor Parkman was murdered." He was taken to see it, too, by nobody but Doctor Holmes. And that evening, at a dinner tendered the distinguished Briton, Henry W. Longfellow related a singular incident regarding Professor Webster.

Longfellow had often been a guest in the Webster home in Cambridge, and on one such occasion, a year or so before the crime, Webster had the lights of the dining room lowered and a servant brought a bowl of burning chemicals which shed a ghastly luminescence on the faces of those at the table. Webster then stood up, said Longfellow, took a rope from beneath the table, and cast it around his own short thick neck, like a noose. He then leaned over the glowing bowl, rolled his eyes, lolled his head to one side, and stuck out his tongue, like one hanged. Some of the guests thought it an odd idea of entertainment.

Perhaps the best bit of folklore, though, concerns sardonic Ben Butler, to whom Harvard had failed to grant an LL.D. While cross-examining a witness in court, and treating him rather roughly, the judge reminded Butler that the witness was no less than a Harvard professor. "Yes, I know, your honor," said Ben. "We hanged one the other day."

For the next half century or more Harvard faculty members were constantly undergoing similar pleasantries, according to the late Albert Bushnell Hart, who told me that the ribbing was still prevalent in his early days at Harvard, in the 1880's. And in recent years, so Harlow Shapley reports, the chief comment on the case concerns wonder that only *one* Harvard professor has murdered another. This fact leaves the incidence of murder among Harvard faculty members very low—one in approximately every three centuries.

Actuarially speaking, the job of teaching there remains a fairly good risk.

The Malefactor

Anton Chekhov

A TINY, very thin little peasant stood before the examining magistrate. He wore a striped shirt and patched trousers; his shaggy beard, his pockmarked face, his eyes scarcely visible under their bushy, overhanging brows gave him a harsh and forbidding expression, to which a mane of matted, unkempt hair added a spider-like ferocity. He was barefoot.

"Denis Grigorieff," began the magistrate, "come nearer and answer my questions. While patrolling the track on the seventh of last July, Ivan Akinfoff, the railroad watchman, found you at the one hundred and forty-first verst unscrewing one of the nuts that fasten the rails to the ties. Here is the nut you had when he arrested you. Is this true?"

"What's that?"

"Did everything happen as Akinfoff reports?"

"Yes, just as he reports."

"Very well. Now, what was your object in unscrewing that nut?"

"What's that?"

"Stop your 'What's that?' and answer my question; why did you unscrew that nut?"

"If I hadn't needed the nut I wouldn't have unscrewed it," grunted Denis, glancing at the ceiling.

"What did you need it for?"

"What for? We make sinkers out of nuts."

"Whom do you mean by 'we?' "

"We—the people, the peasants of Kimoff."

"Look here, man, no playing the idiot! Talk sense, and don't lie to me about sinkers!"

"I never lied in my life," muttered Denis, blinking. "How can one possibly fish without sinkers, your honour? If you baited your hook with a shiner or a roach, do you think it would sink to the bottom without a sinker? You tell me I am lying!" laughed Denis. "A fine bait a shiner would make, floating on the top of the water! Bass and pike and eels always take ground bait; a floating bait would only be taken by a garfish, and they won't often take it. Anyway, we haven't any garfish in our river; they like the open."

"Why are you talking to me about garfish?"

"What's that? Didn't you ask me about fishing? All the gentlemen with us fish like that. The smallest boy knows more than to fish without a sinker. Of course, there are some people who don't know anything, and they go fishing without sinkers. Fools obey no laws."

"So you tell me you unscrewed this nut to use as a weight?"

"What else should I have unscrewed it for? To play knuckle-bones with?"

"But you might have made a weight out of a piece of lead or a bullet or a nail or something."

"Lead does not grow on every bush; it has to be bought; and a nail wouldn't do. There is nothing so good to make a weight of as a nut. It is heavy and has a hole in it."

"What a fool he is pretending to be! You act as if you were one day old or had just dropped from the clouds. Don't you see, you donkey, what the consequences of this unscrewing must be? If the watchman hadn't found you, one of the trains might have run off the track and killed everybody, and *you* would have killed them!"

"God forbid, your honour! Do you think we are wicked heathen?

Praise be to God, kind master, not only have we never killed anybody, we have never even thought of it! Holy Mother preserve us and have mercy upon us! How can you say such things?"

Denis smirked and winked incredulously at the magistrate. "Huh! For how many years has the whole village been unscrewing nuts, and not an accident yet? If I were to carry a rail away, or even to put a log across the track, then, perhaps, the train might upset, but, Lord! a nut—pooh!"

"But can't you understand that the nuts fasten the rails to the ties?"

"Yes, we understand that, and so we don't unscrew them all; we always leave some; we do it carefully; we understand."

Denis yawned and made the sign of the cross over his mouth.

"A train ran off the track not far from here last year," said the magistrate. "Now I know why."

"What did you say?"

"Now, I say, I know why that train ran off the track last year."

"Yes; you have been educated to know these things, kind master; you can understand just why everything is; but that watchman is a peasant who doesn't know anything; he just grabbed me by the coat collar and dragged me away. One ought to judge first and drag afterward. But a peasant has the sense of a peasant. You might write down, your honour, that he hit me twice—in the mouth and in the chest."

"Another nut was found when your house was searched. Where did you unscrew that one, and when?"

"Do you mean the nut that was lying under the little red chest?"

"I haven't any idea where it was lying, but it was found. Where did you unscrew it?"

"I didn't unscrew it; it was given to me by Ignashka, the son of one-eyed Simon. That is, I am speaking of the nut under the little chest; the one in the sleigh in the courtyard, Mitrofan and I unscrewed together."

"Which Mitrofan?"

"Mitrofan Petroff. Haven't you heard of him? He's the man that makes fishingnets and sells them to the gentlemen. He needs a lot of nuts in his business—a dozen to every net."

"Listen! In Article 1081 of the Code it says that 'Whoever intentionally commits an act of injury to a railroad, whereby an accident might result to the trains, and who knows that such an accident might result'—do you hear that? 'who *knows*'—'shall be severely punished.' You could not but have known what this unscrewing would lead to. The sentence is exile and hard labour."

"Of course, you know that better than I do. We people live in darkness. How can we know such things?"

"You know all about it perfectly well. You are lying and shamming ignorance."

"Why should I lie? Ask anybody in the village if you don't believe me. They never catch a thing but roach without a sinker; even gudgeons hardly ever bite unless you use one."

"Now you are going to begin on those garfish again!" smiled the magistrate.

"We don't have garfish in our river. If we let the bait float on the top without a sinker we sometimes catch a perch, but not often."

"Oh, stop talking!"

Silence fell. Denis stood first on one leg and then on the other and stared at the table, winking rapidly as if he saw the sun before his eyes and not a green table-cover. The magistrate was writing quickly.

"I shall have to arrest you and send you to prison."

Denis stopped winking, raised his heavy eyebrows, and looked inquiringly at the magistrate.

"How do you mean—to prison? Your honour, I haven't time! I have to go to the fair to collect the three roubles that Gregory owes me for tallow."

"Stop talking! Don't interrupt!"

"To prison! If there was any reason, of course I'd go, but, living as I do—what is it for? I haven't robbed any one; I haven't even been fighting. If it's the payment of my rent you are thinking about, you mustn't believe what the bailiff says, your honour. Ask any one of the gentlemen; that bailiff is a thief, sir!"

"Stop talking!"

"I'll stop," mumbled Denis. "All the same, I'll swear under oath that the bailiff has muddled his books. There are three brothers in our family—Kuzma and Gregory and I—"

"You are interrupting me. Here, Simon!" called the magistrate, "take this man away."

"There are three brothers in our family," murmured Denis as two strapping soldiers took hold of him and led him out of the room. "I can't be responsible for my brothers. Kuzma won't pay his debts, and I, Denis, have to suffer! You call yourselves judges! If our old master, the general, were alive he would teach you judges your business. You ought to be reasonable, and not condemn so wildly. Flog a man if he deserves it—"

The Right Way to Deal with Pirates

Mark Twain

HESE MURDER and jury statistics remind me of a certain very extraordinary trial and execution of twenty years ago; it is a scrap of history familiar to all old Californians, and worthy to be known by other peoples of the earth that love simple, straight-forward justice unencumbered with nonsense. I would apologize for this digression but for the fact that the information I am about to offer is apology enough in itself. And since I digress constantly, anyhow, perhaps it is as well to eschew apologies altogether and thus prevent their growing irksome.

Capt. Ned Blakely—that name will answer as well as any other fictitious one (for he was still with the living at last accounts, and may not desire to be famous)—sailed ships out of the harbor of San Francisco for many years. He was a stalwart, warm-hearted, eagle-eyed veteran, who had been a sailor nearly fifty years—a sailor from early boyhood. He was a rough, honest creature, full of pluck, and just as full of hard-hearted simplicity, too. He hated trifling conventionalities—"business" was the word, with him. He had all a sailor's vindictiveness against the quips and quirks of the law, and steadfastly believed that the first and last aim and object of the law and lawyers was to defeat justice.

He sailed for the Chincha Islands in command of a guano-ship. He had a fine crew, but his negro mate was his pet—on him he had for years lavished his admiration and esteem. It was Capt. Ned's first voyage to the Chinchas, but his fame had gone before him—the fame of being a man who would fight at the dropping of a handkerchief, when imposed upon, and would stand no nonsense. It was a fame well earned. Arrived in the islands, he found that the staple of conversation was the exploits of one Bill Noakes, a bully, the mate of a trading-ship. This man had created a small reign of terror there. At nine o'clock at night, Capt. Ned, all alone, was pacing his deck in the starlight. A form ascended the side, and approached him. Capt. Ned said:

"Who goes there?"

From *Roughing It*, by Mark Twain. By permission of Harper & Brothers.

"I'm Bill Noakes, the best man on the islands."

"What do you want aboard this ship?"

"I've heard of Capt. Ned Blakely, and one of us is a better man than 'tother—I'll know which, before I go ashore."

"You have come to the right shop—I'm your man. I'll learn you to come aboard this ship without an *in*vite."

He seized Noakes, backed him against the mainmast, pounded his face to a pulp, and then threw him overboard.

Noakes was not convinced. He returned the next night, got the pulp renewed, and went overboard head first, as before. He was satisfied.

A week after this, while Noakes was carousing with a sailor crowd on shore, at noonday, Capt. Ned's colored mate came along, and Noakes tried to pick a quarrel with him. The negro evaded the trap, and tried to get away. Noakes followed him up; the negro began to run; Noakes fired on him with a revolver and killed him. Half a dozen sea-captains witnessed the whole affair. Noakes retreated to the small after-cabin of his ship, with two other bullies, and gave out that death would be the portion of any man that intruded there. There was no attempt made to follow the villains; there was no disposition to do it, and indeed very little thought of such an enterprise. There were no courts and no officers; there was no government; the islands belonged to Peru, and Peru was far away; she had no official representative on the ground; and neither had any other nation.

However, Capt. Ned was not perplexing his head about such things. They concerned him not. He was boiling with rage and furious for justice. At nine o'clock at night he loaded a double-barreled gun with slugs, fished out a pair of handcuffs, got a ship's lantern, summoned his quartermaster, and went ashore. He said:

"Do you see that ship there at the dock?"

"Ay-ay, sir."

"It's the *Venus*."

"Ay-ay, sir."

"You—you know *me*."

"Ay-ay, sir."

"Very well, then. Take the lantern. Carry it just under your chin. I'll walk behind you and rest this gun-barrel on your shoulder, p'inting forward—so. Keep your lantern well up, so's I can see things ahead of you good. I'm going to march in on Noakes—and take him—and jug the other chaps. If you flinch—well, you know *me*."

"Ay-ay, sir."

In this order they filed aboard softly, arrived at Noake's den, the quartermaster pushed the door open, and the lantern revealed the three desperadoes sitting on the floor. Capt. Ned said:

"I'm Ned Blakely. I've got you under fire. Don't you move without orders—any of you. You two kneel down in the corner; faces to the wall —now. Bill Noakes, put these handcuffs on; now come up close. Quartermaster, fasten 'em. All right. Don't stir, sir. Quartermaster, put the key in the outside of the door. Now, men, I'm going to lock you two in; and if you try to burst through this door—well, you've heard of *me*. Bill Noakes, fall in ahead, and march. All set. Quartermaster, lock the door."

Noakes spent the night on board Blakely's ship, a prisoner under strict guard. Early in the morning Capt. Ned called in all the sea-captains in the harbor and invited them, with nautical ceremony, to be present on board his ship at nine o'clock to witness the hanging of Noakes at the yard-arm!

"What! The man has not been tried."

"Of course he hasn't. But didn't he kill the nigger?"

"Certainly he did; but you are not thinking of hanging him without a trial?"

"*Trial!* What do I want to try him for, if he killed the nigger?"

"Oh, Capt. Ned, this will *never* do. Think how it will sound."

"Sound be hanged! *Didn't he kill the nigger?*"

"Certainly, certainly, Capt. Ned—nobody denies that—but—"

"Then I'm going to *hang* him, that's all. Everybody I've talked to talks just the same way you do. Everybody says he killed the nigger, everybody knows he killed the nigger, and yet every lubber of you wants him *tried* for it. I don't understand such bloody foolishness as that. *Tried!* Mind you, I don't object to trying him if it's got to be done to give satisfaction; and I'll be there, and chip in and help, too; but put it off till afternoon—put it off till afternoon, for I'll have my hands middling full till after the burying—"

"Why, what do you mean? Are you going to hang him *anyhow*—and try him afterward?"

"Didn't I *say* I was going to hang him? I never saw such people as you. What's the difference? You ask a favor, and then you ain't satisfied when you get it. Before or after's all one—*you* know how the trial will go. He killed the nigger. Say—I must be going. If your mate would like to come to the hanging, fetch him along. I like him."

There was a stir in the camp. The captains came in a body and pleaded with Capt. Ned not to do this rash thing. They promised that they would create a court composed of captains of the best character; they would impanel a jury; they would conduct everything in a way becoming the serious nature of the business in hand, and give the case an impartial hearing and the accused a fair trial. And they said it would be murder, and punishable by the American courts if he persisted and hung the accused on his ship. They pleaded hard. Capt. Ned said:

"Gentlemen, I'm not stubborn and I'm not unreasonable. I'm always willing to do just as near right as I can. How long will it take?"

"Probably only a little while."

"And can I take him up the shore and hang him as soon as you are done?"

"If he is proven guilty he shall be hanged without unnecessary delay."

"*If* he's proven guilty. Great Neptune, *ain't* he guilty? This beats my time. Why you all *know* he's guilty."

But at last they satisfied him that they were projecting nothing underhanded. Then he said:

"Well, all right. You go on and try him and I'll go down and overhaul his conscience and prepare him to go—like enough he needs it, and I don't want to send him off without a show for hereafter."

This was another obstacle. They finally convinced him that it was necessary to have the accused in court. Then they said they would send a guard to bring him.

"No, sir, I prefer to fetch him myself—he don't get out of *my* hands. Besides, I've got to go to the ship to get a rope, anyway."

The court assembled with due ceremony, impaneled a jury, and presently Capt. Ned entered, leading the prisoner with one hand and carrying a Bible and a rope in the other. He seated himself by the side of his captive and told the court to "up anchor and make sail." Then he turned a searching eye on the jury, and detected Noakes's friends, the two bullies. He strode over and said to them confidentially:

"You're here to interfere, you see. Now you vote right, do you hear?—or else there'll be a double-barreled inquest here when this trial's off, and your remainders will go home in a couple of baskets."

The caution was not without fruit. The jury was a unit—the verdict, "Guilty."

Capt. Ned sprung to his feet and said:

"Come along—you're my meat *now,* my lad, anyway. Gentlemen, you've done yourselves proud. I invite you all to come and see that I do it all straight. Follow me to the cañon, a mile above here."

The court informed him that a sheriff had been appointed to do the hanging, and—

Capt. Ned's patience was at an end. His wrath was boundless. The subject of a sheriff was judiciously dropped.

When the crowd arrived at the cañon, Capt. Ned climbed a tree and arranged the halter, then came down and noosed his man. He opened his Bible, and laid aside his hat. Selecting a chapter at random, he read it through, in a deep bass voice and with sincere solemnity. Then he said:

"Lad, you are about to go aloft and give an account of yourself; and the lighter a man's manifest is, as far as sin's concerned, the better for him. Make a clean breast, man, and carry a log with you that'll bear inspection. You killed the nigger?"

No reply. A long pause.

The captain read another chapter, pausing, from time to time, to impress the effect. Then he talked an earnest, persuasive sermon to him, and ended by repeating the question:

"Did you kill the nigger?"

No reply—other than a malignant scowl. The captain now read the first and second chapters of Genesis, with deep feeling, paused a moment, closed the book reverently, and said with a perceptible savor of satisfaction:

"There. Four chapters. There's few that would have took the pains with you that I have."

Then he swung up the condemned, and made the rope fast; stood by and timed him half an hour with his watch, and then delivered the body to the court. A little later, as he stood contemplating the motionless figure, a doubt came into his face; evidently he felt a twinge of conscience—a misgiving—and he said with a sigh:

"Well, p'raps I ought to burnt him, maybe. But I was trying to do for the best."

When the history of this affair reached California (it was in the "early days") it made a deal of talk, but did not diminish the captain's popularity in any degree. It increased it, indeed. California had a population then that "inflicted" justice after a fashion that was simplicity and primitiveness itself, and could therefore admire appreciatively when the same fashion was followed elsewhere.

The Juryman

John Galsworthy

"Don't you see, brother, I was reading yesterday the Gospel about Christ, the little Father; how He suffered, how He walked on the earth. I suppose you have heard about it?"

*"Indeed, I have," replied Stepanuitch; "but we are people in darkness; we can't read."—*Tolstoi.

MR. HENRY BOSENGATE, of the London Stock Exchange, seated himself in his car that morning during the Great War with a sense of injury. Major in a Volunteer Corps; member of all the local committees; lending this very car to the neighbouring hospital, at times even driving it himself for their benefit; subscribing to funds, so far as his diminished income permitted—he was conscious of being an asset to the country, and one whose time could not be wasted with impunity. To be summoned to sit on a jury at the local assizes, and not even the grand jury at that! It was in the nature of an outrage.

Strong and upright, with hazel eyes and dark eyebrows, pinkish-brown cheeks, a forehead white, well-shaped, and getting high, with greyish hair glossy and well-brushed, and a trim moustache, he might have been taken for that colonel of Volunteers which indeed he was in a fair way of becoming.

His wife had followed him out under the porch, and stood bracing her supple body clothed in lilac linen. Red rambler roses formed a sort of crown to her dark head; her ivory-coloured face had in it just a suggestion of the Japanese.

Mr. Bosengate spoke through the whirr of the engine:

"I don't expect to be late, dear. This business is ridiculous. There oughtn't to *be* any crime in these days."

His wife—her name was Kathleen—smiled. She looked very pretty and cool, Mr. Bosengate thought. To one bound on this dull and stuffy business everything he owned seemed pleasant—the geranium beds beside the gravel drive, his long, red-brick house mellowing decorously in its creepers and ivy, the little clock-tower over stables now converted to a garage, the dovecote, masking at the other end the conservatory which adjoined the billiard-room. Close to the red-brick lodge his two children, Kate and Harry, ran out from under the acacia trees, and waved to him, scrambling bare-legged on to the low, red, ivy-covered wall which guarded his domain of eleven acres. Mr. Bosengate waved back, thinking: "Jolly couple—by Jove, they are!" Above their heads, through the trees, he could see right away to some Downs, faint in the July heat haze. And he thought: "Pretty a spot as one could have got, so close to town!"

Despite the war he had enjoyed these last two years more than any of the ten since he built "Charmleigh" and settled down to semi-rural domesticity with his young wife. There had been a certain piquancy, a savour added to existence, by the country's peril, and all the public service and sacrifice it demanded. His chauffeur was gone, and one gardener did the work of three. He enjoyed—positively enjoyed—his committee work; even the serious decline of business and increase of taxation had not much worried one continually conscious of the national crisis and his own part therein. The country 'had wanted waking up, wanted a lesson in effort and economy; and the feeling that he had not spared himself in these strenuous times had given a zest to those quiet pleasures of bed and board which, at his age, even the most patriotic could retain with a good conscience. He had denied himself many things—new clothes, presents for Kathleen and the children, travel, and that pine-apple house which he had been on the point of building when the war broke out; new wine, too, and cigars, and membership of the two Clubs which he had never used in the old days. The hours had seemed fuller and longer, sleep better earned —wonderful, the things one could do without when put to it! He turned the car into the high road, driving dreamily, for he was in plenty of time.

The war was going pretty well now; he was no fool optimist, but now that conscription was in force, one might reasonably hope for its end within a year. Then there would be a boom, and one might let oneself go a little. Visions of theatres and supper with his wife at the Savoy afterwards, and cosy night drives back into the sweet-smelling country behind your own chauffeur once more teased a fancy which even now did not soar beyond the confines of domestic pleasures. He pictured his wife in new dresses by Jay—she was fifteen years younger than himself, and "paid for dressing" as they said. He had always delighted—as men older than their wives will—in the admiration she excited from others not privileged to enjoy her charms. Her rather queer and ironical beauty, her cool irreproachable wifeliness, was a constant balm to him. They would give dinner parties again, have their friends down from town, and he would once more enjoy sitting at the foot of the dinner table while Kathleen sat at the head, with the light soft on her ivory shoulders, behind flowers she had arranged in that original way of hers, and fruit which he had grown in his hothouses; once more he would take legitimate interest in the wine he offered to his guests—once more stock that Chinese cabinet wherein he kept cigars. Yes—there was a certain satisfaction in these days of privation, if only from the anticipation they created.

The sprinkling of villas had become continuous on either side of the high road; and women going to shop, tradesmen's boys delivering victuals, young men in khaki, began to abound. Now and then a limping or bandaged form would pass—some bit of human wreckage! And Mr. Bosengate would think mechanically: "Another of those poor devils! Wonder if we've had his case before us!"

Running his car into the best hotel garage of the little town, he made his way leisurely over to the court. It stood back from the market-place, and was already lapped by a sea of persons having, as in the outer ring at race meetings, an air of business at which one must not be caught out, together with a soaked or flushed appearance. Mr. Bosengate could not resist putting his handkerchief to his nose. He had carefully drenched it with lavender water, and to this fact owed, perhaps, his immunity from the post of foreman on the jury—for, say what you will about the English, they have a deep instinct for affairs.

He found himself second in the front row of the jury box, and through the odour of "Sanitas" gazed at the judge's face expressionless up there, for all the world like a be-wigged bust. His fellows in the box had that appearance of falling between two classes characteristic of jurymen. Mr. Bosengate was not impressed. On one side of him the foreman sat, a prominent upholsterer, known in the town as "Gentleman Fox." His dark and beautifully brushed and oiled hair and moustache, his radiant linen, gold watch and chain, the white piping to his waistcoat, and a habit of never saying "Sir" had long marked him out from commoner men; he undertook to bury people too, to save them trouble; and was altogether superior.

On the other side Mr. Bosengate had one of those men who, except when they sit on juries, are never seen without a little brown bag, and the appearance of having been interrupted in a drink. Pale and shiny, with large loose eyes shifting from side to side, he had an underdone voice and uneasy, flabby hands. Mr. Bosengate disliked sitting next to him. Beyond this commercial traveller sat a dark pale young man with spectacles; beyond him again, a short old man with grey moustache, mutton chops, and innumerable wrinkles; and the front row was completed by a chemist. The three immediately behind, Mr. Bosengate did not thoroughly master; but the three at the end of the second row he learned in their order of an oldish man in a grey suit, given to winking: an inanimate person with the mouth of a moustachioed codfish, over whose long bald crown three wisps of damp hair were carefully arranged; and a dried, dapperish, clean-shorn man, whose mouth seemed terrified lest it should be surprised without a smile. Their first and second verdicts were recorded without the necessity for withdrawal, and Mr. Bosengate was already sleepy when the third case was called. The sight of khaki revived his drooping attention. But what a weedy-looking specimen! This prisoner had a truly nerveless, pitiable, dejected air. If he had ever had a military bearing it had shrunk into him during his confinement. His ill-shaped brown tunic, whose little brass buttons seemed trying to keep smiling, struck Mr. Bosengate as ridiculously short, used though he was to such things. "Absurd," he thought—"Lumbago! Just where they ought to be covered!" Then the officer and gentleman stirred in him, and he added to himself: "Still, there must be some distinction made!" The little soldier's visage had once perhaps been tanned, but was now the colour of dark dough; his large brown eyes with white showing below the iris, as so often in the eyes of very nervous people—wandered from face to face, of judge, counsel, jury, and public. There were hollows in his cheeks, his dark hair looked damp; around his neck he wore a bandage. The commercial traveller on Mr. Bosengate's left turned, and whispered: *"Felo de se!* My hat! what a guy!" Mr. Bosengate pretended not to hear—he could not bear that fellow!—and slowly wrote on a bit of paper: "Owen Lewis." Welsh! Well, he looked it—not at all an English face. Attempted suicide—not at all an English crime! Suicide implied surrender, a putting-up of hands to Fate—to say nothing of the religious aspect of the matter. And suicide in khaki seemed to Mr. Bosengate particularly abhorrent; like turning tail in face of the enemy; almost meriting the fate of a deserter. He looked at the prisoner, trying not to give way to this prejudice. And the prisoner seemed to look at him, though this, perhaps, was fancy.

The counsel for the prosecution, a little, alert, grey, decided man, above military age, began detailing the circumstances of the crime. Mr. Bosengate, though not particularly sensitive to atmosphere, could perceive a sort of current running through the court. It was as if jury and public were thinking rhythmically in obedience to the same unexpressed pre-

judice of which he himself was conscious. Even the Caesar-like pale face
up there, presiding, seemed in its ironic serenity responding to that current.

"Gentlemen of the jury, before I call my evidence, I direct your attention to the bandage the accused is still wearing. He gave himself this
wound with his army razor, adding, if I may say so, insult to the injury
he was inflicting on his country. He pleads not guilty; and before the
magistrates he said that absence from his wife was preying on his mind"—
the advocate's close lips widened—"Well, gentlemen, if such an excuse is to
weigh with us in these days, I'm sure I don't know what's to happen to
the Empire."

"No, by George!" thought Mr. Bosengate.

The evidence of the first witness, a room-mate who had caught the
prisoner's hand, and of the sergeant, who had at once been summoned,
was conclusive, and he began to cherish a hope that they would get
through without withdrawing, and he would be home before five. But
then a hitch occurred. The regimental doctor failed to respond when his
name was called; and the judge having for the first time that day showed
himself capable of human emotion, intimated that he would adjourn until
the morrow.

Mr. Bosengate received the announcement with equanimity. He would
be home even earlier! And gathering up the sheets of paper he had
scribbled on, he put them in his pocket and got up. The would-be suicide
was being taken out of the court—a shambling drab figure with shoulders
hunched. What good were men like that in these days! What good! The
prisoner looked up. Mr. Bosengate encountered in full the gaze of those
large brown eyes, with the white showing underneath. What a suffering,
wretched, pitiable face! A man had no business to give you a look like
that! The prisoner passed on down the stairs, and vanished. Mr. Bosengate
went out and across the market-place to the garage of the hotel where he
had left his car. The sun shone fiercely and he thought: "I must do some
watering in the garden." He brought the car out, and was about to start
the engine, when some one passing said: "Good evenin'. Seedy-lookin'
beggar that last prisoner, ain't he? We don't want men of that stamp." It
was his neighbour on the jury, the commercial traveller, in a straw hat,
with a little brown bag already in his hand and the froth of an interrupted
drink on his moustache. Answering curtly: "Good evening!" and thinking: "Nor of yours, my friend!" Mr. Bosengate started the car with unnecessary clamour. But as if brought back to life by the commercial
traveller's remark, the prisoner's figure seemed to speed along too, turning
up at Mr. Bosengate his pitifully unhappy eyes. Want of his wife!—queer
excuse for trying to put it out of his power ever to see her again. Why!
Half a loaf, even a slice, was better than no bread. Not many of that
neurotic type in the Army—thank Heaven! The lugubrious figure vanished, and Mr. Bosengate pictured instead the form of his own wife
bending over her "Gloire de Dijon" roses in the rosery, where she gener-

ally worked a little before tea now that they were short of gardeners. He saw her, as often he had seen her raise herself and stand, head to one side, a gloved hand on her slender hip, gazing as it were ironically from under drooped lids at buds which did not come out fast enough. And the word *"Caline,"* for he was something of a French scholar, shot through his mind: "Kathleen—*Caline!"* If he found her there when he got in, he would steal up on the grass and—ah! but with great care not to crease her dress or disturb her hair! "If only she weren't quite so self-contained," he thought. "It's like a cat you can't get near, not really near!"

The car, returning faster than it had come down that morning, had already passed the outskirt villas, and was breasting the hill to where, among fields and the old trees, Charmleigh lay apart from commoner life. Turning into his drive, Mr. Bosengate thought with a certain surprise: "I wonder what she *does* think of! I wonder!" He put his gloves and hat down in the outer hall and went into the lavatory to dip his face in cool water and wash it with sweet-smelling soap—delicious revenge on the unclean atmosphere in which he had been stewing so many hours. He came out again into the hall dazed by soap and the mellowed light, and a voice from half-way up the stairs said: "Daddy! Look!" His little daughter was standing up there with one hand on the banisters. She scrambled on to them and came sliding down, her frock up to her eyes, and her holland knickers to her middle. Mr. Bosengate said mildly:

"Well, that's elegant!"

"Tea's in the summer-house. Mummy's waiting. Come on!"

With her hand in his, Mr. Bosengate went on, through the drawing-room, long and cool, with sunblinds down, through the billiard-room, high and cool, through the conservatory, green and sweet-smelling, out on to the terrace and the upper lawn. He had never felt such sheer exhilarated joy in his home surroundings, so cool, glistening and green under the July sun; and he said:

"Well, Kit, what have you all been doing?"

"I've fed my rabbits and Harry's; and we've been in the attic. Harry got his leg through the skylight."

Mr. Bosengate drew in his breath with a hiss.

"It's all right, Daddy; we got it out again, it's only grazed the skin. And we've been making swabs—I made seventeen—Mummy made thirty-three, and then she went to the hospital. Did you put many men in prison?"

Mr. Bosengate cleared his throat. The question seemed to him untimely.

"Only two."

"What's it like in prison, Daddy?"

Mr. Bosengate, who had no more knowledge than his little daughter, replied in an absent voice:

"Not very nice."

They were passing under a young oak tree, where the path wound round to the rosery and summer-house. Something shot down and clawed Mr. Bosengate's neck. His little daughter began to hop and suffocate with laughter.

"Oh, Daddy! Aren't you caught! I led you on purpose!"

Looking up, Mr. Bosengate saw his small son lying along a low branch above him—like the leopard he was declaring himself to be (for fear of error), and thought blithely, "What an active little chap it is!"

"Let me drop on your shoulders, Daddy—like they do on the deer."

"Oh, yes! Do be a deer, Daddy!"

Mr. Bosengate did not see being a deer; his hair had just been brushed. But he entered the rosery buoyantly between his offspring. His wife was standing precisely as he had imagined her, in a pale blue frock open at the neck, with a narrow black band round the waist, and little accordion pleats below. She looked her coolest. Her smile, when she turned her head, hardly seemed to take Mr. Bosengate seriously enough. He placed his lips below one of her half-drooped eyelids. She even smelled of roses. His children began to dance round their mother, and Mr. Bosengate, firmly held between them, was also compelled to do this, until she said.

"When you've quite done, let's have tea!"

It was not the greeting he had imagined coming along in the car. Earwigs were plentiful in the summer-house—used perhaps twice a year, but indispensable to every country residence—and Mr. Bosengate was not sorry for the excuse to get out again. Though all was so pleasant, he felt oddly restless, rather suffocated; and lighting his pipe, began to move about among the roses, blowing tobacco at the greenfly; in war-time one was never quite idle! And suddenly he said:

"We're trying a wretched Tommy at the assizes."

His wife looked up from a rose.

"What for?"

"Attempted suicide."

"Why did he?"

"Can't stand the separation from his wife."

She looked at him, gave a low laugh, and said:

"Oh dear!"

Mr. Bosengate was puzzled. Why did she laugh? He looked round, saw that the children were gone, took his pipe from his mouth, and approached her.

"You look very pretty," he said. "Give me a kiss!"

His wife bent her body forward from the waist, and pushed her lips out till they touched his moustache. Mr. Bosengate felt a sensation as if he had arisen from breakfast without having eaten marmalade. He mastered it and said:

"That jury are a rum lot."

His wife's eyelids flickered. "I wish women sat on juries."

"Why?"

"It would be an experience."

Not the first time she had used that curious expression! Yet her life was far from dull, so far as he could see; with the new interests created by war, and the constant calls on her time made by the perfection of their home life, she had a useful and busy existence. Again the random thought passed through him: "But she never tells me anything!" And suddenly that lugubrious khaki-clad figure started up among the rose bushes. "We've got a lot to be thankful for!" he said abruptly. "I must go to work!" His wife, raising one eyebrow, smiled. "And I to weep!" Mr. Bosengate laughed—she had a pretty wit! And stroking his comely moustache where it had been kissed, he moved out into the sunshine. All the evening, throughout his labours, not inconsiderable, for this jury business had put him behind time, he was afflicted by that restless pleasure in his surroundings; would break off in mowing the lower lawn to look at the house through the trees; would leave his study and committee papers to cross into the drawing-room and sniff its dainty fragrance; paid a special good-night visit to the children having supper in the schoolroom; pottered in and out from his dressing-room to admire his wife while she was changing for dinner; dined with his mind perpetually on the next course; talked volubly of the war; and in the billiard-room afterwards, smoking the pipe which had taken the place of his cigar, could not keep still, but roamed about, now in conservatory, now in the drawing-room, where his wife and the governess were still making swabs. It seemed to him that he could not have enough of anything. About eleven o'clock he strolled out—beautiful night, only just dark enough—under the new arrangement with Time—and went down to the little round fountain below the terrace. His wife was playing the piano. Mr. Bosengate looked at the water and the flat dark water-lily leaves which floated there; looked up at the house, where only narrow chinks of light showed, because of the Lighting Order. The dreamy music drifted out; there was a scent of heliotrope. He moved a few steps back, and sat in the children's swing under an old lime tree. Jolly—blissful—in the warm, bloomy dark! Of all hours of the day this, before going to bed was perhaps the pleasantest. He saw the light go up in his wife's bedroom, unscreened for a full minute, and thought: "Aha! If I did my duty as a special, I should 'strafe' her for that." She came to the window, her figure lighted, hands up to the back of her head, so that her bare arms gleamed. Mr. Bosengate wafted her a kiss, knowing he could not be seen. "Lucky chap!" he mused; "she's a great joy!" Up went her arm, down came the blind—the house was dark again. He drew a long breath. "Another ten minutes," he thought, "then I'll go in and shut up. By jove! The limes are beginning to smell already!" And, the better to take in that acme of his well-being, he tilted the swing, lifted his feet from the ground, and swung himself toward the scented blossoms. He wanted to whelm his senses in their perfume, and closed his eyes. But instead of the domestic vision he expected, the face of the little Welsh soldier, hare-eyed, shadowy, pinched and dark and pitiful, started up with such disturbing vividness that he

opened his eyes again at once. Curse! The fellow almost haunted one!
Where could he be now—poor little devil! lying in his cell, thinking—
thinking of his wife! Feeling suddenly morbid, Mr. Bosengate arrested
the swing and stood up. Absurd!—all his well-being and mood of warm
anticipation had deserted him! "A d——d world!" he thought. "Such a
lot of misery! Why should I have to sit in judgment on that poor beggar,
and condemn him?" He moved up on to the terrace and walked briskly,
to rid himself of this disturbance before going in. "That commercial
traveller chap," he thought, "the rest of those fellows—they see nothing!"
And, abruptly turning up the three stone steps, he entered the conservatory, locked it, passed into the billiard-room, and drank his barley water.
One of the pictures was hanging crooked; he went up to put it straight.
Still life. Grapes and apples, and lobsters! They struck him as odd for the
first time. Why lobsters? The whole picture seemed dead and oily. He
turned off the light, and went upstairs, passed his wife's door, into his
own room, and undressed. Clothed in his pyjamas he opened the door
between the rooms. By the light coming from his own he could see her
dark head on the pillow. Was she asleep? No—not asleep, certainly. The
moment of fruition had come; the crowning of his pride and pleasure in
his home. But he continued to stand there. He had suddenly no pride, no
pleasure, no desire; nothing but a sort of dull resentment against everything. He turned back, shut the door, and slipping between the heavy
curtains and his open window, stood looking out at the night. "Full of
misery!" he thought. "Full of d——d misery!"

Filing into the jury box next morning, Mr. Bosengate collided slightly
with a short juryman, whose square figure and square head of stiff yellow-
red hair he had only vaguely noticed the day before. The man looked
angry, and Mr. Bosengate thought: "An ill-bred dog, that!"

He sat down quickly, and, to avoid further recognition of his fellows,
gazed in front of him. His appearence on Saturdays was always military,
by reason of the route march of his Volunteer Corps in the afternoon.
Gentleman Fox, who belonged to the corps too, was also looking square;
but that commercial traveller on his other side seemed more *louche,* and
as if surprised in immorality, than ever; only the proximity of Gentleman
Fox on the other side kept Mr. Bosengate from shrinking. Then he saw
the prisoner being brought in, shadowy and dark behind the brightness
of his buttons, and he experienced a sort of shock, this figure was so
exactly that which had several times started up in his mind. Somehow he
had expected a fresh sight of the fellow to dispel and disprove what had
been haunting him, had expected to find him just an outside phenomenon,
not, as it were, a part of his own life. And he gazed at the carven immobility of the judge's face, trying to steady himself, as a drunken man
will, by looking at a light. The regimental doctor, unabashed by the
judge's comment on his absense the day before, gave his evidence like a
man who had better things to do, and the case for the prosecution was

forthwith rounded in by a little speech from counsel. The matter—he said —was clear as daylight. Those who wore His Majesty's uniform, charged with the responsibility and privilege of defending their country, were no more entitled to desert their regiments by taking their own lives than they were entitled to desert in any other way. He asked for a conviction. Mr. Bosengate felt a sympathetic shuffle passing through all feet; the judge was speaking:

"Prisoner, you can either go into the witness box and make your statement on oath, in which you may be cross-examined on it; or you can make your statement there from the dock, in which case you will not be cross-examined. Which do you elect to do?"

"From here, my lord."

Seeing him now full face, and, as it might be, come to life in the effort to convey his feelings, Mr. Bosengate had suddenly a quite different impression of the fellow. It was as if his khaki had fallen off, and he had stepped out of his own shadow, a live and quivering creature. His pinched clean-shaven face seemed to have an irregular, wilder, hairier look, his large nervous brown eyes darkened and glowed; he jerked his shoulders, his arms, his whole body, like a man suddenly freed from cramp or a suit of armour. He spoke, too, in a quick, crisp, rather high voice, pinching his consonants a little, sharpening his vowels, like a true Welshman.

"My lord and misters the jury," he said: "I was a hairdresser when the call came on me to join the army. I had a little home and a wife. I never thought what it would be like to be away from them, I surely never did; and I'm ashamed to be speaking it out like this—how it can squeeze and squeeze a man, how it can prey on your mind when you're nervous like I am. 'Tis not everyone that cares for his home—there's a lots o' them never wants to see their wives again. But for me 'tis like being shut up in a cage, it is!" Mr. Bosengate saw daylight between the skinny fingers of the man's hand thrown out with a jerk. "I cannot bear it shut up away from wife and home like what you are in the army. So when I took my razor that morning I was wild—an' I wouldn't be here now but for that man catching my hand. There was no reason in it, I'm willing to confess. It was foolish; but wait till you get feeling like what I was, and see how it draws you. Misters the jury, don't send me back to prison; it is worse still there. If you have wives you will know what it is like for lots of us; only some is more nervous than others. I swear to you, sirs, I could not help it—" Again the little man flung out his hand, his whole thin body shook and Mr. Bosengate felt the same sensation as when he drove his car over a dog—"Misters the jury, I hope you may never in your lives feel as I've been feeling."

The little man ceased, his eyes shrank back into their sockets, his figure back into its mask of shadowy brown and gleaming buttons, and Mr. Bosengate was conscious that the judge was making a series of remarks; and, very soon, of being seated at a mahogany table in the jury's withdrawing room, hearing the voice of the man with hair like an Irish terrier's saying: "Didn't he talk through his hat, that little blighter!" Conscious, too, of the commercial traveller, still on his left—always on his left! mopping his brow, and muttering: "Phew! It's hot in here to-day!" when an effluvium, as of an inside accustomed to whisky, came from him. Then the man with the underlip and the three plastered wisps of hair said:

"Don't know why we withdrew, Mr. Foreman!"

Mr. Bosengate looked round to where, at the head of the table, Gentleman Fox sat, in defensive gentility and the little white piping to his waistcoat. "I shall be happy to take the sense of the jury," he was saying blandly.

There was a short silence, then the chemist murmured:

"I should say he must have what they call claustrophobia."

"Clauster fiddlesticks! The feller's a shirker, that's all. Missed his wife —pretty excuse! Indecent, I call it!"

The speaker was the little wire-haired man; and emotion, deep and angry, stirred in Mr. Bosengate. That ill-bred little cur! He gripped the edge of the table with both hands.

"I think it's d——d natural!" he muttered. But almost before the words had left his lips he felt dismay. What had he said—he, nearly a colonel of volunteers—endorsing such a want of patriotism! And hearing the commercial traveller murmuring: " 'Ear, 'ear!" he reddened violently.

The wire-headed man said roughly:

"There's too many of these blighted shirkers, and too much pampering of them."

The turmoil in Mr. Bosengate increased; he remarked in an icy voice:

"I agree to no verdict that'll send the man back to prison."

At this a real tremor seemed to go round the table, as if they all saw themselves sitting there through lunch time. Then the large grey-haired man given to winking, said:

"Oh! Come, sir—after what the judge said! Come, sir! What do you say, Mr. Foreman?"

Gentleman Fox—as who should say "This is excellent value, but I don't wish to press it on you!"—answered:

"We are only concerned with the facts. Did he or did he not try to shorten his life?"

"Of course he did—said so himself," Mr. Bosengate heard the wire-haired man snap out, and from the following murmur of assent he alone abstained. Guilty! Well—yes! There was no way out of admitting that, but his feelings revolted against handing "that poor little beggar" over to the tender mercy of his country's law. His whole soul rose in arms against agreeing with that ill-bred little cur, and the rest of this job-lot. He had an impulse to get up and walk out, saying: "Settle it your own way. Good morning."

"It seems, sir," Gentleman Fox was saying, "that we're all agreed to guilty, except yourself. If you will allow me, I don't see how you can go behind what the prisoner himself admitted."

Thus brought up to the very guns, Mr. Bosengate, red in the face, thrust his hands deep into the side pockets of his tunic, and, staring straight before him, said:

"Very well; on condition we recommend him to mercy."

"What do you say, gentlemen; shall we recommend him to mercy?"

" 'Ear, 'ear!" burst from the commercial traveller, and from the chemist came the murmur:

"No harm in that."

"Well, I think there is. They shoot deserters at the front, and we let this fellow off. I'd hang the cur."

Mr. Bosengate stared at that little wire-haired brute. "Haven't you *any* feeling for others?" he wanted to say. "Can't you see that this poor devil suffers tortures?" But the sheer impossibility of doing this before ten other men brought a slight sweat out on his face and hands; and in agitation he smote the table a blow with his fist. The effect was instantaneous. Everybody looked at the wire-haired man, as if saying: "Yes, you've gone a bit too far there!" The "little brute" stood it for a moment, then muttered surlily:

"Well, commend 'im to mercy if you like; I don't care."

"That's right; they never pay any attention to it," said the grey-haired man, winking heartily. And Mr. Bosengate filed back with the others into court.

But when from the jury box his eyes fell once more on the hare-eyed figure in the dock, he had his worst moment yet. Why should this poor wretch suffer so—for no fault, no fault; while he, and those others, and that snapping counsel, and the Caesar-like judge up there, went off to their women and their homes, blithe as bees, and probably never thought of him again? And suddenly he was conscious of the judge's voice:

"You will go back to your regiment, and endeavour to serve your country with better spirit. You may thank the jury that you are not sent to prison, and your good fortune that you were not at the front when you tried to commit this cowardly act. You are lucky to be alive."

A policeman pulled the little soldier by the arm; his drab figure, with eyes fixed and lustreless, passed down and away. From his very soul Mr. Bosengate wanted to lean out and say: "Cheer up, cheer up; *I* understand."

It was nearly ten o'clock that evening before he reached home, motoring back from the route march. His physical tiredness was abated, for he had partaken of a snack and a whisky and soda at the hotel but mentally he was in a curious mood. His body felt appeased, his spirit hungry. To-night he had a yearning, not for his wife's kisses, but for her understanding. He wanted to go to her and say: "I've learnt a lot to-day—found out things I never thought of. Life's a wonderful thing, Kate, a thing one can't live all to oneself; a thing one shares with everybody, so that when another suffers, one suffers too. It's come to me that what one *has* doesn't matter a bit—it's what one does, and how one sympathises with other people. It came to me in the most extraordinary vivid way, when I was on that jury watching that poor little rat of a soldier in his trap; it's the first time I've ever felt—the—the spirit of Christ, you know. It's a wonderful thing, Kate—wonderful! We haven't been close—really close, you and I, so that we each understand what the other is feeling. It's all in that, you know; understanding—sympathy—it's priceless. When I saw that poor little devil taken down and sent back to his regiment to begin his sorrows all over again—wanting his wife, thinking and thinking of her just as you know I would be thinking and wanting you, I felt what an awful outside sort of life we lead, never telling each other what we really think and feel, never being really close. I daresay that little chap and his wife keep nothing from each other—live each other's lives. That's what *we* ought to do. Let's get to feeling that what really matters is—understanding and loving, and not only just saying it as we all do, those fellows on the jury, and even that poor devil of a judge—what an awful life, judging one's fellow-creatures! When I left that poor little Tommy this morning, and ever since, I've longed to get back here quietly to you and tell you about it, and make a beginning. There's something wonderful in this, and I want you to feel it as I do, because you mean such a lot to me."

This was what he wanted to say to his wife, not touching, or kissing her, just looking into her eyes, watching them soften and glow as they surely must, catching the infection of his new ardour. And he felt unsteady, fearfully unsteady with the desire to say it all as it should be said: swiftly, quietly, with the truth and fervour of his feeling.

The hall was not lit up, for daylight still lingered under the new arrangement. He went towards the drawing-room, but from the very door shied off to his study and stood irresolute under the picture of a "Man catching a flea" (Dutch school), which had come down to him from his father. The governess would be in there with his wife! He must wait. Essential to go straight to Kathleen and pour it all out, or he would never do it. He felt as nervous as an undergraduate going up for his *vivâ voce*. This thing was so big, so astoundingly and unexpectedly important. He was suddenly afraid of his wife, afraid of her coolness and her grace, and that something Japanese about her—of all those attributes he had been accustomed to admire; most afraid, as it were, of her attraction. He felt young to-night, almost boyish; would she see that he was not really fifteen years older than herself, and she not really a part of his collection, of all the admirable appointments of his home; but a companion spirit to one who wanted a companion badly? In this agitation of his soul he could keep still no more than he could last night in the agitation of his senses; and he wandered into the dining-room. A dainty supper was set out there, sandwiches, and cake, whisky and cigarettes—even an early peach. Mr. Bosengate looked at this peach with sorrow rather than disgust. The perfection of it was of a piece with all that had gone before this new and sudden feeling. Its delicious bloom seemed to heighten his perception of the hedge around him, that hedge of the things he so enjoyed, carefully planted and tended these many years. He passed it by uneaten, and went to the window. Out there, all was darkening, the fountain, the lime tree, the flower-beds, and the fields below, with the Jersey cows who would come to your call; darkening slowly, losing form, blurring into soft blackness, vanishing, but there 'none the less—all there —the hedge of his possessions. He heard the door of the drawing-room open, the voices of his wife and the governess in the hall, going up to bed. If only they didn't look in here! If only—! The voices ceased. He was safe now—had but to follow in a few minutes, to make sure of Kathleen alone. He turned round and stared down the length of the dark dining-room, over the rosewood table, to where in the mirror above the side-board at the far end, his figure bathed, a stain, a mere blurred shadow; he made his way down to it along the table edge, and stood before himself as close as he could get. His throat and the roof of his mouth felt dry with nervousness; he put out his finger and touched his face in the glass. "You're an ass!" he thought. "Pull yourself together, and get it over. She will see; of course she will!" He swallowed, smoothed his moustache, and walked out. Going up the stairs, his heart beat painfully; but he was in for it now, and marched straight into her room.

Dressed only in a loose blue wrapper, she was brushing her dark hair before the glass. Mr. Bosengate went up to her and stood there silent, looking down. The words he had thought of were like a swarm of bees buzzing in his head yet not one would fly from between his lips. His wife went on brushing her hair under the light which shone on her polished elbows. She looked up at him from beneath one lifted eyebrow.

"Well, dear—tired?"

With a sort of vehemence the single word "No" passed out. A faint, a quizzical smile flitted over her face; she shrugged her shoulders ever so gently. That gesture—he had seen it before! And in desperate desire to make her understand, he put his hand on her lifted arm.

"Kathleen, stop—listen to me!" His fingers tightened in his agitation and eagerness to make his great discovery known. But before he could get a word out he became conscious of that cool round arm, conscious of her eyes half-closed, sliding round at him, of her half-smiling lips, of her neck under the wrapper. And he stammered:

"I want—I must—Kathleen, I—"

She lifted her shoulders again in that little shrug. "Yes—I know; all right!"

A wave of heat and shame, and of God knows what came over Mr. Bosengate; he fell on his knees and pressed his forehead to her arm; and he was silent, more silent than the grave. Nothing—nothing came from him but two long sighs. Suddenly he felt her hand stroke his cheek—compassionately, it seemed to him. She made a little movement towards him; her lips met his, and he remembered nothing but that. . . .

In his own room Mr. Bosengate sat at his wide-open window, smoking a cigarette; there was no light. Moths went past, the moon was creeping up. He sat very calm, puffing the smoke out into the night. Curious thing

—life! Curious world! Curious forces in it—making one do the opposite of what one wished; always—always making one do the opposite, it seemed! The furtive light from the creeping moon was getting hold of things down there, stealing in among the boughs of the trees. "There's something ironical," he thought, "which walks about. Things don't come off as you think they will. I meant, I tried—but one doesn't change like that all of a sudden, it seems. Fact is, life's too big a thing for me! All the same, I'm not the man I was yesterday—not quite!" He closed his eyes, and in one of those flashes of vision which come when the senses are at rest, he saw himself as it were far down below—down on the floor of a street narrow as a grave, high as a mountain, a deep dark slit of a street—walking down there, a black midget of a fellow, among other black midgets—his wife, and the little soldier, the judge, and those jury chaps—*fantoches* straight up on their tiny feet, wandering down there in that dark, infinitely tall, and narrow street. "Too much for one!" he thought. "Too high for one—no getting on top of it. We've got to be kind, and help one another, and not expect too much, and not think too much. That's—all!" And, squeezing out his cigarette, he took six deep breaths of the night air, and got into bed.

My Father Goes to Court

Carlos Bulosan

WHEN I WAS five, I lived with my mother and brothers and sisters in a small town on the island of Luzon. Father's farm had been destroyed in 1918 by one of our sudden Philippine floods, so for several years afterward we all lived in the town, though he preferred living in the country. We had as a next-door neighbor a very rich man, whose sons and daughters seldom came out of the house. While we boys and girls played and sang in the sun, his children stayed inside and kept the windows closed. His house was so tall that his children could

From *The Laughter of My Father*, by Carlos Bulosan. Copyright, 1942, 1943, 1944, by Harcourt, Brace and Company, Inc. Originally published in *The New Yorker*.

look in the windows of our house and watch us as we played, or slept, or ate, when there was any food in the house *to* eat.

Now, this rich man's servants were always frying and cooking something good, and the aroma of the food was wafted down to us from the windows of the big house. We hung about and took all the wonderful smell of the food into our beings. Sometimes, in the morning, our whole family stood outside the windows of the rich man's house and listened to the musical sizzling of thick strips of bacon or ham. I can remember one afternoon when our neighbor's servants roasted three chickens. The chickens were young and tender and the fat that dripped into the burning coals gave off an enchanting odor. We watched the servants turn the beautiful birds and inhaled the heavenly spirit that drifted out to us.

Some days the rich man appeared at a window and glowered down at us. He looked at us one by one, as though he were condemning us. We were all healthy because we went out in the sun every day and bathed in the cool water of the river that flowed from the mountains into the sea. Sometimes we wrestled with one another in the house before we went out to play. We were always in the best of spirits and our laughter was contagious. Other neighbors who passed by our house often stopped in our yard and joined us in laughter.

Laughter was our only wealth. Father was a laughing man. He would go into the living room and stand in front of the tall mirror, stretching his mouth into grotesque shapes with his fingers and making faces at himself; then he would rush into the kitchen, roaring with laughter.

There was always plenty to make us laugh. There was, for instance, the day one of my brothers came home with a small bundle under his arm, pretending that he brought something good to eat, maybe a leg of lamb or something as extravagant as that, to make our mouths water. He rushed to Mother and threw the bundle into her lap. We all stood around, watching Mother undo the complicated strings. Suddenly a black cat leaped out of the bundle and ran wildly around the house. Mother chased my brother and beat him with her little fists, while the rest of us bent double, choking with laughter.

Another time one of my sisters suddenly started screaming in the middle of the night. Mother reached her first and tried to calm her. My sister cried and groaned. When Father lighted the lamp, my sister stared at us with shame in her eyes.

"What is it?" Mother asked.

"I'm pregnant!" she cried.

"Don't be a fool!" Father shouted.

"I'm pregnant, I tell you!" she cried.

Father knelt by my sister. He put his hand on her belly and rubbed it gently. "How do you know you are pregnant?" he asked.

"Feel it?" my sister said.

We put our hands on her belly. There was something moving inside. Father was frightened. Mother was shocked. "Who's the man?" she asked.

"There's no man," my sister said.

"What is it, then?" Father asked.

Suddenly my sister opened her blouse and a bullfrog jumped out. Mother fainted, Father dropped the lamp, the oil spilled on the floor, and my sister's blanket caught fire. One of my brothers laughed so hard he rolled on the floor.

When the fire was extinguished and Mother was revived, we returned to bed and tried to sleep, but Father kept on laughing so loud we could not sleep any more. Mother got up again and lighted the oil lamp; we rolled up the mats on the floor and begun dancing about and laughing with all our might. We made so much noise that all our neighbors except the rich family came into the yard and joined us in loud, genuine laughter.

It was like that for years.

As time went on, the rich man's children became thin and anemic, while we grew even more robust and full of life. Our faces were bright and rosy, but theirs were pale and sad. The rich man started to cough at night; then he coughed day and night. His wife began coughing too. Then the children started to cough, one after the other. At night their coughing sounded like the barking of a pack of seals. We hung outside their windows and listened to them. We wondered what had happened. We knew that they were not sick from lack of nourishing food, because they were still always frying something delicious to eat.

One day the rich man appeared at a window and stood there a long time. He looked at my sisters, who had grown fat with laughing, then at my brothers, whose arms and legs were like the molave, which is the sturdiest tree in the Philippines. He banged down the window and ran through his house, shutting all the windows.

From that day on, the windows of our neighbor's house were always closed. The children did not come outdoors any more. We could still hear the servants cooking in the kitchen, and no matter how tight the windows were shut, the aroma of the food came to us in the wind and drifted gratuitously into our house.

One morning a policeman from the presidencia came to our house with a sealed paper. The rich man had filed a complaint against us. Father took me with him when he went to the town clerk and asked him what it was about. He told Father the man claimed that for years we had been stealing the spirit of his wealth and food.

When the day came for us to appear in court, Father brushed his old Army uniform and borrowed a pair of shoes from one of my brothers. We were the first to arrive. Father sat on a chair in the centre of the courtroom. Mother occupied a chair by the door. We children sat on a long bench by the wall. Father kept jumping up from his chair and stabbing the air with his arms, as though he were defending himself before an imaginary jury.

The rich man arrived. He had grown old and feeble; his face was scarred with deep lines. With him was his young lawyer. Spectators came in and almost filled the chairs. The judge entered the room and sat on a high chair. We stood up in a hurry and then sat down again.

After the courtroom preliminaries, the judge looked at Father. "Do you have a lawyer?" he asked.

"I don't need any lawyer, Judge," he said.

"Proceed," said the judge.

The rich man's lawyer jumped up and pointed his finger at Father. "Do you or do you not agree that you have been stealing the spirit of the complainant's wealth and food?"

"I do not!" Father said.

"Do you or do you not agree that while the complainant's servants cooked and fried fat legs of lamb or young chicken breasts you and your family hung outside his window and inhaled the heavenly spirit of the food?"

"I agree," Father said.

"Do you or do you not agree that while the complainant and his children grew sickly and tubercular you and your family became strong of limb and fair of complexion?"

"I agree," Father said.

"How do you account for that?"

Father got up and paced around, scratching his head thoughtfully. Then he said, "I would like to see the children of the complainant, Judge."

"Bring in the children of the complainant."

They came in shyly. The spectators covered their mouths with their hands, they were so amazed to see the children so thin and pale. The children walked silently to a bench and sat down without looking up. They stared at the floor and moved their hands uneasily.

Father could not say anything at first. He just stood by his chair and looked at them. Finally he said, "I should like to cross-examine the complainant."

"Proceed."

"Do you claim that we *stole* the spirit of your wealth and became a laughing family while yours became morose and sad?" Father asked.

"Yes."

"Do you claim that we *stole* the spirit of your food by hanging outside your windows when your servants cooked it?" Father asked.

"Yes."

"Then we are going to *pay* you right now," Father said. He walked over to where we children were sitting on the bench and took my straw hat off my lap and began filling it up with centavo pieces that he took out of his pockets. He went to Mother, who added a fistful of silver coins. My brothers threw in their small change.

"May I walk to the room across the hall and stay there for a few minutes, Judge?" Father asked.

"As you wish."

"Thank you," Father said. He strode into the other room with the hat in his hands. It was almost full of coins. The doors of both rooms were wide open.

"Are you ready?" Father called.

"Proceed," the judge said.

The sweet tinkle of the coins carried beautifully into the courtroom. The spectators turned their faces toward the sound with wonder. Father came back and stood before the complainant.

"Did you hear it?" he asked.

"Hear what?" the man asked.

"The spirit of the money when I shook this hat?" he asked.

"Yes."

"Then you are paid," Father said.

The rich man opened his mouth to speak and fell to the floor without a sound. The lawyer rushed to his aid. The judge pounded his gavel.

"Case dismissed," he said.

Father strutted around the courtroom. The judge even came down from his high chair to shake hands with him. "By the way," he whispered, "I had an uncle who died laughing."

"You like to hear my family laugh, Judge?" Father asked.

"Why not?"

"Did you hear that, children?" Father said.

My sisters started it. The rest of us followed them and soon the spectators were laughing with us, holding their bellies and bending over the chairs. And the laughter of the judge was the loudest of all.

The Trial of the Knave of Hearts

Lewis Carroll

THE KING and Queen of Hearts were seated on their throne when they arrived, with a great crowd assembled about them—all sorts of little birds and beasts, as well as the whole pack of cards: the Knave was standing before them, in chains, with a soldier on each side to guard him; and near the King was the White Rabbit, with a trumpet in one hand, and a scroll of parchment in the other. In the very middle of the court was a table, with a large dish of tarts upon it: they looked so good, that it made Alice quite hungry to look at them—"I wish they'd get the trial done," she thought, "and hand round the refreshments." But there seemed to be no chance of this, so she began looking at everything about her to pass away the time.

Alice had never been in a court of justice before, but she had read about them in books, and she was quite pleased to find that she knew the name of nearly everything there. "That's the judge," she said to herself, "because of his great wig."

The judge, by the way, was the King, and as he wore his crown over the wig (look at the frontispiece if you want to see how he did it), he did not look at all comfortable, and it was certainly not becoming.

"And that's the jury-box," thought Alice, "and those twelve creatures" (she was obliged to say "creatures," you see, because some of them were animals, and some were birds), "I suppose they are the jurors." She said this last word two or three times over to herself, being rather proud of it: for she thought, and rightly too, that very few little girls of her age knew the meaning of it at all. However, "jurymen" would have done just as well.

The twelve jurors were all writing very busily on slates. "What are they doing?" Alice whispered to the Gryphon. "They can't have anything to put down yet, before the trial's begun."

"They're putting down their names," the Gryphon whispered in reply, "for fear they should forget them before the end of the trial."

"Stupid things!" Alice began in a loud indignant voice, but she

From *Alice's Adventures in Wonderland*.

491

stopped herself hastily, for the White Rabbit cried out, "Silence in the Court!" and the King put on his spectacles and looked anxiously round, to make out who was talking.

Alice could see, as well as if she were looking over their shoulders, that all the jurors were writing down "stupid things!" on their slates, and she could even make out that one of them didn't know how to spell "stupid," and that he had to ask his neighbor to tell him. "A nice muddle their slates'll be in before the trial's over!" thought Alice.

One of the jurors had a pencil that squeaked. This, of course, Alice could *not* stand, and she went round the court and got behind him, and very soon found an opportunity of taking it away. She did it so quickly that the poor little juror (it was Bill, the Lizard) could not make out at all what had become of it; so, after hunting all about for it, he was obliged to write with one finger for the rest of the day; and this was of very little use, as it left no mark on the slate.

"Herald, read the accusation!" said the King.

On this the White Rabbit blew three blasts on the trumpet, and then unrolled the parchment scroll, and read as follows:

> *"The Queen of Hearts, she made some tarts,*
> *All on a summer day:*
> *The Knave of Hearts, he stole those tarts,*
> *And took them quite away!"*

"Consider your verdict," the King said to the jury.

"Not yet, not yet!" the Rabbit hastily interrupted. "There's a great deal to come before that!"

"Call the first witness," said the King; and the White Rabbit blew three blasts on the trumpet, and called out, "First witness!"

The first witness was the Hatter. He came in with a teacup in one hand, and a piece of bread-and-butter in the other. "I beg pardon, your majesty," he began, "for bringing these in: but I hadn't quite finished my tea when I was sent for."

"You ought to have finished," said the King. "When did you begin?"

The Hatter looked at the March Hare, who had followed him into the court, arm-in-arm with the Dormouse. "Fourteenth of March, I *think,* it was," he said.

"Fifteenth," said the March Hare.

"Sixteenth," added the Dormouse.

"Write that down," the King said to the jury, and the jury eagerly wrote down all three dates on their slates, and then added them up, and reduced the answer to shillings and pence.

"Take off your hat," the king said to the Hatter.

"It isn't mine," said the Hatter.

"*Stolen!*" the King exclaimed, turning to the jury, who instantly made a memorandum of the fact.

"I keep them to sell," the Hatter added as an explanation: "I've none of my own. I'm a hatter."

Here the Queen put on her spectacles, and began staring hard at the Hatter, who turned pale and fidgeted.

"Give your evidence," said the King; "and don't be nervous, or I'll have you executed on the spot."

This did not seem to encourage the witness at all; he kept shifting from one foot to the other, looking uneasily at the Queen, and in his confusion he bit a large piece out of his teacup instead of the bread-and-butter.

Just at this moment Alice felt a very curious sensation, which puzzled her a good deal until she made out what it was: she was beginning to grow larger again, and she thought at first she would get up and leave the court; but on second thoughts she decided to remain where she was as long as there was room for her.

"I wish you wouldn't squeeze so," said the Dormouse, who was sitting next to her. "I can hardly breathe."

"I can't help it," said Alice very meekly: "I'm growing."

"You've no right to grow *here*," said the Dormouse.

"Don't talk nonsense," said Alice more boldly: "you know you're growing too."

"Yes, but *I* grow at a reasonable pace," said the Dormouse; "not in that ridiculous fashion." And he got up very sulkily and crossed over to the other side of the court.

All this time the Queen had never left off staring at the Hatter, and, just as the Dormouse crossed the court, she said to one of the officers of the court, "Bring me the list of the singers in the last concert!" on which the wretched Hatter trembled so, that he shook both his shoes off.

"Give your evidence," the King repeated angrily, "or I'll have you executed, whether you're nervous or not."

"I'm a poor man, your majesty," the Hatter began in a trembling voice, "and I hadn't but just begun my tea—not above a week or so—and what with the bread-and-butter getting so thin—and the twinkling of the tea——"

"The twinkling of *what?*" said the King.

"It *began* with the tea," the Hatter replied.

"Of course twinkling begins with a T!" said the King sharply. "Do you take me for a dunce? Go on?"

"I'm a poor man," the Hatter went on, "and most things twinkled after that—only the March Hare said——"

"I didn't!" the March Hare interrupted in a great hurry.

"You did!" said the Hatter.

"I deny it," said the March Hare.

"He denies it," said the King: "leave out that part."

"Well, at any rate, the Dormouse said——" the Hatter went on, looking anxiously round to see if he would deny it too: but the Dormouse denied nothing, being fast asleep.

"After that," continued the Hatter, "I cut some more bread-and-butter——"

"But what did the Dormouse say?" one of the jury asked.

"That I can't remember," said the Hatter.

"You *must* remember," remarked the King, "or I'll have you executed."

The miserable Hatter dropped his teacup and bread-and-butter, and went down on one knee. "I'm a poor man, your majesty," he began.

"You're a *very* poor *speaker,*" said the King.

Here one of the guinea pigs cheered, and was immediately suppressed by the officers of the court. (As that is rather a hard word, I will just explain to you how it was done. They had a large canvas bag, which tied up at the mouth with strings: into this they slipped the guinea pig, head first, and then sat upon it.)

"I'm glad I've seen that done," thought Alice. "I've so often read in the newspapers, at the end of trials, 'There was some attempt to applause, which was immediately suppressed by the officers of the court,' and I never understood what it meant till now."

"If that's all you know about it, you may stand down," continued the King.

"I can't go no lower," said the Hatter: "I'm on the floor, as it is."

"Then you may *sit* down," the King replied.

Here the other guinea pig cheered, and was suppressed.

"Come, that finishes the guinea pigs!" thought Alice. "Now we shall get on better."

"I'd rather finish my tea," said the Hatter, with an anxious look at the Queen, who was reading the list of singers.

"You may go," said the King, and the Hatter hurriedly left the court, without even waiting to put his shoes on.

"And just take his head off outside," the Queen added to one of the officers; but the Hatter was out of sight before the officer could get to the door.

"Call the next witness!" said the King.

The next witness was the Duchess' cook. She carried the pepper-box in her hand; and Alice guessed who it was, even before she got into the court, by the way the people near the door began sneezing all at once.

"Give your evidence," said the King.

"Shan't," said the cook.

The King looked anxiously at the White Rabbit, who said in a low voice, "Your majesty must cross-examine *this* witness."

"Well, if I must, I must," the King said with a melancholy air, and, after folding his arms and frowning at the cook till his eyes were nearly out of sight, he said in a deep voice, "What are tarts made of?"

"Pepper, mostly," said the cook.

"Treacle," said a sleepy voice behind her.

"Collar that Dormouse!" the Queen shrieked out. "Behead that Dormouse! Turn that Dormouse out of court! Suppress him! Pinch him! Off with his whiskers!"

For some minutes the whole court was in confusion, getting the Dormouse turned out, and, by the time they had settled down again, the cook had disappeared.

"Never mind" said the King, with an air of great relief. "Call the next witness." And he added in an under-tone to the Queen, "Really, my dear, *you* must cross-examine the next witness. It quite makes my forehead ache!"

Alice watched the White Rabbit as he fumbled over the list, feeling very curious to see what the next witness would be like—"for they haven't got much evidence *yet*," she said to herself. Imagine her surprise, when the White Rabbit read out the name "Alice!"

"Here!" cried Alice, quite forgetting in the flurry of the moment how large she had grown in the last few minutes, and she jumped up in such a hurry that she tipped over the jury-box with the edge of her skirt, upsetting all the jurymen on to the heads of the crowd below, and there they lay sprawling about, reminding her very much of a globe of gold-fish she had accidentally upset the week before.

"Oh, I *beg* your pardon!" she exclaimed in a tone of great dismay, and began picking them up again as quickly as she could, for the accident of the gold-fish kept running in her head, and she had a vague sort of idea that they must be collected at once and put back into the jury-box, or they would die.

"The trial cannot proceed," said the King in a very grave voice, "until all the jurymen are back in their proper places—*all*," he repeated with great emphasis, looking hard at Alice as he said so.

Alice looked at the jury-box, and saw that, in her haste, she had put the Lizard in head downwards, and the poor little thing was waving its tail about in a melancholy way, being quite unable to move. She soon got it out again, and put it right; "not that it signifies much," she said to herself; "I should think it would be *quite* as much used in the trial one way up as the other."

As soon as the jury had a little recovered from the shock of being upset, and their slates and pencils had been found and handed back to them, they set to work very diligently to write out a history of the accident, all except the Lizard, who seemed too much overcome to do any thing but sit with its mouth wide open, gazing up into the roof of the court.

"What do you know about this business?" the King said to Alice.

"Nothing," said Alice.

"Nothing *whatever?*" persisted the King.

"Nothing whatever," said Alice.

"That's very important," the King said, turning to the jury. They were just beginning to write this down on their slates, when the White Rabbit interrupted; *"Un*important, your majesty means, of course," he said in a very respectful tone, but frowning and making faces at him, as he spoke.

*"Un*important, of course, I meant," the King hastily said, and went on to himself in an undertone, "important—unimportant—unimportant—important——" as if he were trying which word sounded best.

Some of the jury wrote it down "important," and some of them "unimportant." Alice could see this, as she was near enough to look over their slates; "but it doesn't matter a bit," she thought to herself.

At this moment the King, who had been for some time busily writing in his note-book, called out "Silence!" and read out from his book, "Rule Forty-two. *All persons more than a mile high to leave the court.*"

Everybody looked at Alice.

"I'm not a mile high," said Alice.

"You are," said the King.

"Nearly two miles high," added the Queen.

"Well, I shan't go, at any rate," said Alice; "besides, that's not a regular rule; you invented it just now."

"It's the oldest rule in the book," said the King.

"Then it ought to be Number One," said Alice.

The King turned pale, and shut his note-book hastily. "Consider your verdict," he said to the jury, in a low trembling voice.

"There's more evidence to come yet, please your majesty," said the White Rabbit, jumping up in a great hurry; "this paper has just been picked up."

"What's in it?" said the Queen.

"I haven't opened it yet," said the White Rabbit, "but it seems to be a letter, written by the prisoner to—to somebody."

"It must have been that," said the King, "unless it was written to nobody, which isn't usual, you know."

"Who is it directed to?" said one of the jurymen.

"It isn't directed at all," said the White Rabbit; "in fact, there's nothing written on the *outside*." He unfolded the paper as he spoke, and added "It isn't a letter after all; it's a set of verses."

"Are they in the prisoner's handwriting?" asked another of the jurymen.

"No, they're not," said the White Rabbit, "and that's the queerest thing about it." (The jury all looked puzzled.)

"He must have imitated somebody else's hand," said the King. (The jury all brightened up again.)

"Please your majesty," said the Knave, "I didn't write it, and they can't prove I did: there's no name signed at the end."

"If you didn't sign it," said the King, "that only makes the matter worse. You *must* have meant some mischief, or else you'd have signed your name like an honest man."

There was a general clapping of hands at this: it was the first really clever thing the King had said that day.

"That *proves* his guilt," said the Queen.

"It proves nothing of the sort," said Alice. "Why you don't even know what they're about!"

"Read them," said the King.

The White Rabbit put on his spectacles. "Where shall I begin, please your majesty?" he asked.

"Begin at the beginning," the King said, gravely, "and go on till you come to the end: then stop."

These were the verses the White Rabbit read:

> *"They told me that you had been to her,*
> *And mentioned me to him:*
> *She gave me a good character,*
> *But said I could not swim.*
>
> *He sent them word I had not gone*
> *(We know it to be true):*
> *If she should push the matter on,*
> *What would become of you?*
>
> *I gave her one, they gave him two,*
> *You gave us three or more;*
> *They all returned from him to you,*
> *Though they were mine before.*
>
> *If I or she should chance to be*
> *Involved in this affair,*
> *He trusts to you to set them free.*
> *Exactly as we were.*
>
> *My notion was that you had been*
> *(Before she had this fit)*
> *An obstacle that came between*
> *Him and ourselves, and it.*
>
> *Don't let him know she liked them best.*
> *For this must ever be*
> *A secret, kept from all the rest,*
> *Between yourself and me."*

"That's the most important piece of evidence we've heard yet," said the King, rubbing his hands; "so now let the jury—"

"If any one of them can explain it," said Alice (she had grown so large in the last few minutes that she wasn't a bit afraid of interrupting him), "I'll give him sixpence. *I* don't believe there's an atom of meaning in it."

The jury all wrote down on their slates, "*She* doesn't believe there's an atom of meaning in it," but none of them attempted to explain the paper.

"If there's no meaning in it," said the King, "that saves a world of trouble, you know, as we needn't try to find any. And yet I don't know," he went on, spreading out the verses on his knee, and looking at them with one eye; "I seem to see some meaning in them, after all—*'said I could not swim'*—you can't swim, can you?" he added, turning to the Knave.

The Knave shook his head sadly. "Do I look like it?" he said, (Which he certainly did *not,* being made entirely of cardboard.)

"All right, so far," said the King, and he went on muttering over the verses to himself: " *'We know it to be true'*—that's the jury, of course— *'I gave her one, they gave him two'*—why, that must be what he did with the tarts, you know—"

"But it goes on *'they all returned from him to you,'* " said Alice.

"Why, there they are!" said the King triumphantly, pointing to the tarts on the table. "Nothing can be clearer than *that.* Then again—*'before she had this fit'*—you never had fits, my dear, I think?" he said to the Queen.

"Never!" said the Queen furiously, throwing an inkstand at the Lizard as she spoke. (The unfortunate little Bill had left off writing on his slate with one finger, as he found it made no mark; but he now hastily began again, using the ink, that was trickling down his face, as long as it lasted.)

"Then the words don't *fit* you," said the King looking round the court with a smile. There was a dead silence.

"It's a pun," the King added in an angry tone, and everybody laughed. "Let the jury consider their verdict," the King said, for about the twentieth time that day.

"No, no!" said the Queen. "Sentence first—verdict afterward."

"Stuff and nonsense!" said Alice loudly. "The idea of having the sentence first!"

"Hold your tongue!" said the Queen, turning purple.

"I won't!" said Alice.

"Off with her head!" the Queen shouted at the top of her voice. Nobody moved.

"Who cares for you?" said Alice (she had grown to her full size by this time). "You're nothing but a pack of cards!"

At this the whole pack rose up into the air, and came flying down upon her; she gave a little scream, half of fright and half of anger, and tried to beat them off, and found herself lying on the bank, with her head in the lap of her sister, who was gently brushing away some dead leaves that had fluttered down from the trees on to her face.

"Wake up, Alice dear!" said her sister; "why, what a long sleep you've had!"

"Oh, I've had such a curious dream!" said Alice, and she told her sister, as well as she could remember them, all these strange adventures of hers that you have just been reading about; and when she had finished, her sister kissed her, and said, "It *was* a curious dream, dear, certainly; but now run in to your tea; it's getting late." So Alice got up and ran off, thinking while she ran, as well she might, what a wonderful dream it had been.